...tion of Living Primates

ATES

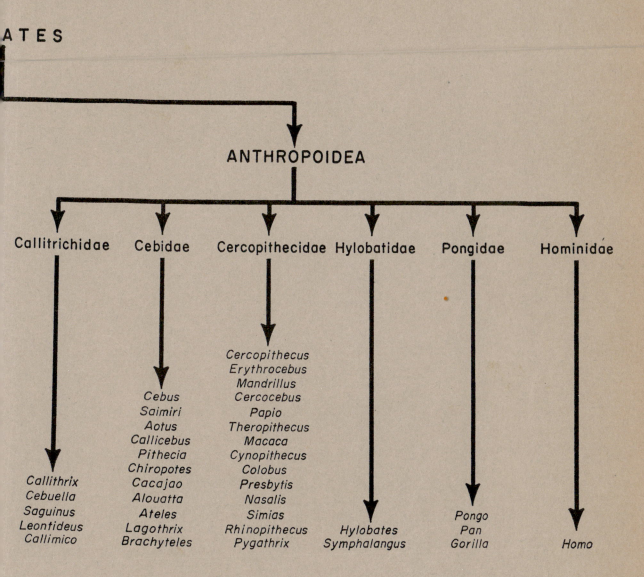

ANTHROPOIDEA

Callitrichidae	Cebidae	Cercopithecidae	Hylobatidae	Pongidae	Hominidae
		Cercopithecus			
		Erythrocebus			
		Mandrillus			
	Cebus	*Cercocebus*			
	Saimiri	*Papio*			
	Aotus	*Theropithecus*			
	Callicebus	*Macaca*			
	Pithecia	*Cynopithecus*			
	Chiropotes	*Colobus*			
Callithrix	*Cacajao*	*Presbytis*			
Cebuella	*Alouatta*	*Nasalis*		*Pongo*	
Saguinus	*Ateles*	*Simias*	*Hylobates*	*Pan*	
Leontideus	*Lagothrix*	*Rhinopithecus*	*Symphalangus*	*Gorilla*	*Homo*
Callimico	*Brachyteles*	*Pygathrix*			

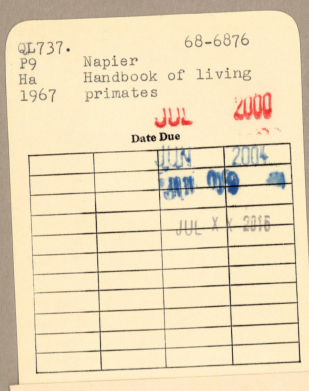
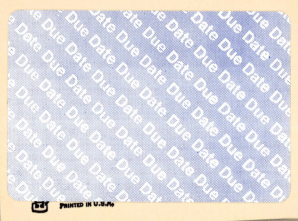

A
HANDBOOK
of
LIVING
PRIMATES

Papio ursinus, juvenile (by courtesy of C. K. Brain)

A
HANDBOOK
of
LIVING
PRIMATES

Morphology, Ecology and Behaviour
of Nonhuman Primates

J. R. NAPIER
Unit of Primatology and Human Evolution
Royal Free Hospital School of Medicine, London

AND

P. H. NAPIER

1967

ACADEMIC PRESS
LONDON · NEW YORK

ACADEMIC PRESS INC. (LONDON) LTD.
Berkeley Square House
Berkeley Square
London, W.1.

U. S. Edition published by
ACADEMIC PRESS INC.
111 Fifth Avenue
New York, New York 10003

PRINTED IN GREAT BRITAIN BY ROBERT MACLEHOSE AND CO. LTD
THE UNIVERSITY PRESS, GLASGOW

Preface

The idea for this book grew out of a collection of study notes for student classes on primate biology. During one annual revision, an impulse to extend and elaborate the notes resulted in the accumulation of a mass of data, which now constitute the skeleton of the present handbook. Just as study-notes can become handbooks, handbooks can grow into multi-volume monographs, a progression that we have tried to avoid by presenting the data in a systematic, concise, and, where possible, tabular form.

It is unlikely that the method we have chosen for presentation of the data will appeal to everyone. There are some, no doubt, for whom a reference book setting is an anathema. However, we have adopted this method simply because we feel that there is a great need among medical research scientists, human biologists and zoologists for the type of book where up-to-date, factual information on primate biology is readily available. The first handbook in this field, having a format not dissimilar to the present volume, was written by H. O. Forbes and published in Allen's Naturalists' Library in 1894. Until the publication during the last decade of W. C. Osman Hill's major treatises, Forbes' book was one of the few systematic accounts of the Primates in the English language; indeed it still serves as the principal *vade mecum* for many primate biologists.

As a result of the fervour to establish man's place in nature in the post-Darwin era of the 19th century, anatomists and zoologists gave the morphology of primates a thorough, if typological, going-over, and remarkably little can be added to their accounts of myology and osteology. On the other hand, animal behaviour, ecology and genetic biology, which today dominate basic research trends in primate biology, were unexplored fields. The sections on 'Habits' which embody behaviour and ecology in Forbes' Handbook rely wholly on the brief anecdotes of field naturalists. Today, our knowledge of the behaviour of free-ranging primates, though still desperately meagre in certain quarters, is increasing year by year as, happily, more workers enter the field armed with more and more generous grants.

In many ways primate biology is still in the "cataloguing and collecting" phase as it has been called; this must be regarded as an essential stock-taking exercise during which language and methodology develop and the bricks and mortar of the subject—the basic facts of primate taxonomy, morphology and behaviour—are collected and disseminated. Without these facts and without, at least, an awareness of the gaps in our knowledge, the subject cannot hope to fulfil its great promise. Basically this book is a catalogue of material, a collection of facts and a guide to deficiencies; but we hope it is a little more than that. Catalogues are not usually selective, they would hardly fulfil their purpose if they were. In the present handbook we have tried to avoid the mere propagation of unsifted and undigested fact by attempting a critical selection of the material. All that glisters is not gold—and primate biology possesses more than a fair share of lodes rich in iron pyrites. Where data are based on anecdotal, very limited or even single observations, we have introduced a note of caution by using the symbol *. To have omitted such limited data would have been to reduce the value of the handbook as even the most extravagant anecdote or unique observation may provide invaluable clues for further research.

In pursuance of the handbook principle we have adopted a shorthand style in the presentation of the data in Part II, which constitute the profiles for each genus. We have also used a numerical method of citing authorities. The authorities and dates of the relevant publications are to be found at the end of each profile; the full references are arranged alphabetically at the end of the book.

An alphabetical arrangement of profiles in Section II was selected in preference to a taxonomic one. We have also preferred to use the genus name as the principal heading for the profile rather than the familiar one. Familiar names show considerable regional variation, for instance the ubiquitous *Cercopithecus* of the *aethiops* group is known variously throughout Africa as the savannah monkey, the grivet, the vervet and the green monkey. Genus names, on the other hand, controversial issues aside, are as international as Linnaeus intended. A list of familiar names in common use in the English-speaking world, France, Germany and Holland, and their generic and specific synonyms appears in Section III. Vernacular names of purely indigenous usage are, for the most part, omitted. Common scientific synonyms are also listed in this section.

The taxonomy and nomenclature of primates, as no one will deny, are in a very fluid state; and as laboratory interest in these animals grows, and as more and more collecting and field study expeditions are set up, the confusion is bound to get worse before it gets better. Our principal aim in writing this book is to make primate biology as comprehensible to as wide a section of scientists as possible without indulging in the half-truths of over-simplification. Nowhere is this intention more difficult to realize than in systematics and nomenclature. It would be easy to accept the simplest classification available and to ignore the complicating emendations, however authoritative, on the grounds of expediency. But to adopt such a procedure is to misunderstand the aims of systematics which are not to provide merely a convenient *aide-mémoire* for the student, but to express in a biological, meaningful way the neontological and phylogenetic relationships between animal groups. If relationships between groups of primates should, on further study, turn out to be more complicated than was supposed, then one must accept any nomenclatorial complexities that result. Happily the trend deriving from the modern concept of species is on the whole towards "lumping" rather than "splitting"; however even a reduction of the number of genera and species can be as confusing as the addition of new taxa. Primarily we have based our classification on G. G. Simpson's "A Classification of Mammals" (1945) which is probably the best known and most widely accepted system in use today. But in a number of instances where this classification has seemed to us inadequate in the light of more recent knowledge, we have adopted the most *up to date and authoritative* work on the subject. In the face of conflicting opinions we have tended to follow the more conservative line believing that for the majority of primate biologists, stability of nomenclature is the most important consideration. Where nomenclatorial changes are sufficiently radical to warrant it, as in the case of marmosets and tamarins, we have included a table of synonyms. Where nomenclature is subject to current dispute we have tried to summarize both the problem and our own attitude towards it, in a Taxonomic Note to be found in Part III. In instances where genus names have been shown to be invalid on the grounds of non-availability we have followed the convention of including the rejected name in square brackets e.g. *Leontideus* [*Leontocebus*].

We did not set out to revise the taxonomy of primates; there are plenty of authors, bolder and better informed than we, who will do just this. We have only aimed to present the *facts* of primate biology in a comprehensible way and we believe that familiarity is the best framework for our intentions.

There is a mounting tide of opinion against the inclusion of the treeshrews among the primates. Van Valen (1965), in a palaeontological review, concludes that the tupaiid-primate relationship is "possible but unlikely". The posthumous paper of the embryologist J. P. Hill (1965) strikes heavily at one of the pillars on which this association rests—the characteristics of the placenta. Recent studies of the treeshrews, carried out at the Max Planck Institute by

Bob Martin (1966), argue against their inclusion on grounds of maternal behaviour. On the other hand there are a number of anatomical features, particularly in the dentition, the presence of a postorbital bar and other structural correlates of an advanced visual mechanism, that ally these forms closely with the primates. Goodman's (1962) evidence from immuno-logical studies of serum proteins affines the treeshrews with the primates rather than with non-primate mammalian groups. The situation with regard to the primate affinities of tree-shrews is equivocal to say the least. We have followed Simpson (1945), Clark (1959), Fiedler (1956), etc., in accepting their primate affiliations—however remote they may prove to be.

Part I of the book consists of an account of the morphology of primates; its purpose is to provide an overall survey of the principal functional characters which distinguish primates from the other mammals and from each other. Throughout this section, indeed throughout the book as a whole, we have tried to present the data with a proper balance between structure, function and behaviour.

In Part II the data for each genus are presented under several main headings; Geographical Range; Ecology; Morphology; Genetic Biology; Behaviour; Reproduction and Develop-ment; Captivity, etc. This sequence is pursued in Part III, the appendix, where explanatory notes will be found amplifying, discussing or defining terms and concepts used in the profiles of Part II; for example the vegetational zones and vertical classification of the forest canopy are discussed; and the differing types of primate locomotion and hand function are classified and defined.

In order to make it easier to compare certain characters of one genus with another, much of the quantitative data included in the profiles (e.g. weights, hand proportions, limb proportions, chromosome numbers etc.) are given collectively in tabular form under the appropriate sections in Part III.

It is not easy to write a book of this sort without making mistakes. These can creep into the text at any one of its many stages of preparation and, in spite of assiduous proof-reading, can appear shining like a beacon in its final published form. We have done our best to see that the unavoidable errors are kept to a minimum and that the avoidable errors, which are entirely the result of our own ignorance, are not too obtrusive. Having admitted the inevitability of error we can only apologize sincerely to those authors whom we have misquoted or mis-interpreted and to those readers whom, thereby, we may mislead.

We are exceedingly grateful to a large number of friends and colleagues who have provided us with practical help. Without their generosity we could not have written this book.

J. R. NAPIER

P. H. NAPIER

May 1967

Acknowledgements

We are happy to acknowledge the generosity of the following who have supplied us with photographs: David Attenborough, Molly Badham, C. K. Brain, John Buettner-Janusch, Harry Butler, C. R. Carpenter, John Crook, John Doidge, Frank Dumond of the Monkey Jungle, Florida, John Ellefson, Jane Goodall (Jane van Lawick-Goodall), R. E. Greed, Manfred Grüner, the late Professor K. R. L. Hall, J. K. Hampton, Barbara and Tom Harrisson, Caroline Jarvis, Phyllis Jay, Hans Kummer, Masao Kawai, Lim Boo Liat, Gilbert Manley, Stephen Peet, Jean Jacques Petter, Duane Rumbaugh, Reg Salmon of Fox Photos, Laurie Smith, Eric and Doris Sorby for many excellent photographs, Dr. Heinrich Sprankel, Alan Walker and Sherwood L. Washburn.

We are indebted to the following who have helped us in many ways: Molly Badham and Nathalie Evans of Twycross Zoo Park, Sam Berry, John Buettner-Janusch, Dr. A. W. China, Bob Cooper, R. K. Davenport, Michael Day, Mr. L. G. Ellis, Erik Erikson, Mr. R. A. Fish and his staff at the Zoological Society's Library, Mr. Philip Hershkovitz, Mr. J. E. Hill and his staff in the Mammalogy Section of the British Museum (Natural History), Osman Hill who has contributed so much to Primatology, Caroline Jarvis of the London Zoo, Phyllis Jay, Cliff Jolly, Masao Kawai, Judith King of the Osteology Section of the British Museum (Natural History), Rainer Lorenz, Gilbert Manley, Bill Montagna of the Oregon Regional Primate Research Center, Desmond Morris, Jean Jacques Petter, George Pournelle, Curator of Mammals at the San Diego Zoo, George B. Rabb, Adolph Schultz whom every primate biologist has reason to thank, Laurie Smith, Head Keeper of the Monkey House at the London Zoo who knows more about primates than is contained in this book, John Sparkes, Dr. Heinrich Sprankel, Jack Trevor, Sherwood L. Washburn and Adrienne Zihlmann.

We warmly thank our friends who have been involved in this book from conception to parturition: Audrey Besterman who prepared the diagrams, Barbara Dickson who typed much of the manuscript and provided unlimited encouragement, Frances Ellis and her staff of the Photographic Department of the Royal Free Hospital School of Medicine, Colin Groves who has read every word of this book and corrected many of them, and Alan Walker whose personal communications from Uganda and Madagascar have been invaluable.

We are very happy to acknowledge the support given to one of us (J.R.N.) over a number of years by the Wenner-Gren Foundation for Anthropological Research and the Boise Fund of Oxford University.

Finally, we should like to thank Academic Press, and in particular the production staff, whose advice and help have been invaluable.

Contents

PART II
Profiles of Primate Genera

Index to Profiles

PART III

Supplementary and Comparative Data

Taxonomy and Nomenclature

Habitats of Primates

Limbs and Locomotion

Data on Macaques

Vital Statistics of Primates

PART I

Functional Morphology of the Primates

Functional Morphology of the Primates

From the point of view of their morphology the living primates are best considered in twelve natural groups or Families.

Tupaiidae		
Lemuridae		
Indriidae	Malagasy families	Prosimian families
Daubentoniidae		
Lorisidae		
Tarsiidae		
Callitrichidae	New World monkey families	
Cebidae		
Cercopithecidae	Old World monkey family	Anthropoid families
Hylobatidae		
Pongidae	Ape and human families	
Hominidae		

PROSIMIAN FAMILIES

1. Tupaiidae
This family comprehends the treeshrews which comprise five genera: *Tupaia, Dendrogale, Urogale, Anathana* and *Ptilocercus*. Geographically they are widely distributed throughout the Far East.

2. Lemuridae
A Madagascan family comprising *Lemur, Hapalemur, Lepilemur, Cheirogaleus, Microcebus* and *Phaner*.

3. Indriidae
This family includes the long-legged Madagascan lemurs—*Indri, Propithecus* and *Avahi*.

4. Daubentoniidae
A monotypic family comprising the aberrant Madagascan lemur *Daubentonia*, the Aye-aye.

5. Lorisidae
The family of lorises and galagos which has representatives in the Far East (*Nycticebus, Loris*) and in Africa (*Perodicticus, Arctocebus* and *Galago*).

6. Tarsiidae
A monotypic family containing the single living representative *Tarsius*. Tarsiers are found on many islands of the East Indies, e.g. Borneo, Philippines.

ANTHROPOID FAMILIES

7. Callitrichidae

South American family consisting of five genera of marmosets and tamarins, *Callithrix*, *Cebuella*, *Saguinus*, *Leontideus* and *Callimico*.

8. Cebidae

The largest family of South American monkeys comprehending all remaining genera, i.e. *Aotus*, *Callicebus*, *Pithecia*, *Chiropotes*, *Cacajao*, *Cebus*, *Saimiri*, *Alouatta*, *Ateles*, *Lagothrix* and *Brachyteles*.

9. Cercopithecidae

Monkeys of the Old World (Africa and Asia). An historically continuous family now sub-divided geographically into *Presbytis*, *Nasalis*, *Simias*, *Rhinopithecus*, *Pygathrix*, *Cynopithecus* (Asia); and *Papio*, *Colobus*, *Cercopithecus*, *Erythrocebus*, *Theropithecus*, *Cercocebus*, *Mandrillus* (Africa). Only one genus *Macaca*, is common to both regions.

10. Hylobatidae

Lesser apes of the Far East ranging from Assam in the West to Borneo in the East. The family comprehends two genera: *Hylobates* and *Symphalangus*.

11. Pongidae

Great Apes of the Old World. Africa: *Pan* and *Gorilla*. South-East Asia: *Pongo*.

12. Hominidae

Represented by a single world-wide polytypic species, *Homo sapiens*.

The morphology of these 12 families link them together at ordinal level to form the Primates. The primate affinities of 10 out of 12 families are unequivocal, the two aberrant taxa being the treeshrews and the Madagascan genus *Daubentonia*, the Aye-aye. At one time, naturalists swayed by the morphology of the teeth included the Aye-aye with the rodents, but their primate affinities can hardly, now, be questioned. The treeshrews are still refused admittance by a number of authorities, notably W. C. Osman Hill. Certain authors (Evans 1942; Roux, 1947; Henckel, 1928) see difficulty in separating the treeshrews from the elephant-shrews in the Mentophyla section of the Insectivora on the basis of osteology. On the other hand, Clark on neurological (1932) and developmental (1959) grounds finds no such problem (but see J. P. Hill's (1965) posthumous paper on placentation in *Tupaia* and Campbell's (1966) preliminary note on the lamination of the lateral geniculate nucleus). Van Valen (1965) regards tupaiid-primate relationship as "possible but unlikely" on palaeontological grounds. Palaeontological evidence is equivocal but the morphology of living forms and, in particular, the evidence derived from serological techniques (Goodman, 1962a, b, 1963, etc.) still appear to be valid arguments in favour of retaining the treeshrews among the primates.

The list of families in the order presented, as well as being a horizontal section through a systematic scheme of living primates, also corresponds approximately to a *scala naturae* of primate evolution. The existence of a graded series among living primates recapitulating, in an approximate way, the phylogenetic stages of the fossil record, is a feature of the primate order that has been well-recognized since 1876 when T. H. Huxley wrote: "Perhaps no order of mammals presents us with so extraordinary a series of gradations as this—leading us insensibly from the crown and summit of the animal creation down to creatures from which there is but a step, as it seems, to the lowest, smallest and least intelligent of the placental mammals."

While such a state of affairs, unique among mammals, is most helpful to the primate palaeontologist, there is the constant danger that students will read into such a graded series, a linearity of descent that most certainly did not exist.* The graded series of living primates represents, as Clark (1959) has taken great pains to emphasize, the terminal products of many diverging lines of evolution. Stripped of their more obvious later specializations, they provide, however, a working model of the successive grades of organization in primate phylogeny from the lowest to the highest (Fig. 1).

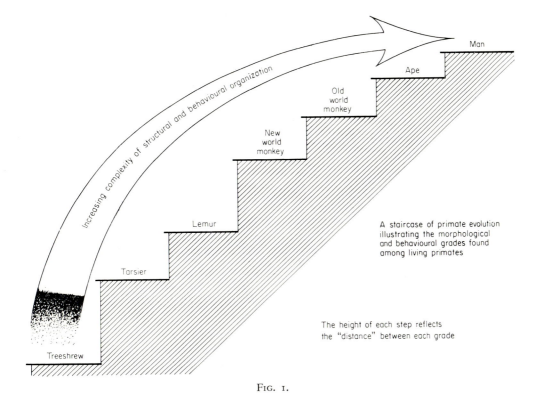

A staircase of primate evolution illustrating the morphological and behavioural grades found among living primates

The height of each step reflects the "distance" between each grade

FIG. 1.

CHARACTERS OF THE ORDER

In 1873 St. George Mivart defined primates in the following terms:

"... an ungiculate, claviculate, placental mammal with orbits encircled by bone; three kinds of teeth at least at one time of life; brain always with a posterior lobe and a calcarine fissure; the innermost digits of at least one pair of extremities opposable; hallux with a flat nail or

* Students can hardly be blamed for falling into this trap which was so neatly and innocently set by Darwin in his "Origin" and so industriously placed in the path of the unwary by Huxley and Haeckel in their respective books. The erroneous concept of the "missing link", the inevitable derivative of this way of thought, is the one "fact" that everybody thinks they know about evolution.

none; a well-marked caecum; penis pendulous; testes scrotal; always two pectoral mammae."

Professor F. Wood Jones in his book "Man's place among the Mammals" (1929) takes these criteria and examines them one by one; he concludes *à propos* of Mivart's definition "There is no single character . . . which constitutes a peculiarity of the Primates; for a primate animal may only be diagnosed by possessing an aggregate of them all" (p. 75). This important observation was also made by Clark (1959) who points out the difficulties of providing a clear-cut definition of the Order as a whole and observes (p. 42) that "There is no distinguishing feature which characterizes them all"—except a negative one, their lack of specialization. Clark supplies a list of evolutionary trends characteristic of the Order constituting a more useful and more meaningful diagnostic key than that provided by Mivart, whose definition does little more than supply a list of primitive mammalian features of which, to be sure, primates have a more than generous share. However, it must be remembered that Mivart was the first zoologist to attempt a comprehensive definition of primates that, *inter alia*, excluded the bats.

Clark's "evolutionary trends" are as follows:

1. Preservation of a generalized structure of the limbs with a primitive pentadactyly and the retention of certain elements of the limb skeleton (such as the clavicle) which tend to be reduced or to disappear in some groups of mammals.
2. An enhancement of the free mobility of the digits especially the thumb and big toe (which are used for grasping purposes).
3. The replacement of sharp, compressed claws by flattened nails associated with the development of highly sensitive tactile pads on the digits.
4. The progressive abbreviation of the snout or muzzle.
5. The elaboration and perfection of visual apparatus with development of varying degrees of binocular vision.
6. Reduction of the apparatus of smell.
7. The loss of certain elements of the primitive mammalian dentition and the preservation of a simple cusp pattern of the molar teeth.
8. Progressive elaboration of the brain affecting predominantly the cerebral cortex and its dependencies.
9. Progressive and increasingly efficient development of those gestational processes concerned with the nourishment of the foetus before birth.

Two further evolutionary trends may be added to the list:

10. Progressive development of truncal uprightness leading to a facultative bipedalism.
11. Prolongation of post-natal life periods.

The value of this key lies in its applicability to fossil as well as to living primates; with the exception of Trend 9, all the characters listed can be evaluated directly or indirectly from fossil material. Not *all* these trends are shown by *all* primates; nor do all primates show these trends to an equal extent. The overall judgment of affinity needs to be made not on the basis of the presence or absence of isolated characters but rather on total morphological pattern.

While essentially a morphological catalogue, Clark's list implies the acquirement of certain functional and behavioural traits that can be regarded as correlates of the structural ones. For instance, the preservation of a generalized structure of the limb skeleton can be interpreted in behavioural terms as the preservation of a generalized locomotor pattern that includes climbing, leaping and running, irrespective, for the most part, of the nature of the habitat. As an example of this inherent locomotor plasticity, spider monkeys which are in nature among the most habitually arboreal of all Anthropoidea, can be maintained successfully in captivity in a totally "terrestrial" environment. Baboons and patas monkeys, on the other hand, in spite of extensive ground-living adaptations, remain sufficiently generalized to move and sleep in trees. Clark's second trend, interpreted in a functional and behavioural sense, can be considered in the light of the manipulative power of the hand and foot, the acquirement of an opposable thumb and big toe and independently mobile digits. Such behavioural characters as hand-feeding, grooming, tool-using and tool-making can be correlated with these functions in the hand, and certain locomotor specializations, particularly those shown by the anthropoid apes, with the analagous functions of the foot.

An automobile is composed of separate elements which, if properly assembled and supplied with a power source, will function on the test bench. So far so good, but it is not until the automobile is tested in its natural environment that the success or otherwise of the design can be judged. Only on the road can its behaviour be studied; and the best behaved cars are the ones the customers buy. Similarly, in nature, it is on behaviour that natural selection operates. Structure, function and behaviour are interdependent, and the success of an organism can be marred by imperfections at any one of these three levels; but whatever the underlying cause, the fate of an organism is finally decided by its behavioural responses to its natural environment.

In the following section, therefore, Clark's list of morphological trends in evolution are discussed principally in terms of their functional significance and behavioural correlations.

1. THE LIMBS AND VERTEBRAL COLUMN

All primates retain, in addition to a clavicle, a separate radius and ulna capable of the relative movements of pronation and supination which reach their maximal expression in the Hylobatidae, Pongidae and Hominidae. Apart from the Tarsiidae, in which the tibia and fibula are fused in the distal half of their length, a separate fibula is also a characteristic of primates (Barnett and Napier, 1953). All primates have five free digits on hand and foot with the exception of *Ateles*, *Brachyteles* and *Colobus* and certain of the Lorisidae. In *Ateles*, *Brachyteles* and *Colobus* the free thumb is secondarily reduced to a tubercle or is wholly absent; in these species however the metacarpal element is retained. A thumb markedly reduced in length and robustness is found in the Pongidae.

In the Lorisidae the 2nd digit of both hand and foot is considerably shortened; in certain Cercopithecidae also (e.g. *Theropithecus* and *Erythrocebus*) the 2nd digit is reduced in length. The carpal skeleton of primates, though subject to functional modification in the relative size of its components, is comprised of nine bones (including the pisiform and a single *os centrale*); the *os centrale* invariably fuses with the neighbouring scaphoid before birth in Hominidae and during post-natal growth in Hylobatidae and Pongidae; a fused centrale is also usually found in Indriidae, in some Lemuridae (*Lepilemur*) and occasionally in some Cercopithecidae (e.g. *Presbytis cristatus*). The tarsus varies little within the Order with regard to component bones, although considerable changes in relative proportions are seen (Schultz, 1963a). The primitive digital projection formula 3.4.2.5.1. for the hand, is retained tenaciously, the functional axis of the hand being the line of the 3rd digit; the only common variant of this formula (in Lemuridae, Indriidae and Lorisidae) is 4.3.2.5.1. or 4.3.5.2.1., the functional axis being shifted to the 4th digit.

VERTEBRAL COLUMN

The vertebral column (less caudal components) of primates as a whole shows a basic mammalian pattern and consists of 26–33 elements, the principal variations of functional importance occurring in the lumbar and sacral regions. The shortening of the lumbar region is probably the most fruitful indicator of locomotor function. The key elements, as Erikson (1963) points out, are in "the number of segments, shape of the vertebral bones, total lengths of the region, functional role of the joints, and the cranial extension of the lumbar type of articulation" (p. 152). In marmosets, which Erikson (*loc. cit.*) classifies as "springers", the lumbar vertebrae vary in number between 6 and 7. In New and Old World quadrupedal forms such as *Cebus* and *Macaca* the modal number is 6 or 7. In gibbons 5 lumbar vertebrae are commonly found but, in New World semibrachiators such as *Ateles* and *Lagothrix*, the commonest number is 4 as it is in the large anthropoid apes. Old World semibrachiators, on the other hand, possess 7 lumbar vertebrae suggesting a fundamental locomotor difference between Old World and New World semibrachiating groups. Man commonly possesses 5 lumbar vertebrae. Hylobatidae, Pongidae and Hominidae invariably possess 4–5 sacral vertebrae and the remaining taxa only 3 (except lorisoid primates which usually have between 5 and 9 sacral vertebrae). Anticlinal vertebrae are present in all families except those of the apes and man and in certain lorisoids, e.g. *Loris* and *Nycticebus*.

In the potto (*Perodicticus*) the cervical spines are elongated below C.2; the last cervical and the first thoracic spines are extremely long and bear a horny cap on their tips which penetrate the skin of the neck. This unique adaptation supposedly acts in defence. A remarkable specialization of the ribs has developed in another lorisiform *Arctocebus*, the angwantibo. The ribs from the 4th downwards are markedly broadened in the region of the costal angle and overlap one another like roofing tiles. This unique feature is presumably also a defensive specialization and helps to protect this slow moving and vulnerable animal from predator attack.

A long tail is a common primate feature, its reduction in a wide variety of genera (*Indri*, *Macaca*, *Cacajao*, *Perodicticus*, *Loris*, etc.) and its complete absence in Hylobatidae, Pongidae and Hominidae might lead one to regard it as a minor evolutionary trend. In the New World family Cebidae, the two sub-families the Atelinae and the Alouattinae, possess a prehensile tail having an area on the ventral surface covered with a specialized integument incorporating pressure pads, flexion creases and ridge-forming skin. A number of other New World families show a certain degree of functional prehensility. The capuchins (*Cebus*) for instance frequently coil the tail lightly round a branch at rest. The titis (*Callicebus*) and the night-monkeys (*Aotus*) may be seen sitting with the tail intertwined with that of a companion. Even among the Old World families, in which a prehensile tail is not regarded as characteristic, the infants of certain forms, e.g. mangabeys and olive colobus may show this trait for a brief period in the post-natal stage. According to recent observations (A. C. Walker—unpublished) the adults of the *albigena* group of mangabeys have semi-prehensile tails.

A recent study by Ankel (1965) of the lumen of the sacral canal of the primates has shown that the Sacral Canal Index changes from its cranial to its caudal end in proportion to the number of caudal vertebrae present; thus the diameter of the lumen varies in tail-less, short tailed and long-tailed primates. One particular application of this Index is to determine the length of the tail in fossil primates; for instance Ankel (*loc. cit.*) has shown that *Pliopithecus* of the Miocene of Europe—a probable hylobatine—must have had a long tail, a fact that was previously unsuspected. This deduction provides an effective demonstration of the value of neontological studies in the interpretations of primate palaeontology.

LIMBS AND TRUNK

The relative length of the fore- and hindlimbs to each other and to the length of the vertebral column shows considerable variation among the primates. This is not a surprising finding in view of the wide adaptive range of primate locomotion. It is assumed, on palaeontological grounds, that the common ancestral primate possessed short limbs and a long vertebral column. One of the adaptive trends of primate evolution has been the lengthening of both fore- and hindlimbs and a shortening of the vertebral column. Short limbs have been retained in treeshrews for instance which possess relatively the shortest limbs among primates; other short-limbed forms are found among the lorisoid members of the Lorisidae, e.g. *Arctocebus*, *Perodicticus* and *Nycticebus*, and in the Callitrichidae. In all remaining primates, one or both limbs are longer than the vertebral column. The vertebral column also varies in length although not to the same degree as the limbs. While anthropoid apes and man have extremely long arms, they also have short vertebral columns, so that relative limb-length indices (Schultz, 1956) are higher in consequence. Generally speaking the vertebral column is long in leaping forms such as *Presbytis* and *Colobus* and short, though for differing reasons, in ground-living quadrupeds such as *Papio*; it is also short in brachiators such as *Hylobates* and semibrachiators such as *Ateles* (Erikson, 1963).

Long limbs relative to trunk length are an adaptation to ground-living and their function is to lengthen the stride. Short limbs are an adaptation to certain types of arboreal locomotion, particularly arboreal quadrupedalism, where their function is to lower the centre of gravity and, thus, to ensure stability. Other forms of arboreal locomotion, such as the brachiation of the gibbons, are associated with *lengthening* of the forelimbs. Although the forces acting on the forelimb in brachiation are reversed (inasmuch as the forelimbs are suspending the body rather than supporting it from below) the lengthening of the limb is functionally analagous to that of ground-living forms; its effect is to increase the length of the "arm-stride". Relative lengthening of the hindlimbs is the characteristic adaptation of Vertical Clinging and Leaping forms such as *Galago*, *Indri* and *Tarsius*. Thus, the lengths of the limbs relative to the length of the trunk reflect both the habitat and the nature of the locomotor habit:

Short limbs   — Arboreal   — Adaptation for quadrupedal gait.
Long limbs   — Ground-living — Adaptation for quadrupedal gait.
Long forelimbs — Arboreal   — Adaptation for brachiation.
Long hindlimbs — Arboreal   — Adaptation for vertical clinging and leaping.

The bones of the forelimb show considerable variation in form, and in the nature of their articular surfaces, between locomotor groups while those of the hindlimb are much more conservative throughout the Order. The explanation is a functional one: that in spite of all the varied locomotor patterns of primates, there is little variation in the dynamics of the hindlimb; the bones and joints of the hindlimb are subject only to compressional forces whereas those of the forelimbs, which show considerable functional variation, are subject to both tensional *and* compressional forces. The conservatism of the hindlimb is reflected, *inter alia*, in the relative constancy of the Crural Index, (*see* Part III p. 393).

Although both arms and legs tend to become elongated in primate phylogeny the ratio between arm and leg length varies considerably. Three distinct patterns are discernible when the relative lengths of arms and legs are compared by means of the Intermembral Index:

$$\text{Length Humerus} + \text{Radius} \times 100 \ / \ \text{Length Femur} + \text{Tibia}.$$

The three patterns are as follows:

1. Short arms and long legs   — Intermembral index 50–80
2. Arms and legs subequal   — Intermembral index 80–100
3. Long arms and short legs   — Intermembral index 100–150

The ranges correspond with the three major locomotor patterns of primates: (1) Vertical Clingers; (2) Quadrupeds; (3) Brachiators. (Plate 5.)

The scapula shows a broad range of intrinsic adaptation in relation to the differing functions of the primate forelimb during locomotion, particularly between major locomotor groups such as brachiators and quadrupeds (Ashton and Oxnard, 1963).

2. OPPOSABILITY OF THUMB AND BIG TOE

Acquirement of prehensility of the hands and feet and of "opposability" of the thumb and big toe are among the most striking and important evolutionary trends of the primates.

PREHENSILITY OF HAND

The hand of treeshrews is typical of that of generalized mammals being non-prehensile and capable only of convergence and divergence of the digits. Treeshrews have short digits and long "thumbs". The term "thumb" is barely applicable as the pre-axial digit is hardly differentiated from the remaining digits either structurally or functionally. In one respect however the progressive hand of higher primates is adumbrated in the unique arrangement of the contrahentes muscles in *Tupaia* which favour, in their arrangement, the independent movement of the thumb. All other primates possess prehensility by virtue of relatively long digits and a divergent and mobile thumb, by which means objects held in the hand can be stabilised. The behavioural correlate of prehensility is the ability to hold food items in one hand; squirrels for instance, lacking prehensility, are habitually two-handed feeders.

OPPOSABILITY OF THUMB

A distinction should be made between true opposability of Hylobatidae, Cercopithecidae, Pongidae and Hominidae and the pseudo-opposability of remaining families (for a discussion of these terms *see* Part III p. 396). All primates that possess separate thumbs (Tupaiidae and Callitrichidae excepted) are capable of some sort of opposability at the carpo-metacarpal joint although the tarsier is an exception (Plate 1). In this animal the carpo-metacarpal joint is practically immobile and movement occurs at the metacarpo-phalangeal joint. The range of movement shown by the tarsier in the metacarpo-phalangeal joint is never wholly lost in primate phylogeny and is still an important movement in the human hand (Napier, 1952, 1961).

Opposability of the thumb in Cercopithecidae and Hominidae is associated with a specialized type of carpo-metacarpal joint and with the differentiation of thenar muscles particularly the deep head of flexor pollicis brevis (Day and Napier, 1963).

In the Pongidae, as a result of specializations of the hand for brachiation, the metacarpals and phalanges of digits 2–5 have become elongated; the thumb ray did not share in this elongation; on the contrary it underwent a certain amount of regression. Consequently,

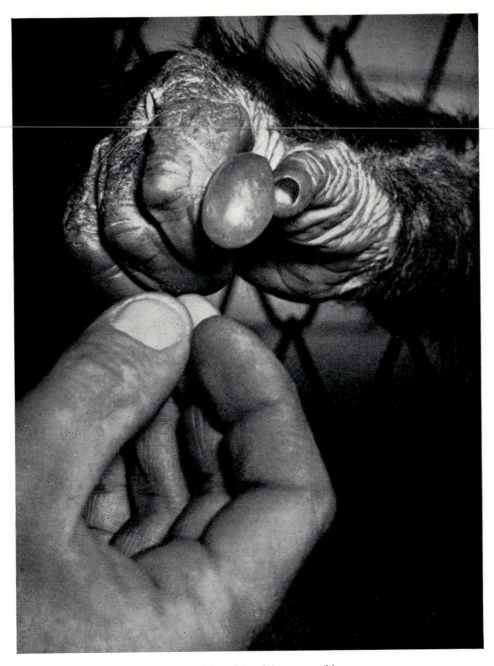

PLATE 1. Opposition of thumb in a young chimpanzee.

functional opposition, the behavioural ability to place thumb and finger tips together in the performance of precision grip, is considerably impaired in the large anthropoid apes. The length of the fingers and shortness of the thumb has the effect of making procedures such as picking up a grape (Plate 1) an effective but, in human terms, an imprecise activity.

The gibbons, an ancient offshoot of the Old World monkey stock, have acquired opposability of the thumb in a manner which is unique among primates. The carpo-metacarpal joint is not a typical "saddle" joint as it is in all other Old World monkeys, but a form of "ball and socket" joint. This specialization of gibbons associated with the deep cleft existing between their thumb and index fingers appears to be an adaptation, not so much for brachiation, as for climbing vertical tree trunks, an activity for which a wide span to the hand is required.

OPPOSABILITY OF BIG TOE

"Opposability" of the big toe is in reality a pseudo-opposability, in the sense that axial rotation of the metatarsal is absent. All primates except Tupaiidae and Hominidae possess "opposable" big toes irrespective of the degree to which opposability of the thumb is present. Fossil evidence derived from the Eocene lemuroid, *Notharctus*, strongly suggests that the "opposability" of the big toe is a more ancient possession of primates than opposability of the thumb. Among living primates the combination of an opposable big toe and a virtually non-opposable thumb is found in *Tarsius* and *Callithrix*.

Unlike the thumb, the big toe is never totally reduced in primates, although in the orangutan there is evidence of reduction affecting the nail-bearing terminal phalanx; this reduction is more common in females than in males (Tuttle and Rogers, 1966) and in Sumatran than Bornean orangs (Lyon, 1908). The big toe, however, varies in relative length and robusticity (Schultz, 1963a, 1964). The stoutest big toes are found in the Lorisidae, Indriidae and Lemuridae (Plate 2) where they constitute the principal means of support during clinging and climbing. The shortest big toes are found in marmosets, in ground-living Cercopithecidae such as geladas and patas monkeys, and in the orang-utan amongst the Pongidae. The reduction of the big toe in both length and robusticity in the gelada baboon (*Theropithecus*) is accompanied by other changes in relative metacarpal robusticity that show convergence with the adaptations of the feet of carnivora (Jolly, 1964). Man has both a long and extremely stout big toe which provides the principal leverage element during striding bipedalism. Apart from treeshrews, man is the only primate whose big toe is not divergent; the gorilla—particularly the highland race, *G. g. beringei*—shows the nearest approach to the human condition.

The importance of locomotor habit in relation to foot structure is well demonstrated in the Cercopithecinae. The savannah-living and therefore large terrestrial baboons have relatively short big toes; in contrast, in the more arboreal, forest-living drills and mandrills the big toe is very strongly developed. Habitat alone, however, is not responsible for the length of the hallux, large big toes being seen in savannah-living forms (man) and forest-living forms (mandrill). Short big toes are found in ground-living geladas and arboreal orang-utans. It is clear therefore that the robustness of the big toe depends on the adaptive characters of the gait itself rather than simply on habitat.

PLATE 2. Hands and feet of primates: a. Treeshrew hand; b. Potto hand; c. Tarsier hand; d. Tarsier foot; e. Macaque hand; f. Potto foot; g. Gorilla foot; h. Baboon foot.

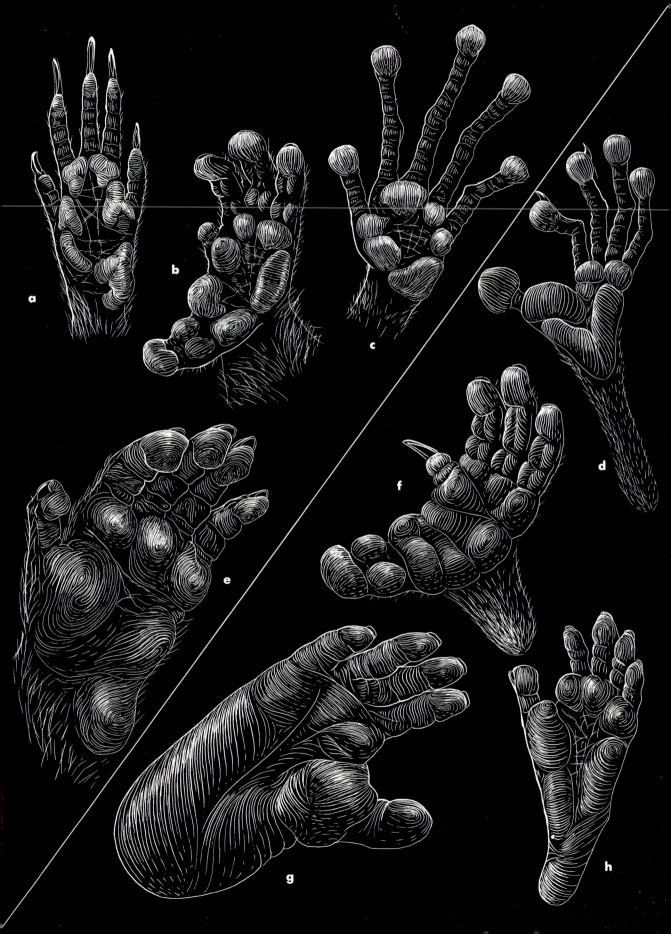

a

b

c

d

e

f

g

h

3. NAILS, CLAWS AND PADS

Modifications of the nails and of the palmar and plantar pads are closely associated with the development of specializations in the thumb and big toe of primates.

NAILS

All living primates with the exception of Tupaiidae, Daubentoniidae and Callitrichidae are provided with flat or flattish nails on the ends of their digits. The broader the terminal phalanges, the broader and flatter is the nail; thus, in most primates, the thumb or the big toe bears the flattest nail. The claw-like nail of the Callitrichidae has been the subject of much controversy. Some authorities have regarded it as a secondary *reversion* from a flat nail to a claw but Clark (1936) after an histological analysis of claws and nails, concluded that it was a progressive structure, a modified claw intermediate between a true claw and a nail. Only in the Tupaiidae does the big toe bear a claw; in all other families it carries a flat nail; in Lemuridae, Lorisidae and Indriidae, the second toe bears a claw ("toilet claw"); in Tarsiidae, the second and third toes bear toilet claws. In 60% of orang-utans, in association with the grossly reduced function of the hallux, there is complete absence of the nail.

PADS

The prosimian families show a primitive arrangement of the palmar and plantar pads; each of the eleven pads form discrete hillocks. The single exception to this generalization is the indris where palmar and plantar pads are not differentiated. In the New and Old World anthropoid families, the palmar and plantar pads are much reduced and are more-or-less confluent with the skin of the palm (Plate 2). In digitigrade primates such as baboons the interdigital pads are somewhat enlarged to constitute walking pads, functionally analogous to the heel of a plantigrade foot. In the Hylobatidae, Pongidae and, particularly, the Hominidae, the primary pads are barely discernible except for their characteristic dermatoglyphic patterns which continue to form part of the surface architecture of the foot and hand.

CUTANEOUS END ORGANS

Primates are characterized by possession of muco-cutaneous end-organs and Meissner-like endings in hairless skin (Winkelman, 1963). Meissner's corpuscles are best developed in Pongidae and Hominidae and least developed in Lorisidae; of all primates, man shows the most complex Meissner's corpuscles. Although Tupaiidae (e.g. *Urogale*) apparently lack all organized endings in glabrous skin, the typical mammalian end-organs have not yet been found (*loc. cit.*).

The specialization of the thumb and big toe, the independence and elaboration of digital movements, the confluence of palmar and plantar pads, the replacement of claws by nails and the increasing complexity of the peripheral sensory mechanisms subserving tactile discriminatory functions, constitute the correlated series of trends that characterize the primate hand and foot.

4. MUZZLES, NOSES AND THE OLFACTORY SENSE

Broadly speaking the importance of the olfactory sense in primates is inversely proportional to the development of the mobility and sensitivity of the hands, as outlined in the last two sections, and to the evolution of overlapping visual fields to be discussed in the next.

The possession of a well-developed olfactory sense in some prosimian families is often used as an argument in favour of a ground-living origin for the primates, on the basis that a good sense of smell is of little advantage to tree-dwellers. However it is manifest that non-primate tree-dwellers, such as the squirrels, find plenty of reasons for retaining this special sense. It seems more likely that the debasement of olfaction in higher primates is an outcome of their *specialized* arboreality which has little in common with that of squirrels or any other tree-living Eutherian mammal.* The principal adaptations of primate arboreality are their manipulative and visual abilities. Improvement in these functions provided a much more effective—three-dimensional—means of exploring the environment than olfaction, which was thus gradually superseded as a prime sense. The morphological correlates of specialized visual and olfactory functions (the frontality of the orbits and a well-developed olfactory snout) are to some extent incompatible; in the Tarsiidae, for instance, the frontality and gross enlargement of the orbits have led to an actual physical compression of the nasal space: clearly, however, this is a special case.

The existence of a projecting muzzle or a strongly prognathic face in primates is not necessarily correlated with a highly developed sense of smell; nor is the presence of a complicated turbinal system wholly indicative of the importance of olfaction, for olfactory nerve-endings are not widely distributed over the mucous membrane of the nose but are rather strictly limited to the upper part of the cavity. A muzzle or snout may be associated with (*a*) a highly evolved olfactory sense as in Tupaiidae, or (*b*) an enlarged masticatory apparatus as in some Cercopithecidae (e.g. *Papio*) and some Pongidae (e.g. *Gorilla*), or (*c*) an enlargement of the larynx as in some Cebidae (e.g. *Alouatta*).

OLFACTORY MUZZLE

An "olfactory" muzzle is characteristic of certain Lemuridae and Lorisidae. The crucial factor which determines an "olfactory" muzzle in primates is not the length of the snout so much as the presence of a moist, naked rhinarium, curved nostrils, a naked philtrum and a tethered upper lip (strepsirrhine condition). In the majority of Cebidae the nostrils are wide apart (platyrrhine condition) but in the Cercopithecidae and ape and human families they are separated by only a narrow septum (catarrhine condition). The absence of a primitive type of philtrum allows the musculature of the face to spread across the upper lip and so facilitate its mobility; the mobile upper lip constitutes an important component of facial expression and vocal communication.

A progressive reduction in the importance of "marking" behaviour above prosimian level is associated with the debasement of the olfactory sense. The morphological basis of "marking" lies in the specialized cutaneous glands (allied to sweat glands) that are so prominent in Lemuridae and Tupaiidae. "Marking" behaviour is not wholly lost in anthropoid families, for

* Some Metatherian mammals such as the phalangers have become adapted to tree-life in a manner which is convergent with that of primates.

the Cebidae indulge in a form of urine marking similar to that seen in Lorisidae (Hill, 1957). Even in the Hylobatidae, Pongidae and Hominidae, although marking activity is absent, specialized glands are retained in certain regions of the body (e.g. in the axilla in *Homo*).

DENTAL MUZZLE

A "dental" muzzle is characteristic of certain of the ground-living Cercopithecidae, particularly the baboons* and the mandrills; in the latter genus the prognathism is exaggerated by the presence of striking paranasal bony swellings covered by highly coloured skin which appear to have little organic function and therefore, by default, are considered to be adornments having a social or sexual significance as signalling devices. Most of the remaining Cercopithecidae, the guenons and the colobine monkeys of Africa and Asia, are relatively flat-faced as are the Hominidae and the typical Cebidae (Plate 3). Among the Pongidae, the gorilla and the chimpanzee are the most prognathic; the orang-utan, *Pongo*, has a "dished" face that reveals that it is the forward growth of the upper and lower jaw that produces the prognathic effect seen in all great apes, rather than growth of the nasal bones, which in *Pongo* remain quite short. Likewise in the gelada baboons (*Theropithecus*) the face is moderately prognathic due to the presence of heavy jaws and large teeth but the nose is short and retroussé.

NOSES

Noses in the sense of an external nose consisting of nasal bones and fleshy and cartilaginous elements are not unduly obtrusive in the non-human primates; only among the colobine sub-family of Cercopithecidae and in Pongidae (e.g. *Gorilla*) are they remarkable. Among the Colobinae, both *Rhinopithecus* and *Simias* have short triangular-shaped tip-tilted or snub noses; in *Colobus*, on the other hand, particularly the black and white variety, the nose is rounded and overhangs the upper lip. However, it is in *Nasalis* that the colobine nose reaches its apogee; in the female the nose is triangular-shaped and projecting in profile view; in the male it is an enormously protuberant, fleshy organ that overhangs the mouth; the nares are completely inverted, opening on its undersurface. The external nose of *Nasalis* has no olfactory function; it has generally been regarded as a secondary sex characteristic. Functionally, it acts as an accessory vocal organ. The honking sound emitted by the adult male proboscis monkey owes its reverberating character to the resonating chamber effect produced by the nose. The nose is also used effectively by the male in threat display. The gorilla has a broad prominent nose formed by long nasal bones and by thickening and expansion of the alar folds; in this character it is clearly distinguished from most chimpanzees (except the occasional old male. Keith, 1899).

5. EYES AND VISION.
EARS AND THE AUDITORY SENSE

The elaboration of the visual mechanism in diurnal primates is an adaptation to specialized arboreal life in which a high premium is placed on the ability to judge distances accurately in

---

* Scott (1963) points out that, in baboons, both dental *and* olfactory factors account for the prominence of the muzzle.

PLATE 3. Lateral view of the skulls of primates: a. Chimpanzee $\times \frac{1}{2}$; b. Gibbon $\times \frac{2}{3}$; c. Marmoset $\times 1$; d. Treeshrew $\times \frac{3}{4}$; e. Guenon $\times \frac{5}{8}$; f. Spider monkey $\times \frac{3}{5}$; g. Potto $\times 1$; h. Patas monkey $\times \frac{3}{5}$; i. Macaque $\times \frac{2}{3}$; j. Mouse lemur $\times \frac{4}{5}$; k. Baboon $\times \frac{1}{2}$. Scales approximate.

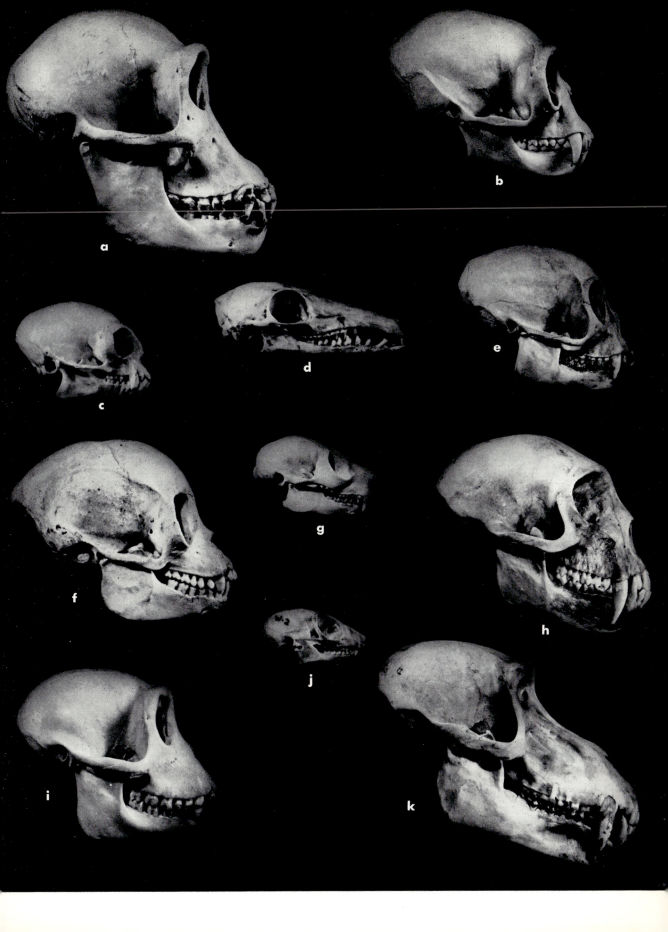

jumping and leaping and on the finer discriminatory functions required in searching for and manipulating food. Visual judgment of spatial relationships depends on two factors, overlapping of the visual fields and the presence of a cone-type retina with a *fovea centralis*.

OVERLAPPING OF VISUAL FIELDS

In the earliest known fossil primate, *Plesiadapis* of the Palaeocene of North America and Europe, the orbits are directed laterally and lack an outer rim, the so-called post-orbital bar, both generalized mammalian characteristics. By the Eocene the lemur-like Adapidae possessed a degree of frontality of the orbits, a post-orbital bar but no total post-orbital closure. In the Upper Eocene European tarsioids such as *Necrolemur* showed complete frontality but the post-orbital closure, though incipient, was incomplete. (Simons 1963; Simons and Russell, 1960).

The evolutionary trend towards frontality of the orbits has not proceeded as far in the prosimian as in the anthropoid families. Treeshrews retain a mammal-like divergence of the orbits whose axes subtend an angle of approximately 140°; a post-orbital bar, however, is present. In the Lemuridae this angle has been reduced to 60°–70° and, in anthropoid families, to 30°. It must be noted however that the visual axis and the axis of the orbital cavity do not correspond, the latter being always more divergent than the former; in Cercopithecidae for instance the optical axes are parallel in spite of a 30° divergence of the orbits. Stereoscopic vision increases as the angle between the optical axes is reduced; when the two fields of vision wholly overlap one another, a point in space is then focused on both retinae at once.

The post-orbital bar (present in all living primate families) and total post-orbital closure (present in all living anthropoid families) are structural modifications of the skull that develop in response to the mechanical demands for forwardly directed orbits (Plate 3).

While frontality of the orbits is associated with the acquisition of binocular vision it is also accompanied by a reduction of the total field of vision. In *Tarsius* and in other members of the Vertical Clinging and Leaping group (e.g. *Indri*) for whom a wide field of vision is a great advantage, an exaggerated range of neck rotation can presumably be regarded as a "compensatory" adaptation.

Reduction of the length of the "olfactory" muzzle also tends to be associated with the acquirement of binocular vision for general reasons already given in the previous section. The skull of the baboon demonstrates, however, that a long muzzle and frontally-facing orbits are not incompatible. As a consequence of the marked degree of flexion of the cranial base, which results in the ventral displacement of the nasal chamber and the dentary in respect of the neurocranium, these animals have a clear field of vision over the top of the muzzle (Plate 3k).

RETINAL ANATOMY

All primates except the few nocturnal forms possess photoreceptors of two kinds in the retina, rods and cones. In nocturnal primates, as in nocturnal mammals, the cones are wanting. The function of the cones, which respond to changes at high light intensity, is greater resolving power and therefore fine discrimination, and colour vision; rods have a lower threshold and therefore are able to respond to low intensity light. Cones predominate towards the centre of the retina where there is a yellow pigmented region of high cone-density known as the macula; a small depression, the fovea, is found in the centre of the macula. The fovea, which is the point of maximal visual acuity, is avascular and composed entirely of cones which are separated from the cavity of the eye only by the inner limiting membrane of the retina. Pure rod retinae are found in all the nocturnal Lorisidae (*Loris, Perodicticus, Galago,* etc.) and in some of the Lemuridae (e.g. *Cheirogaleus, Microcebus*) and in *Tarsius.* Among anthropoid families the only monkey to lack cones is the cebid genus *Aotus,* the night-monkey or Douroucouli. A macula is present in all primates; but with the exception of *Tarsius,* prosimians have no true fovea (Polyak, 1957). Le Gros Clark (1959) has discussed the phylogenetic implications of the retina of *Tarsius* and *Aotus* which possesses a fovea (the anatomical correlate of photopic or cone vision) and yet is entirely lacking in cones.

The majority of primates have become adapted to specialized arboreal life by *acquiring* stereoscopic vision and *retaining* a mammalian rod and cone retina. The nocturnal forms have, to a varying extent, *acquired* stereoscopy but have lost their cones. The possession of a high visual acuity in primates is complementary to the high degree of manipulative accuracy of the hands. Henry J. Watt, in 1925, wrote: "The fovea refines and distinguishes positions and forms, while accommodation sharpens the object of attention and dissipates the rest; stereoscopy adds a new character to a group of forms that may persist for indefinite periods of observations; delicate skin gives greater sensitivity to variations of pressure and the prehensile hand implies a very great refinement in the positions and forms in the derived articular sense. In the hand this becomes a fine mobile tri-dimensional sense that, like the stereoscopic eye, thus almost can go round and through things, isolating them from their surroundings."

AUDITORY REGION

The structure of the bony, external and middle ear of primates provides characters which are of considerable taxonomic and phylogenetic valency, inasmuch as they display little adaptive variation within major taxa.* The osseous floor of the tympanum or middle ear in all primates is derived from the petrous part of the temporal bone. In all prosimian families the floor of the middle ear is ballooned out to form a tympanic bulla; this character is also found in the New World families. The lateral wall of the tympanic cavity in all anthropoid families and in the Tarsiidae and Lorisidae is formed by the tympanum or ear drum which is encircled by a bony ring, the tympanic ring. In Lemuridae and Tupaiidae the tympanic ring, which is derived from the ectotympanic portion of the temporal bone, is enveloped within the bulla; the lateral wall of the bulla is derived from the petrous temporal bone, itself, and not from the ectotympanic bone, which has a completely separate developmental history.† The presence of a tympanic ring *within* the bulla, is a distinguishing character of lemurs and treeshrews. The external auditory meatus, which is a lateral prolongation of the tympanic ring to form a bony tube, is seen in *Tarsius* and in Old World families. In Lorisidae and New World families, the ring is exposed on the side of the skull and the bony external auditory tube is absent or very short. To summarize these important diagnostic characters: (i) A tympanic bulla is present in Tupaiidae, Tarsiidae, Lemuridae, Indriidae, Daubentoniidae, Lorisidae, Callitrichidae and Cebidae; (ii) An exposed tympanic ring is present in Lorisidae, Callitrichidae and Cebidae;

---

* The ossicles of the middle ear which have been studied by Doran (1879) show certain variable characters of taxonomic moment. The form of the inner ear, on the other hand, shows little variation in primates.

† Van Valen (1965) states that the bulla of treeshrews is formed from an entotympanic ossification and is probably not, therefore, a homologue of the primate bulla. Spatz (1966) agrees with this derivation but reaches an opposite phylogenetic conclusion.

B

(iii) an external auditory meatus is present in Tarsiidae, Cercopithecidae, Hylobatidae, Pongidae and Hominidae.

All primates possess ears potentially capable of being moved; this is true even in man. Mobility may be both intrinsic and extrinsic, or purely extrinsic. Intrinsic movement refers to the ability of certain primates—usually those of nocturnal habit—to fold the pinna on itself in a concertina-like fashion; extrinsic movement describes the ability to "scan" with the ears by altering their orientation with reference to the head. This function may be highly developed in certain nocturnal prosimian forms such as galagos or restricted to a simple retraction or flattening movement of very limited magnitude in the anthropoid families; broadly speaking primate ears can be classified into mobile and (relatively) immobile types.

The mobile ear is large, membranous and dish-like; on the inner surface of the pinna there are a number of alternating ribs and grooves that represent the sites of intrinsic folding which is activated by an intrinsic muscular system—the corrugator pinnae; the extrinsic muscles, both pre- and post-auricular in position are also well-developed. The mobile ear is most highly specialized in *Galago* and *Tarsius* and is seen in a less extreme form in some of the Lemuridae (e.g. *Microcebus*, *Phaner*) and in *Ptilocercus* among the Tupaiidae. All primate forms in which the highly mobile ear is found are nocturnal in habit. The diurnal treeshrew, *Tupaia*, possess a small rounded, relatively immobile and flattened pinna, reminiscent of the anthropoid ear. Clark (1959) observes that the subfamily that comprehends the nocturnal lorises (e.g. *Nycticebus*, *Loris*) possesses less specialized ears than the subfamily Galaginae; he suggests that this may be related to the differing requirements for temperature regulation in the slow-climbing lorises and in the rapid, energetic, leaping galagos.

The remainder of prosimian families and all the anthropoid families (including the nocturnal cebid *Aotus*) possess relatively immobile ears. They are generally small, oval or nearly circular in shape and show some degree of inrolling at their free edge. Mobility is largely extrinsic and varies considerably. Lemuridae show a moderate degree of protraction and retraction. Cercopithecidae show only retraction of a limited degree and in Pongidae the ears are practically immobile as they are in the Hominidae. Van Hooff (1962) has observed that among the Cercopithecidae the greatest degree of retraction is found in the wholly or partly ground-living genera (*Papio*, *Macaca*, *Mandrillus* and *Cercocebus*).

In addition to an auditory function, the ears of primates serve as signalling devices. In *Callithrix*, the variety of ear tufts and plumes of different form and colour constitute a highly visual means of species recognition. The role of the ears as components in communication through facial expression in anthropoid families has been discussed by Van Hooff (1962).

The external morphology of the ear is dealt with in a number of monographs by Pocock (1918, 1920, 1925a), and the musculature of the ear by Huber (1931). The malleus and the incus have been studied by Masali and Chiarelli (in press) with particular reference to the taxonomic position of the gibbons, which they find, in respect of morphometric characteristics, closer to the Cercopithecidae than to the Pongidae.

6. THE TEETH, DIGESTION AND DIET

A heterodont dentition consisting of incisors, canines and two sorts of cheek teeth is a primitive mammalian possession which has been tenaciously retained by all primates with the single exception of the dentally aberrant genus *Daubentonia*. The principal changes from the primitive mammalian dentition are a reduction in the *number* of teeth from 44 to 32 or 36, a functional specialization in incisors and canines, and a modification of the cusp pattern of the cheek teeth.

DENTAL FORMULA

The primitive mammalian formula is assumed to have been: $\frac{3}{3}\frac{1}{1}\frac{4}{4}\frac{3}{3}=44$. No living primates have retained three incisors in the upper jaw and the only family to have retained the 3rd incisor in the lower jaw is the Tupaiidae. The premolars have been reduced from four to three in the prosimian families and in New World monkey families; in the remainder—the Old World monkey, ape and human families—a further reduction to two has taken place. In the molar series the primitive number of $M.\frac{123}{123}$ is generally retained but there is a tendency among primates for the reduction or loss of the 3rd molar, thus:

Habitually absent: *Callithrix, Cebuella, Saguinus, Leontideus*.
Frequently absent: *Hylobates, Homo*.
Retrogressive changes: *Propithecus, Indri, Aotus, Callicebus, Saimiri, Cebus, Lagothrix, Ateles, Brachyteles, Callimico, Pan, Tupaia* (M.$\frac{3}{}$ only): *Perodicticus* (M.$\frac{3}{}$ only).

All the genera listed fall into the category of "short-faced" primates. The Cercopithecidae, a family which contains many "long-faced" genera, show the opposite trend, that is to say towards an enlargement of M.$\frac{3}{3}$. In addition the lower 3rd molar frequently bears a 5th cusp, (*Papio, Mandrillus, Colobus* etc., but not *Cercopithecus* or *Erythrocebus*). Long-faced monkeys constitute the more specialized group of the Cercopithecidae, at least as far as their jaws and dentition are concerned. Both *Gorilla* and *Pongo* (Pongidae) show a similar reversal of the trend, having M.$\frac{}{3}$ often larger than M.$\frac{}{2}$. *Pongo* even shows a high incidence of supernumerary molars. The less dentally specialized *Pan* and *Homo* show a common tendency for M.$\frac{3}{3}$ to be smaller than M.$\frac{2}{2}$. In *Homo*, M.$\frac{3}{3}$ are quite frequently absent. Agenesis of 3rd molar is reported to be greatest in Eskimoes (Moorees, 1957) and lowest in Negroes (Fanning, 1960). In white females Nanda (1954) found true agenesis in 9%. Among the Hylobatidae, the larger genus, *Symphalangus* shows no sign of reduction of M.$\frac{3}{3}$ while in the relatively small gibbons (*Hylobates*) these teeth are frequently absent.

The Miocene fossil species *Proconsul africanus*, generally regarded as closely related to the ancestral line of living chimpanzees, shows retrogressive changes in upper 3rd molar (Clark and Leakey, 1951). *Proconsul africanus* was also a "short-faced" form as has been recently shown (Davis and Napier, 1963). All in all, it would seem that loss of M.$\frac{3}{3}$ is an evolutionary trend of the primate order, although certain specialized forms (principally the large ground-living primates) show a trend in the opposite direction.

INCISORS AND CANINES

Among the primates the anterior teeth are much less conservative in their morphology than are the cheek teeth. Their position at the front of the mouth, and hence their deployment for functions other than those concerned with seizing and chopping food, seems to offer a possible explanation for the variety of forms they display. The upper incisors show little variety although they tend to be small and peg-like in the prosimians (apart from *Daubentonia*) and broad and spatulate in the anthropoid families. In *Daubentonia* both upper and lower incisors are reduced to a single pair and have assumed a rodent-like shape and growth pattern. The lower incisors of certain Cebidae (e.g. *Cacajao, Pithecia* and *Chiropotes*) show procumbency of a moderate degree, but it is in the prosimian families (excluding Tarsiidae and Dauben-toniidae) that extreme procumbency is found. In Lorisidae, Indriidae and Lemuridae, the lower central and lateral incisors, plus the canines, form a series of slender closely-packed, horizontally-projecting teeth which constitute the so-called dental comb. A similar, though less specialized, arrangement is seen in the treeshrews. The significance of the dental comb has been discussed recently by Buettner-Janusch and Andrew (1964) who regard it primarily as a grooming device; any alimentary function that it possesses is purely secondary.

Found under the tongue in lemurs and lorises is a horny denticulated structure, the sublingua. This structure is functionally associated with the dental comb and has been aptly described by Clark (1959) as a "toothbrush"; its principal function being to rid the comb of hairs and debris. The sublingua is vestigial in the Anthropoidea being represented by a fold of mucous membrane, the plica fimbriata.

The canines show considerable variation in primates in respect of size, shape, projection and degree of interlocking; the canines also show sexual dimorphism in certain genera. Apart from the Hominidae, all families show some degree of projection of canines beyond the tooth row; this is usually more pronounced in the upper jaw than in the lower. Even in man the upper canines may project below the occlusal surface of the tooth row to a greater degree than the lower canines. The degree of projection and stoutness of the tooth varies considerably, particularly among the Cebidae. *Callicebus*, for instance, shows relatively little projection while in *Chiropotes*, the canines are long and extremely stout. The longest and sharpest canines are found among ground-living Cercopithecidae; and the most massive among the Pongidae.

The occurrence of sexual dimorphism in canine size in Cercopithecidae and Pongidae suggests that their prime function, (and therefore their significance in natural selection) is not wholly alimentary. However there is no doubt from the massive form and from the evidence of wear in the *Gorilla* for instance, that they are not mere adornment: and are probably used by this animal for stripping bark. The slender, dagger-like canines of baboons (which being vegetarians have no need for carnivorous adaptations) have a non-alimentary function which would appear to be associated with the rôle of the male in the social organization of the troop. In baboon troops the dominant male controls the troop, limits intra-group fighting and protects the young; all these functions are performed with the minimum of actual aggression; the threat of aggression being the principal device. When troop relationships are stabilized, even threat is rare (Hall, 1964). Threat also operates in predator defence, an aggressive display by large males being very often sufficient to discourage attack by cheetahs or leopards. These remarks apply equally to the macaques, a genus in which sexual dimorphism in canine size (as well as body size) is also striking. Some families, such as the Hylobatidae, show little or no sexual dimorphism in canine (or body-) size. The social structure of gibbons and siamangs is based on the family unit rather than on the troop and it would seem that a different explanation for the large canine size of Hylobatidae is required. Carpenter (1940) found little evidence of inter-group aggression in wild populations of gibbons although recent observations of Frisch (1963) on the frequency of broken canines in gibbons suggest that fighting between different groups does occur and that the males are the protagonists. New light has been thrown on the territoriality of one species of gibbon, *Hylobates lar*, by the field observations of Ellefson (in press) who describes inter-group aggression as commonplace leading not infrequently to actual physical encounters between males.

Other aspects of primate behaviour such as communication through facial expression need to be studied, to understand this aspect of the role of the front teeth; there is little doubt that the grin-face of most primates, the "snarl" of the baboon and mandrill and the smile of man as well as other expressions that expose the teeth, such as yawning, are displays of profound significance for primate communication.

PREMOLARS AND MOLARS

The evolutionary trend in both the molar and premolar series has been to increase the number of cusps, though primates may be regarded as the most conservative of mammals in this respect. The primitive premolars are homodont and unicuspid; in non-human anthropoid families, with the exception of the anterior lower premolars, they are bicuspid, an additional medial cusp having been derived from the cingulum. The anterior lower premolar in Cercopithecidae and Pongidae is a unicuspid tooth modified to form a shearing surface against which the upper canine plays; this type of tooth is usually referred to as sectorial.

In Hominidae, both fossil and living, both upper and lower premolars are homodont and bicuspid.

In prosimian families on the whole a unicuspid condition prevails but in this group the anterior and posterior premolars tend to become specialized away from the typical premolar form. The anterior premolar assumes a caniniform form and function in certain Lemuridae (e.g. *Phaner*, and to a lesser extent in *Lepilemur*) and the posterior premolar becomes molarized in Lorisidae and Tupaiidae, though not in Lemuridae or Tarsiidae.

The primitive Eutherian condition of tritubercular upper molars, with a raised trigone and a talon basin persists in Tupaiidae and Tarsiidae. The evolutionary trend in primates as far as the *upper molars* are concerned, is the development of a true hypocone. In the Lemuridae and Indriidae several stages of this metamorphosis are seen: the molars are tritubercular in Cheirogalinae; they present an incipient hypocone in *Lemur* and *Hapalemur*; a hypocone is present on M.^{2} in *Lepilemur* and *Phaner*, and full quadritubercular status is shown by Indriidae. The Lorisidae also show four cusps although the size of the hypocone varies from genus to genus.

Among the anthropoid families, only Callitrichidae retain tritubercular molars; all other families show the quadri- or quinquetubercular condition. In Cercopithecidae the upper molars show marked waisting between anterior and posterior pairs of cusps; each pair of cusps is united by a strong transverse ridge (bilophodont condition). The dentition of the gelada baboon shows these characteristics in a most exaggerated form (Jolly, 1964). In the ape and human families, there is no bilophodonty; instead the antero-internal and postero-external cusps are joined by an oblique ridge (a similarly disposed ridge is also found in the New World genera *Ateles* and *Alouatta*).

The trend in the *lower molars* has been towards a modification of the original trigonid by the loss of one cusp (paraconid); the elevation of the talonid basin until the occlusal surfaces of trigonid and talonid are level; the enlargement of the talonid cusps (hypoconid and entoconid) to form a quadricuspid tooth; and the development of a 5th cusp, postero-lateral in position—the hypoconulid. The quadricuspid lower molar is seen in all Prosimian families, other than Tupaiidae and Tarsiidae; it is also seen in the Cebidae, Callitrichidae and Cercopithecidae. In the Pongidae the lower molars bear five cusps (Y5 pattern) and are further distinguished from those of Cercopithecidae by the absence of bilophodonty. Most genera of Cercopithecidae have a fifth cusp on the talonid of M.$_{\overline{3}}$, the exceptions being *Erythrocebus* and *Cercopithecus*. In the human family the quadricuspid condition ($+4$ pattern) is often seen.

DIET AND DIGESTION

The relationship between tooth form, alimentary tract morphology and diet in the primates is not a very obvious one. Hill (1956b) listed the vegetable and animal components of primate diet in an arboreal environment:

Vegetable: Fruits, flowers, leaves, bark, pith, seeds, roots, tubers and nuts.
Animal: Birds, birds' eggs, lizards, spiders, insects, frogs and crustacea.

To extend this list to embrace the diet of ground-living, extra-forest forms, one would need to include grasses and small mammals. Both the patas monkey (*Erythrocebus*) and the baboon (*Papio*) include large quantities of grass in the staple diet; in the latter genus, occasional meat-eating is well established (Dart, 1963; Washburn and De Vore, 1963; De Vore, 1965). Recent evidence from field studies (Goodall, 1963) reveal that the eating of freshly-killed meat is occasionally observed in chimpanzees. The general impression gained from reports of meat-eating among primates is that it is very much an *ad hoc* affair, a matter of learned behaviour. This view receives support from the fact well known to zoo authorities that primates in captivity, even *Gorilla* which is a strict vegetarian in nature, will readily eat meat if presented (Crandall, 1964).

Generally speaking, primates are omnivorous: relatively few of them are restricted in diet and none are restricted to the extent found in some non-primate mammals such as for instance the koala bear and the giant panda. The leaf-eating monkeys and certain of the lemurs are probably the only primates which can be regarded as having a narrowly specialized diet in the wild. Leaf-eating monkeys include the Asian langurs and African colobus monkeys (Colobinae), *Alouatta* (the howler monkey) and the Madagascan family, Indriidae. In captivity,

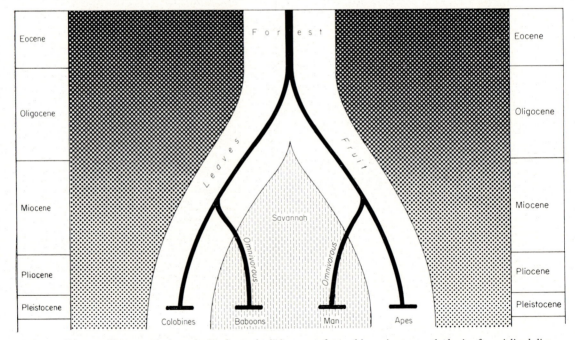

FIG. 2. Diagram illustrates the hypothesis of an early dichotomy of catarrhine primates on the basis of specialized diet. Secondary occupation of a savannah niche by progressive Cercopithecoidea (leading to modern baboons) and progressive Hominoidea (leading to modern man) was accompanied, *inter alia*, by adoption of an omnivorous diet.

colobs, langurs and howler-monkeys do well on fruit and vegetables. The aberrant aye-aye (Daubentonia) is largely insectivorous but also eats fruit; galagos may be largely insectivorous in the wild. Some of the Pithecinae (*Pithecia*, *Chiropotes*) are reported to be wholly frugivorous as judged from stomach-content analysis (Fooden, 1964b).

In primates dental adaptations to diet, as might be expected from this lack of specialization, are not particularly obtrusive. The most extreme behavioural adaptation is that of *Daubentonia* which adopts a rodent-like gnawing action for excavating wood-boring insects. Other adaptations that can be correlated with the diet are the large size of the molar series in *Gorilla* which is a bulk vegetarian, the sharply-pointed molar cusps of *Tarsius*, *Aotus* and *Galago* etc. related to their largely insectivorous habits; and the unique form of upper and lower molars in the leaf-eating howler monkeys. Other striking dental characters such as the broad spatulate upper incisors of Pongidae and the bilophodont pattern of cercopithecid molars may also be dietetic specializations; these dental characters may indeed be of considerable phylogenetic significance indicating a separation of the early catarrhine primates into two main ecological types; fruit-eaters and leaf-eaters. Although these dietary distinctions are somewhat blurred in modern catarrhine families as a result, it is presumed, of secondary ecological shifts, the ancient dichotomy is still apparent between the leaf-eating Colobinae and the fruit-eating Pongidae and Hylobatidae (Fig. 2).

DIGESTIVE SYSTEM

A similar lack of specialization is seen in the alimentary systems of primates. Characters of the visceral system thus provide important evidence, as do the teeth, of phylogenetic relationships within the Order. Adaptive changes in the alimentary tract, which can satisfactorily be correlated with diet, affect principally the stomach, the caecum and the colon. Among leaf-eaters, for example, the stomach is large and shows some tendency towards sacculation (particularly in Colobinae); the caecum and colon are voluminous. Defaecation patterns vary considerably with the nature of the diet. Highland gorillas which are bulk eaters defaecate five or six times a day whereas the Western race, whose diet contains a higher proportion of fruit, seldom defaecate more than once daily. This physiological difference may probably be correlated with the observation that nests of Western gorillas are usually free of excreta; the highland race almost invariably foul their nests.

Leaf-eating primates also exhibit large salivary glands. Cheek pouches, another adaptation that might loosely be regarded as alimentary, are seen in the family Cercopithecidae; these capacious extensions of the cheeks that extend below the ramus of the mandible to meet almost in the midline, are crammed with food which is then pushed back into the mouth by hand, chewed and swallowed at leisure. It has been suggested that cheek pouches have much the same physiological function as the modified stomachs of leaf-eating monkeys, thus either one or other are present in catarrhine monkeys but not both. While the latter fact is undoubtedly so, the suggested analogy seems unlikely; there is no indication that digestion is occurring while the food is held in the cheek pouches; and recovery from cheek pouches can not really be regarded as analogous to the regurgitation of ruminants. Furthermore, leaf-eating monkeys never ruminate or regurgitate their food (Ayer, 1948). The leaf-eating stomach is not comparable to the ruminant stomach but is merely an exaggeration of the typically tripartite primate stomach. The adaptive significance of cheek pouches is not at all easy to understand; they occur throughout the Cercopithecinae (but are absent in Colobinae) and therefore must be presumed to be a relatively recent possession. Their survival value to modern cercopithecines, many of whom obtain their food by raiding native plantations, is obvious, but it is not so easy to see their significance for past populations. This feeding habit however may indicate that in the past the Cercopithecinae were more ground-living than they are today. Cheek pouches would be a highly advantageous adaptation for monkeys living at the forest edge or in a forest-savannah mosaic type habitat and foraging in open savannah.

Tomes (1923) pointed out that there was less variation in the teeth of primates than in their diet. The validity of this statement is questionable, for the diet, with few exceptions, is remarkably homogeneous from the point of view of composition and consistency, and the teeth show a great many adaptive specializations within the framework of the generalized primate dentition. Not all these adaptations however are related to diet (*vide supra*). The teeth would undoubtedly have shown greater adaptation to such dietary differences as exist, were it not for the early differentiation of the forelimbs as prehensile organs. Hands which are capable of seizing food, manipulating and breaking it up, can take over effectively many of the functions that in mammals without specialized hands, are performed by the teeth. Food which is picked by hand does not require to be bitten off; and food which is torn apart in the hands requires less mastication. Man, as a result of his cultural advances in the use of fire for cooking and tools for eating, has now taken the process one stage further by relieving even his hands of these responsibilities.

JAW SIZE

Generally speaking among the primates the expansion of the brain and thus of the brain case, and the reduction in jaw size associated with a secondment to the hands of some of the food-getting functions of mammals, has made unnecessary the addition to the skull vault of a sagittal crest for the hypertrophied jaw muscles. The neurocranium supplies a sufficiently wide area of attachment for the temporalis muscle in most primates to obviate the mechanical need for a sagittal crest. In larger primates such as baboons, gorillas and orangs which possess heavy jaws, sagittal crests are commonly seen in the male and only rarely seen in females. It is well known that whereas the relative size of the brain case *decreases* as the absolute body size of an animal *increases*, the relative size of the jaws increases with the body size. In the skulls of large monkeys such as baboons and mandrills the brain-case looks relatively small compared with the facial skeleton; the reverse is true in small monkeys such as talapoins. This is an expression of allometric growth. It has been shown that there is a constant relationship between body size and facial length in *Papio* (Freedman, 1957, 1962; Jolly, 1964); this correlation is independent of sex however. Because of the sexual dimorphism which exists in baboon populations, the longest faces (and therefore the largest sagittal crests), naturally, are found in males. The combination of relatively large jaws and relatively small neurocrania makes the provision of additional bone surface obligatory for attachment of the jaw musculature. In chimpanzees a very low sagittal crest is occasionally found in males but only very occasionally in females (Ashton and Zuckerman, 1956); this may be attributed to the relatively small size of chimpanzees compared with gorillas, to their essentially frugivorous diet and to the somewhat retrogressive nature of the third molar tooth. Ashton and Zuckerman (*loc. cit.*) found low crests in male *Cercopithecus ascanius*. Small crests in the region of the lambda are also seen in male *Colobus*. In fact they can be found in any primate that possesses large jaws and a small braincase although, for reasons stated above, there is a tendency for these adaptive features to be found most often in the larger species. The position of sagittal crests on the vault of the skull depends on the degree of prognathism of the face and the arrangement of the fibres of the temporalis muscle. In *Papio* in which the snout is strongly developed, the posterior oblique element of the fan-shaped temporalis muscle is larger than the anterior-vertical component. Thus, the crest appears first in—and may be limited to—the region of the lambda (Jolly, 1964). In *Theropithecus*, a baboon-like primate but with a less prominent snout, the crest extends further forward to the region of the bregma.

The occurrence of the nuchal crest, and raised flange of bone in the occipital region is largely (though not wholly) related to the postural adaptations of the skull, and is discussed in Section 9.

The following table lists the average body weight of male and female anthropoid apes. Figures are also given (Schultz, 1956) of the average body weight of females in percentage of the average body weight of males. These comparative figures may serve to rationalize the presence or absence of sagittal crests in these hominoid genera.

TABLE I

	Average weight adult male	Average weight adult female	♀ weight in % ♂ weight	Sagittal crests
Chimpanzee	49 kg	41 kg	84%	Occasional low crest in male (16%). Only very occasionally in female
Orang-utan	79 kg	37 kg	47%	Large in male. Rarely in female
Gorilla	160 kg	92 kg	58%	Large in male. Occasional occurrence in females (30%)

7. THE BRAIN

The wholly imaginary hippocampus minor, the subject of a major scientific bloomer of the post-Darwinian era, and the *vera causa* for a delightful parody in "The Water Babies", serves as a trenchant reminder that no new structure is to be found in the human brain that is not found in the brain of other primates. The differences between the brains of the highest and lowest of the primate grades lie, principally, in the progressive elaboration, differentiation and reorganization of the cerebral cortex and cerebellum (Plate 4). Many of the modifications are linked with the development of an advanced visual system and with the evolution of prehensility, opposability and tactile acuity in the hand (Noback and Moskowitz, 1963).

Treeshrews are still classified by some authorities with the elephant-shrew in the Menotyphla division of the Insectivora but in the development of the neopallium these forms differ profoundly from each other (Clark, 1932b). The brain of the diurnal *Tupaia* is large for its body size and, by comparison with certain insectivores such as *Echinosorex* (a nocturnal form), the olfactory bulbs, tracts and tubercles are reduced. The piriform lobe is largely concealed by the growth of the temporal lobe of the neopallium; the visual cortex is expanded to cover the mid-brain and part of the cerebellum. There are no sulci on the lateral surface of the hemisphere but a small calcarine sulcus, delimiting the visual cortex, is apparent on the medial side. Associated with these external cortical changes, there is a differentiation of cellular elements of the striate cortex and of the thalamic nuclei (Clark, 1929). Correlated with the lack of

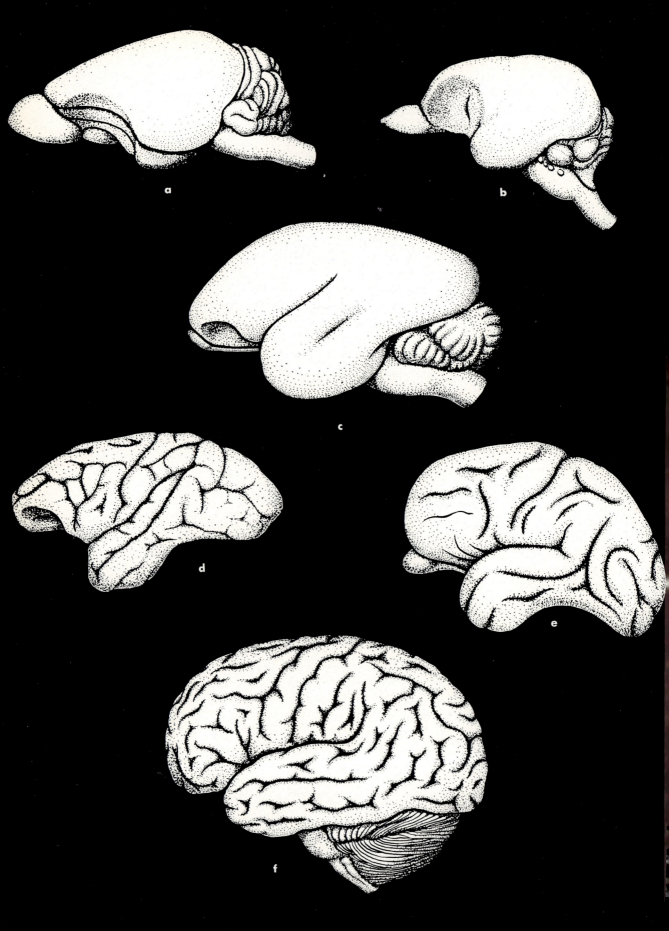

frontality of the orbits of *Tupaia*, there are no uncrossed fibres in the optic chiasma (cf. *Tarsius* 25–35% uncrossed fibres; Cercopithecoidea 40%; Hominoidea 40%. In all these, orbital frontality is fully established).

The brain of Lemuridae is known principally from the work of Clark (1931) on *Microcebus* which shows the most primitive condition of all Lemuriformes. In many ways *Microcebus* shows little advance on the tupaiid brain. The olfactory lobes are relatively large in all Lemuridae and the piriform lobe of the cortex, as in *Tupaia*, still forms the lower pole of the temporal lobe; in *Lemur*, however, it has become completely concealed. The occipital lobe of *Microcebus* remains relatively unexpanded and the posterior horn of the lateral ventricle is absent; the visual area of the cortex however is larger than in *Tupaia* though it still extends well on to the lateral surface of the hemisphere. A retrocalcarine sulcus, characteristic of all primates above tupaiid level, is in evidence on the medial surface of the cerebral hemisphere. The lateral cerebral surface of *Microcebus* shows a lateral sulcus but is otherwise lacking in fissures; in *Lemur* several longitudinal sulci are apparent; in Indriidae the cortex shows the most complex fissural pattern among the Lemuriformes. It must be remembered however, in this respect, that the complexity of fissural patterns of cerebral cortex are correlated with size. In other mammalian Orders e.g. Perissodactyla, increased fissuration has evolved hand in hand with increase in body size (Edinger, 1948).

In terms of cyto-architectonics, the cortex of Lemuridae shows considerable advances on that of the Tupaiidae, particularly in the primary projection areas and to a lesser extent in parietal and temporal association areas: these latter regions are concerned with the storage and integration of all sensory memories (visual, tactile, auditory, etc.). In the thalamus, the lateral geniculate nucleus has become elaborated in connection with the increasing importance of the visual mechanisms; in lemurs, the lateral geniculate nucleus shows a distinct lamination of the cellular layers. The lamination is somewhat irregularly displayed in *Tupaia* and inversion is absent. In the anthropoid families, similar lamination and differentiation of the lateral geniculate body has occurred, but the pattern is quite different, the whole nucleus becoming rotated ventrally and "everted" (Clark, 1932a; Chacko, 1955).

In many ways the brain of *Tarsius* is less advanced than that of *Microcebus* despite its apparent anthropoid-like contour (Plate 4b). This is due principally to the size of the visual cortex which produces a prominent occipital pole, and to the reduction in the olfactory apparatus. The cerebral hemispheres lack any surface fissural pattern except a short lateral sulcus and a deep calcarine sulcus. As might be expected from the size of the visual cortex, the lateral geniculate nucleus is large and shows laminated differentiation of the "inverted" or lemuroid type.

In view of the specialized locomotor functions of *Tarsius*, which involve precise leaps from vertical support to vertical support, it is surprising (Clark, 1959) that the cerebellum lacks the enlargement and fissuration of the lateral lobes that might well be expected. An increase in the fibre connections between cerebrum and cerebellum, which facilitates muscular co-ordination, is reflected in the size of the cortico-pontine-cerebellar tracts, the size of the pontine nuclei and in the size and differentiation of the lateral cerebellar lobes. Elaboration of this system is a progressive feature seen in the ascent from lower to higher primates.

The simplest brain among the Anthropoidea is found in the Callitrichidae. Even so it is far in advance of the brain of prosimian families, being relatively very large compared with body

---

PLATE 4. Brains of primates. Lateral aspect of cerebral hemisphere of: a. Treeshrew × 3; b. Tarsier × 2½; c. Marmoset × 2¼; d. Macaque × 1; e. Gorilla × ½; f. Man × ½ (a, b, c, and e after Le Gros Clark, 1959). Scales approximate.

weight (Plate 4c). The olfactory parts of the brain are more reduced than in the prosimians and the visual parts (Tarsiidae excepted) are more advanced. The common marmosets (*Callithrix*) show little or no fissural patterning of the cerebral cortex beyond a lateral sulcus and in a calcarine system, but the larger representatives of New World anthropoid families, e.g. Cebidae, possess a richly convoluted cerebrum. *Cebus*, for example, shows a number of vertically orientated and arcuate sulci (cf. the longitudinal arrangement of sulci in the larger Lemuridae). As in all the Anthropoidea, the lateral geniculate nucleus of *Callithrix* is of the everted type.

CEREBRAL CORTEX

The expansion of the cerebral cortex, characteristic of the Anthropoidea, is a result of two factors; firstly, an increase in the size of ascending and descending fibre tracts that connect the cortex with sub-cortical centres and the spinal cord; secondly an elaboration of the association areas and of the intrinsic fibre systems that connect them with the primary motor and sensory projection areas on the same and opposite sides of the brain. The primary motor projection area constitutes both the pre-central gyrus and the area immediately anterior to it. The primary sensory areas are those areas of cortex related to vision (occipital), hearing (temporal) and general sensation (parietal). The remainder of the cortex consists of association areas whose function is concerned with the storage of acts or sensations learned and remembered.

The manipulative power of the hand and its role in sensory acuity, is reflected both in the size of the relevant motor and sensory association areas, and in the cortical representation of the hand in the primary motor and sensory projection areas. The size of the specific area of cortical representation for the hand, determined by means of neurophysiological experiment, forms an ascending series in Callitrichidae, Cebidae, Cercopithecidae and Hominidae (Noback and Moskowitz, 1963). The expression of the primate trend towards a higher functional differentiation of the brain (corticalization) is a concept whereby the cortex assumes the dominant role over the lower centres. The relative extent of corticalization in anthropoid families is apparent following selective cortical ablations in monkeys, chimpanzees and man. Ablation of the primary motor area of the cortex in Pongidae leads to more severe and more persistent ill-effects than in Cercopithecidae, and in Cercopithecidae than in Cebidae; the brunt of the disability falling on skilled motor acts. Ablations of the sensory cortex result in severe impairment of discriminatory functions which are more affected in man than in the chimpanzee, and in the chimpanzee than in the monkey.

During primate phylogeny, it would seem that with the evolution of the Anthropoidea a plateau was reached with respect to visual mechanisms. Studies of recent anthropoid families do not indicate any profound qualitative differences in the structure of the visual pathway. It is true that differences exist in the lateral geniculate body, in the number and arrangement of the laminae and in the ratio of cells and neurones between monkeys (Cercopithecidae, Cebidae) and the ape and human families, which suggest refinements in vision, particularly peripheral vision (Noback and Moskowitz, 1963). Differences also exist in the boundaries of the striate area in the occipital lobes. In the Cercopithecidae, most of the striate area is sited on the lateral surface of the occipital pole whereas in man, and to a lesser extent in the Pongidae, it is largely confined to the medial surface, lining the depths of the calcarine fissure; this displacement is presumably brought about by an expansion of parietal, occipital and temporal association areas among the higher primate grades that have resulted in an "infolding" of the occipital pole.

The external morphological correlates of a highly evolved visual sense, the frontality of the orbits and the development of a post-orbital closure, are already apparent in the fossil catarrhine frontal bone discovered in the Fayum of the Egyptian Lower Oligocene. This bone has been attributed provisionally by Simons (1962) to *Oligopithecus*. An enhanced visual system would thus seem to have been established early in catarrhine phylogeny. The central nervous correlates of manipulative ability and sensory acuity of the hand however, show a progressive "improvement" through the anthropoid grades from Cebidae to Cercopithecidae, to Pongidae, to Hominidae. This "improvement" which is apparent in living forms, accords well with the palaeontological evidence, which suggests that the total emancipation of the hand from the function of weight-bearing and its secondary deployment as a tool-using and tool-making device was a relatively recent event in primate evolution.

Holloway (1966), in a stimulating review of the significance of cranial capacity as a parameter of hominization, points out that the comparison of cranial capacities between man and sub-human primates is nonsensical (*sic*) in as much as it is not based on the comparison of equal units. That is to say, 1 cc of chimpanzee cortex is not equivalent to 1 cc of human cortex. Anatomical studies have shown that cell density *decreases* as brain size increases (Tower, 1954). This may be due to an increase in size of the nerve cells themselves, or an increase in dendritic branching, or even an increase in neuroglial cells (Hawkins and Olszewski, 1957). Thus a fourfold increase in brain size, for instance, does not mean that there are four times as many neurones. Holloway (*loc. cit.*) suggests that the essential differences between the brains of lower and higher primates is a matter of neural reorganization. He states (p. 106) that "quantitative shifts between components or substructures of the brain, as measured in terms of area or volume, have taken place under natural selection such that the outputs of the systems are different between species. By shifting interactions between components in quantitative ways, the product of the whole is altered."

At sub-cortical level attention has centred on the limbic system and particularly on the amygdaloid component of the rhinencephalon. The importance of the amygdala for olfaction still remains uncertain; for instance in the human brain, in spite of the phylogenetic debasement of olfaction as a sensory function, the amygdala remains large as it does indeed in anosmatic mammals like the porpoise. Stimulation experiments in animals and ablative operations in man produce conflicting evidence of the extent of the primary olfactory representation in the amygdala. The amygdaloid nucleus, however, is clearly involved in some way, at present unknown, in the expression of the rage reaction. Bard and Mountcastle (1948) showed, in the cat, that there was a marked depression of the rage threshold following bilateral amygdalectomy.

Experimental evidence seems to point to the amygdala and other parts of the limbic system as being modulatory in function. Rothfield and Harmon (1954) showed that placidity resulted from experimental neocortical ablations in animals providing that the limbic system was left intact. If the fornix fibres were severed, the rage threshold was lowered; the modulatory function of the limbic system was thus reduced. The effect of the disturbance produced by these lesions on those mechanisms which normally allow the selection of a behaviour pattern adequate for a given situation, was to produce an indiscriminate and inappropriate rage reaction.

In direct contrast to the findings of Bard and Mountcastle (1948), the bilateral excision of the amygdala in monkeys has been shown to alter the relative hierarchical positions of a group of male rhesus monkeys, previously dominant individuals becoming peripheral (Rosvold *et al.*, 1954). Chance (1962) has discussed the evolution of the amygdaloid nucleus in primates with particular reference to the genesis of the rage-controlling ability of man. The results of amygdalectomy in man however are as equivocal as they are in animals (see Gloor, 1960). Changes for the worse in maternal behaviour of female monkeys has also been noted after bilateral amygdalectomy (Thomson and Walker, 1950; Walker, Thomson and McQueen, 1953).

Attention of anatomists and physiologists has also been directed to the fornix-mamillo-thalamic system. Simpson (1952) and Daitz (1953) counted fornix fibres in monkeys and in man and their results show a fourfold increase in the fibres of the human sub-callosal fornix over the macaque. Powell, Guillery and Cowan (1957) demonstrated the relatively large size of the human fornix-mamillo-thalamic system compared with that of *Macaca mulatta*, and conclude that this system plays a "relatively important, though unknown part in the organization of the human brain," a statement which coincides with the general consensus (Gloor, 1960). Holloway (1966) stresses that the results of these and many other studies of sub-cortical systems indicate the dangers of overemphasizing the role of cortical elaboration in evolution of the primate brain.

8. PLACENTATION

Recent advances in immunochemistry of primates have confirmed some old theories and led to new concepts of taxonomic relationship within the Order (Goodman, 1962a, b, 1963). The progressive improvement of primate placental structure, and thus the increase of intimacy between foetal and maternal circulations, is pivotal to the theory which states that certain proteins such as albumin are stable in an evolutionary sense and can be employed as markers to indicate phylogenetic affinity.

In the formation of the mammalian chorioallantoic placenta, the embryo becomes attached to the uterine wall by means of its outer covering membranes, and it is through this attachment that the embryonic circulation is drawn. The more rapidly this circulation is established and the more intimately the blood systems of the mother and embryo mingle, the more efficient is the nutrition of the developing embryo. The intimacy of the two blood systems, in the terms of Goodman's theory, leads to exchange of proteins, iso-immunization of the mother to the foetal antigens and thus to immunological attack on the foetal proteins by the maternal antibodies which have passed into the foetal circulation.

Two types of placentation in Grosser's classification are found among primates although each type shows a number of variations:

1. Epitheliochorial. In this type, placental formation is diffuse, the outer membrane of the embryo (the chorion) invades the whole of the uterine wall to a limited depth; the maternal and foetal bloodstreams are separated by several epithelial and endothelial layers so that there exists a barrier across which protein exchange is limited. After birth, the placenta is stripped off the uterine wall bringing no maternal layers with it (non-deciduate type). Epitheliochorial placentae are found in Lemuridae and Lorisidae.*

2. Haemochorial. In this form of placentation the chorionic membrane of the embryo becomes intimately attached to a restricted area of the wall of the uterus by an eroding action of the chorionic processes which eventually break through the walls of the maternal blood vessels. In the fully established placenta, the vascular chorionic processes are bathed in crypts of

---

* According to Gerard (1929, 1931, 1932) the placenta of *Galago demidovii* is of an endotheliochorial type, but see J. P. Hill (1965).

maternal tissue containing maternal blood; thus in this type there are fewer layers to interfere with the free exchange of serum proteins. Haemochorial placentae are found in Tarsiidae among prosimians and in all anthropoid families. The placenta of *Tupaia* which is unique among mammals is said to show certain structural advances towards a haemochorial type (Meister and Davis, 1956, 1958). However J. P. Hill, in a posthumous paper published in 1965, points out that the placenta is unique to primates being of a bidiscoidal, endotheliochorial type.

At one time it was thought that the explanation of placental exchange lay in diffusion and filtration across the foetal and maternal membranes; the rate of diffusion would thus be expected to vary with the number of intervening layers, being greatest in Grosser's type IV, the haemochorial placenta. It now appears (Amoroso, 1959) that placental transfer depends on cytological and cytochemical structure as well as on the disposition of placental blood vessels. Evidence points to an active cellular participation by the placenta.

Goodman's immunological theory, based on the evolution of a haemochorial placenta, is as follows: the process of speciation among higher primates has largely been controlled by acceleration of the rate of variation in the specificity of serum proteins. A protein is composed of polypeptide chains whose component amino-acid sequence is under genetic control: a single gene mutation can produce a change in amino-acid sequence, a change, in other words, in the primary structure of the protein. This means that a new factor is introduced into the "foetal environment" which at this level, may be advantageous or disadvantageous in natural selection. Advantageous mutations in protein synthesis are what Goodman (1963) refers to as "molecular adaptation". The occurrence of a haemochorial placenta, which permits an intimate contact of maternal and foetal circulations and therefore transference of serum proteins, would facilitate maternal iso-immunization against a mutant or variant protein; this would tend to increase the evolutionary stability of proteins such as albumin which are synthesized early in foetal life. This state of affairs does not operate (or rather operates to a lesser extent) in animals which possess the less efficient epitheliochorial placenta since these animals tend—by virtue of the presence of a less "penetrable" placental barrier—to produce greater variation in protein synthesis and thus a greater potential for phenotypic variation.

If Goodman's theory is correct, not only the form of the placenta but also the length of the gestation period adversely affects the survival of mutant proteins by prolonging the period during which immunological attack by maternal antibodies can operate. The effect of prolonged gestation, therefore, would be to slow down the rate of divergence of a given species from its ancestral pattern. The gamma-globulins, serum proteins which appear late in ontogeny, would be less likely to be attacked by maternal antibodies. That these proteins have evolved more rapidly in anthropoid evolution is suggested by the much greater differences in gamma-globulin than in albumin antigenic reactions between anthropoid family groups such as those of the Old and New World monkeys (Goodman, 1962a, b). Goodman postulates that the main phylogenetic lines of advance of the primates were those in which there was an early elaboration of the haemochorial placenta and a marked prolongation of the gestation period. This hypothesis is supported when the fate of the epitheliochorial lemuroid families is compared with that of the haemochorial anthropoid families. Among the lemurs there has been a widely adaptive, but non-progressive, form of evolution; the many terminal products of lemuriform evolution, including the numerous forms now extinct, all have about equal status, fairly low in the grade system of primate phylogeny; this type of evolution is characterized by an early splitting into a number of derived types and is called *cladogenesis*. Anthropoid families on the other hand have shown the type of evolutionary change known

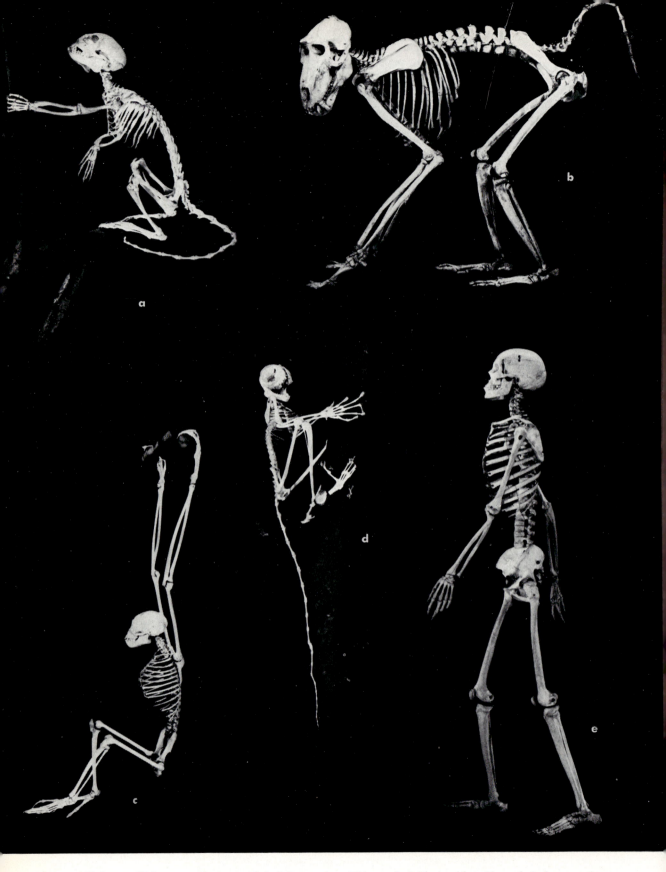

PLATE 5. Skeletons of Primates: a. Marmoset ×⅓; b. Baboon ×⅛; c. Gibbon ×⅛; d. Tarsier ×⅓; e. Man ×⅙. Scales approximate.

as *anagenesis*, that is to say the anthropoid stock has been characterized by its progressive improvement and *lack* of diversification.

There is no doubt in the minds of primate biologists that the past patterns of prosimian and anthropoid evolution, as judged largely by neontological considerations, were very different indeed. It is still to be proved however whether Goodman's theory, attractive though it is, provides an adequate explanation for this difference in the light of modern theories of protein transference.

New serological data on primates has already led to revision of the taxonomy of the primates, particularly of the Pongidae and their relationship with the Hominidae. The classification of the superfamily Hominoidea into three families: (i) The Hominidae, containing the chimpanzee, gorilla and man; (ii) the Pongidae, containing a monotypic genus, *Pongo*, the orang-utan, and (iii) the Hylobatidae for the gibbon and siamang, is becoming a popular device. It has also led, unhappily, to the grouping of the gorilla and chimpanzee in a single genus, *Pan*, (Simpson, 1963).

9. THE SKULL AND TRUNCAL ERECTNESS

In addition to the list of principal evolutionary trends presented by Clark (1959) and used as a basis for this essay, there are certain progressive adaptations of the primate skull, particularly those relating to posture, which must be referred to. It is clear that the skull reflects in many of its characters the trends already discussed on pp. 6–7. For instance the expansion of the neurocranium, the frontality and isolation of the orbits from the infratemporal fossa, the prognathism of the face and length of the jaws are correlated with evolutionary changes occurring in related systems. The part played by the evolution of the brain, the visual system and the masticatory system of primates in shaping the skull has already been discussed. In addition to the progressive adaptations related to posture, there are certain non-progressive features that nevertheless constitute important differences between members of the primate order; the morphology of the bony ear is of particular importance in this respect (*see* Section 5) and constitutes, with the dentition (Section 6), the principal region of the skull employed in taxonomic judgments.

POSTURAL ADAPTATIONS OF THE SKULL

The foramen magnum of the typical mammalian skull is directed posteriorly while that of primates is directed inferiorly although this is not an absolute distinguishing mark as will be seen. It seems likely that the ventral migration of the foramen magnum is partly an adaptation to the vertical posture of the trunk, which itself can be regarded as a major evolutionary trend of primates, and partly consequent upon the enlargement of the cerebrum (particularly in the occipital region) which has had the effect of "rolling-up" the occiput. The nuchal surface and foramen magnum become progressively displaced from their primitive posterior position to their specialized ventral one as the cerebrum enlarges through the evolutionary grades.

The majority of primates are capable of sitting, clinging or hanging in the vertical position and many of standing and walking with the trunk held vertically (Plate 5). Even in the Tupaiidae, truncal erectness is occasionally seen. Certain prosimian families (Tarsiidae, Indriidae, Lorisidae and Lemuridae) include a number of genera in which a vertical resting posture is habitual: these genera are grouped in the locomotor category Vertical Clingers and Leapers (*see* Part III p. 387). They include *Tarsius, Indri, Propithecus, Avahi, Lepilemur, Galago,* and certain extinct Eocene prosimians such as *Necrolemur.* These forms show a constellation of morphological characters which typify the group, including a projecting occiput, globular brain case and a foramen magnum placed well forward on the base of the skull; in these adaptations, and others relating particularly to the limbs, they are to be distinguished from other genera of these particular prosimian families in which vertical clinging and leaping behaviour is absent, or modified. *Lemur catta,* for instance, though generally regarded as a quadruped, displays in its locomotor behaviour a number of characteristics reminiscent of the Vertical Clinging and Leaping group; *Hapalemur* also probably belongs to this group. In all anthropoid families the erectness of the trunk constitutes at least a part of the postural behavioural repertoire.

Among Cercopithecidae and Hylobatidae, long periods of sitting particularly during night-resting (Washburn, 1957) are facilitated by the presence of specialized pads surmounting the ischium—the ischial callosities (Plate 6). These pads are lacking in Cebidae which usually adopt a horizontal sleeping posture. Ischial callosities show considerable variation between genera. In the more arboreal forms, *Hylobates* and *Cercopithecus* for instance, they are small and well separated; in ground-living members of the Cercopithecinae (e.g. *Papio, Mandrillus*) they are large in males and fused across the midline. The discrete or fused nature of the callosities however is not wholly a matter of habitat but rather of taxonomic affinity. The patas monkey (*Erythrocebus*), for instance, while entirely ground-adapted, possesses discrete ischial callosities, a character that underlines its evolutionary relationship to *Cercopithecus.* The mangabeys on the other hand, which are wholly or partly arboreal according to species, possess fused callosities typical of the baboons. This fact, *inter alia,* reflects the close relationship of *Cercocebus* and *Papio* which has sufficiently impressed a number of authorities for them to include both genera (with *Macaca* and *Mandrillus*) in a single subfamily Papioninae (Hill, 1966), or in a separate tribe Cercocebini (Jolly, 1964). The Pongidae and Hominidae sit frequently and also display truncal uprightness and bipedalism in varying degrees. Hominidae are habitually bipedal while Pongidae are only facultatively so. Occasional bipedalism however is not limited to the human and ape families but is observed in Cebidae and Cercopithecidae (Hewes, 1961).

Truncal uprightness is an ancient primate possession as Wood Jones (1916) emphasized in "Arboreal Man"; the fossil tarsioids of the Eocene such as *Necrolemur, Nannopithex* and *Hemiacodon* show both cranial and post-cranial adaptations to a saltatory type of locomotion (Clark, 1959; Simons, 1963). The foramen magnum of *Necrolemur* lies almost as far ventrally as it does in modern *Tarsius.* All primates, with one or two exceptions, have a foramen magnum which is directed downwards rather than backwards, although the degree to which it is displaced orally varies considerably. As Schultz has observed (1955), in the foetal and infantile stages of all anthropoid families, the foramen magnum is placed far forward on the ventral aspect of the skull. During the rapid post-natal growth of the face, the foramen gradually shifts backwards. Even in man, some aboral shift occurs (Ashton and Zuckerman, 1956), though the amount of change is less than in anthropoid apes. The aboral shift of the foramen is greater in primates which show marked prognathism than in the short-faced forms; among the Cebidae, the short-faced squirrel monkey (*Saimiri*) for instance possesses a foramen sited almost as far forward as it is in man, while in the markedly prog-nathic *Pongo* and *Gorilla* the foramen is directed as much posteriorly as it is ventrally. Only in the howler monkey (*Alouatta*) among the Cebidae does the foramen magnum occupy a near-

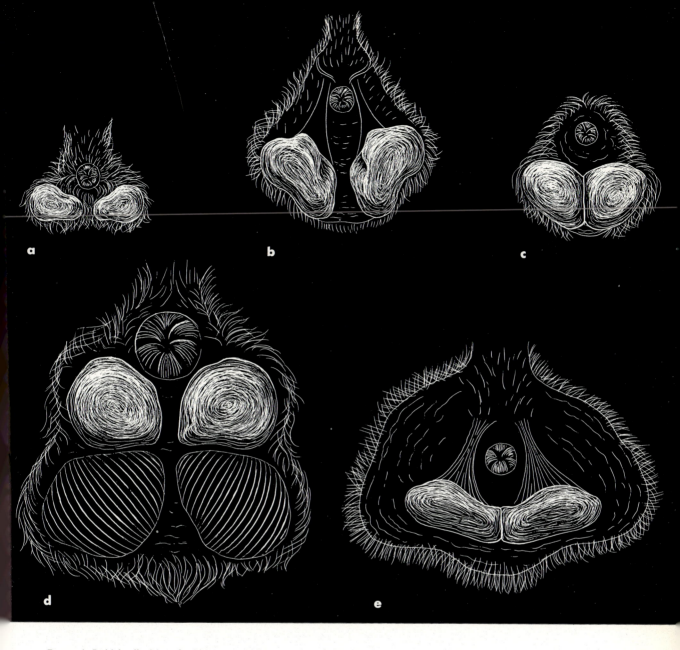

PLATE 6. Ischial callosities of primates: a. ♂ Mona monkey; b. ♂ Pigtailed Macaque; c. ♂ Barbary ape; d. ♂ Gelada baboon; e. ♂ Guinea baboon.

mammalian position; this character is associated in howlers with other remarkable modifications of skull topography, which are generally regarded as expressions of the highly specialized nature of the vocal apparatus in this genus.

In man the forward position of the foramen magnum and thus of the occipital condyles allows the head to be balanced on the top of the vertebral column without the need of a powerful set of neck muscles to offset the weight of the face and jaws; but in *Gorilla*, for instance, the face and jaws are so heavy, and the pivot so far back, that extremely strong muscles are required at the back of the neck to provide a counterbalancing force. In *Gorilla* and other genera such as *Pongo*, *Papio* and *Mandrillus* in which this imbalance operates, the nuchal area of the skull is enormously expanded to provide an additional area of attachment for the bulky posterior neck muscles; in *Gorilla* and *Pongo* a raised flange, the nuchal crest, which is a functional analogue of the sagittal crest, is usually present in the adult males (Ashton and Zuckerman, 1956). The functional relationship between the sagittal and nuchal crests in primates has been the subject of considerable controversy particularly with respect to the occurrence of such crests in the Australopithecinae (Robinson, 1958). Nuchal and sagittal crests owe their formation to two distinct biomechanical forces, the one concerned with posture and the other with jaw size. In certain forms the two forces operate with equal intensity. Therefore nuchal crests may develop in the absence of sagittal crests as in *Colobus polykomos*, (Vogel, 1962), or sagittal crests may develop in the absence of nuchal crests as in *Nycticebus coucang* (Seth, 1964) and *Colobus verus* (Vogel, *loc. cit.*), or sagittal and nuchal crests may develop together in confluence, as in *Gorilla* and *Pongo*.

In conclusion it would seem that the displacement ventrally and orally of the foramen magnum and occipital condyles is primarily an adaptation for truncal erectness and is an evolutionary trend of primates. It would also seem that the conflicting demands of the masticatory apparatus have led, secondarily, to an aboral migration of the foramen in certain long-faced and heavy-jawed forms.

10. GROWTH RATES AND THEIR EFFECTS

The structural characters of an adult primate are ultimately dependent on the genetical constituents of the zygote nucleus. Some characters appear in early foetal life, some are present at birth, some appear during early post-natal life, in others development is delayed until adult life; certain characters are directly related to the primary gene product, others are the result of interactions during ontogeny of environmental factors such as diet, climate and so on.

Embryonic and foetal development and post-natal growth, though frequently presented to the student as discrete and separate events, are a continuous process; and it is not until the fully adult stage is reached that the "final product" is ripe for taxonomic assessment in the totality of its characters. Even then, as Schultz (1956) has pointed out, ontogeny is by no means over. Although it is probably legitimate to regard such later changes as occur, as degenerative, they are still species-specific and therefore of phylogenetic significance. Characters of sub-adult, even infant, primates *can* however be used intraspecifically in taxonomic practice and in palaeontology, provided they are compared with other specimens of comparable developmental age; interspecific comparisons are more dangerous for as Schultz (1963) points out: ". . . every single feature can independently shift its place in the sequence of ontogenetic processes in either direction" (p. 89). As an example of this, the fusion of the *os centrale* of the carpus may be quoted; the fusion of this bone to the neighbouring scaphoid (navicular) occurs early in the pre-natal stage of ontogeny in man, soon after birth in the great apes and in late adult life in gibbons and some monkeys. The fusion of the *os centrale* in man, viewed in this perspective, loses its unique "qualitative" nature and becomes a non-specific quantitative character. Absence of an *os centrale* is, none-the-less, a character of taxonomic significance in man, but only in the *time* of its disappearance as a separate entity and not in the fact of its fusion. The early fusion of the *os centrale* in man is an example of acceleration of the growth process. Other accelerations in man (relative to non-human primates) are the early descent of the testes, the fusion of the sternebrae, the early closure of the premaxillary suture and the early development of a mastoid process. Retardations or "foetalisations" as they were termed in Bolk's (1926) theory, are an important source of human specializations but, as is now clearly appreciated, not the only source. Alterations in growth rates that are generally regarded as retardations (Schultz, 1950) include the retention of the foetal position of the head on the vertebral column, lack of forward growth of the orbits and of the face, and lack of rotation of the great toe. Many of these growth modifications such as the position of the head on the vertebral column and the lack of rotation of the big toe are foetal "retentions" rather than foetal retardations. Little if any change occurs in the foetal position of the head in modern man throughout ontogeny. Modern man has "foetalized" as far as he can go by retaining precisely the foetal condition.

Reduction, that is to say the disappearance of structures, is a relatively rare phenomenon but when it occurs, it is liable to be regarded as a qualitative distinction; in fact, as Schultz has shown, reduction is merely the extreme expression of the retardation mechanism and is therefore essentially quantitative. Such reductions in man include the disappearance of the *os penis*, an apparently unique human character. The fact that man's closest simian relative, the gorilla, possesses an *os penis*, albeit very small, while man has no trace of such a structure, is on the face of it, a major distinction. From the lemurs to anthropoid apes, a relative reduction in size of the *os penis* is apparent; but from gorilla to man there is, apparently, to use Simpson's term, a quantum jump. The final reduction in man of the *os penis* is the culmination of an evolutionary trend, as Schultz has shown, characterizing the primates. Like so many qualitative distinctions that in the past have been proposed for man and found, on further study, to be merely quantitative, the disappearance of the *os penis* will, no doubt, be demonstrated as a continuous and gradual process when the fossil record of early hominids is more complete. The disappearance of the shaft of the pisiform in man is another example.

Accelerations, retardations, retentions and reductions are some of the mechanisms by which innovations in the genotype are reflected in the specificity of the phenotype; these processes act by modifying the differential growth velocities and new phenotypes—new species—may then evolve. Normally regulatory forces, which have a genetic basis, hold the growth processes involved in ontogeny in pre-determined channels. Tanner (1962) has demonstrated the action of these forces by plotting maturity gradients in various parts of the human body. Maturity gradients in the lower limb, for instance, show that at all ages of development the length of the foot is nearer its adult status than the length of the leg below the knee; and that this segment is similarly nearer the adult status than the thigh segment. The maturity gradient is thus from the foot to the thigh. In the individual, disturbances of the regulatory forces lead to developmental abnormalities; in populations, subject to natural selection, disturbances in differential growth rates may, if beneficial, lead to new adaptations. Reference in this discussion principally has been made to man, but it should be clear that the same processes operate for all non-human primates; if man, however incorrectly, can be called a "neotenous ape", *Cercopithecus* monkeys can be described as "neotenous baboons".

Tanner (1962) has shown that the characteristic shape of human weight growth curves is shared with chimpanzees and rhesus monkeys. There is no reason to doubt that other Old World monkeys and apes, indeed other primates, show similar curves; it is merely that growth studies have been limited so far to these two forms. Gavan and Swindler in a recent paper (1966) point out that the similarity in shape of growth rate among chimpanzees, rhesus monkeys and human infants, is not due so much to a basic primate growth curve as to a basic mammalian one.

A trend to prolong post-natal life is apparent in the primates. The data, which are far from complete or certain, are presented in Table II and indicate that the normal life span has become extended from 14 years in the prosimians to 75 years in modern man. In past human populations, however, the average expectancy of life was considerably lower than 75 years; such figures include deaths in infancy and deaths from plagues and warfare, so that they constitute more of a social index of life expectancy than a biological one; there is no evidence for instance, that in past populations, the juvenile phase was of shorter duration than it is now. The period which shows the least change between the apes and man is the foetal phase or gestation period; whereas the duration of infantile, juvenile and adult phases has doubled, the intra-uterine phase has remained the same. In some respects man's intra-uterine development is accelerated but in most features such as ossification, brain size and myelination of peripheral nerves, his development is clearly retarded compared with that of other primates. Man produces absolutely and relatively the largest infant at birth of all primates, but the ossification

TABLE II

Duration of Life Periods

	Foetal phase (days)	Infantile phase (years)	Juvenile phase (years)	Adult phase (years)	Life span (years)
Lemur	126	?	?2	11 +	14
Macaque	168	$1\frac{1}{2}$	6	20	27–28
Gibbon	210	?2	$6\frac{1}{2}$	20 +	30 +
Orang-utan	233	$3\frac{1}{2}$	7	20 +	30 +
Chimpanzee	238	3	7	30	40
Gorilla	265	3 +	7 +	25	?35
Modern Man	266	6	14	50 +	70–75

Table shows duration of life periods of primates derived from many sources. Foetal phase is equivalent to gestation period. Life span is the summation of the three post-natal phases. Uncertainty is indicated by ? or a + sign.

of the bones of the hand lags far behind that of macaques, and somewhat behind that of chimpanzees.

At birth the human infant's brain is 25% of its adult size compared with the 70% of the brains of macaques and gibbons. Thereafter the brain grows rapidly in man, the maximum growth period being in the first three years; at the end of this time the brain is 75% of its adult size having an average cranial capacity of 1225 cc. Thereafter the infantile brain "spurt" subsides and further growth occurs *pro rata* with the growth of the body. Similar "spurts" in body weight growth occur in non-human primates but start earlier in the post-natal period and are of shorter duration. The retardation and prolongation of the brain-growth period in humans reflects the complexity of the neuronal organization and connections in the adult.

The absolute size of the human brain at birth, which weighs on average 350 g, can be correlated with the fact that the human gestation period has not become extended as have all his other life periods. Prolongation of the intra-uterine phase by, for example, three months, would mean that the brain would weigh approximately 526 g. The size of the infant's head would then be incompatible with the size of the birth canal. The gestation period is terminated in man (and other primates) when the size of the head is consonant with a safe delivery.

Selection for increased pelvic dimensions in man would seem a possible way in which nature could meet this critical situation, but the pelvic dimensions are fixed by the demands of upright bipedal walking. Thus two evolutionary trends, the increased size of the human brain and the adaptations of the pelvis consonant with bipedalism, are at variance. The solution, as in the case of most adaptations, is an evolutionary compromise.

Tanner (1962) points out that the essential change between higher primates (monkeys and apes) and mammals is the postponement of menarche in the females and puberty in the males until growth is nearly complete. In the rhesus monkey (*M. mulatta*) as in man, the adolescent growth spurt precedes the onset of puberty in males (Fig. 3). The magnitude of the difference between the male and female adolescent spurts reflects, in part, the degree of sexual dimorphism in the adults.

Tanner (1962) regards the existence of an adolescent spurt as an evolutionary trend of primates. The postponement of puberty until growth is nearing completion may be advantageous for the evolution of social life among the higher primates. Postponement of puberty ensures a tractable, non-sexually competitive group of juveniles within a band or troop. Such

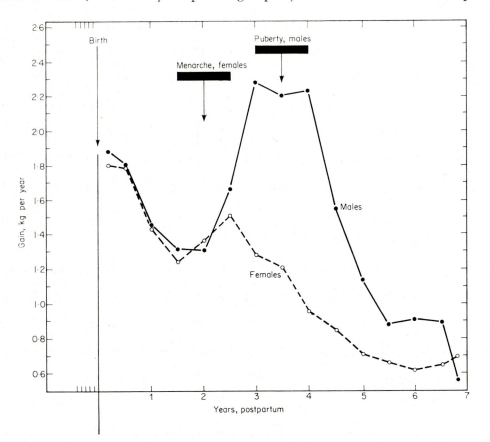

FIG. 3. Weight velocity curves for the rhesus monkey. Curves resemble those of man and show the adolescent spurt in males and females. [From J. M. Tanner (1962), "Growth at Adolescence", 2nd Ed. Blackwell, Oxford.]

an arrangement has obvious advantages in a baboon troop for instance where group-survival is in the hands of a few dominant and fully adult males; the presence of hordes of sexually mature, though physically immature juveniles, would lead to intragroup aggression and fighting, a feature which is so markedly lacking in free-ranging baboon troops.

The trend for prolongation of life periods in the primates is closely related to the increasing importance of learned behaviour in the Order. The period of immaturity is a period of dependency and during this time the infant primate is learning, through his mother and other members of the group, the *mores* of his complex social life.

PART II

Profiles of Primate Genera

Index to Profiles

Profiles are arranged alphabetically according to generic name. The common name equivalents of each genus are listed below in alphabetical order.

COMMON NAME	GENERIC NAME	
Pagai Island Langur	*Simias*	p. 314–315
Patas monkey	*Erythrocebus*	p. 143–147
Pentailed Treeshrew	*Ptilocercus*	p. 289–292
Philippine Treeshrew	*Urogale*	p. 337–339
Pinché	*Saguinus*	p. 299–308
Potto	*Perodicticus*	p. 258–261
Proboscis monkey	*Nasalis*	p. 228–233
Pygmy marmoset	*Cebuella*	p. 84–86
Rhesus monkey	*Macaca*	p. 207–219
Saki	*Pithecia*	p. 264–266
Siamang	*Symphalangus*	p. 316–319
Sifaka	*Propithecus*	p. 284–288
Slender loris	*Loris*	p. 203–206
Slow loris	*Nycticebus*	p. 234–237
Smooth-tailed treeshrew	*Dendrogale*	p. 141–142
Snub-nosed Langur	*Rhinopithecus*	p. 295–298
Spider monkey	*Ateles*	p. 59–63
Sportive lemur	*Lepilemur*	p. 200–202
Squirrel monkey	*Saimiri*	p. 309–313
Talapoin	*Cercopithecus*	p. 115–116
Tamarin	*Saguinus*	p. 299–308
Tarsier	*Tarsius*	p. 320–325
Titi	*Callicebus*	p. 72–75
Treeshrew	*Tupaia*	p. 330–336
Uakari	*Cacajao*	p. 69–71
Woolly monkey	*Lagothrix*	p. 182–187
Woolly spider monkey	*Brachyteles*	p. 66–68

Use of asterisk in Profiles denotes data based on very limited or even single observations. Small numbers used in text indicate authorities who are listed in numerical order at the end of each profile.

ALOUATTA† Lacépède, 1799   Howlers

5 species: 21 subspecies[1, 2, 3, 11]

A. villosa [= *A. palliata*]	Mantled Howler	8 subsp.
A. seniculus	Red Howler	5 subsp.
A. belzebul (Type species)	Red-handed Howler	5 subsp.
A. fusca [= *A. guariba*]	Brown Howler	3 subsp.
A. caraya	Black Howler	0 subsp.

GEOGRAPHICAL RANGE [2, 4]

Central and South America. *Alouatta* are found from sea level to 6560 ft. (2000 m) in altitude. *A. villosa* found in coastal forests of Mexico, throughout central America (save Yucatan) and in Pacific coastal forests of S. America as far as 3° S. Remaining species are found throughout forested areas of S. America; *A. caraya* extends into the Gran Chaco. Also found in mountains of the S.E. littoral of Brazil (*A. fusca*).

ECOLOGY

HABITAT:[5] Tropical rain forest and mixed deciduous forest. Upper and middle canopy of forest preferred; generally avoid secondary growth. Feed in the smaller branches of emergent trees. ACTIVITY RHYTHM: Diurnal. DIET:[6] Predominantly a leaf-eater; also buds, flowers and fruit, particularly figs [*see* Carpenter (1934) for list of food plants of *A. villosa*].

MORPHOLOGY

External Characters

Large, robust prehensile-tailed monkeys with long fur, black in *A. villosa*, brown in *A. fusca*, copper-red in *A. seniculus*, and black with reddish hands, feet and tailtip in *A. belzebul*. Sexual dichromatism in *A. caraya*: ♂ black, ♀ and juvenile olive-buff.[7] In all species, face is bare and deeply pigmented. Nostrils close together.[8] Swelling beneath the chin, accommodating the specialized larynx, is outlined by a beard in the ♂; it is much more prominent in the ♂ than in the ♀. The head is set low on the shoulders giving a hunched appearance. The tail is very mobile; the distal quarter of the underside bears naked skin with papillary ridges. Arms and legs subequal. Big toe divergent and opposable. HAND: Digital formula: 3.4.2.5.1. or 3=4.2.5.1. Genitalia of both sexes are prominent. MAMMAE: 2 nipples situated near the axilla.[4]

Weights and Dimensions[3, 4, 16, 9]

	♂	♀	♀ in % ♂
Average weight (g)	7392 (4♂♂)	5720 (4♀♀)	77
Head and body length range (mm)	465–720 (35♂♂)	390–573 (34♀♀)	81
Tail length range (mm)	490–748 (35♂♂)	490–711 (34♀♀)	93

Considerable sexual dimorphism in weight, e.g. Schultz (1956) gives ♀ in % of ♂=81% (198 specimens). Dimorphism less marked in tail length.

† *See* Taxonomic Notes, p. 370.

PLATE 8. *Alouatta villosa*, on Barro Colorado Island (by courtesy of C. R. Carpenter)

PLATE 7. *Alouatta seniculus* ♂ (San Diego Zoo)

Internal Characters

For details of laryngeal anatomy, *see* Boker (1932), Negus (1949) and Kelemen and Sade (1960). SKULL: of unusual shape having basicranial axis almost in line with basifacial; foramen magnum directed backwards. Angular region of mandible greatly enlarged.[10-12] Manubrium sterni tends to be bifurcate. All the foregoing skeletal characters probably related to hyo-laryngeal specialization. Hyoid bone expanded into egg-shaped sacculation forming a resonance chamber which is larger in ♂ than in ♀. Largest hyoid bone seen in *A. seniculus*. STOMACH: large; intestine short but capacious (associated with leaf-eating diet).[16] DENTITION: D.F.: $\frac{2}{2}\frac{1}{1}\frac{3}{3}\frac{3}{3}=36$. Molars show adaptations for predominantly leaf-eating diet.[17,18]

Genetic Biology

CHROMOSOMES:[19] 2n=44 (2♂♂ *A. seniculus*). *Karyotype*: 30 acrocentrics, 6 subterminals, 6 metacentrics, plus X and Y chromosomes. SEROLOGY: No information available at present on blood groups.

BEHAVIOUR

Locomotor Behaviour[6,20]

AUTHORS' CLASSIFICATION: Quadrupedalism. New World Semibrachiation sub-type. (Erikson's category: Brachiator.) Rather deliberate and essentially quadrupedal gait, the prehensile tail always ready to give support, or actually grasping intermittently. Howlers hang by arms or tail alone while feeding on slender terminal branches but "arm-swinging" behaviour is not marked. Avoid leaps; a long jump (3–4 m) may be made after much hesitation. Seldom seen on the ground but in captivity they occasionally walk quadrupedally with interphalangeal joints of hands and feet flexed. Able to swim if necessary. LIMB PROPORTIONS: Both fore- and hindlimbs longer than vertebral column and subequal in relative length. Arm longer than forearm. *See* Part III, p. 393, for Indices.

Hand Function[8,20,21]

Hand prehensile, thumb pseudo-opposable. Effective grasp between thumb and index finger, and remaining digits. Fine manipulative movements not observed.

Resting Posture[6]

Sit on rump with knees flexed. Sometimes lie face-down on a branch with arms and legs dangling; always with tailtip tightly coiled around branch.

Social Behaviour

Principal field studies are those of Carpenter (1934, 1942b, 1965), Collias and Southwick (1952) and Altmann (1959). *A. villosa* live in groups of from 2–45 animals, average: about 18. AVERAGE GROUP COMPOSITION: 3 adult ♂, 8 adult ♀, 3 infants, 4 juveniles. ADULT SEX RATIO: 1♂: 2·3 ♀♀ (average of 51 groups). Individual adult ♂♂ occasionally live in temporary isolation. Each group is nomadic within a fairly well-defined territorial range which is defended against intrusion by other groups. Territory is defended by howling, accompanied by shaking and breaking of branches; this substitutes for physical aggression. Howling sessions take place regularly at dawn and help to localize the position of groups. Intra-group behaviour is generally communal, co-operative and placid. There is no clear-cut ♂ dominance, even during the 2- or 3-day oestrous period when the ♀ may copulate with every ♂ in the group. Rhythmic tongue movements are displayed by both sexes as a preliminary to copulation. GROOMING: rarely observed. PLAY: most prominent at about 18 months, then declines sharply. CARE OF YOUNG: Both ♂ and ♀ help young by bridging wide gaps between trees during progression, and by retrieving them when they fall. It is not known how far these observations apply to species of *Alouatta* other than *A. villosa*.

REPRODUCTION AND DEVELOPMENT

Births take place throughout the year although variations in frequency occur. Births are usually single, but twinning has been recorded.[24] GESTATION: not known. LACTATION: 18–24 months (estimated).[6] MATURITY: $3\frac{1}{2}$–4 years.[6] SIZE OF NEWBORN: Head and Body (mm) 170, 240: Tail (mm) 230, 315 (2♂♂ *A. seniculus*).[4]

CAPTIVITY

LONGEVITY RECORD: *A. villosa* 3 years 9 months, Bronx Zoo, New York.[25, 27] Alouatta are unsuited to captivity; their aloof, unadaptable temperaments need companionship, tranquillity, and lack of change in the environment. Physically, they need warmth and a suitable diet, but information on the subject is very limited.[4]

REFERENCES

1. Cabrera, A. (1957)
2. Hall, E. R. and Kelson, K. R. (1959)
3. Hershkovitz, P. (1949a)
4. Hill, W. C. Osman (1962a)
5. Collias, N. E. and Southwick, C. H. (1952)
6. Carpenter, C. R. (1934)
7. Miller, F. W. (1930)
8. Pocock, R. I. (1920)
9. Sanderson, I. T. (1949)
10. Hofer, H. (1954)
11. Lawrence, Barbara (1933)
12. Bolk, L. (1915)
13. Böker, H. (1932)
14. Negus, V. E. (1949)
15. Kelemen, G. and Sade, J. (1960)
16. Fooden, J. (1964b)
17. James, W. Warwick (1960)
18. Pocock, R. I. (1925c)
19. Bender, M. A. and Chu, E. H. Y. (1963)
20. Erikson, G. E. (1963)
21. Hofer, H. (1960)
22. Carpenter, C. R. (1942b)
23. Carpenter, C. R. (1965)
24. Schultz, A. H. (1921)
25. Jones, M. L. (1962)
26. Schultz, A. H. (1956)
27. Crandall, L. S. (1964)
28. Altmann, S. A. (1959)

C

ANATHANA Lyon, 1913   Madras Treeshrews

1 species: 3 subspecies[1,2]

Anathana ellioti Waterhouse, 1849

GEOGRAPHICAL RANGE[2]

India, S. of the R. Ganges. LIMITS OF GENUS: Latitudes: 8°–26° N. Longitudes: 72°–88° E.

ECOLOGY*

HABITAT: Tropical rain forest, monsoon forest and thorn woodland. Probably similar to *Tupaia* in being both terrestrial and arboreal. ACTIVITY RHYTHM: Diurnal. DIET: As for *Tupaia*.

MORPHOLOGY

External Characters[2]

Bushy-tailed squirrel-like animals, very similar to *Tupaia* but with larger better-haired ears and shorter heavier snout. The fur, redbrown or greybrown coarsely speckled with black, is paler on the flanks and underparts; it is rather stiff and smooth in texture. There is an oblique pale shoulder stripe. The naked part of the nose is more coarsely reticulated than that of *Tupaia*, and is cut squarely across. MAMMAE: 3 pairs. Hands and feet are clawed.

Weights and Dimensions[2,3]

	♂	♀	♀ in % ♂
Head and body length average and range (mm)	171 (160–180) (5♂♂)	181 (177–185) (3♀♀)	106
Tail length average and range (mm)	184 (169–195) (5♂♂)	179 (165–187) (3♀♀)	97

Internal Characters[2]

See *Tupaia*; only differences noted here. SKULL: Facial skeleton short and heavy. Fenestra in zygoma small and inconspicuous. DENTITION: D.F.: $\frac{2}{3}\frac{1}{1}\frac{3}{3}\frac{3}{3}=38$. Lower canine much reduced in size, especially compared with *Urogale* where it is conspicuously developed. Hypocones on $M.^{1}$ and $M.^{2}$ very well developed. ALIMENTARY TRACT: A long caecum is present (25–30 mm).

CAPTIVITY

Anathana has very rarely been observed either in the wild or in captivity. The only record of its exhibition in a Zoo is in Calcutta in 1876.[4]

REFERENCES

1. Ellerman, J. R. and Morrison-Scott, T. C. S. (1951)
2. Lyon, M. W. (1913)
3. British Museum (Natural History) Records
4. Jones, M. L. (1962)

AOTUS Illiger, 1811 Douroucoulis

1 species: 9 subspecies

A. trivirgatus Humboldt, 1811   Douroucouli or Night Monkey

GEOGRAPHICAL RANGE[1-4]

Widely distributed through Central and South America. In S. America they are found in forested regions S. of R. Orinoco to the Amazon basin and as far W. as foothills of Andes; thence southward into the Gran Chaco as far as confluence of R. Parana and R. Paraguay. Found from sea level up to 9000 ft (2769 m) altitude.

ECOLOGY

HABITAT: Inhabitants of tropical rain forest, mixed deciduous forest and old secondary forest where they are usually found from the canopy down to shrub layers of floor (3–30 m).[5] Also found in gallery forests and forest outliers in the eastern Chaco.[6] Sleep in hollows of tree-trunks.[7] DIET: Fruit, insects and small mammals;[3] said to require very little water.[6] ACTIVITY RHYTHM: nocturnal.

MORPHOLOGY

External Characters[3, 8, 9]

Medium sized. Thick soft coat except on face where hair is sparse. Colour of fur is a neutral brown or grey with lighter coloured ventrum. Colour and texture of fur subject to seasonal and altitudinal variation. On head there are three longitudinal dark stripes (very variable) separated by white semilunes above eyes which are large, golden-brown, and slightly protuberant. Ears small and unobtrusive. Nose prominent and internarial septum relatively narrow; face orthognathous. No overt sexual dimorphism. Tail usually longer than body and semiprehensile in young.[5]* LIMBS: legs longer than arms. DIGITAL FORMULA (Hand): 3.4.2.5.1.

Weights and Dimensions[3, 24, 25, 22]

			♀ in % of ♂
Weight range (g)	825, 1020 (2♂)	780, 1249 (2♀)	88(11 specimens)
Head and body length range (mm)	240–475 (20♂ + ♀)		
Tail length range (mm)	220–418 (20♂ + ♀)		

Internal Characters

SKULL: low, short and broad, auditory bullae greatly expanded. Orbits are large and forwardly directed and malar bones prominent. VERTEBRAL COLUMN: Long and slender having usually 7 lumbar vertebrae. Lumbar length exceeds thoracic length by 22%.[10] DENTITION: D.F.: $\frac{2}{2}\frac{1}{1}\frac{3}{3}\frac{3}{3} = 36$. Canines only moderately large; upper molars are quadricuspid with sharp

PLATE 9. *Aotus trivirgatus* (Fox Photos)

pointed cusps and prominent hypocones. M.[3] recessive. HANDS AND FEET: Tactile pads are prominent and somewhat "mammalian" in form.[12] Deep head of flexor pollicis brevis absent; opponens pollicis present; adductor pollicis undifferentiated; contrahentes 2, 4, 5 present.[13] VISUAL SYSTEM: Retina composed wholly of rods, but a macula and fovea are present.[11] RESPIRATORY SYSTEM: Ventral air sac communicates with larynx.[3] CUTANEOUS GLANDS: Diffuse glandular area on ventral surface of base of tail; better developed in ♂♂.[3]

Genetic Biology

CHROMOSOMES:[14] 2n = 54.* No karyotype available.

BEHAVIOUR

Locomotor Behaviour

AUTHORS' CLASSIFICATION: Quadrupedalism. (Erikson's Category: Springer). Run, walk and leap quadrupedally with tail used as a balancing organ. Illustrated by Enders (1930) in a vertical clinging posture on trunk of a sapling, a posture reminiscent of *Lepilemur*, *Indri*, etc. LIMB PROPORTIONS: *See* Part III, p. 393, for Indices. Hindlimbs are considerably longer than forelimbs; humerus longer than radius.

Hand Function

Hands are used in a form of grooming consisting of scratching and picking,[16] also for parting the fur.[5] Finger tips much used for sensory discrimination. Hands of *Aotus* show a single prehensive pattern as in Prosimii.[17] HAND PROPORTIONS: *See* Part III, p. 401, for Indices.

Resting Posture

Rest in quadrupedal hunched posture. For night-resting, *see* Ecology. Some mutual tail-entwining observed.[5]

Social Behaviour

Principal field study is that of Moynihan (1964) summarized here: GROUP SIZE: Family groups consisting of 2 adults and young. HOME RANGE AND TERRITORIALITY: Groups tend to remain within their territories, inter-group contacts are few. Occasional crossing of boundaries to a fruiting tree may bring a group of 4 or 5 animals together, but it soon breaks up. Aggression occurs between adults of the same sex. VOCALIZATION is adapted to nocturnal life; at least 9 distinctive calls have been described. DISPLAYS are rare; arching the back (threat) and swaying from side to side have been observed. MALE DOMINANCE is slight. PLAY: Lack of play patterns in young. MARKING BEHAVIOUR (CAPTIVITY): Washing of hands and feet in urine stream. Rubbing of the perineal region against a branch has been observed and may be associated with territorial marking. GROOMING: Self-grooming consists of scratching with hands and feet. Social grooming is associated with copulatory behaviour and is usually performed by the ♂, using hands and teeth.

REPRODUCTION AND DEVELOPMENT

GESTATION PERIOD: not known. BIRTH SEASON: Captivity birth records do not indicate any seasonality.[3] Single births. English (1934) reports birth and development in captivity of a single specimen. Moynihan (1964) observed that, for the first few days, infant clings to mother's belly, later being carried on her back. From about the 9th day, infant may be carried by the father, except when being nursed by the mother. (Cf. *Callicebus*).

CAPTIVITY

LONGEVITY RECORD:[20] *Aotus trivirgatus trivirgatus* 11 years 7 months, London: Zoological Gardens. BIRTHS IN CAPTIVITY:[21] Between 1959 and 1963, 8 births have been recorded in World Zoos. DIET: Douroucoulis have been fed successfully on fruit, bread, mealworms, eggs and milk.[8] *See also* Crandall (1964).

REFERENCES

1. Hershkovitz, P. (1949a)
2. Hall, E. R. and Kelson, K. R. (1959)
3. Hill, W. C. Osman (1960)
4. Allen, J. A. (1916)
5. Moynihan, M. (1964)
6. Kreig, H. (1930)
7. Bates, H. W. (1863)
8. Sanderson, I. T. (1957)
9. Pocock, R. I. (1920)
10. Erikson, G. E. (1963)
11. Polyak, S. (1957)
12. Clark, W. E. Le Gros (1959)
13. Day, M. H. and Napier, J. R. (1963)
14. Bender, M. A. and Chu, E. H. Y. (1963)
15. Enders, R. K. (1930)
16. Bishop, Alison (1964)
17. Bishop, Alison (1962)
18. English, W. L. (1934)
19. Hill, W. C. Osman (1959a)
20. Jones, M. L. (1962)
21. International Zoo Year Book, Vols. 1–5 (1959–1965)
22. Schultz, A. H. (1956)
23. Crandall, Lee S. (1964)
24. Hubbell, G. (Personal Communication)
25. Veterinary Officer's Reports: Zoological Society of London

ARCTOCEBUS Gray, 1863 Angwantibos

1 species: 2 subspecies

Arctocebus calabarensis Smith, 1860 2 subsp.

GEOGRAPHICAL RANGE [1,2]

Africa. Tropical forests of W. Africa. Probable range is limited by four rivers: to the West, the Cross R.; to the East, the Ubangi R.; to the South, the Ogowe R., and to the South-East, the Congo R.

ECOLOGY *

HABITAT:[1] Tropical forests including high deciduous forest, rain forest and secondary forest. Usually found in high trees. ACTIVITY RHYTHM: Nocturnal, but is sometimes seen to be active in daytime. DIET: Unknown in the wild; presumed to be largely insectivorous.

MORPHOLOGY

External Characters

Much smaller than *Perodicticus*. Fur is thick and woolly and rust-red or yellowish brown above, fawn or pale grey on underparts. In *A. c. aureus* general colour is golden-rust, underparts being lighter.[2] Face is longer and sharper than in the potto. Tail is lacking. Thumb and big toe extremely divergent; digits are relatively smaller, less hairy and more webbed than those of pottos. All digits bear flat nails except 2nd pedal digit; index finger reduced to a nailless tubercle, middle finger also reduced. Limbs are short, robust and subequal in length. MAMMAE: 3 pairs.[3]

Weights and Dimensions

Body weight[4] (g)	266–465 (Number and sex not stated)	
Head and body length range[1] (mm)	220–251 (6♂♂)	231, 263 (2♀♀)
Tail length[1] (mm)	8 approx. (6♂♂)	8 approx. (2♀♀)

Rode (1937) gives head and body length as 250–400 mm (number and sex not stated).

Internal Characters

See *Perodicticus*. Only principle differences noted here. SKULL: Neurocranium less globular, rostrum more produced; premaxillaries fuse in midline to form a projecting keel. Short external auditory meatus. POST-CRANIAL SKELETON: Cervical and upper thoracic vertebrae long, but none project through skin.[3] Dorsal parts of ribs uniquely specialized; they are notably broadened and overlap like tiles.[10] HUMERUS: entepicondylar foramen absent.

PLATE 10. *Arctocebus calabarensis*

PHALANGES: Only two phalanges on index finger, full complement, though much reduced, on middle finger. DENTITION: $\frac{2}{2} \frac{1}{1} \frac{3}{3} \frac{3}{3} = 36$. Diastemata between canine, anterior premolar and second premolar well-marked. Upper anterior premolar somewhat caniniform and with a cingulum. Upper molars with well-developed hypocones and pointed cusps; M.$\frac{3}{}$ tritubercular and relatively large. Lower molars all quadricuspid with sharp tall cusps. ALIMENTARY TRACT: Colon forms simple loop, unsacculated and without taeniae.[3] VASCULAR: Retia mirabilia present affecting main arteries to hands and feet.[6]

BEHAVIOUR

Locomotor Behaviour

AUTHORS' CLASSIFICATION: Quadrupedalism. Subtype: Slow-climbing. See *Perodicticus*; *Arctocebus*, however, said to be more active. LIMB PROPORTIONS: *See* Part III, p. 393, for Indices.

Hand Function

See *Perodicticus*.

REPRODUCTION AND DEVELOPMENT [7]

Polyoestrous cycling believed to occur. Recorded oestrus lengths are 45, 36, 37 and 38 days. GESTATION PERIOD:* 131 days; birth was followed by post-partum oestrus on death of infant.

CAPTIVITY

Angwantibos are not suited to captivity conditions. Maximum lifespan at London Zoo: $3\frac{1}{2}$ years.[8] LONGEVITY RECORD[9] (up to 1962): 4 years 6 months, Berlin Zoo. Between 1959–63, only one birth (at Amsterdam) has been recorded from World Zoos.[8]

REFERENCES

1. Sanderson, I. T. (1940)
2. Booth, A. H. (1958)
3. Hill, W. C. Osman (1953)
4. Oregon Regional Primate Research Center
5. Rode, P. (1937)
6. Wislocki, G. B. and Straus, W. L. (1933)

7. Manley, G. H. (1966a)
8. International Zoo Year Books, Vols. I–V (1959–1965)
9. Jones, M. L. (1962)
10. Schultz A. H. (1961)

ATELES   E. Geoffroy, 1806   Spider Monkeys

4 species: 16 subspecies[1]

A. paniscus (Type species)	Black Spider Monkey	2 subsp.
A. belzebuth	Long-haired Spider Monkey	3 subsp.
A. fusciceps	Brown-headed Spider Monkey	2 subsp.
A. geoffroyi	Black-handed Spider Monkey	9 subsp.

GEOGRAPHICAL RANGE [1,2]

Coastal forests of Mexico to Lat. 23° N. Throughout Central America and parts of South America including Pacific coastal forests, upper tributaries of R. Amazon and R. Orinoco, North bank of lower Amazon including the Guianas, South bank of lower Amazon between R. Tocantins and R. Tapajos. Southern latitudinal limit: 16° S.

ECOLOGY

HABITAT: Found in lowland rain forest and montane forest on the slopes of Andes; tend to occupy small branches of high strata of canopy. DIET:[3] 90% fruits and nuts; also buds and flowers. ACTIVITY RHYTHM: diurnal.

MORPHOLOGY

External Characters

Slender body with long slender limbs, long prehensile tail and a prominent abdomen. Head is small with well-marked muzzle; the fur is very variable in colour, texture and length, even within species. Coat colour is variable; black (*A. paniscus*); black or brownish-black (*A. fusciceps*); black or brown, generally with paler underparts and a pale triangular patch on the forehead (*A. belzebuth*); golden, red, buff or dark brown with hands and feet generally black (*A. geoffroyi*). (For detailed colour key, *see* Kellogg and Goldman, 1944.) Hair on crown is generally directed forward. ♀ tends to be heavier and larger than ♂.[4] LIMBS: Arms and legs long relative to trunk, but arms longer than legs. Big toe divergent but relatively small. Hand is prehensile and thumb is vestigial or absent; DIGITAL FORMULA: $3=4>2=5$. MAMMAE: single pair in axilla. GENITALIA: pendulous clitoris.

Weights and Dimensions

	♂	♀	♀ in % of ♂
Body weight range[7]	5470, 6887 (2♂)	5824 (1♀)	103[4]
Head and body length range[1] (mm)	370–590 (17♂)	344–660 (30♀)	105†
Tail length range[1] (mm)	630–823 (17♂)	613–920 (30♀)	107†

† (♀ in % of ♂ based on midpoint of ranges)

PLATE 11. *Ateles belzebuth* (San Diego Zoo), *see* p. 60.

Internal Characters

SKULL: ♀ skull larger than ♂; foramen magnum directed downwards. VERTEBRAL COLUMN:[8] usually 4 lumbars; length of lumbar col. 43% of thoracic. THORAX:[8] flattened ventrally, sternum broad, scapula elongated and dorsally displaced, humeral head globular (arm-swinging adaptations). NEUROLOGY: Brain is large and shows certain affinities with Old World monkeys and apes, particularly in occipital region. (For bibliography, *see* Hill, 1962a.) TAIL: glabrous skin bearing dermatoglyphics and containing eccrine sweat glands[9] and Meissner's corpuscles[10] on ventral surface of distal third. CUTANEOUS GLANDS: Paired glands found on either side of manubrium, histologically of a tubular type.[11] DENTITION: D.F. $\frac{2}{2}\frac{1}{1}\frac{3}{3}\frac{3}{3} = 36$. Incisor $\frac{1}{-}$ grooved anteriorly. UPPER CANINE: large and vertically implanted. MOLARS: quadritubercular; tendency for $M\frac{3}{3}$ to be reduced or lost.[12]

Genetic Biology

CHROMOSOMES:[13] 2n = 34 which is the lowest number recorded for a primate. Karyotype shows only 2 pairs of acrocentric chromosomes. P.T.C. TASTING:[14] 100% non-tasters (13 individuals). BLOOD GROUPS:[25] Five specimens (*A. paniscus, A. fusciceps, A. belzebuth*) have been tested. Four proved to be Group A and one Group B of the Human-Type ABO groups. Saliva negative for Lewis substance.

BEHAVIOUR

Locomotor Behaviour

AUTHORS' CLASSIFICATION: Quadrupedalism. Sub-type: New World semibrachiation. Regarded as a brachiator by Erikson (1963). Basically quadrupedal but capable of rapid progression with legs extended, by swinging below branches by means of arms and tail. Frequently make long jumps outwards and downwards, or long vertical drops.[3] Quadrupedal when on ground but also capable of bipedalism in which case tail is held in a curve parallel to the back. When walking quadrupedally on ground, fingers are occasionally flexed at proximal interphalangeal joints.[8] LIMB PROPORTIONS: Arms and legs very long relative to trunk height. *See* Part III, p. 393 for Indices.

Hand Function[15, 16]

Hand is prehensile and thumb is vestigial or absent. Main prehensile function of the hand is the hook-grip. "Precision" element achieved by digits by means of scissor-like action. Tail frequently employed in lieu of hand for picking up small objects, e.g. shelled peanuts. HAND PROPORTIONS: *see* Part III, p. 401, for Indices.

Resting Posture

Rest with body erect and hands either free, supporting body above head or wrapped around legs.

Social Behaviour

Relatively little information available. Principal studies are those of Carpenter (1935), Wagner (1956), Eisenberg and Kuehn (1966) and Hofer (1958). Information relates to

PLATE 12. *Ateles geoffroyi* (San Diego Zoo), *see* p. 61.

A. geoffroyi. RANGE: Semi-nomadic; range is presumed to vary with seasonal variation in food supply.[3] POPULATION DENSITY: 200 per sq. mile.[18] GROUP SIZE varies according to habitat[26] from family groups to large troops of 100.[17] ADULT SEX RATIO: 1♂: 1·6♀♀.[19] GROUP STRUCTURE: Strict linear hierarchy cannot easily be defined. Male dominance behaviour not evident; female groups with offspring are the most cohesive units in an otherwise loose constitution.[26] SOCIAL GROOMING:[26] Of relatively low valency but demonstrating rank order within the group; high-ranking individuals groom more than they are groomed. VOCALIZATION: *see* Eisenberg and Kuehn (1966). PLAY:[3] Great variety of active play patterns among young.

REPRODUCTION AND DEVELOPMENT

MENSTRUAL CYCLE: every 24–27 days.[21] GESTATION:* 139 days approx.[22] Single births. No evidence of discrete breeding season.[3, 11] YOUNG AT BIRTH: 7% of adult ♀ weight.[4] Young are carried on mother's abdomen for about four months, later on her back; infants use prehensile tail to hold on to mother's tail. In *A. geoffroyi*,[3] infant is black for 6 months, during which time it is almost completely dependent on its mother; adult colouration is not completely acquired until 10 months. First permanent teeth (incisors) at 11–13 months. Weight at 1 year: 2000 g (1 specimen).

CAPTIVITY

Gentle temperament; easily tamed though capable of unprovoked outbursts of rage.[20] Accept a wide variety of foods. Successfully maintained in outdoor colonies at several zoos in U.S. (e.g. San Francisco and San Diego). LONGEVITY RECORD:[23] *A. paniscus* 20 years, Prospect Park, Brooklyn, U.S. 7 or 8 years is not uncommon, but average zoo life of *A. geoffroyi* is 4½ years.[24] BIRTHS IN CAPTIVITY:[24] 62 births have been reported in World Zoos between 1959–63.

REFERENCES

1. Kellogg, R. and Goldman, E. A. (1944)
2. Hall, E. R. and Kelson, K. R. (1959)
3. Carpenter, C. R. (1935)
4. Schultz, A. H. (1956)
5. Midlo, C. and Cummins, H. (1942)
6. Biegert, J. (1961)
7. Hill, W. C. Osman (1962a)
8. Erikson, G. E. (1963)
9. Ellis, R. A. and Montagna, W. (1963)
10. Winkelmann, R. K. (1963)
11. Wislocki, G. B. and Schultz, A. H. (1925)
12. Clark, W. E. Le Gros (1959)
13. Bender, M. A. and Chu, E. H. Y. (1963)
14. Chiarelli, B. (1963b)
15. Bishop, Alison (1964)
16. Hofer, H. (1958)
17. Wagner, H. O. (1956)
18. Sanderson, I. T. (1949)
19. Carpenter, C. R. (1942b)
20. Sanderson, I. T. (1957)
21. Harms, J. W. (1956)
22. Asdell, S. A. (1946)
23. Crandall, L. S. (1964)
24. International Zoo Year Book (1959–65)
25. Wiener, A. S., Moor-Jankowski, J. and Gordon, E. B. (1966)
26. Eisenberg, J. F., and Kuehn, R. E. (1966)

AVAHI†   Jourdan, 1834   Avahis

1 species: 2 subspecies[1]

Avahi laniger Gmelin, 1788   2 subsp.

GEOGRAPHICAL RANGE [2]

Madagascar. North-west Sambirano forest region and in forested regions of eastern littoral extending into foothills of central plateau.

ECOLOGY [2]

HABITAT: Eastern and N.W. rain forest where they are found clinging on to vertical trunks and larger branches; during the day found sleeping among foliage some distance from trunk. ACTIVITY RHYTHM: nocturnal. DIET: from captivity studies assumed to be leaves, bark, fruit and flowers.

MORPHOLOGY [3, 4]

External Characters

Smallest member of Indriidae. Fur is thick, soft and woolly. Colour is an overall grey-brown having a somewhat grizzled appearance due to change in colour of individual hairs from grey at base through brown to black at tip. Underparts grey or white with rufous tinge. Tail, hands and feet rusty. White band on forehead. Face is rounded, muzzle short and rhinarium naked; ears are small and hidden. Eyes very large with pupil forming a vertical slit. Hindlimbs much longer than forelimbs. Hands long and slender; 3rd, 4th and 5th digits syndactylous. Feet also show webbing of 3rd, 4th and 5th digits, and a widely divergent big toe; claw on 2nd toe. DIGITAL FORMULA: 4.3.5.2.1.

Weights and Dimensions* [3]

Body weight—no information.	
Head and body length (mm)	300–330 (2 specimens)
Tail length (mm)	390–395 (2 specimens)

Internal Characters[3]

For further details see *Propithecus*; differences only noted here. SKULL: Neurocranium small and broad, orbits very large. Mandible has long and very oblique symphysis. FEMUR: Adaptations typical of vertical clinging and leaping locomotor group (see *Propithecus*). ALIMENTARY SYSTEM: Salivary glands, especially parotid, particularly large. Viscera are bulky and capacious as in all Indriidae. Stomach shows some incipient sacculation. Gall bladder absent.* GENITALIA:[5] Penis bears only 2 large spines; clitoris is long and thin. CUTANEOUS GLANDS:[2] Paired gland below angles of jaw in ♂ and ♀, and glands in the region of scrotum in ♂. DENTITION: D.F.: $\frac{2}{2}\frac{1}{0}\frac{2}{2}\frac{3}{3}=30$. INCISORS: I.[1,2] minute, peglike

---

† *See* Taxonomic Notes, p. 370.

structures; in lower jaw they form a dental comb. CANINES: C.[1] stout but not particularly prominent. Lower canines absent. MOLARS: Upper molars are quadricuspid. In lower jaw, first and third molars are quinquecuspid.

Genetic Biology

No information available.

BEHAVIOUR

Locomotor Behaviour

AUTHORS' CLASSIFICATION: Vertical Clinging and Leaping. For details see *Propithecus*. LIMB PROPORTIONS: legs are much longer than arms. For Indices, *see* Part III, p. 393.

Hand Function*

Hand prehensile and thumb pseudo-opposable. Prehensile function is typical of lemuriformes consisting of a single pattern of movement. Ulnar border of hand provides dominant grip in locomotion. HAND PROPORTIONS: For Indices, *see* Part III, p. 401.

Resting Posture[2]

Normally rest in vertical clinging position but in sleep curl up among leaves remote from the trunk.

Social Behaviour*

GROUP SIZE:[2] Family units of 2–4 individuals. VOCALIZATION:[2] Calls are not prominent. Repertoire consists of grunts, soft whistles and high-pitched prolonged whistles. MARKING BEHAVIOUR has not been observed in the wild or in captivity.

REPRODUCTION AND DEVELOPMENT [5]

Single mating season. Give birth to single young; infants are born at end of August in Madagascar. LACTATION: 5 months duration. Infants are carried on abdomen, and later shift to mother's back.

CAPTIVITY

A specimen was exhibited in London at the Zoological Gardens in 1889.

REFERENCES

1. Schwarz, E. (1931c)
2. Petter, J. J. (1962c)
3. Hill, W. C. Osman (1953)
4. Forbes, H. O. (1897)
5. Petter-Rousseaux, A. (1964)
6. Grandidier, D. and Petit, G. (1932)
7. Napier, J. R. and Walker, A. C. (1967)

BRACHYTELES Spix, 1823

1 species : 0 subspecies

B. arachnoides E. Geoffroy, 1806

GEOGRAPHICAL RANGE [1]

South America. Confined to Tupi forests of S.E. Brazil between Bahia and Sao Paulo and inland into montane forest of Minas Gerais.

ECOLOGY *

HABITAT: Inhabitants of tropical and montane rain forest where they are said to frequent the open strata of the canopy and emergents.[2] DIET: Fruits, leaves and seeds.[1] ACTIVITY RHYTHM: Diurnal.

MORPHOLOGY

External Characters[1]

Large robust animal with thick coat, elongated limbs and absent thumb. [Size and coat reminiscent of woolly monkeys; long limbs and thumbless state reminiscent of spider monkeys.] Tail prehensile. Abdomen prominent. Nostrils not markedly platyrrhine. Colour ranges from grey to brown with varying shades of yellow which are more pronounced in ♂ than ♀. Face is naked and flesh-coloured when young but probably darkens in adults.

Weights and Dimensions

	♂	♀	♀ in % of ♂
Body weight[3] *(g)**	—	9500 (adult ♀)	—
Head and body length range[1, 3] *(mm)*	462–630 (6♂)	470–565 (3♀)	95
Tail length range[1, 3] *(mm)*	650–741 (6♂)	740–800 (3♀)	111

(♀ in % of ♂ based on midpoint of ranges)

Internal Characters

SKULL: generally similar to *Lagothrix* but having a larger angular region to mandible. VERTEBRAL COLUMN:[4] usually 4 lumbar vertebrae; length of lumbar column 55% of

PLATE 13. *Brachyteles arachnoides.* Juvenile ♀ (Zoological Society of New York)

thoracic. THORAX:[4] Arm-swinging adaptations in thorax and shoulder girdle (see *Ateles*). ARM: Entepicondylar foramen is absent. HAND:[4] long and slender; thumb represented by a minute metacarpal and single phalanx. DENTITION:[5] D.F. $\frac{2}{2}\frac{1}{1}\frac{3}{3}\frac{3}{3}=36$. Canines relatively small. Molars are quadricuspid with oblique crests (cf. *Ateles*). M.$\frac{3}{}$ retrogressive.

Genetic Biology*

CHROMOSOMES:[6] 2n = 34 (tentative). No karyotype available.

BEHAVIOUR

Locomotor Behaviour

AUTHORS' CLASSIFICATION: Quadrupedalism. Sub-type: New World semibrachiation. (Erikson's (1963) category: Brachiator.) No field observations but in captivity frequently swing themselves by arms, tail and/or legs.[4] When walking quadrupedally fingers are flexed at interphalangeal joints. LIMB PROPORTIONS: for Indices *see* Part III, p. 393.

Hand Function[4]

Prehensile; hand function much as in *Ateles*.

Resting Posture[4]

Common resting posture is to hang by arms and tail or by all five extremities.

Social Behaviour

No information.

REPRODUCTION AND DEVELOPMENT

Unknown.

CAPTIVITY

Seldom kept in captivity. Zoo life usually very short. LONGEVITY RECORD:[7] 1 year 8 months. Breslau Zoo (now Wroclaw, Poland). No record of births in captivity.[8]

REFERENCES

1. Hill, W. C. Osman (1962a)
2. Burmeister, H. C. C. (1854–6)
3. Erikson, G. E. quoted by Hill, W. C. Osman (1962a)
4. Erikson, G. E. (1963)
5. James, W. Warwick (1962)
6. Chiarelli, B. (1961) quoted in Bender, M. A. and Chu, E. H. Y. (1963)
7. Jones, M. L. (1962)
8. International Zoo Year Book, vols. I–V (1959–65)

CACAJAO Lesson, 1840 Uakaris

3 species: 2 subspecies[1]†

C. calvus	Bald Uakari	o subsp.
C. melanocephalus (Type species)	Black-headed Uakari	o subsp.
C. rubicundus	Red Uakari	2 subsp.

GEOGRAPHICAL RANGE [2, 3, 4]

South America. Upper Amazonia between (i) R. Branco-Negro and R. Japura (*C. melano-cephalus*); (ii) narrow zone between R. Japura and R. Içá (*C. calvus*); (iii) South of R. Içá (Putumayo); W. of R. Jurua and E. of R. Ucayali (*C. rubicundus*). Latitudinal limits: 4° N.–7° S.

ECOLOGY *

HABITAT:[5, 6] Tropical rain forest subject to periodic flooding. Found in higher (open) strata of canopy and in emergent trees. Move through forest at lower (closed) canopy level on stout branches. Never seen on ground. ACTIVITY RHYTHM: Diurnal. DIET: Fruits, buds, seeds, leaves and epiphytes.

MORPHOLOGY

External Characters

Medium-sized monkeys with short tail. Most familiar species (*C. rubicundus*) has bright crimson face and forehead and shaggy red-brown coat.

Colour key	Body fur	Face and forehead
C. calvus	Silvery grey or white	Pink and bare
C. rubicundus	Red-brown	Crimson and bare
C. melanocephalus	Chestnut-brown with black extremities	Black and bare

Coat is long, coarse and shaggy. LIMBS: Legs longer than arms. HANDS: D.F.: 4.3.2 = 5.1.[17]

Weights and Dimensions[7, 8]

	♂	♀	♀ in % of ♂
Head and body length range (mm)	435–485 (4♂)	365–445 (3♀)	90
Tail length range (mm)	155–185 (4♂)	150–165 (3♀)	92

Internal Characters

VERTEBRAL COLUMN: Unique among Old and New World monkeys in possessing 4 or 5 sacral vertebrae (Schultz, 1961). ALIMENTARY TRACT: long intestinal tract; length said by Forbes (1897) to exceed that of any other platyrrhine monkey. HANDS: Thenar muscles not

† *See* Taxonomic Notes, p. 370.

differentiated but two heads of adductor pollicis well-defined; other contrahentes: 2.4.5.
DENTITION: D.F.: $\frac{2}{2}\frac{1}{1}\frac{3}{3}\frac{3}{3}=36$. Upper incisors projecting; lower incisors are procumbent and somewhat compressed from side-to-side giving the appearance almost of the prosimian dental comb. Large canines with wide diastemata in upper jaw. Molars are quadricuspid and show characteristically grooved wear pattern (cf. *Pithecia*). Premolars are heterodont.

Genetic Biology

CHROMOSOMES:[10]* 2n = 46 (1 ♂ *C. rubicundus*). HAEMOGLOBINS:[11] (*C. rubicundus*) Show two components on starch gel electrophoresis.

BEHAVIOUR

Locomotor Behaviour

AUTHORS' CLASSIFICATION: quadrupedalism. (Erikson's category: climber). Few field observations available. Although Uakaris are reputedly lethargic and poor leapers (*see* Hill, 1960) in captivity they can be very active, leaping "recklessly".[13] Observers report some arm-swinging activity and occasional bipedalism.[5] During quadrupedal walking on level surfaces, hands are markedly externally rotated.[14]*

Hand Function

Hand prehensile, thumb non-opposable. Main functional axis of hand between index and middle fingers; however, thumb is used selectively for picking up small objects which are gripped at interphalangeal joint or between tip of thumb and thenar pad.[15] Uakaris manipulate food between the wrists held in supination.[2]

Social Behaviour

Behaviour in the wild is unknown. Said to be gregarious and to move about in small groups, although one observer has reported groups of 100.[16]

CAPTIVITY

LONGEVITY RECORD:[18] *C. calvus* 3 years 2 months. New York: Bronx Zoo. *C. rubicundus* 8 years 9 months. Philadelphia Zoological Gardens. Births at Monkey Jungle, Florida, during 1963 and San Diego Zoo in 1966. For notes on these animals in captivity *see* Crandall, 1964.

REFERENCES

1. Cabrera, A. (1957)
2. Hill, W. C. Osman (1960)
3. Fiedler, W. (1956)
4. Forbes, H. O. (1897)
5. Bates, H. W. (1863)
6. Ashton, E. H. and Oxnard, C. E. (1964b)
7. Thomas, O. (1928b)
8. Lönnberg, E. (1938)
9. Day, M. H. and Napier, J. R. (1963)
10. Bender, M. A. and Chu, E. H. Y. (1963)
11. Buettner-Janusch, J. and Buettner-Janusch, V. (1964)
12. Erikson, G. E. (1963)
13. Hubbell, G. (1964) Personal communication
14. Authors' observation
15. Bishop, Alison (1964)
16. Lönnberg, E. (1938)
17. Pocock, R. I. (1920)
18. Jones, M. L. (1962)
19. Schultz, A. H. (1961)
20. Crandall, L. S. (1964)
21. Priemel, G. (1937)

PLATE 14. *Cacajao rubicundus* (San Diego Zoo)

CALLICEBUS Thomas, 1903

Titis

3 species: 14 subspecies[1, 2]

C. torquatus	Widow monkey	3 subsp.
C. moloch	Dusky Titi	7 subsp.
C. personatus (Type species)	Masked Titi	4 subsp.

RANGE [1, 2]

South America. Found around the S. and W. tributaries of the R. Orinoco; in the Amazon basin W. and S. of the R. Negro and S. into Paraguay as far as the Chaco Boreal; on the S. bank of R. Amazon E. and W. of R. Tapajos. Also found in the Tupi forests of E. coast of Brazil (C. personatus). Latitudinal limits: 5°N.–23°S. Western limits: the Andes. North-eastern limits: the R. Negro and the R. Amazon. For locality maps, see Hershkovitz (1963).

ECOLOGY

HABITAT: Tropical rain forest. C. torquatus seen among high trees.[3] In western and southern part of range C. moloch occupies low canopy, thickets and underbrush, generally near water;[4] occasionally move on the ground.[5, 18] DIET:[5] fruit, insects, birds' eggs and small birds. ACTIVITY RHYTHM:[6] diurnal or possibly crepuscular.

MORPHOLOGY

External Characters

Small to medium in size. Coat has long, bushy, lustrous fur.

Colour key	Back	Underparts	Head	Limbs	Tail
C. personatus	Darkbrown with long buffy tips	Similar to back or rufous (not sharply defined)	Sharply contrasting black mask, or similar to back	Hands and feet black, sharply contrasting with buff limbs	Redbrown
C. moloch	Grey, reddish or brown	Similar to back, or sharply defined orange-red or buff	Forehead with grey or black band; or similar to back	Hands and feet similar to limbs; grey, red, dark brown or blackish	Dark grey, sometimes with whitish tip
C. torquatus	Reddish-black	Similar to back	White, buff or orange throatpatch or ruff	Black forearms, legs and feet. White or yellow hands (exc. 1 subsp. with black hands)	Black

For detailed colour key of C. moloch and C. torquatus, see Hershkovitz (1963).

Face orthognathous and external nares typically platyrrhine. Tail is non-prehensile (but *see* Social Behaviour) and much longer than body. Limbs short; legs longer than arms. HANDS:[20] Digits bear nails which are strongly curved transversely. Digital formula: 3.4.2.5.1. Palmar pads, six in number; interdigital pads sharply defined, hypothenar pad very prominent; two or three supplementary pads in centre of palm as in *Aotus*.

Weights and Dimensions[1]

	C. moloch	*C. torquatus*
Head and body length range (mm)	287–390 (5♂♂3♀♀)	310–375 (16♂♂3♀♀)
Tail length range (mm)	331–480 (5♂♂3♀♀)	420–493 (16♂♂3♀♀)
Body weight (g)	681 (1♂)	

Internal Characters

SKULL: Foramen magnum somewhat backwardly directed and angular region of mandible notably expanded; hyoid bone dilated ventrally. These features are reminiscent of *Alouatta* (*see* Social Behaviour: vocalization). POSTCRANIAL SKELETON: *see* comparative table in Part III, p. 390, after Priemel.[7] DENTITION: D.F. $\frac{2}{2}\frac{1}{1}\frac{3}{3}\frac{3}{3} = 36$. Canines barely project beyond tooth row; upper premolars are frequently tricuspid;[1] lower premolars retain a simple, almost unicuspid form.[8] Upper molars are tritubercular with pseudohypocone reminiscent of *Notharctus*.[9] Lower molars quadricuspid.

Genetic Biology[10]*

CHROMOSOMES: 2n = 46. (1♂). KARYOTYPE: 24 acrocentrics, 10 subterminals, 10 meta-centrics, X = subterminal, Y = acrocentric.

BEHAVIOUR

Locomotor Behaviour

AUTHORS' CLASSIFICATION: Quadrupedalism. (Erikson's category: Springer.) Essentially quadrupedal but most observers[4, 7, 12, 13] refer to well-developed jumping and leaping ability; *Callicebus* is said to have a "squirrel-like agility in climbing and jumping."[4] Tail is used for balancing. In captivity its movements are restless, rapid and jerky.[14] LIMB PROPORTIONS:* *see* Part III, p. 393, for Indices.

Hand Function

Hand prehensile, thumb non-opposable. During manipulation uses the whole hand as a unit, thumb being barely differentiated functionally; there is some differentiation between index and middle fingers.[15] HAND PROPORTIONS:* *see* Part III, p. 401, for Indices.

Resting Posture

Normally rests with body hunched and supported on all four limbs. During rest and sleep, pairs usually entwine tails.[19] (*See* Plate 15.)

Social Behaviour

A preliminary report of a field study of *C. moloch* (Mason, In press) is summarized here. GROUP SIZE: Live in pairs or family groups which average 3 but may be 4, or 5 at most; in certain ecological situations family groups may combine. TERRITORIALITY: Family unit occupies a relatively small fixed area which contains its sleeping and feeding trees; territory may actually be defended. When groups confront each other on the boundaries of their territories, as they do almost daily, defensive behaviour consists of vocalization accompanied by arching the back, erecting the hair, and lashing the tail. VOCALIZATION: Howler-like quality to voice; calls are extremely elaborate and distinctive; calling sessions take place early in the morning[4, 13] (reminiscent of territorial behaviour of *Alouatta*). Vocalization has been studied by Moynihan (in press). CHEST-RUBBING: Rubbing the chest along a branch, or squeezing and rubbing it with the hands, was observed most frequently after inter-group encounters. SEXUAL BEHAVIOUR: Pairs form a strong and stable relationship; ♂ and ♀ usually keep close together. SOCIAL GROOMING and other sensory contacts (e.g. sitting for long periods side by side with tails entwined) have been observed. MALE DOMINANCE is not marked; either sex may lead progression to food trees.

REPRODUCTION AND DEVELOPMENT

Birth season is not fixed, but in an 11-month field study in eastern Colombia from May through March, six births were recorded in the December to March period only.[18] Single young. ♂ carries infant except when it is being fed by its mother.[18] (cf. *Callithrix*). Infant clings with hands, feet and tail.[19]

CAPTIVITY

Can be easily tamed and thrive moderately well in zoos. LONGEVITY RECORD:[16] *C. moloch* 4 years 2 months, Bronx Zoo, New York. BIRTHS IN CAPTIVITY:[17] In World Zoos, one birth was recorded between 1959–63.

REFERENCES

1. Hershkovitz, P. (1963)
2. Hill, W. C. Osman (1960)
3. Humboldt, A. de and Bonpland, A. (1812)
4. Kreig, H. (1930)
5. Bates, H. W. (1863)
6. Cabrera, A. (1900) *In* Hershkovitz, P. (1963)
7. Priemel, G. (1937)
8. Clark, W. E. Le Gros (1959)
9. Gregory, W. K. (1920)
10. Bender, M. A. and Chu, E. H. Y. (1963)
11. Erikson, G. E. (1963)
12. Deville, E. (1855) *In* Hershkovitz, P. (1963)
13. Miller, L. E. (1916) *In* Hershkovitz, P. (1963)
14. Napier, J. R. (1964)—personal observation
15. Bishop, Alison (1964)
16. Jones, M. L. (1962)
17. International Zoo Year Book, Vols. 1–5 (1959–1965)
18. Mason, W. A. (In press)
19. Moynihan, M. (In press)
20. Biegert, J. (1961)

PLATE 15. *Callicebus moloch* (San Diego Zoo)

CALLIMICO† Ribiero, 1911 Goeldi's Marmosets

1 species: 0 subspecies

Callimico goeldii Thomas, 1904

RANGE [1, 2]

Found in only three areas on the upper tributaries of R. Amazon, E. of R. Ucayali between latitudes 7°–11° S. and longitudes 68°–75° W. Found on high ground 650–2000 ft (185–615 m) above sea level.

ECOLOGY *

HABITAT: Inhabitants of tropical rain forest where they are found in the canopy, level unrecorded. DIET: not known. ACTIVITY RHYTHM: Diurnal.

MORPHOLOGY

External Characters[3, 4]

Small, lightly-built monkeys. Coat is thick, straight and silky in texture and is predominantly black with minute pale tips to the hairs. Long hairs on back and sides of head stand out, giving a "bouffant" appearance. Young are almost entirely brownish-black. Face is orthognathous; bridge of nose is depressed, giving snub-nosed look. Tail is considerably longer than body. Fingers and toes bear modified claws; big toe has a nail and is small but divergent; the thumb is long, in line with the fingers and is non-opposable. DIGITAL FORMULA: $3 = 4.2.5.1$.[11] MAMMAE: 1 pair in axillary position.[3]

Weights and Dimensions[1, 15]

Average weight (g)	472 (11 ♂♂ and ♀♀)	
Head and body lengths (mm)	190, 215 (2♂)	190 (1♀)
Tail lengths (mm)	255, 325 (2♂)	270 (1♀)

Internal Characters

For details of anatomy *see* monograph by Hill (1959b). In many characters *Callimico* is like the Marmosets and Tamarins but in others it bears a strong resemblance to Cebidae, e.g. retention of $M_{\frac{3}{3}}$, verticality of lower incisors and form of nails which are less claw-like than in Callitrichidae. *Callimico* shows a number of prosimian (particularly tarsioid) features especially in muscular system, e.g. retention of 4 contrahentes muscles in the hand. SKULL: dolichocephalic and orthognathous. Mandible has a very prominent backwardly-curving coronoid and a moderate chin. DENTITION:[5] D.F.: $\frac{2}{2}\frac{1}{1}\frac{3}{3}\frac{3}{3} = 36$. $M.\frac{3}{3}$ present but retrogressive. Hypocones on upper molars are diminutive and teeth are virtually tricuspid.[6]

See Taxonomic Notes, Part III, p. 371.

PLATE 16. *Callimico goeldii* (San Diego Zoo)

Genetic Biology*

CHROMOSOMES:[7] 2n=48 (1♀). KARYOTYPE: 16 acrocentrics, 30 subterminals, 2 meta-centrics. P.T.C. TASTING:[8] Non-taster (1 specimen).

BEHAVIOUR

Locomotor Behaviour

AUTHORS' CLASSIFICATION: Quadrupedalism. (Erikson's (1963) category: Springer). Little is known of locomotor behaviour in the wild but it is presumed to be similar to that of marmosets and tamarins. LIMB PROPORTIONS: For Indices *see* Part III, p. 393.

Hand Function

Hand prehensile, thumb non-opposable but thumb is slightly more divergent than in *Leontideus*.[10] HAND PROPORTIONS: For Indices *see* Part III, p. 401.

Resting Posture

Rest on all fours as in marmosets; tail may be curled round a branch.[12]

Social Behaviour

Unknown in the wild state. VOCALIZATION: voice is said to be similar to that of tamarins.[13]

REPRODUCTION AND DEVELOPMENT

Unknown.

CAPTIVITY

Seldom seen in captivity (but see Lorenz 1966a). LONGEVITY RECORD[14] (up to 1962): 2 years 4 months, Bronx Zoo, New York.

REFERENCES

1. Hill, W. C. Osman (1957)
2. Thomas, O. (1928b)
3. Hill, W. C. Osman (1959b)
4. Cruz Lima, E. da (1945)
5. James, W. Warwick (1960)
6. Dollman, G. (1937) *In* Hill, W. C. Osman (1957)
7. Bender, M. A. and Chu, E. H. Y. (1963)
8. Chiarelli, B. (1963b)
9. Erikson, G. E. (1963)
10. Bishop, Alison (1964)
11. Biegert, J. (1961)
12. Ribiero, A. de Miranda (1940)
13. Sanderson, I. T. (1957)
14. Jones, M. L. (1962)
15. Lorenz, R. and Heinemann, H. (1967)
16. Lorenz, R. (1966a)

CALLITHRIX† Erxleben, 1777   Marmosets

= *Hapale* Illiger, 1811]

8 species: 8 subspecies[1, 28]

Callithrix [= *Mico*] *argentata*	Black-tailed Marmoset	4 subsp.
Callithrix aurita	White-eared Marmoset	2 subsp.
Callithrix flaviceps	Buff-headed Marmoset	0 subsp.
Callithrix geoffroyi	White-fronted Marmoset	0 subsp.
Callithrix jacchus	Common Marmoset	0 subsp.
Callithrix penicillata	Black-eared Marmoset	2 subsp.
Callithrix humeralifer	Santarem Marmoset	0 subsp.
Callithrix chrysoleuca	Golden Marmoset	0 subsp.

GEOGRAPHICAL RANGE [2]

South America. Brazil, south of the R. Amazon, between R. Tocantins and R. Madiera, Northern tributaries of R. Paraguay in the Mato Grosso. Extensive distribution in E. Brazil; range is limited by the coast to the E. and by the R. Parana and the R. Parnaiba to the W. On the E. coast the probable latitudinal limit is 28° S.

ECOLOGY *

HABITAT: Equatorial rain forest. Woodland savanna (chapadao) of Mato Grosso. Move on the larger branches of upper strata[3] (open canopy) also in the shrub layer of high forest or forest patches. DIET:[2] Largely insectivorous but also fruit and vegetable matter (based on stomach contents).[4] ACTIVITY RHYTHM: diurnal.

MORPHOLOGY

External Characters

Very small animals. Fur is thick and silky; for colour of fur and skin, *see* Colour Key. LIMBS: legs considerably longer than arms; forearms short, hands long. Digits clawed, except big toe which bears flat nail.[5] Thumb long and non-opposable. Digital formula: 3.4.2.5.1. TAIL: non-prehensile. GENITALIA: Scrotum white and hairless.

Weights and Dimensions[2, 6, 7, 8]

	♂	♀	% ♀ of ♂
Body weight range (g)	175–360 (4♂)	167–335 (9♀)	93
Head and body length range (mm)	173–220 (50♂)	158–240 (43♀)	101
Tail length range (mm)	243–375 (50♂)	247–385 (43♀)	102

N.B. % size ♀ of ♂ estimated from midpoint of ranges.

† *See* Taxonomic Notes, Part III, p. 371.

Colour Key

	Body Fur	*Ears*	*Face*	*Tail*
C. argentata	Silvery white or light brown	Bare; crimson or pink	Bare, crimson or pink	Black, *not* ringed
C. jacchus	Black and grey marbling	White tufts	Hairy, pale. White blaze on forehead	Ringed, black and grey
C. flaviceps	Black and grey marbling, yellow head	Yellow tufts	Hairy, pale	Ringed, black and grey
C. aurita	Black and brown marbling	White tufts	Hairy, pale. White blaze on forehead	Ringed, black and yellow or grey
C. penicillata	Black and brown marbling	Black whisker-like tufts	Hairy, pale. White blaze on forehead	Ringed, black and grey
C. chrysoleuca	White, rump yellowish	White tufts, growing from pinna	Bare, flesh-coloured	Yellowish, faintly ringed
C. humeralifer	Brownish-black, grizzled	White or buff tufts growing from pinna	Pigmented. Pink muzzle	Black at base, faintly ringed distally
C. geoffroyi	Reddish, grizzled	Black whisker-like tufts	Hairy, pale. White blaze on forehead extends to vertex	Ringed, black and grey

Internal Characters

For general anatomy, *see* Beattie, 1927; Hill, 1957. VERTEBRAL COLUMN: Lumbar vertebrae —6. ARM: Entepicondylar foramen absent in humerus; LEG: 3rd trochanter present on femur. HANDS: Palmar pads relatively inconspicuous; modified claws (tegulae) on ends of digits.[5] THENAR MUSCLES: Adductor pollicis not differentiated; other contrahentes to 3.4 and 5; opponens pollicis absent. C.N.S.: Cerebral hemispheres show few convolutions, a primitive feature.[10] EYE: macula present; rods and cones in retina.[11] CUTANEOUS GLANDS: small

PLATE 17. *Callithrix jacchus.* Adult ♂ carrying two young aged 7½ weeks (by courtesy of Gerhard Budich)

sebaceous glands scattered all over scrotum in ♂ and labia in ♀ extending to circumanal region. DENTITION: $\frac{2}{2} \frac{1}{1} \frac{3}{3} \frac{2}{2} = 32$. Lower incisors almost as long as canines ("short-tusked"). Upper canines long; longer in ♀ than in ♂.[12] $M^{1,2}$ tricuspid, $M^{\underline{2}}$ very small; $M_{\overline{1,2}}$ quadricuspid, $M_{\overline{2}}$ cusps retrogressive.

Genetic Biology

CHROMOSOMES: $2n = 46$ (*C. chrysoleuca*[13] 1♂, 2♀; *C. jacchus*[14] 4♂). Karyotype of *C. chrysoleuca*: 4 metacentrics, 10 acrocentrics, 30 sub-terminals, X = subterminal, Y = metacentric. P.T.C. TASTING: 100% tasters in series of 10 individuals.[15] BLOOD GROUPS: Thirty-one marmosets have been tested for Human-type ABO groups; all specimens proved to be Group A. Saliva negative for Lewis substance.[16]

BEHAVIOUR

Locomotor Behaviour

AUTHORS' CLASSIFICATION: Quadrupedalism. (Erikson's category—Springer). Movement is squirrel-like in agility, speed and jerkiness. Leaping however is not marked though statements are contradictory (*see* Krieg, 1930). Moves essentially on main boughs rather than slender branches.[3] Tail used for balancing during locomotion and to assist upright sitting.[18] LIMB PROPORTIONS: For Indices *see* Part III, p. 393, also Wettstein (1963).

Hand Function

Hand is prehensile and digits are widely divergent[9] to give a strong clawed grip on bark. Single-handed feeding with object gripped between flexed and converged digits and proximal palm. For proportions, *see* Part III, p. 401.

Resting Posture

Sit on all fours but during grooming adults will sit upright.[18] May rest with abdomen in contact with branch and limbs on either side.

Social Behaviour

Little information is available on behaviour in the wild. HOME RANGE AND TERRITORIALITY: unknown. GROUP ORGANIZATION: Live in family groups of 3–8 individuals[4] but may be seen in the wild in much larger groups.[19] In captivity Fitzgerald[18] describes well-developed social sense and parental responsibility (*C. jacchus*). SEXUAL DISPLAY:[18] minimal; tend to be monogamous. VOCALIZATION: wide range of high-pitched calls but no scientific study available. GROOMING: mutual grooming observed in captivity[18] but scratching with hind claws is common form of self-toilet. MARKING BEHAVIOUR: this has been observed, using secretion from scrotal and perineal glands.[2]

REPRODUCTION AND DEVELOPMENT

Generally regarded as polyoestrous. Cyclical circumgenital swelling reported in one species.[20*]

No evidence of restricted breeding season in captivity.[21] GESTATION PERIOD: 140 days.[26] Normally 2 young at birth (occasionally 1 or 3). Infants weaned at 6 months; sexual maturity at 14 months. Ear tufts develop between 6 and 9 months.[26] ♂ parent takes a major part in carrying and protecting infants. (*See* Plate 17.)

CAPTIVITY

For information on welfare and husbandry, *see* Lucas *et al.* (1927); Crandall (1964); Fitzgerald (1935); Hume (1957); Grüner and Krause (1963). BREEDING RECORD: 45 births in world zoos from 1959–63.[24] LONGEVITY: potential zoo lifespan is approximately 10 years. LONGEVITY RECORDS:[25] *C. argentata*, 8 years, 9 months, New York: Bronx Zoo; *C. jacchus*, 12 years, 0 months, London: Zoological Gardens; *C. penicillata*, 6 years, 1 month, London: Zoological Gardens. DIET:[18, 22] Very varied but animal protein, fruit, vegetables and additives essential, particularly Vitamin D. U.V. light exposure generally recommended.

REFERENCES

1. Cabrera, A. (1957)
2. Hill, W. C. Osman (1957)
3. Bates, H. W. (1863)
4. Kreig, H. (1930)
5. Clark, W. E. Le Gros (1936)
6. Lucas, N. S., Hume, E. M. and Smith, H. H. (1927)
7. Wettstein, E. B. (1963)
8. Lönnberg, E. (1940a)
9. Beattie, J. (1927)
10. Clark, W. E. Le Gros (1959)
11. Polyak, S. (1957)
12. Schultz, A. H. (Private Communication)
13. Bender, M. A. and Chu, E. H. Y. (1963)
14. Benirschke, K., Anderson, J. M. and Brownhill, L. E. (1962)
15. Chiarelli, B. (1963b)
16. Wiener, A. S., Moor-Jankowski, J. and Gordon, E. B. (1966)
17. Erikson, G. E. (1963)
18. Fitzgerald, A. (1935)
19. Sanderson, I. T. (1957)
20. Russell, A. E. and Zuckerman, S. (1935)
21. Zuckerman, S. (1953)
22. Hume, E. M. (1957)
23. Grüner, M. and Krause, P. (1963)
24. International Zoo Year Book Vols. I–V (1959–1965)
25. Jones, M. L. (1962)
26. Lucas, N. S., Hume, E. M. and Smith, H. H. (1937)
27. Crandall, L. S. (1964)
28. Hershkovitz, P. (1966b)

CEBUELLA†   Gray, 1866   Pygmy Marmosets

1 species: 2 subspecies[1]

C. pygmaea Spix, 1823

GEOGRAPHICAL RANGE [1]

S. America. Found on N. and S. banks of upper R. Amazon extending from W. bank of R. Purus and R. Japura to the foothills of Andes. Also found on banks of R. Putumayo in Colombia.

ECOLOGY

HABITAT: Equatorial rain forest. Minor habitat unknown. Sleep in holes of trees.[2] ACTIVITY RHYTHM: Diurnal. DIET: in the wild, insects, fruit, birds' eggs and birds;[2] in captivity as for *Callithrix*.

MORPHOLOGY

External Characters[3]

Smallest platyrrhine primate. Fur is brown with yellow or green sub-terminal colouration of hairs giving tawny grizzled effect on back, neck and flanks and a vague banded effect on tail. Underparts white or fawn. Face is hairy, hair being swept back from muzzle, concealing ears. *No ear tufts.* Nostrils platyrrhine. Digits clawed, except for big toe which has a flat nail. DIGITAL FORMULA:[4] 3.4.5.2.1. Two mammae in axillary position.

Weights and Dimensions[4, 5]

Head and body length range (mm)	130–144 (6♂ + ♀)
Tail length range (mm)	197–210 (6♂ + ♀)

Internal Characters

For details of anatomy, see *Callithrix*. SKULL: Apart from size, differs from *Callithrix* in the absence of post-glenoid process, convexity of mastoid region and more spherical bullae.[3] DENTITION: D.F.: $\frac{2}{2}\frac{1}{1}\frac{3}{3}\frac{2}{2} = 32$. As for *Callithrix*. Lower incisors may be as long as canines; upper incisors large. CANINES: Lower canines barely project above level of incisors ("short-tusked" condition).

Genetic Biology[10]

CHROMOSOMES: 2n = 44.*

---

† *See* Taxonomic Notes, Part III, p. 371.   PLATE 18. *Cebuella pygmaea*, adult ♀ (by courtesy of Kurt Ochs)

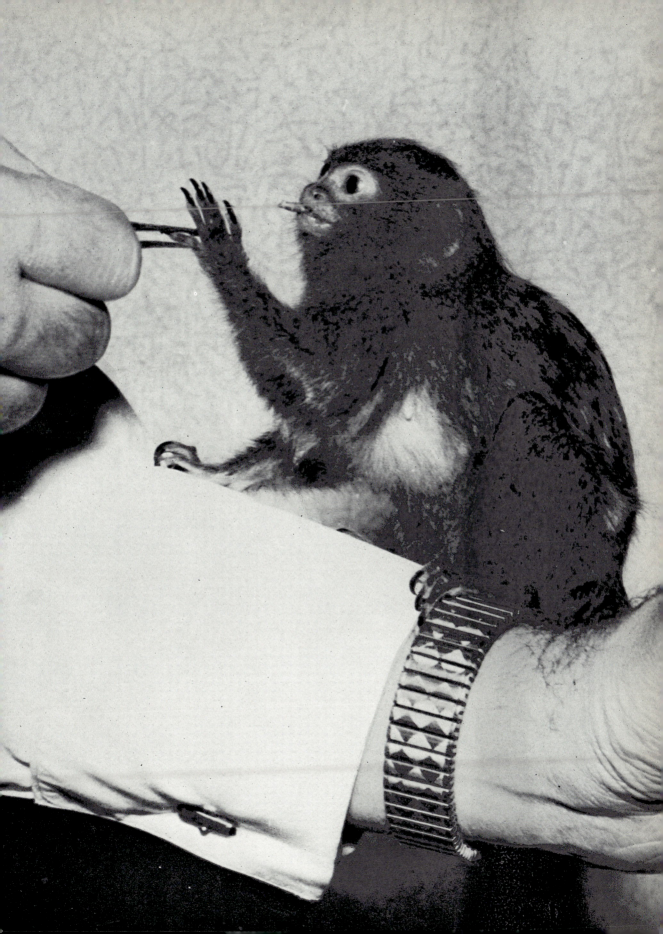

BEHAVIOUR

Locomotor Behaviour

AUTHORS' CLASSIFICATION: Quadrupedalism. Move in scurrying fashion of squirrels. LIMB PROPORTIONS:* For Indices, *see* Part III, p. 393.

Social Behaviour

Pygmy marmosets are so difficult to observe in the wild that nothing is known of their behaviour. Reports of behaviour in captivity are rare.[2, 7]

REPRODUCTION AND DEVELOPMENT

Normally two young at birth (occasionally one or three). Stages of post-natal development observed by Ochs (1964) in captive pair:

Birth–6 weeks:	remain clinging to ♂ parent.
6–8 weeks:	move independently; take solid foods.
12 weeks:	fully self-supporting.
24 weeks:	infant grown to size of adult.

CAPTIVITY

LONGEVITY RECORD:[8] 4 years, 11 months. New York: Bronx Zoo. BREEDING RECORDS:[9] 10 births were recorded in World Zoos between 1959–63.

REFERENCES

1. Cabrera, A. (1957)
2. Ochs, K. (1964)
3. Hill, W. C. Osman (1957)
4. Authors' observations
5. Lönnberg, E. (1940a)
6. Schultz, A. H. (1929)
7. Sanderson, I. T. (1957)
8. Crandall, L. S. (1964)
9. International Zoo Year Book Vols. I–V (1959–1965)
10. Bender, M. A. and Chu, E. H. Y. (1963)

CEBUS   Erxleben, 1777   Capuchins

4 species: 33 subspecies[1, 2]

C. capucinus (Type species)	White-throated capuchin	5 subsp.
C. albifrons	White-fronted capuchin	12 subsp.
C. nigrivittatus	Weeper capuchin	5 subsp.
C. apella	Black-capped capuchin	11 subsp.

Most authorities[1, 3, 4] recognize two groups within the genus: Tufted capuchins—*C. apella*; Untufted capuchins—*C. capucinus*, *C. nigrivittatus* and *C. albifrons*. The major distinguishing characters between the two groups are specifically mentioned in the appropriate sections of the following profile. *See also* Plate 19.

GEOGRAPHICAL RANGE[3, 5]

Central and South America. Most northerly species (*C. capucinus*) found in Honduras, Lat. 16° N. Thence southwards throughout most forested areas of central and south America as far as Lat. 30° S. where *C. apella* is found in mountainous areas of the S.E. littoral of Brazil. *C. apella* occurs up to approximately 2150 m altitude (7000 ft).

ECOLOGY

HABITAT: Dwellers in the canopy of all types of tropical forest up to 2150 m altitude;[6] wholly arboreal but descend to ground to drink and, in certain regions, to raid plantations.[3] On Barro Colorado Island, capuchins occupy tops of smaller trees or lower levels of tall trees.[7] ACTIVITY RHYTHM: diurnal. DIET: fruit, insects; no leaves.[7, 8] Omnivorous in captivity.[44]

MORPHOLOGY

External Characters[1, 3]

Medium-sized monkeys with round heads, robust bodies and a relatively short semi-prehensile tail. *Tufted group* are usually larger and more robust than untufted. In both groups, coat is either black (*C. capucinus*) or various shades of brown: generally dark brown in *C. apella*, light brown or cinnamon in *C. albifrons*, and either light or dark brown in *C. nigrivittatus*. The face, throat, chest, shoulders and upper arms are whitish in *C. capucinus* and buff in *C. albifrons*. FACE AND HEAD: *Untufted group*: crown of the head bears a dark-coloured smooth V-shaped patch of variable extent; there is no dark pre-auricular band. *Tufted group*: the cap is broad and is composed of long, dark, erect hairs which may form ridges or "horns" on either side of the crown; the hair tufts are variable. *Tufted group* also show a darkish pre-auricular band on the face extending from the cap and ending below the chin. Sexual dimorphism apparent in *C. albifrons* where ♀ may have a superciliary brush of erect hairs. LIMBS: legs somewhat longer than arms. THUMB of medium length and moderately well differentiated. DIGITAL FORMULA: variable, 4th digit may be longer, equal or shorter than 3rd. Big toe large and divergent. TAIL: distal third may be rolled when at rest, reflecting incipient prehensility. EXTERNAL GENITALIA: may lead to confusion in sexing as clitoris is prominent and pendulous, and scrotum sessile.

a

b

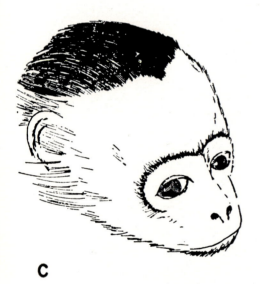

c

d

e

f

Weights and Dimensions

	♂	♀	♀ in % of ♂†
Body weight range (g) (all species)[3, 9]	1150–3320 (18♂)	—	—
Head and body length range (mm) (all species)[1, 3]	320–565 (77♂)	323–480 (51♀)	91
Tail length range (mm) (all species)[1, 3]	342–560 (77♂)	290–510 (51♀)	89

† Schultz (1956) gives the ♀ weight in % ♂: *C. capucinus* 77% (61 specimens), *C. apella* 79% (20 specimens).

In the above table, there is some evidence of sexual dimorphism in body size and tail length; Schultz' figures imply an even greater difference in body weight. Percentage of ♀ in terms of ♂ based on midpoint of range.

Internal Characters

SKULL: Relatively minor differences between "tufted" and "untufted" groups summarized by Hershkovitz (1949a). Old ♂♂ of *C. apella* show sagittal crest. POSTCRANIAL: Lumbar vertebrae 5 or 6 in both groups.[1, 20] GENITALIA: Os penis present. C.N.S.: Relatively large brains, richly convoluted.[11] SKIN INNERVATION:[12] Dermal and hair follicle nets not prominent; Meissner-like endings in glabrous skin. DENTITION: D.F.: $\frac{2}{2}\frac{1}{1}\frac{3}{3}\frac{3}{3}=36$. Incisors implanted vertically; canines large (♂>♀); premolars bicuspid; molars quadricuspid, $M.\frac{1}{1}>M.\frac{2}{2}>M.\frac{3}{3}$; $M.\underline{3}$ very small; oblique ridges absent. GASTRO-INTESTINAL: *C. nigrivittatus* has short caecum (correlated with insect-eating diet),[8] and a short, straight colon as in *Tarsius* and *Saimiri*.

Genetic Biology

CHROMOSOMES:[13] 2n=54 (10 specimens). KARYOTYPE: 26 acrocentrics, 20 subterminals, 6 metacentrics, plus X and Y chromosomes. BLOOD GROUPS:[14] Part of B antigen (B₃) present on R.B.C. of *C. apella*, but lack B.1 and B.2 component of apes and man. Lewis secretion negative. *See* Wiener *et al.* (1964, 1966). P.T.C. TASTING:[16] 32 tasters: 4 non-tasters. IMMUNOLOGICAL REACTIONS: *see* Goodman (1963) and Williams (1964). HAEMO-GLOBINS:[19] One major Hb which moves essentially as does human A on starch-gel electrophoresis (*C. albifrons*).

BEHAVIOUR

Locomotor Behaviour

AUTHORS' CLASSIFICATION: Quadrupedalism. (Erikson's category: Climber.) Extremely active and agile. Travel by running and walking on all fours. When leaping, usually land quadrupedally but sometimes spreadeagled.[21] Said to swim.[22] Use the slight prehensile ability of tail to aid locomotion. Occasional bipedalism.[23] LIMB PROPORTIONS: For Indices *see* Part III, p. 393.

PLATE 19. Head patterns of *Cebus*. Untufted group: a. *C. albifrons*; b. *C. albifrons* (♀ with moderately developed superciliary brush); c. *C. capucinus*; d. *C. nigrivittatus*. Tufted group: e. and f. *C. apella* with prominent and moderately developed tufts, respectively. [From P. Hershkovitz, *Proc. U.S. nat. Mus.* **98**, 323–427, (1949)]

PLATE 21. *Cebus capucinus* (Eric Kirkland)

PLATE 20. *Cebus apella* ♂, 7 years old (by courtesy of Twycross Zoo Park; photo by John Doidge)

Hand Function

Hand is prehensile and thumb pseudo-opposable.[24] Considerable manipulative skill in handling objects.[11, 22, 25, 26] Tool-using and handling proclivities well-known; *see* Hill (1960) who quotes many instances; also Vevers and Weiner (1963) and ciné film.[27] Agonistic throwing behaviour frequently reported in captivity (Kortlandt and Kooij, 1963). HAND PROPORTIONS: For Indices *see* Part III, p. 401.

Resting Posture

Exhibits true sitting posture as in catarrhines. Sleeps either with limbs hanging either side of branch or curled up with hands under head.

Social Behaviour

Capuchins have not yet been studied, *per se*, in the wild; most observations are anecdotal, incidental to other studies, or made in captivity (*see* Bernstein, 1965). RANGE AND TERRITORIALITY: In an area of small residual forest in Brazil, *C. apella* have a very small home-range, not exceeding a few hundred metres.[35] Limited territorial behaviour; no evidence of inter-generic aggression with howlers on Barro Colorado Island,[7] or elsewhere with other monkey species.[30] GROUP SIZE: 8–30+. Reputedly, capuchins have a highly developed social structure. VOCALIZATION:[26, 32, 33, 34] in the wild, capuchins produce a wide variety of sounds some of which may be regarded as spacing mechanisms; no extensive spectrographic study available at present. FACIAL EXPRESSION: *see* van Hooff (1962). GROOMING: social grooming more developed than in *Ateles* or *Alouatta*.[37]

REPRODUCTION AND DEVELOPMENT

Menstrual cycle somewhat variable: 15–20 days; menstrual bleeding (*C. apella*) lasting 2–7 days.[38] No evidence of a restricted breeding season.[39] GESTATION PERIOD: 180 days approximately.[40] Twinning rare. Infant at birth weighs 8·5% of adult ♀.[10]

Age grades in *C. apella*[41]

Infant I	Incomplete deciduous dentition	1 to 6–8 months
Infant II	Complete deciduous dentition	6–8 to 14–18 months
Juvenile	Mixed deciduous and permanent dentition	14–18 to 36–40 months
Sub-adult	Incomplete permanent dentition	36 to 42 months
Adult	Unworn complete permanent dentition	36–42 months to 8–10 years
Old adult	Worn permanent dentition	8–10 to 15–20 years

CAPTIVITY

Breeding in captivity relatively rare considering success as zoo animals. BREEDING RECORDS: 133 births in world zoos, 1959–63.[42] LONGEVITY RECORD:[43] *C. apella* 40 years approximately. San Diego Zoo. *See also* Crandall (1964).

REFERENCES

1. Hershkovitz, P. (1949a)
2. Cabrera, A. (1957)
3. Hill, W. C. Osman (1960)
4. Fiedler, W. (1956)
5. Hall, E. R. and Kelson, K. R. (1959)
6. Tate, G. H. H. (1939)
7. Collias, N. E. and Southwick, C. H. (1952)
8. Fooden, J. (1964b)
9. Veterinary Officer's Reports, Zoological Society of London
10. Schultz, A. H. (1956)
11. Klüver, H. (1933)
12. Winkelman, R. K. (1963)
13. Bender, M. A. and Chu, E. H. Y. (1963)
14. Dahr, P. (1937) quoted in Franks, D. (1963)
15. Franks, D. (1963)
16. Chiarelli, B. (1963b)
17. Goodman, M. (1963)
18. Williams, C. A. (1964)
19. Buettner-Janusch, J. and Buettner-Janusch, V. (1964)
20. Erikson, G. E. (1963)
21. Belt, J. (1874)
22. Kühlhorn, F. (1953)
23. Authors' observations
24. Napier, J. R. (1962)
25. Vevers, G. M. and Weiner, J. S. (1963)
26. Nolte, A. (1958)
27. Film in authors' possession
28. Kortlandt, A. and Kooij, M. (1963)
29. Bernstein, I. S. (1965)
30. Sanderson, I. T. (1957)
31. Kühlhorn, F. (1954)
32. Kühlhorn, F. (1939)
33. Chapman, F. M. (1937)
34. Garner, R. L. (1900) quoted in Hill, W. C. Osman (1960)
35. Causey, O. R., Laemmert, H. W. and Hayes, G. S. (1948)
36. Hooff, J. A. R. A. M. van (1962)
37. Carpenter, C. R. (1935)
38. Hamlett, G. W. D. (1939)
39. Zuckerman, S. (1953)
40. Asdell, S. A. (1946)
41. Gilmore, R. M. (1943)
42. International Zoo Year Book, Vols. I–V (1959–1965)
43. Hill, C. A. (1964)
44. Crandall, L. S. (1964)
45. Wiener, A. S., Moor-Jankowski, J. and Gordon, E. B. (1966)

CERCOCEBUS E. Geoffroy, 1812 Mangabeys

2 species groups: 5 species: 8 subspecies†[1, 2]

Albigena Group	*C. albigena* Grey-cheeked mangabey	3 subsp.
	C. aterrimus Black mangabey	0 subsp.
Torquatus Group	*C. torquatus* White-collared mangabey	0 subsp.
	C. atys (Type species) Sooty mangabey	2 subsp.
	C. galeritus Agile mangabey	3 subsp.

GEOGRAPHICAL RANGE [3]

Africa. Genus ranges from French Guinea (15° W.) to W. Uganda (33° E.). One species, *C. galeritus*, reported from Tana River in E. Kenya.[4] Western mangabeys (*atys* and *torquatus*) occupy coastal forest belt of W. Africa; *C. atys* is found W. of Greenwich meridian to 15° W. and *C. torquatus* to the E. from the Lower Niger to the Congo Rivers. *C. galeritus* is found N. of the Congo R. from the R. Ubangi eastwards as far as Uganda.[3] *C. albigena* has a similar distribution but extends further into Uganda, as far as 33° E. *C. aterrimus* is found S. of R. Congo in the enclave formed by this river and its continuation, the R. Lualaba.

ECOLOGY

HABITAT: Tropical rain forest. Mangabeys occupy two major ecological niches within high forest. *Albigena* Group are wholly arboreal, preferring mainly swampy areas of low-lying forest.[5] Seldom descend below middle stratum of canopy.[6] *Torquatus* Group are largely ground-living: *C. atys*[2] found in secondary forest, rarely ascends above lower stratum of canopy. *C. galeritus*[4, 7, 8] found on river banks, seldom more than a few metres above ground. *C. torquatus*:[7] Primary and secondary forest and banks of streams. Arboreal only for eating and sleeping. DIET: *Torquatus* group are crop-raiders. Palm-nuts, seeds, hard and soft fruits, leaves. ACTIVITY RHYTHM: Diurnal. PREDATORS: Monkey-eating eagle (*Stephanoaetus coronatus*) and leopard.

MORPHOLOGY

External Characters[1, 9, 10, 11, 12]

Large monkeys with slender bodies, longish limbs and tails.

Torquatus Group varies from a light mushroom colour (*C. galeritus*) to dark smoky grey (*C. atys*). Limbs, particularly forearms, legs, hands and feet, darker than body; underparts fawn or cream. Head adornments consist of cap of contrasting colour e.g. *C. atys*—dark brown; halfmoon of white hairs on back of crown in *C. a. lunulatus*; *C. torquatus*—chestnut red. Eyelids and supra-orbital skin strikingly white. *C. torquatus* is characterized by white flashes on cheeks extending below the chin to form the "white-collar" of its common name.

Albigena Group are predominantly black in colour with greyish underparts; cheek tufts and throat are light grey. Adornments consist of tufts above eyes and of an occipital tuft in *C. albigena*; in *C. aterrimus* the crown hair forms a vertical pointed crest like a coconut. Eyelids of Albigena Group are either dark (*C. albigena*) or light-coloured (*C. aterrimus*).

---

† *See* Taxonomic Notes, Part III, p. 372. PLATE 22. White-collared mangabey, *Cercocebus torquatus* (Eric Kirkland)

Distinguishing characters of the two groups are as follows:

Torquatus Group	*Albigena Group*
1. Hairs of coat are short	1. Hairs of coat are long
2. Mushroom to grey hairs with tendency to speckling	2. Black hairs with no speckling
3. No crest on head	3. Crest on head

All species have prominent ischial callosities which are fused in the midline in ♂, the junction being marked by a vertical linear groove.[32]

Weights and Dimensions[13]

Torquatus Group: *C. galeritus*	♂	♀	♀ in % ♂
Head and body length (mm)	543 (515–580) (10♂♂)	473 (440–520) (10♀♀)	87
Tail length (mm)	748 (690–785) (10♂♂)	643 (590–695) (10♀♀)	86
Albigena Group: *C. albigena*			
Head and body length (mm)	576 (540–615) (15♂♂)	503 (435–580) (14♀♀)	87
Tail length (mm)	886 (820–940) (15♂♂)	810 (740–895) (14 ♀♀)	91

Note moderate degree of sexual dimorphism in tail length and body size. In *C. albigena* ♀ tail is relatively longer than ♂ tail.

Internal Characters

See *Macaca* and *Cercopithecus* for details of special characters of Cercopithecinae; only principle differences from these two forms noted here. SKULL: Differ from *Cercopithecus* and *Macaca* in the presence of suborbital (paranasal) depression.[14] Muzzle is moderately elongated; degree of prognathism approximately that of *Macaca*. According to Rode (1936), face of *Cercocebus* is longer than that of *Cercopithecus* and, associated with this, has a longer palatal length and a more acute zygomatico-frontal angle. EXTREMITIES: Hands and feet do not differ in any constant particular from those of *Cercopithecus* but are longer and more slender than those of *Macaca*.[32] ALIMENTARY SYSTEM: Cheek pouches as in all Cercopithecinae; stomach simple. GENITALIA: Penis long and large to ensure penetration of swollen ♀ genital opening as in some macaques. Sexual skin of ♀♀ is of moderate extent and swelling does not reach gross proportions of baboons and some macaques. DENTITION: D.F.: $\frac{2}{2}\frac{1}{1}\frac{2}{2}\frac{3}{3}=32$. M.$\frac{}{3}$ bears 5th cusp on talonid as in *Macaca*.

Genetic Biology

CHROMOSOMES:[15, 16] 2n = 42 (all species). In *C. aterrimus* all chromosomes are metacentric.[16] HAEMOGLOBINS:[14, 17, 18] Three species tested (*C. atys*, *C. albigena* and *C. galeritus*) show an abnormal Hb in contrast to other Old World monkeys where rate of migration revealed by

---

PLATE 23. Sooty mangabey, *Cercocebus atys* (Eric Kirkland)

paper electrophoresis is identical with normal human A. P.T.C. TASTING:[19] Predominantly "tasters" as 33 : 2 (all species less *C. atys*).

BEHAVIOUR

Locomotor Behaviour

AUTHORS' CLASSIFICATION: Quadrupedalism. Capable of running, climbing and jumping in trees and of running on ground. *C. albigena* somewhat deliberate in trees. Tail is carried in a high arch,[12] sometimes arched over back.[20] *C. torquatus* said to swim readily.[7] *Torquatus* Group are digitigrade when ground-walking, *Albigena* Group are plantigrade.[21] LIMB PROPORTIONS: For Indices, *see* Part III, p. 394. Limbs moderately elongated relative to trunk height but not as long as in *Papio*.

Hand Function

Hands prehensile, thumb fully opposable and relatively long compared with index finger, making thumb-index precision movements possible. HAND PROPORTIONS: For Indices, *see* Part III, p. 401.

Resting Posture

Rest and sleep in sitting position (associated with ischial callosities). Tail has some prehensile qualities, often being coiled around branch while resting and feeding.[13, 31]

Social Behaviour

No extensive field studies have been made of this genus. For general field information, *see* Haddow (1952). HOME-RANGE: *C. albigena* said to have a smaller range than *C. torquatus*. COMMUNICATION: VOCALIZATION: On the whole mangabeys are reputed to be rather silent but references to "noisy bands" are common.[7] Studies employing sound spectrographs[22] indicate that vocalization in many ways is transitional between *Cercopithecus* and *Papio*; of particular interest is the recognition of "segmented grunts" comparable to those of *Papio*.[22] FACIAL EXPRESSION:[23] *Cercocebus* shares a number of facial expressions with *Papio* and *Macaca* rather than with *Cercopithecus*. In this connection, the relation of the infra-orbital fossa to muscles of facial expression controlling the upper lip, is discussed by Rode (1936). INTRA-GROUP BEHAVIOUR: Day-bands of *C. albigena* consist of 20–40 animals[5] but at night sleeping-groups of 4–5 are commonest. Solitary ♂♂ are often seen.[12] SEXUAL BEHAVIOUR: Overt sexual behaviour has not been observed in nature but "presenting behaviour", whatever its motivation, has been observed in captivity.[25]

REPRODUCTION AND DEVELOPMENT *

Menstrual cycle is regular and lasts approximately 29–33 days;[26, 27] it is accompanied by a moderate degree of swelling and colour change in the "sexual skin". Colour changes of perineum, however, have not been observed in *C. albigena*.[12] Birth season in N. Hemisphere: April–November.[28] Gestation period is unrecorded.

CAPTIVITY

BIRTHS IN CAPTIVITY: Between 1959–63, 49 births were recorded in World Zoos.[29]
LONGEVITY RECORD (up to 1962):[30] *C. atys*, 20 years 9 months, National Zoological Park,
Washington; *C. torquatus*, 20 years 4 months, London; Zoological Gardens.

REFERENCES

1. Schwarz, E. (1928a)
2. Booth, A. H. (1956a)
3. Schouteden, H. (1947)
4. Allen, G. M., Lawrence, B. and Loveridge, A. (1936) quoted in Tappen, N. C. (1960)
5. Haddow, A. J., Smithburn, K. C., Mahaffy, A. F. and Bugher, J. C. (1947)
6. Ashton, E. H. and Oxnard, C. E. (1964b)
7. Malbrant, R. and Maclatchy, A. (1949)
8. Allen, G. M. and Loveridge, A. (1942)
9. Sanderson, I. T. (1957)
10. Elliot, D. G. (1913)
11. Forbes, H. O. (1897)
12. Haddow, A. J. (1952)
13. Allen, J. A. (1925)
14. Tappen, N. C. (1963)
15. Bender, M. A. and Chu, E. H. Y. (1963)
16. Klinger, H. P. (1963)
17. Jacob, G. F. and Tappen, N. C. (1957)
18. Jacob, G. F. and Tappen, N. C. (1958)
19. Chiarelli, B. (1963b)
20. Lydekker, R. (1893–94)
21. Jolly, C. J. (1964)
22. Andrew, R. J. (1963)
23. Hooff, J. A. R. A. M. van (1962)
24. Rode, P. (1936)
25. Zuckerman, S. (1932)
26. Zuckerman, S. (1930)
27. Zuckerman, S. (1937)
28. Zuckerman, S. (1953)
29. International Zoo Year Book, Vols. I–V (1959–1965)
30. Jones, M. L. (1962)
31. Walker, A. C. (Unpublished data)
32. Pocock, R. I. (1925a)

CERCOPITHECUS Linnaeus, 1758   Guenons

SUBGENUS: *Cercopithecus* (Linnaeus, 1758)

Cercopithecus (Cercopithecus) 9 species groups: 21 species: 67 subspecies†[,1]

Aethiops Group	*C. aethiops*	Grivets	7 subsp.
	C. pygerythrus	Vervets	13 subsp.
	C. sabaeus	Green monkeys	0 subsp.
Cephus Group	*C. cephus*	Moustached monkeys	2 subsp.
Diana Group	*C. diana* (Type species)	Diana monkeys	3 subsp.
Lhoesti Group	*C. lhoesti*	L'Hoest's monkeys	0 subsp.
	C. preussi	Preuss' monkeys	0 subsp.
Hamlyni Group	*C. hamlyni*	Hamlyn's or Owl-faced monkeys	0 subsp.
Mitis Group	*C. mitis*	Blue monkeys	8 subsp.
	C. albogularis	Sykes' monkeys	12 subsp.
Mona Group	*C. mona*	Mona monkeys	0 subsp.
	C. campbelli	Campbell's monkeys	2 subsp.
	C. wolfi	Wolf's monkeys	3 subsp.
	C. pogonias	Crowned guenons	4 subsp.
	C. denti	Dent's monkeys	0 subsp.
Neglectus Group	*C. neglectus*	De Brazza's monkeys	0 subsp.
Nictitans Group	*C. nictitans*	Spot-nosed guenons	3 subsp.
	C. petaurista	Lesser spot-nosed guenons	2 subsp.
	C. ascanius	Redtails	5 subsp.
	C. erythrotis	Red-eared Guenons	3 subsp.
	C. erythrogaster	Red-bellied Guenons	0 subsp.

GEOGRAPHICAL RANGE

Africa. Widely-spread group which are found over most of the rain forest, woodland and savannah habitats of sub-Saharan Africa from Senegal in the W., Ethiopia and Sudan in the E., and S. to the Cape. One species, *C. sabaeus*, was introduced into St. Kitt's, W. Indies and into St. Jago, Cape Verde islands in the 17th century, and another, *C. mona*, to Grenada, W. Indies. For further details of geographical range of species groups, *see* table of distinguishing characters and Dandelot (1959) for distribution of *Aethiops* group.

ECOLOGY

HABITAT: Rain forest, secondary forest, montane forest, woodland savannah and open savannah.[2] Rarely found in arid zones but *C. aethiops* reported from Aïr Massif (18° N., 8° E.).[3] *C. lhoesti* inhabits montane forest up to 8000 ft (2438 m),[4] and *C. mitis* up to 10,000 ft (3048 m) in mountains bordering Great Rift Valley.[5] Predominantly dwellers of closed canopy (*see* Part III, p. 383), living close to forest edges and river banks. Some species, e.g. *C. diana*, occupy open canopy and emergent layers. ACTIVITY RHYTHM: Diurnal; one species,

---

† *See* Taxonomic Notes, Part III, p. 372.   PLATE 24. *Cercopithecus aethiops tantalus* ♂ (Eric Kirkland)

C. hamlyni, reputedly nocturnal[6] (improbable). DIET:[7, 8, 9, 10] Leaves, green shoots, fruits, cultivated native crop plants. Principle crop-raiding species: *C. ascanius*, *C. aethiops*, *C. lhoesti*, *C. mitis*,[8] *C. campbelli*.[11, 40] *C. mitis* and *C. aethiops* said to be partly insectivorous;[9, 12] *C. diana* is entirely frugivorous (stomach contents).[10] *Cercopithecus* (*Cercopithecus*) not observed drinking in nature except *C. pygerythrus* in arid zones. Principal feeding periods are early a.m. and early p.m.[8, 9] PREDATORS: Man, the monkey-eating eagle (*Stephanoaetus coronatus*), the Martial Hawk Eagle and, to some extent, leopard.[8] *See* Table on p. 109 for details of habitat.

MORPHOLOGY

External Characters

Medium to large size. Fur is thick, soft and short. Predominant colours are green, yellow, rufous and black; many of the coats show ticking or flecking. Genus is characterized by localized flashes and bars of brilliant colours and by striking adornments such as nose-spots (*C. nictitans*), moustaches (*C. cephus*) and beards (*C. diana*, *C. neglectus*). Face is moderately orthognathous, body is slender and graceful and tail is longer than combined head and body length in all species. Ischial callosities are small and well separated (cf. *Papio*). Nipples approximate in midline. Scrotum of ♂ is characteristically blue in colour, particularly vivid in *C. aethiops* group. For detailed account of colour variability between species, see table of distinguishing characters (p. 109).

Weights and Dimensions

Body weight range (g) *C. ascanius*:[8]	3178–6356 (38♂♂)	1816–3859 (36♀♀)
Head and body length range[6, 8] (mm) (all species)	410–645 (107♂♂)	315–520 (96♀♀)
Tail length range[6, 8] (mm) (all species)	575–1090 (107♂♂)	480–1020 (96♀♀)

Based on means, weight of ♀ is 70% of ♂.

Internal Characters

SKULL: Typical of Cercopithecinae but lacking prognathism, heavy jaws and skull buttressing of some genera, e.g. *Papio*. Distinguished from *Colobus* by relatively narrow inter-orbital width.[13] Skull differences from *Cercocebus* discussed by Rode (1936). *See also* Verheyen (1962) for comparative craniology and craniometry of genus. VERTEBRAL COLUMN: Commonly C.7, T.12, L.7 and S.3.[15] ARMS: Humerus shows marked antero-posterior and lateral curvatures, deltoid insertion well defined; humeral head points backwards. HANDS: Digital formula: 3.4.2.5.1. Deep head of flexor pollicis brevis and other thenar muscles well differentiated. FOOT: D.F.: 3.4.2.5.1.; big toe relatively short compared with prosimians and *Pan* and *Gorilla*.[39] ALIMENTARY SYSTEM: Small cheek pouches present (cf. *Macaca*); stomach is simple. DENTITION: D.F.: $\frac{2}{2}\frac{1}{1}\frac{2}{2}\frac{3}{3} = 32$. Main distinguishing characteristic from *Papio* and *Macaca* is absence of 5th cusp on lower 3rd molar. M.$\underline{3}$ tends to be reduced (cf. *Papio* and *Macaca*).

Genetic Biology

CHROMOSOMES:[16] *C. aethiops* 2n = 60; *C. diana* 2n = 58–60; *C. neglectus* 2n = 58–62; *C. cephus*, *C. mona*, *C. nictitans* 2n = 66; *C. mitis*, *C. lhoesti* 2n = 72. HAEMOGLOBINS:* *Cercopithecus* sp.:

PLATE 25. Hamlyn's owl-faced monkey, *Cercopithecus hamlyni* ♂

Hb identical with Human A,[17] though this disputed by Buettner-Janusch (1963b). Some indication of Hb polymorphism in *C. aethiops*.[19] P.T.C. TASTING:[20] Non-tasters predominate, e.g. *C. diana* 19 : 2, *C. hamlyyni* 12 : 2, *C. nictitans* 21 : 2, *C. aethiops* 29 : 1. BLOOD GROUPS (*C. pygerythrus*): Human groups A and B.

BEHAVIOUR

Locomotor Behaviour

AUTHORS' CLASSIFICATION: Quadrupedalism. Capable of climbing, jumping and running on the ground. Cross gaps in canopy by considerable downward jumps. During locomotion, tail is carried in varied positions which are species-specific.[8] All species probably capable of swimming, an activity that has been observed in *C. aethiops*,[4, 21] *C. neglectus*[12] and *C. mona*. During early stages, tail of infant *C. ascanius* shows considerable prehensile power in maintaining grip on mother.[8] LIMB PROPORTIONS: Forelimb shorter than hindlimb but not greatly so; for Indices *see* Part III, p. 394.

Hand Function[22, 23]

Thumb fully opposable but thumb-index precision grip imperfect owing to relative disproportion (*see* Hand Indices, Part III, p. 401). Power-grip used to support balance on slender branches.

Resting Posture

All species bear ischial callosities which are believed to be associated with sitting and night-resting posture.[24] Most species sleep amongst small branches in dense foliage. Night-resting habits have been extensively studied in connection with epidemiology of yellow fever;[25, 26] for *C. aethiops see* Hall and Gartlan (1965) and Brain (1965).

Social Behaviour

Knowledge of the naturalistic social behaviour of this genus depends largely on two field studies, that of Haddow (1952) on *C. ascanius*, and that of Hall and Gartlan (1965) on *C. aethiops*. HOME RANGE:[8, 9] Home range in *C. ascanius* is ½ sq mile (1·3 sq km). On Lolui I. (*C. aethiops*) maximum day range is 550 yds (500 m); home ranges of adjacent groups overlap. Size of range varies with food conditions e.g. *C. aethiops* reported covering 11 miles (17·6 km) in 24 hours in time of food shortage.[27] GROUP SIZE:[8, 9] Maximum size of bands 40–50 but variable in size and constitution at different parts of day; usually consists of 10 or more during feeding and travelling; smaller units of 3–5 individuals with 1 adult ♂ are found during night resting.[25, 26] ADULT SEX RATIO: (*C. aethiops*): 1♂ : 1·4♀♀. Groups contain 45% immatures. Solitary ♂♂ have been noted in *C. ascanius*,[8] *C. mitis*, *C. neglectus* and *C. aethiops*.[28] COMMUNICATION: VOCALIZATION: Calls in the wild are said to have a high-pitched chirping quality.[8] In captivity a wide range of sounds has been recorded in *C. aethiops*, *C. diana* and *C. neglectus*.[29, 30] FACIAL EXPRESSION: *Cercopithecus* have a relative immobility of face compared to ground-living Cercopithecinae;[31] lip-smacking and grinning seldom seen, though former has been observed.[32] THREAT DISPLAY:[8, 9] Tail is raised and head is lowered with arms held stiffly. Body action is accompanied by branch throwing or dropping, defaecation, urination and vocalization against intruder. INTRA-GROUP BEHAVIOUR: Male

PLATE 26. ♀ Samango monkey, *Cercopithecus mitis*, grooming a ♂ (by courtesy of C. K. Brain)

PLATE 27. Left: *Cercopithecus albogularis kolbi*, adult ♀; right: *Cercopithecus mona* (Eric Kirkland), *see* p. 106

PLATE 29. *Ceropithecus erythrotis*, adult ♂ aged 7 years (by courtesy of Doris M. Sorby)

PLATE 28. De Brazza's monkey, *Cercopithecus neglectus*, ♀ with infant (by courtesy of Twycross Zoo Park; photo by John Doidge), *see* p. 107

TABLE I

Range, Habitats and Pelage Characters of *Cercopithecus (Cercopithecus)*

Species Group	Range	Habitat	Colour of Coat	Skin and Adornment of Face
aethiops	Senegal to Ethiopia and Sudan to S. Africa. Most northerly range 18° N. 8° E.	Ground living. Gallery forest and river banks. Woodland savannah and open savannah.	Shoulder, back and tail yellowish to olive. Underparts white or yellowish. Pale grey or black on lower outer surface of limbs.	Face black. White or yellowish superciliary band, face fringe and ear tufts.
cephus	Tropical rain forest of Gabon and Congo (Brazzaville). Limited to N. by Sanaga R. and to the S. by Congo and Ubangi Rivers.	Arboreal. Frequents areas of secondary forest where oil-palm abounds. Usually found in closed canopy.	*C. cephus.* Coat is predominantly greenish brown; speckling is produced by bars of grey, yellow or black on individual hairs. Outer aspects of forelimbs and hands dark brown or black. Throat white and remaining underparts grey.	Face naked and, except for lips and eyelids, violet blue in colour. White bar between mouth and nose and a black rim to upper lip giving a "moustache" effect.
diana	W. Africa. From Sierra Leone to Ghana W. of the R. Volta.	Arboreal. Frequents highest or middle strata of tropical rain forest. Seldom descends to shrub layer or ground.	*C. diana.* Predominantly blue-black and white. Chest and upper abdomen creamy white. Chestnut saddle on back. Orange-brown on inner aspect of thighs and genital region. Rest of body blue-black.	Face black. Short white beard (*C. diana*); long white beard (*C. diana roloway*). White stripe down outside of thigh.
lhoesti	Central and E. Africa. Lowland forest of Congo (Leopoldville) and Western mountainous region of Uganda. *C. preussi* occupies similar habitat in Cameroun and Fernando Póo.	Arboreal and ground living. The montane form found in forest valleys up to 2500 m. Crop-raider.	Hair is long and soft and predominantly dark grey with chestnut saddle. Throat and chest white, remaining underparts blackish-brown.	Pale infraorbital markings. Thick grey tufts at side of face running upwards and backwards.
hamlyni	Range not known. Found in Eastern Congo basin in N.W. Ruanda.	Arboreal. Detailed ecology not known.	Hair of head, neck and body is speckled olive grey giving place to silvery colour in sacral region and proximal tail. Ventral surface and forelimbs are jet black. Hindlimbs greyish on outside, jet black on inner.	Prominent stripe of white hairs from forehead to philtrum of nose. Pale, diffuse supraorbital band.
mona	Widely distributed in W. Africa from French Guinea to Cameroon; in Central Africa from Cameroun and Gabon to Uganda. *C. mona* extends from W. of R. Volta to just S. of R. Sanaga. Latitudinal limits: 9° N.–8° S.	Arboreal. All types of rain forest habitat. Mainly occupy upper stratum during day and middle stratum at night.	*C. mona.* Crown of head is black flecked with yellow and green. Body is red-brown, speckled with black, blending with dark grey of outer thighs. Underparts, including throat, chest and inner aspect limbs, white. Oval white spot on each side of tail.	White frontal band fading laterally, narrow black stripe from corner of eye to ear. Facial tufts very bushy and extending on to cheeks.

TABLE I (*continued*)

Species Group	Range	Habitat	Colour of Coat	Skin and Adornment of Face
neglectus	Widely distributed in E. and Central Africa; throughout Congo basin to borders of Uganda and Kenya. Longitudinal Limits: 12° E.–35° E. Latitudinal Limits: 2° N.–11° S.	Arboreal and ground-living. An inhabitant of riverine and swamp forest. Frequently found on banks of streams.	Crown, body, outer thighs and arms dark grizzled effect of black and yellow due to annulation of hairs. Hands, feet, tail (except root) are black. White stripe on outside of thigh.	Ginger supraorbital band of white-tipped hairs; above, a dense black band from ear to ear. Lower nose and mouth white. Full white beard. Cheek tufts speckled yellow and black.
nictitans	Widely distributed group found in W. Africa, Cameroun, Central Africa, Congo (Leo.) N. and E. of R. Congo. S. Uganda, W. Kenya, N.-W. Tanzania, N. Zambia, N. and E. of Angola. Latitudinal Limits: 9° N.–12° S. Longitudinal Limits: 17° W.–30° E.	*C. ascanius*: Arboreal. Inhabitant of lowland and upland rain forest and swamp forest. Found principally at forest edges or on river banks. Prefers middle and lower (closed) parts of canopy and shrub layer.	*C. ascanius*: Back, arms and thighs dark brown with orange flecking; forearms and legs are dark grey; hands and feet black. Tail grades from black to chestnut to red towards tip. Underparts pale. The scrotum in this group is blue to blue-black in colour.	*C. ascanius*: Tip of nose bears conspicuous heart-shaped spot of white hairs. Narrow black band in superciliary area. Cheek tufts are very bushy and white in colour or white tipped with black. White nose spots in all other members of this species group except *C. nictitans* in which spot is yellow and oval in shape.
mitis	Widely distributed from S. Sudan to S. Africa (Drakensburg); and from Ethiopia to Congo (Braz.), E. of R. Ubangi. Angola.	Arboreal. Typical of Montane forest but also found in sub-types of Lowland forest and gallery forest, savannah woodland and even scrub forest.	Coat is blue-grey with yellow ticking. Crown of head, forelimbs, hands and feet and terminal tail are black. Throat and underparts are pale blue-grey grading to black on belly.	Light coloured rather diffuse diadem on forehead; narrow black supra-orbital band running towards ear. Nose and circumnasal and circum-oral hair lighter than rest of face.

dominance behaviour said to be rather "low-grade". SOCIAL GROOMING: Seldom seen except in *C. aethiops*.[9] SEXUAL BEHAVIOUR: Copulation rarely observed in the wild. Diurnal copulation has been observed in the wild in *C. mitis*, *C. albogularis* and *C. aethiops*; also in captivity in these species and *C. neglectus*. Copulation has been described by Booth (1962); it is completed in a single mounting unless the animals are disturbed.

REPRODUCTION AND DEVELOPMENT [5, 8, 33]

Cycle is regular and lasts approximately 30 days. There is apparently no fixed breeding season for a given species but there is evidence of seasonal variation of birth rate. Sexual skin changes do *not* occur. GESTATION PERIOD: approx. 180–213 days.[34] Single births, twinning rare,[35] but *see* Stott (1946). PARTURITION: delivery behaviour of *C. mona* has been reported.[37] LACTATION: Lasts for 6 months; owing to proximity of mother's nipples, infant may take both in its mouth when suckling.[5] INFANT GROWTH:[8] Following stages have been noted in *C. ascanius*: (i) Walking independently—7 days; (ii) Very active—30 days; (iii) Taking solid food—60 days; (iv) Fully independent—180 days at which time milk dentition is complete.

CAPTIVITY

Very successful animals in Zoo collections both from longevity and breeding points of view.[34]
See Crandall (1964) for captivity observations. LONGEVITY RECORDS[38] (up to 1962):

C. diana roloway	31 years	National Zoological Park, Washington
C. mona	$22\frac{1}{2}$ years	Rotterdam Zoo
C. mitis	19 years	San Diego Zoo
C. pygerythrus	$22\frac{1}{2}$ years	National Zoological Park, Washington

REFERENCES

1. Hill, W. C. Osman (1966b)
2. Tappen, N. C. (1960)
3. Bigourdan, J. and Prunier, R. (1937) quoted by Tappen, N. C. (1960)
4. Haddow, A. J., Smithburn, K. C., Mahaffy, A. F. and Bugher, J. C. (1947)
5. Booth, C. (1962)
6. Allen, J. A. (1925)
7. Sanderson, I. T. (1940)
8. Haddow, A. J. (1952)
9. Hall, K. R. L. and Gartlan, J. S. (1965)
10. Booth, A. H. (1956a and b)
11. Mackenzie, A. F. (1952)
12. Haddow, A. J. (1956)
13. Verheyen, W. N. (1962)
14. Rode, P. (1936)
15. Schultz, A. H. (1961)
16. Chiarelli, B. (1966b)
17. Jacobs, G. F. and Tappen, N. C. (1958)
18. Buettner-Janusch, J. (1963b)
19. Buettner-Janusch, J. and Buettner-Janusch, V. (1964)
20. Chiarelli, B. (1963b)
21. Thomas, O. and Hinton, M. A. C. (1923)
22. Napier, J. R. (1961)
23. Bishop, Alison (1964)
24. Washburn, S. L. (1957)
25. Lumsden, W. H. R. (1951)
26. Buxton, A. P. (1951)
27. Brain, C. K. (1965)
28. Sclater, W. L. (1900)
29. Andrew, R. J. (1963)
30. Andrew, R. J. (1964)
31. Hooff, J. A. R. A. M. van (1962)
32. Bolwig, N. (1959)
33. Zuckerman, S. (1933)
34. International Zoo Year Book, Vols. I–V (1959–1965)
35. Schultz, A. H. (1948)
36. Stott, R. (1946)
37. Takeshita, H. (1961–62)
38. Jones, M. L. (1962)
39. Schultz, A. H. (1963a)
40. Booth, A. H. (1955)
41. Dandelot, P. (1959)
42. Crandall, L. S. (1964)

CERCOPITHECUS   Linnaeus, 1758   Guenons

SUBGENUS: *Allenopithecus* Lang, 1923

1 species: 0 subspecies

Cercopithecus (Allenopithecus) nigroviridis Pocock, 1907   Allen's swamp monkey

GEOGRAPHICAL RANGE [1, 2, 3, 4]

Africa. Congo. Specimens have been collected from the left bank of R. Congo opposite Mossaka; S.W. of R. Congo on R. bank of R. Tshuapa; from island in R. Congo near Bolobo, and from the Lac Leopold II area.

ECOLOGY *

HABITAT: Swamp forest. ACTIVITY RHYTHM: Diurnal. DIET: Unknown in the wild.

MORPHOLOGY

External Characters[2, 5]

Stockily-built guenon of moderate size, rather "baboon"-like. Limbs short and robust; hands short and broad. Tail relatively short. Sexual dimorphism in body size greater than in *Cercopithecus* generally. Coat has a soft silky texture. Face pigmented but eyelids and chin pale. Narrow superciliary band extends towards ears; cheeks pale and upper lip blackish. Hairs of head, shoulders, arms and hands, back and flanks are black with yellowish bands giving a speckled effect. Outer legs yellower than back. Chin, throat, chest, belly and inner legs yellowish-white. Tail blackish, darkening distally. Ischial callosities more developed than in *Cercopithecus (Cercopithecus)*, rectangular in shape and occasionally continuous across midline in ♂.[2, 6] Sexual skin in both sexes is bright red.

Weights and Dimensions[2, 4]

Head and body length (mm)	460, 510 (2♂♂)	410 (1♀)
Tail length (mm)	500, 525 (2♂♂)	355 (1♀)

HAND: Length/breadth index = 32. FOOT: Length/breadth index = 21·5.

Internal Characters

As for *Cercopithecus (Cercopithecus)*. Main differences noted herewith. *See also* Hill (1964a) and Pocock (1907, 1925b). SKULL: Moderately prognathic, facial bones stouter than in Talapoin; postglenoid tubercle prominent as in cercopitheques generally. Low sagittal crest seen in ♂.[4*] Verheyen (1962) provides a list of relatively minor craniological distinctions from C. (*Cercopithecus*). Craniometrically the two subgenera cannot be distinguished. HANDS:[2] Broad and short with stubby fingers recalling *Papio*; digital pads are prominent being separated by deep flexure creases. There is marked interdigital webbing between II to V digits. EXTERNAL GENITALIA:[2] in form and length, penis resembles that of *Cercocebus atys*. DENTITION:[4*]

PLATE 30. *Cercopithecus (Allenopithecus) nigroviridis*, adult ♂ (San Diego Zoo)

Molars are broad basally and cusps are drawn together towards their apex, forming a narrow longitudinal groove on occlusal surface. M.$\overline{3}$ lacks 5th cusp.

BEHAVIOUR

There are no published records of behaviour of this monkey in captivity or in the wild.

CAPTIVITY [8, 9]

Fairly uncommon in captivity but San Diego Zoo has had a breeding pair since 1953. First record of birth in captivity: June, 1959 (San Diego Zoo). LONGEVITY RECORD (up to 1962):[10] 8 years 8 months San Diego Zoo.

REFERENCES

1. Lang, H. (1923)
2. Hill, W. C. Osman (1964a)
3. Schouteden, H. (1947)
4. Allen, J. A. (1925)
5. Pocock, R. I. (1907)
6. Schwarz, E. (1928b)

7. Pocock, R. I. (1925a)
8. Pournelle, G. H. (1959)
9. Pournelle, G. H. (1962)
10. Jones, M. L. (1962)
11. Verheyen, W. N. (1962)

CERCOPITHECUS Linnaeus, 1758   Guenons

SUBGENUS: *Miopithecus* (I. Geoffroy, 1842)

1 species: 4 subspecies[1]

Cercopithecus (Miopithecus) talapoin Schreber, 1774   Talapoin, mangrove monkey

GEOGRAPHICAL RANGE [2]

West central Africa along Atlantic coast from S. Cameroun to N. Angola. Eastern longitudinal limit: 10° E.

ECOLOGY *

HABITAT:[3] Mangrove swamp, swamp forest; also gallery forest. Frequently found on river banks. ACTIVITY RHYTHM: Diurnal. DIET: Not known in the wild. Said to be crop-raiders.[3]

MORPHOLOGY

External Characters

Smallest of all species of *Cercopithecus*. Predominantly green in colour speckled with black on the back. Paler—more yellowish—on arms and legs. Underparts and inner sides of limbs are pale. Tail is olive grading to black at the tip. Adornments are not marked. Orange rings around eyes. Cheek tufts yellow, radiating in a fan-like arrangement. Black streak from corner of eye to ear, and black smudge on cheek. There is said to be sexual dimorphism in coat colour of this sub-genus. Tail is approximately equal to body length. A sexual skin which undergoes cyclical changes is apparent in females.

Weights and Dimensions[1, 2]

Body weight (g)	1230, 1280 (2♂♂)	745, 820 (2♀♀)
Head and body length (mm)	350 (1♂)	340, 370 (2♀♀)
Tail length (mm)	375 (1♂)	360, 380 (2♀♀)

Internal Characters

As for *Cercopithecus (Cercopithecus)*. SKULL: Less prognathous than other cercopitheques, face being rather short and mandibular angle approx. 90°. Cranium is relatively large and zygoma is very slender. Post-glenoid tubercle absent. Pocock (1907) remarks on its neotenous appearance. "The small face and large cranium of the adult recall those of the young of other species in this genus." (p. 740). Verheyen (1962) states that, craniologically, Talapoins cannot be sufficiently distinguished from other cercopitheques to justify generic or subgeneric distinction; on craniometric grounds however they can be so distinguished. DENTITION:[4, 5] Owing probably to a *lapsus calami* on the part of I. Geoffroy (1842) M.$\overline{3}$ was stated to have only three cusps, a statement perpetuated by Elliot (1913) among others. Schwarz (1928b) pointed this out and observed that M.$\underline{3}$ occasionally has three cusps only (*see* James, 1960, fig. 51b). GENITALIA: clitoris long.[5]

E

PLATE 31. *Cercopithecus (Miopithecus) talapoin*, adult ♀ with infant aged 3 days (by courtesy of W. C. Osman Hill; photo by Larry Bowling)

BEHAVIOUR

There is no reason to suppose that the locomotor behaviour, hand function or resting posture differ greatly from those of *Cercopithecus (Cercopithecus)*. No field studies are available so social behaviour is unknown.

REPRODUCTION AND DEVELOPMENT

Sexual skin undergoes cyclic changes.[9] GESTATION PERIOD: 196 days.*[13]

CAPTIVITY

Births in captivity are uncommon.[10, 13] LONGEVITY RECORD (up to 1962):[11] 22 years 3 months, Philadelphia Zoo.

REFERENCES

1. Poll, M. (1940)
2. Flower, S. S. (1929)
3. Bates, G. L. (1905)
4. Pocock, R. I. (1907)
5. Pocock, R. I. (1925b)
6. Elliot, D. G. (1913)
7. Schwarz, E. (1928b)
8. James, W. Warwick (1960)
9. Zuckerman, S. (1933)
10. International Zoo Year Book, Vols. I–V (1959–65)
11. Jones, M. L. (1962)
12. Verheyen, W. N. (1962)
13. Hill, W. C. Osman (1966a)

CHEIROGALEUS   E. Geoffroy, 1812 Dwarf Lemurs

3 species:[1] 2 subspecies[2]

C. major (Type species)	Greater Dwarf Lemur	2 subsp.
C. medius	Fat-tailed Dwarf Lemur	o subsp.
C. trichotis†	Hairy-eared Dwarf Lemur	o subsp.

GEOGRAPHICAL RANGE [1, 2]

Madagascar. *C. major* found only in eastern rain forest. In the W. and S. it is replaced by *C. medius*. Exact range is not known. Type locality of both species: Fort Dauphin.[1]

ECOLOGY

HABITAT:[2] Inhabitants of tropical forest of both wet and dry types where they are seen on the thick and medium-sized horizontal branches, usually low down. Nest in holes in trees.[3] ACTIVITY RHYTHM:[2] Nocturnal: these animals show periods of torpidity which vary interspecifically, being short (2–3 days) in *C. major* and long (several weeks) in *C. medius* (cf. thickness of base of tail). DIET: Less insectivorous than mouse-lemurs; predominantly fruit-eaters.

MORPHOLOGY

External Characters[1, 4, 5]

Small animals approximately the size of a large rat. Largest species: *C. major*, smallest: *C. trichotis*. Muzzle short; ears not tufted in two commoner species, and thin, membranous and of simple form. Tail thick at base and shorter than body; thickness most marked in *C. medius*. Colour is brownish-red or grey, the underparts being of lighter colour, completely white in *C. medius*, extending dorsally towards neck. Face bears dark eye-rings and in *C. medius* a white nasal stripe which also occurs occasionally in *C. major*. Hindlimbs longer than fore-limbs. HANDS: nails pointed and keeled. DIGITAL FORMULA: 4.3.2.5.1. MAMMAE: usually two pairs—pectoral and inguinal. Full complement of mammalian vibrissae present.

Weights and Dimensions

Head and body length range (mm)	190–267 (5 specimens: *C. medius* and *C. major*)
Tail length range (mm)	165–250 (5 specimens: *C. medius* and *C. major*)

Internal Characters[4]

For general characters of Lemuridae, see *Lemur*; and of Cheirogaleinae, see *Microcebus*. Only principal differences noted here. SKULL: Facial portion more flexed upon neurocranium than in *Microcebus* but otherwise as in the latter genus. ALIMENTARY SYSTEM:[6, 7] Colon primitive as in *Microcebus* and *Tarsius*, lacking an ansa coli. Caecum very short and globular. DENTITION: D.F.: $\frac{2}{2}\frac{1}{1}\frac{3}{3}\frac{3}{3} = 36$. Can be distinguished from *Microcebus* by prominent P.M.[1] which is caniniform and by well-developed lingual cusp on PM.[3].

---

† Extremely rare, only known from type specimen; may now be extinct.

Genetic Biology*

CHROMOSOMES:[8] 2n = 66 (1 ♂ *C. major*).

BEHAVIOUR [2, 9]

Locomotor Behaviour

AUTHORS' CLASSIFICATION: Quadrupedalism. Moves about in darting, squirrel-like fashion though not with so much agility as mouse-lemurs; often seen moving quadrupedally on relatively stout branches with a slow "creeping" gait reminiscent of *Perodicticus*. Leaping less common than in *Microcebus*.[2]

Hand Function

As in *Microcebus*, though hand is less frequently used for eating and toilet purposes. During locomotion, principle axis of grasp falls between 2nd and 3rd digits.

Resting Posture

Seldom adopts sitting posture at rest; during sleep, or periods of physiological torpidity, *Cheirogaleus* are rolled up in a tight ball.

Social Behaviour

GROUP SIZE: In the wild, Dwarf Lemurs are generally seen as solitary animals or, at most, in pairs; can be kept in large groups in captivity providing there is numerical sex equality. MARKING BEHAVIOUR apparently not intensive; branches are marked by urine and excreta.

REPRODUCTION AND DEVELOPMENT [10]

(*C. major*): Polyoestrous. Seasonal sexual cycles without menstruation limited to certain months of the year. DURATION OF CYCLE: approx. 30 days. OESTRUS: 2–5 days. The ♀ external genitalia show changes similar to those of *Microcebus* during the sexual cycle.[10] Copulation has been observed and described (Petter-Rousseaux, 1964). GESTATION: 70 days. NO. OF YOUNG: 2 or 3. At birth the young are relatively immature (Head and body 75 mm, Tail 70 mm, weighing 18 g approx.). Eyes closed at birth, opening on 2nd day. Post-natal development in early stages is faster than in *Microcebus*. Infants are carried in the mother's mouth.

CAPTIVITY

Births in captivity have been recorded.[13] Dwarf lemurs are tame and affectionate (cf. *Microcebus*). LONGEVITY RECORD:[11, 12] 8 years 8 months. London, Zoological Gardens.

REFERENCES

1. Schwarz, E. (1931c)
2. Petter, J. J. (1962a)
3. Rand, A. L. (1935)
4. Hill, W. C. Osman (1953)
5. Forbes, H. O. (1897)
6. Mitchell, P. Chalmers (1905)
7. Mitchell, P. Chalmers (1916)
8. Chu, E. H. Y. and Bender, M. A. (1962)
9. Shaw, G. A. (1879)
10. Petter-Rousseaux, A. (1964)
11. Jones, M. L. (1962)
12. International Zoo Year Book, Vol. 4 (1962)
13. Bourlière, F., Petter-Rousseaux, A. and Petter, J. J. (1962)

PLATE 32. Dwarf lemur: above: *Cheirogaleus major*; below: *Cheirogaleus medius* (by courtesy of Alan C. Walker) [Photographed in the same cage to show relative sizes]

CHIROPOTES Lesson, 1840   Bearded Sakis

2 species: 2 subspecies[1]

C. satanas (Type species)	Black Saki	2 subsp.
C. albinasus	White-nosed Saki	o subsp.

GEOGRAPHICAL RANGE [1, 2]

South America. *C. satanas* is sparsely distributed between S. bank of R. Orinoco and N. bank of R. Amazon and R. Negro, extending eastwards into Guianas; it is also probably to be found E. and W. of R. Tocantins in the region of Cameta, the type site (also recorded on Upper Amazon*). *C. albinasus* is found S. of R. Amazon, limited westwards by R. Madiera and eastwards by R. Xingu; the range may include the northern Mato Grosso.

ECOLOGY

HABITAT: Inhabitants of tropical rain forest particularly gallery forest in unflooded areas[3] and on river banks;[4] probably wholly arboreal. ACTIVITY RHYTHM: Diurnal. DIET: Wholly frugivorous[5, 6]* (latter study based on stomach contents of 2 specimens).

MORPHOLOGY

External Characters[2, 7]

Medium-sized monkeys. Coat is thick, long, predominantly black. In *C. satanas* there is a variable degree of chestnut-brown colouration on back, shoulders and limbs; *C. albinasus* is uniformly black on body. Face is black and naked in *C. satanas*; with a pinkish nose and upper lip in *C. albinasus*. Head hair arises from a centre on the vertex and falls over the side of the head as in a Japanese doll, sometimes (*C. satanas*) in a "bouffant" style. There is a full bushy black beard. Nose has a broad septum with widely separated nostrils which are directed laterally; bridge of nose is narrow (cf. *Pithecia* where bridge of nose is broad). TAIL is long and thick, and does not taper. LIMBS: Legs considerably longer than arms. HANDS: Digital formula: $3.4.2 = 5.1.$ or $3 = 4.2.5.1.$; nails markedly convex in both planes. MAMMAE: 1 pair in axillary position.[2]

Weights and Dimensions[4, 6]

Body weights (g)	2770, 3130 (2♂)	—
Head and body lengths (mm)	400, 406, 407 (3♂)	460 (1♀)
Tail lengths (mm)	380 (1♂)	350 (1♀)

Internal Characters

SKULL: As in all Pitheciinae. ALIMENTARY CANAL: comparatively long small intestine, caecum and colon, possibly correlated with largely frugivorous diet.[6] DENTITION:[9] D.F.: $\frac{2}{2}\frac{1}{1}\frac{3}{3}\frac{3}{3} = 36$. Upper incisors long and projecting; lower incisors somewhat procumbent; canines strong and projecting with well-marked diastemata in upper jaw. Molars quadricuspid, $M\frac{3}{3}$ tend to be small, particularly $M\underline{3}$.

PLATE 33. Bearded Saki, *Chiropotes satanas* (by courtesy of Cologne Zoo)

Genetic Biology

Unknown.

BEHAVIOUR

Locomotor Behaviour

AUTHORS' CLASSIFICATION: Quadrupedalism. (Erikson's category: Climbers). Little known of behaviour in the wild but said to move "cautiously and deliberately, lacking power of leaping."[2,*] LIMB PROPORTIONS: Relatively long hindlimbs. For Indices *see* Part III, p. 394.

Hand Function

Hand prehensile and thumb pseudo- or non-opposable; functional axis of hand is between digits 2 and 3. Humboldt and Bonpland (1812) observed that they used the hand to drink by dipping it in water and licking it dry.

Social Behaviour*

Said to live in small groups; no further information.

CAPTIVITY

LONGEVITY RECORD:[12] *C. satanas*: 15 years. San Diego Zoo.

REFERENCES

1. Cabrera, A. (1957)
2. Hill, W. C. Osman (1960)
3. Bates, H. W. (1863)
4. Cruz Lima, E. da (1945)
5. Boker, H. (1932)
6. Fooden, J. (1964b)
7. Sanderson, I. T. (1957)
8. Pocock, R. I. (1925c)
9. James, W. Warwick (1960)
10. Erikson, G. E. (1963)
11. Humboldt, A. de and Bonpland, A. (1812)
12. Jones, M. L. (1962)

COLOBUS† Illiger, 1811   Guerezas

3 subgenera: 5 species: 41 subspecies[12, 39]

SUBGENUS: *Colobus* Illiger, 1811   Black and White Colobus

2 species: 22 Subspecies[12, 39]

C. polykomos (Type species)	King colobus	12 subsp.
C. guereza [=*abyssinicus*]†	Abyssinian colobus	10 subsp.

GEOGRAPHICAL RANGE [1–3]

Africa. Widely distributed in high forest of lowland and montane type from Senegal to Ethiopia and from Angola throughout the Congo basin to montane forests of Tanzania and Malawi; vagrant in Zambia (*C.p. angolensis*).[4] The northerly species is *C. guereza* and the most southerly ranging is *C. polykomos*. *C. guereza matschiei* and *C.g. uellensis* live at high altitudes in Uganda in montane forest.

ECOLOGY

HABITAT: Inhabitants of tropical rain and montane forest; also outliers and gallery forest. *C. polykomos* found in closed canopy and *C. guereza* in higher "open" canopy. ACTIVITY RHYTHM: Diurnal. DIET: Almost exclusively leaves, determined by field observations and stomach contents.[5] PREDATORS: Man; much hunted for meat and skins.

MORPHOLOGY

External Characters[6–9]

Large monkeys with slender bodies and long tails. Coat is predominantly glossy black, long-haired, particularly in the montane forms, and silky. The extent of the white mantles and fringes varies both inter- and intraspecifically: *C. guereza*: White adornments take the form of a heavy fringe along the whole flank to meet in the midline of the lower back (*C.g. guereza* and *C.g. kikuyuensis*). Tail brush is scanty with a white tip (*C.g. guereza*) or full and white throughout (*C.g. kikuyuensis*). There is usually a white superciliary band, white whiskers and white beard. Hair on the crown in *C. guereza* forms an upstanding cap or bonnet. *C. polykomos*: White fur is restricted to narrow brow band, cheeks, neck, shoulders, thighs and tail (e.g. *C.p. vellerosus* and *C.p. angolensis*). In *C.p. satanas* the coat is wholly black. "Bonnet" is absent in *C. polykomos*. The nose is prominent and slightly overhangs the upper lip.[8] Ischial callosities are of moderate size and are close together in the ♂ but widely separated in the ♀.[8] The thumb is suppressed and is represented by a tubercle; the feet are long and slender and the big toe of moderate size. Sexual dimorphism in canine and body size is only slight.

---

† *See* Taxonomic Notes, Part III, p. 372.

Weights and Dimensions[10]

C. guereza

	♂	♀	♀ in % ♂
Head and body length average and range (mm)	593 (535–690)(16♂♂)	554 (485–640)(13♀♀)	93
Tail length average and range (mm)	811 (670–885)(16♂♂)	773 (715–825)(13♀♀)	95

C. polykomos

	♂	♀	♀ in % ♂
Head and body length average and range (mm)	581 (490–640)(21♂♂)	561 (505–610)(15♀♀)	97
Tail length average and range (mm)	824 (720–890)(21♂♂)	800 (645–880)(15♀♀)	96

Internal Characters

For general anatomy of *Colobus*, *see* Polak (1908); for detailed study of skull, *see* Verheyen (1962). SKULL: Somewhat prognathous with marked post-orbital narrowing. Prominent temporal lines which frequently unite to form a raised crest posteriorly in ♂♂ associated with a high nuchal crest.[13] Zygomatic arch shows considerable variation in convexity and stoutness.[10] Interorbital space wider than in Cercopithecinae.[12] Orbits oval with narrow superciliary ridges. DENTITION: D.F.: $\frac{2}{2}\frac{1}{1}\frac{2}{2}\frac{3}{3} = 32$. Typically catarrhine, having high-cusped molars. Differs from *Cercopithecus* by presence of 5th cusp on M.$\overline{3}$ and from *C. (Procolobus) verus* by the frequent occurrence in the latter of a 6th cusp derived from doubling of the 5th cusp.[7] THORAX: Relatively wider in antero-posterior dimension than in Cercopithecinae.[11] LARYNX: Laryngeal air-sac absent but subhyoid sac and laryngeal saccules present as in *Presbytis*. ALIMENTARY TRACT:[14] Cheek pouches absent. Stomach is enlarged, particularly in the cardiac portion, sacculated and folded upon itself; two longitudinal muscular bands (taeniae) are present. This modification displaces both the spleen and liver from their normal positions; the physiology of the stomach has been studied by Kuhn (1964).

Genetic Biology

CHROMOSOMES:[16] 2n=44 (♀ *C. polykomos*). HAEMOGLOBINS:[17] *Colobus* sp.: Hb exhibit degree of mobility faster than Human A on starch-gel electrophoresis. P.T.C. TASTING:[18] Tasters 6: non-tasters 1 (*C. polykomos*).

PLATE 34. *Colobus guereza kikuyuensis*, ♀ and white infant (San Diego Zoo)

BEHAVIOUR

Locomotor Behaviour*

AUTHORS' CLASSIFICATION: Quadrupedalism. Subtype: Old World Semibrachiation. Commonest form of gait is plantigrade and quadrupedal but frequently swing by arms below branches. Have been seen to leap considerable distances and "brake" their flight by grabbing at the branch with the hands.[19, 20] Tail acts as an airbrake.[19] Seldom seen on ground for any length of time. LIMB PROPORTIONS. Hindlimbs considerably longer than forelimbs. *See* Part III, p. 394, for Indices.

Hand Function

Hand prehensile. Thumb lacking or reduced to stump. During arm swinging locomotion, uses "hook" grip. Seizes objects between fingers and palm; some independent control of index finger apparent against the stump of thumb,[21] i.e. precision pattern of grip is retained. HAND PROPORTIONS: *See* Part III, p. 401.

Social Behaviour*

Little is known about behaviour either in the wild or in captivity. The following observations are derived principally from Haddow (1952). RANGE AND TERRITORIALITY:[38] Well-defined home range; conflicts between groups have clearly a territorial character. Territorial aggressiveness consists of a vocal and physical display which is more pronounced in ♂♂. *Colobus* is frequently found in association with *Cercopithecus*.[22, 23] GROUP SIZE: *C. guereza* varies from 2–15 or more.[24, 38] Solitary ♂♂ are frequently seen. Male dominance behaviour is conspicuous in *C.* (*Colobus*) (cf. *C.* (*Procolobus*) and *C.* (*Piliocolobus*)).[23] NIGHT-RESTING: Bands consist of 4–5 individuals in W. Uganda.[25] VOCALIZATION: Resonant calls that are freely used[22] (cf. *C.* (*Procolobus*) and *C.* (*Piliocolobus*)). SEXUAL BEHAVIOUR is unrecorded.

REPRODUCTION AND DEVELOPMENT

Breeding is believed to continue throughout the year in *C. guereza*.[22] GESTATION PERIOD: Unrecorded. Newborn of *C.* (*Colobus*) is almost wholly white at birth and is handled from the moment of birth by adult and subadult ♀♀ of the colony and occasionally also by the male[26] (see *Presbytis*).

CAPTIVITY

Black and white *Colobus* are reasonably successful in captivity but births are relatively rare. In World Zoos between 1959 and 1963, 16 infants were born.[27] LONGEVITY RECORD:[28] *C. guereza*, 24 years, San Diego Zoo.

(For References, *see* p. 131.)

PLATE 35. *Colobus guereza kikuyuensis* (San Diego Zoo)

COLOBUS Illiger, 1811   Guerezas

SUBGENUS: *Procolobus* Rochebrune, 1887   Olive Colobus

1 species: 0 subspecies[12, 39]

C. verus Van Beneden, 1838

GEOGRAPHICAL RANGE [2, 23]

West Africa. Found in high forest from Sierra Leone and S.E. French Guinea to the Dahomey Gap.

ECOLOGY

HABITAT:[2, 23] Arboreal. Inhabits the forest floor, thickets and low stratum of the canopy but may move into middle stratum to sleep and escape from predators; never ascends to upper stratum. Also found in secondary forest close to rivers. ACTIVITY RHYTHM: Diurnal. DIET:[23] Strictly vegetarian (stomach contents analysis).

MORPHOLOGY

External Characters[14, 29]

Relatively small animal with short-haired olive-grey pelage, totally lacking in adornments. Individual hairs grade from yellow to black. Underparts grey; tail similar in colour to body. Head rounded and orthognathous. Small sagittal crest of hairs on the frontal area of head (cf. *C. (Piliocolobus)*); stiff, bristle-like brow hairs radiating from supra-orbital margin. Face relatively bare, cheek tufts pale and inconspicuous. The nares, which are separated by a relatively broad septum, are slit-like and open somewhat laterally. Slender untufted tail is longer than the body. HANDS: Thumb is reduced to a tubercle. Ischial callosities separate in ♂[8] (cf. *C. (Colobus)*).

Weights and Dimensions[23]

	♂	♀	♀ in % ♂
Body weight			
average and range (g)	3800 (3300–4400)(7♂♂)	3600 (2900–4100)(5♀♀)	95
Head and body length			
average and range (mm)	458 (430–480)(8♂♂)	465 (435–490)(6♀♀)	101
Tail length			
average and range (mm)	594 (570–640)(8♂♂)	610 (570–640)(6♀♀)	103

Internal Characters[7, 10, 12, 14]

For the important craniological distinctions from and similarities with *C.* (*Colobus*) and *C.* (*Piliocolobus*), *see* Verheyen (1962). SKULL: Small jaws and relatively large braincase. Face orthognathous. Sagittal crest in lambdoid region extending well forward, feeble occipital crest. Skull shows no sexual dimorphism.[12] DENTITION: D.F.: $\frac{2}{2}\frac{1}{1}\frac{2}{2}\frac{3}{3} = 32$. Similar to *Colobus* (*Colobus*) and most catarrhines. A 6th pseudo-cusp on $M._{\overline{3}}$ is said to be common.[7, 12] Sexual dimorphism in canine size is least pronounced of all *Colobus*.[12] VISCERAL ANATOMY: Stomach as in other genera of Colobinae but fundus uniquely modified;[5] other visceral specializations have been noted by Hill (1952). LARYNX: Laryngeal air-sac absent as in all *Colobus*; larynx is small and specialized.[10] GENITO-URINARY:[10] Penis shows a degree of epithelial keratinization unique in the Colobinae; the testes are exceptionally large as are the seminal vesicles. In the ♀ there is a swollen sexual skin involving vulva, perineum and circumanal region.

BEHAVIOUR

Locomotor Behaviour

See *Colobus* (*Colobus*).

Social Behaviour*

The only recorded field study is that of A. H. Booth (1957). The following account is a summary of his findings except where stated. GROUP SIZE: Varies from 5–20 individuals, commonly consisting of 10–15. GROUP COMPOSITION: Uncertain, but groups certainly contain more than one adult male. INTRA-GROUP BEHAVIOUR: Male dominance (if present) is of low intensity. Feeding groups are compact. PLAY GROUPS are not seen. RELATIONS WITH OTHER PRIMATES: Forms mixed feeding parties with guenons; in view of diet preferences there is no competition. VOCALIZATION:[30] Voice is little used. Characteristic call is a complex one, alto in pitch, ending in a scream. Resonant calls characteristic of subgenus *Colobus* have not been heard.

REPRODUCTION AND DEVELOPMENT

Sexual swelling in the ♀ has no apparent relationship with the menstrual cycle, but Booth (1957) states that it appears to be much reduced in pregnant and lactating ♀♀. GESTATION PERIOD: Unknown. INFANT DEVELOPMENT:[10] Infant is carried in mother's mouth for several weeks after birth (? behaviour related to absent thumb of genus); later infant is transferred to mother's belly where it is self-supporting. There is some evidence for the belief that the infant's tail may be partially prehensile.[10] Colour of infant resembles that of adult [cf. *Colobus* (*Colobus*)].

CAPTIVITY

Seldom obtained alive; survive only a few days in captivity. Not recorded in European or U.S. Zoos.[27, 31]

(For References, *see* p. 131.)

COLOBUS Illiger, 1811   Guerezas

SUBGENUS: *Piliocolobus* Rochebrune, 1887   Red Colobus

2 species: 19 subspecies[12, 32, 39]

C. badius (Type species)	Red Colobus	19 subsp.
C. kirkii	Kirk's Colobus	0 subsp.

GEOGRAPHICAL RANGE [2, 7]

W., Central and E. Africa. A widely distributed tropical forest species. Races are distributed from Senegal to Uganda, except for Nigeria, S. Cameroun and Gabon; the range extends as far as the E. Coast in Tanzania and at one time included the island of Zanzibar where *C. kirkii* was found up to 1886;[33] now found on the mainland of the E. African coast.

ECOLOGY

HABITAT: Tropical rain forest, forest outliers and gallery forest. Highly arboreal form which occupies upper storey (open canopy) in Ghana;[34] occasionally descends to lower levels to feed. ACTIVITY RHYTHM: Diurnal. DIET: Leaves, also fruits of *Leguminosae*.[15]

MORPHOLOGY

External Characters

Large slender monkeys with long tails. The coat is predominantly glossy black. The black, in *C.b. badius*, extends from forehead over head, neck, shoulders, upper arms, along the back to the outer side of thighs. The remainder, including the forearms, legs and underparts, is chestnut red. The tail is dark red in its basal half, and black distally.[29, 35] In *C.b. waldroni* the forehead is dark red, also the outer side of the thighs; the tail is jet black.[29] The back is slightly speckled with red in *C.b. preussi* and the tail is red for proximal two-thirds.[35] Generally speaking there is less black in the coat among the central and eastern races in which black colour of body is replaced by brown or mahogany. The hair of the head shows neither tufts nor crests.[36] Fingers are relatively longer than in *Colobus* (*Colobus*) and the thumb tubercle apparent in *C.* (*Colobus*) and *C.* (*Procolobus*) is totally absent.[36] The hallux is shorter relatively than in *C.* (*Colobus*).[36] In the ♀ there is a moderately prominent sexual swelling between the callosities but not involving the anus; the swelling extends into the base of the tail. In the ♂ the callosities are well separated (cf. *C.* (*Colobus*)).

Weights and Dimensions[10]

	♂	♀	♀ in % ♂
Head and body length range (mm)	455–610 (34♂♂)	470–600 (23♀♀)	98
Tail length range (mm)	550–800 (34♂♂)	412–790 (23♀♀)	97

Note small degree of sexual dimorphism in body size; individual ♀♀ may be larger than some ♂♂. (♀ in % of ♂ based on midpoint of ranges).

Internal Characters

For discussion of craniological and craniometric differences between this and other subgenera, *see* Verheyen (1962). Hill (1952) discusses the differences in visceral anatomy (larynx, lungs, gastro-intestinal tract and genito-urinary system) between *C.* (*Piliocolobus*) and *C.* (*Procolobus*). The form and physiology of the stomach has been described by Kuhn (1964). SKULL: Orbits are angular with thick superciliarly ridges with distinct supraorbital groove or foramen [not present in *C.* (*Procolobus*) or *C.* (*Colobus*)]. Sagittal crest almost invariable in ♂♂.

BEHAVIOUR

Locomotor Behaviour

See *Colobus* (*Colobus*).

Social Behaviour

Although *C.* (*Piliocolobus*) is both a numerous and widespread subgenus, remarkably little is known about its behaviour in the wild or in captivity. Both Booth (1957) and Haddow (1952) have made incidental observations. Groups or individuals of Red Colobus are often found feeding with *Cercopithecus*. Solitary males are very rare (cf. *C.* (*Colobus*)). Male dominance behaviour is of low intensity.

REPRODUCTION AND DEVELOPMENT

Sexual swelling of the ♀ has no apparent relationship to the phases of the sexual cycle. INFANT: The coat colour of the newborn resembles that of the adult.[37]

CAPTIVITY

Seldom survives long in captivity. Breeding in Zoos has never been reported. LONGEVITY RECORD:[31] *Colobus* (*Piliocolobus*) *badius*, 2 years, Bronx Zoo, New York.

REFERENCES

1. Tappen, N. C. (1960)
2. Booth, A. H. (1958)
3. Rosevear, D. R. (1953b)
4. Ansell, W. F. H. (1960)
5. Booth, A. H. (1956b)
6. Lydekker, R. (1905)
7. Rode, P. (1937)
8. Pocock, R. I. (1925a)
9. Schwarz, E. (1929)
10. Allen, J. A. (1925)
11. Polak, C. (1908)
12. Verheyen, W. N. (1962)
13. Vogel, C. (1962)
14. Hill, W. C. Osman (1952)
15. Kuhn, H.-J. (1964)
16. Chiarelli, B. (1963a)
17. Buettner-Janusch, J. and Buettner-Janusch, V. (1964)
18. Chiarelli, B. (1963b)
19. Haddow, A. J. (Personal communication)
20. Goodall, J. (Personal communication)
21. Bishop, Alison (1964)
22. Haddow, A. J. (1952)
23. Booth, A. H. (1957)
24. Hall, K. R. L. (Personal communication)
25. Lumsden, W. H. R. (1951)
26. Zoonooz (1964a)
27. International Zoo Year Book, Vols. I–V (1959–1965)
28. Zoonooz (1964b)
29. Hayman, R. A. (1935)
30. Hill, W. C. Osman and Booth, A. H. (1957)
31. Jones, M. L. (1962)
32. Schwarz, E. (1938c)
33. Forbes, H. O. (1897)
34. Booth, A. H. (1954)
35. Rosevear, D. R. (1935b)
36. Pocock, R. I. (1936)
37. Dekeyser, P. L. (1955)
38. Schenkel, R. and Schenkel-Hulliger, Lotte (in press)
39. Hill, W. C. Osman (Personal communication)

CYNOPITHECUS† I. Geoffroy, 1835 Celebes Black Ape

1 species: 2 subspecies[1]

Cynopithecus niger Desmarest, 1822

GEOGRAPHICAL RANGE [2]

Northern peninsula of Celebes and some small adjacent islands including Lembeh I. off the northeastern tip; also Batjan I. in the Moluccas (probably introduced). Sea level to 6500 ft (2030 m). LIMITS OF GENUS: 2° N.–1° S.: 119°–128° E.

ECOLOGY *

HABITAT: Tropical rain forest in lowlands and mountainous country. Arboreal, occasionally descending to the ground to invade plantations and orchards.[2, 3] ACTIVITY RHYTHM: Diurnal. DIET: Fruits (very little information available).

MORPHOLOGY

External Characters[2, 4]

Medium to large monkeys with black or very dark brown fur, limbs of almost equal length and rudimentary tail (10–20 mm). Conspicuous brow ridges, depressed posteriorly; long upright crest of hair on centre of crown, sometimes projecting beyond back of head in old ♂♂, less developed in ♀♀ and young. Face is black and bare with broad flat muzzle due to longitudinal bony ridges on either side of nose which, in old ♂♂, are sometimes as prominent as the nose itself. Nostrils are directed outwards and downwards as in *Macaca*; long broad upper lip. The ischial callosities consist of 2 pairs of smooth, hard, pink pads, united by softer skin, and closely surrounded by fur; in the ♂ the pairs of pads are united on the midline ventrally* but in the ♀ they are separated. Large cheek pouches. 2 pectoral mammae.

Weights and Dimensions[2, 5, 6, 7, 24]

	♂	♀	♀ in % ♂
Weight average and range (kg)	10·43 (10–11·2) (3♂♂)	6·57 (5·1–7·7) (9♀♀)	63
Head and body length average and range (mm)	638 (520–800)(4♂♂)	545 (500–610)(4♀♀)	85
Tail length range (mm)	10–20	10–20	100

---

† *See* Taxonomic Notes, Part III, p. 373.　　PLATE 36. Celebes Black Ape, *Cynopithecus niger*, adult ♂ (San Diego Zoo)

Internal Characters

Similar to *Macaca*, and to *Macaca maurus* in particular. The few known distinguishing characters are noted here: SKULL: Strongly developed supra-maxillary ridges; these ridges, and the lateral depressions beneath them, are present even in the young of both sexes.[2] GENITALIA: Penis is long and slender, attached to the short deep glans by a narrow neck; no baculum.[8]* ISCHIAL CALLOSITIES: These are distinctive (*see* External Characters) but variations have been described by Büttikofer (1917). Swelling of the sexual skin at oestrus extends laterally and does not involve tail.[8] HANDS: Similar to *M. fascicularis* and *M. radiata*; FOOT, with long hallux, is similar to *M. nemestrina*.[8] MYOLOGY has been described, on a single specimen, by Patterson (1942). DENTITION: D.F.: $\frac{2}{2}\frac{1}{1}\frac{2}{2}\frac{3}{3}=32$. Upper canines: grooved anteriorly. Considerable sexual dimorphism in upper canine length. M.$\overline{3}$ bears 5th cusp.

Genetic Biology

CHROMOSOMES: 2n=42. Chiarelli (1962b) compares the karyotype with 11 species of *Macaca* with which he considers it to be congeneric. BLOOD GROUPS: For informaton on blood groups and serology, *see* the work of Moor-Jankowski *et al.* (1964) and Wiener *et al.* (1964, 1966); a "new" blood factor of *C. niger* red cells has been demonstrated with rabbit antisera.[15] Jolly and Barnicot (1966) found polymorphic variation of blood proteins to be notably frequent in *C. niger*. Saliva contains Lewis substance.[14] P.T.C.-TASTING:[17] 6 tasters: 1 non-taster.

BEHAVIOUR

Locomotor Behaviour*

AUTHORS' CLASSIFICATION: Quadrupedalism. LIMB PROPORTIONS: For Indices *see* Part III, p. 394. In relative proportions limbs are more similar to *Papio* than to *Macaca*.

Social Behaviour

Little information either in captivity or in the wild; it has been described as living in small "herds".[18] COMMUNICATION: Preliminary studies on an immature captive ♂ indicate that *Cynopithecus*' facial expressions are similar to though less varied than those of Macaques. Raising the eyebrows and retracting the scalp depresses the crest; and baring the teeth and gums causes transverse furrows in the skin over the maxillary ridges.[23]

REPRODUCTION AND DEVELOPMENT

MENSTRUAL CYCLE (mode): 31 days (6 observations).[19] GESTATION: About 165 days (155–175 days range; number of observations not stated).[24]

CAPTIVITY

BIRTHS IN CAPTIVITY:[20] 5 births have been recorded in World Zoos during the years 1959–63. LONGEVITY RECORD:[21] 16 years 7 months, San Diego Zoo.

PLATE 37. *Cynopithecus niger*, adult ♀ and infant (San Diego Zoo)

REFERENCES

1. Laurie, E. M. O. and Hill, J. E. (1954)
2. Büttikofer, J. (1917)
3. Wallace, A. R. (1869)
4. Forbes, H. O. (1897)
5. Zoological Society of London: Veterinary Officer's Reports
6. British Museum (Natural History) Records
7. Sody, H. J. V. (1949)
8. Pocock, R. I. (1925a)
9. James, W. Warwick (1960)
10. Chiarelli, B. (1962b)
11. Moor-Jankowski, J., Wiener, A. S. and Rogers, C. M. (1964)
12. Moor-Jankowski, J. and Wiener, A. S. (1964)
13. Wiener, A. S., Moor-Jankowski, J. and Gordon, E. B. (1964)
14. Wiener, A. S., Moor-Jankowski, J. and Gordon, E. B. (1966)
15. Moor-Jankowski, J., Wiener, A. S. and Gordon, E. B. (1965)
16. Jolly, C. J. and Barnicot, N. A. (1966)
17. Chiarelli, B. (1963b)
18. Sarasin, P. and F. (1905)
19. Spiegel, A. (1954)
20. International Zoo Year Book, Vols. I–V (1959–1965)
21. Jones, M. L. (1962)
22. Patterson, E. L. (1942)
23. Sparks, J. (Personal communication)
24. Oregon Regional Primate Research Center

DAUBENTONIA   E. Geoffroy, 1795   Aye-aye

1 species: 0 subspecies[1]

Daubentonia madagascariensis Gmelin, 1788

GEOGRAPHICAL RANGE [1, 2]

Madagascar. Probable range limited to forested parts of E. coast (Latitudes: 13° S.–21° S.) extending inland to 3250 ft (1000 m) level; also probably extends across northern forested zones to the Sambirano rain forest in Northwest. Available specimens have no definite locality.[1]

ECOLOGY [2, 3, 4]

HABITAT: Large branches and trunks of trees in rain forest; nests constructed high in trees where branch forks. ACTIVITY RHYTHM: Nocturnal. Sleeps in nests in mangoes and litchis high above ground. DIET: Preferred diet is larvae of wood-boring beetles (particularly *Oryctes*); also favoured are the larvae buried in stone of *Terminalia* fruit. Fruits eaten include mango, litchi and coconut; the pulp is clawed out of a small hole in the nut with elongated 3rd digit.

MORPHOLOGY

External Characters[3, 5]

Fur is coarse and long, predominantly dark brown to black; white basal portion of hairs shows through especially in region of face and underparts where a lighter colour prevails; hairs on neck are long and tipped with white. Tail is black or greyish, and bushy. Face is short and broad with a tapering muzzle; eyes large and forwardly facing; ears large, oval and membranous. Full complement of facial vibrissae is present. LIMBS short, legs longer than arms; tail longer than body. FEET: Hallux pseudo-opposable but very divergent and stout. Atypical claws on all digits of hands and feet except hallux which has a flat nail.[6] Middle finger of hand extremely attenuated and elongated, described as "wire-like" (*see* Hand Function). Single pair of mammae, inguinal in position.

Weights and Dimensions*[3]

Head and body length (mm)	400
Tail length (mm)	560–600

Internal Characters[3, 7]

For the detailed anatomy, reference should be made to Owen (1866) and Zuckerkandl (1900); and to Hill (1953) for a summation of anatomical characters. Some of the many aberrant characters of the Aye-aye are noted here. SKULL: Ovoid in shape, the neurocranium continuing into the face without any depression in region of glabella. Foramen magnum inferiorly

PLATE 39. *Daubentonia madagascariensis* (by courtesy of Jean Jacques Petter)

directed. Glenoid articulation wide and flat. Orbits face forwards and upwards and are circled by bone. Premaxillae unusually large and extending to meet lacrimals. Mandible has an extremely short horizontal ramus which is almost in the same axis as ascending ramus. Symphysis, fibrous allowing a small range of movement. POST-CRANIAL: Hand is very long constituting 42% of total length of upper limb; Metacarpal III twice the length of Metacarpal II and narrowing at distal end. C.N.S.: Brain aberrant and, according to Elliot-Smith (1902), shows characters intermediate between insectivores and primates, e.g. olfactory bulbs, tracts and lobes extremely prominent; true Sylvian fissure absent. SPECIAL SENSES: olfactory turbinal system is very primitive. ALIMENTARY: as in *Lemur* except that sublingua is not denticulated. DENTITION:[11] D.F.: $\frac{1}{1} \frac{0}{0} \frac{1}{0} \frac{3}{3} = 18$. Incisors are long, rodent-like and continuously growing. Enamel found only on buccal surface of upper incisors, dentine being exposed

PLATE 38. *Daubentonia madagascariensis*; above: searching: or a grub in the wood. Below: gnawing the bark with the upper incisors to expose the grub (by courtesy of Jean Jacques Petter)

posteriorly; thus, differential wear between two surfaces produces a chisel-edge. Imbedded portion of incisors reaches far backwards, beyond molar row in lower jaw and as far as M.^{2} in upper. Wide diastema between I. and P.M. PREMOLARS: P.M.^{3} is very small. MOLARS: Small and show flat wear pattern. DECIDUOUS DENTITION: D.F.: $\frac{2}{2} \frac{1}{0} \frac{0}{0} \frac{2}{2} = 18$.

BEHAVIOUR

Locomotor Behaviour[2]

AUTHORS' CLASSIFICATION: Quadrupedalism—possibly a modified vertical clinging form. *Lemur*-like in the generalized nature of quadrupedal gait but capable of climbing vertical trunks (cf. *Lepilemur* and other vertical clinging and leaping forms). On ground, walks quadrupedally with tail elevated in the sigmoid-curve fashion of *Lemur*. LIMB PROPORTIONS: For Indices, *see* Part III, p. 394.

Hand Function

Hand is prehensile. Functional axis of hand is between thumb and index finger. USE OF HAND IN FEEDING: In nature, larvae are located by olfactory and auditory signals; the bark is percussed with the 3rd digit of hand, the bore-holes are enlarged with the incisor teeth and the 3rd digit used to crush and extract grub.[13] Shaw (1883) notes that Aye-ayes do not hold food in the hand but use the hand to steady the food.

Resting Behaviour[2, 4]

Similar to that of *Lemur*. In sleep it generally rolls itself into a ball with tail wrapped over body. Sleeps in nests.

Social Behaviour

GROUP SIZE: Solitary. Only seen singly although more than one animal may be observed in the same region. HOME RANGE:[4] approximately 12 acres. VOCALIZATION: Characteristic sound is a sharp prolonged call—"cree-e-e-e", frequently repeated. Other calls noted.[2, 14, 15] SEXUAL BEHAVIOUR: unknown.

CAPTIVITY

Rarely exhibited but said to be relatively hardy in captivity with a life-span of over 3 years.[16] DIET IN CAPTIVITY:[3] Milk, honey, fruit of all kinds, birds' eggs.

REFERENCES

1. Schwarz, E. (1931c)
2. Petter, J. J. (1962c)
3. Hill, W. C. Osman (1953)
4. Petter, J. J. and Petter-Rousseaux, A. (in press)
5. Forbes, H. O. (1897)
6. Clark, W. E. Le Gros (1936)
7. Clark, W. E. Le Gros (1959)
8. Owen, R. (1866)
9. Zuckerkandl, E. (1900)
10. Elliot-Smith, G. (1902)
11. James, W. Warwick (1960)
12. Shaw, G. A. (1883)
13. Sandwith, H., quoted by Owen, R. (1866)
14. Lavauden, L. (1933)
15. Lamberton, C. (1911)
16. International Zoo Year Book, Vol. IV (1962)

DENDROGALE Gray, 1848

Smooth-tailed Treeshrews

2 species: 2 subspecies[1, 2]

Dendrogale murina (Type species)	Northern smooth-tailed treeshrew	o subsp.
Dendrogale melanura	Southern smooth-tailed treeshrew	2 subsp.

GEOGRAPHICAL RANGE [1, 2, 3]

South-East Asia. *D. murina* is found in S. Vietnam, S. E. Thailand and Cambodia; *D. melanura* in the mountains of N.E. Borneo from 3000–11,000 ft (915–3100 m). Banks (1949) reports the occurrence of *Dendrogale* in the mountains of western Sarawak. LIMITS OF GENUS: Latitudes: 15° N.–0°. Longitudes: 102°–117° E.

ECOLOGY

HABITAT: Tropical rain forest and montane forest. *D. melanura* is a mountain species and has not been found below 3000 ft (915 m) in N.E. Borneo. The type specimen was found on the top of Mt. Dulit at 5000 ft (1524 m) among moss-covered stunted jungle.[5] ACTIVITY RHYTHM: Diurnal. DIET: Insects.[6]

MORPHOLOGY

External Characters[7]

Dendrogale is about the size of a large mouse and is the smallest of the treeshrews. Fur is soft, close and velvety; the smooth, short-haired, rather short tail ends in a point. *D. murina* is greybrown with lighter underparts and a conspicuous dark streak on the face running from nose to ear, with a lighter stripe above and below; *D. melanura*, a dark grey species, has an orange mark on the cheek and around the eye. The naked part of the nose is cut squarely across as in *Tupaia glis*; the ears are slightly larger and more hairy than those of *Tupaia*. Single pair of inguinal mammae. Hands and feet are clawed.

Weights and Dimensions[3, 7]

	♂	♀	♀ in % ♂
Head and body length average and range (mm)	115 (103–130)(9♂♂)	120 (107–150)(7♀♀)	104
Tail length average and range (mm)	129 (110–145)(9♂♂)	125 (105–145)(7♀♀)	97

Internal Characters

See *Tupaia*; only differences noted here. SKULL: Fenestra in zygoma reduced to a very small foramen; braincase is less angular and temporal crests are inconspicuous.[7] For anatomy of *Dendrogale*, *see* Davis (1938).

CAPTIVITY

As far as is known, *Dendrogale* has never been exhibited in a Zoo.[8]

REFERENCES

1. Ellerman, J. R. and Morrison-Scott, T. C. S. (1951)
2. Chasen, F. N. (1940)
3. British Museum (Natural History) Records
4. Banks, E. (1949)
5. Hose, C. (1893)
6. Harrison, J. L. (1954)
7. Lyon, M. W. (1913)
8. Jones, M. L. (1962)
9. Davis, D. Dwight (1938)

ERYTHROCEBUS Trouessart, 1897 Patas monkeys

1 species: 4 subspecies[1]

E. patas patas Schreber, 1774	Patas monkey	Western race
E. patas villiersi	Aïr Red monkey	Aïr massif population
E. patas pyrronotus	Nisnas monkey	Eastern race
E. patas baumstarki	Ikoma Patas monkey	N. Tanzania

GEOGRAPHICAL RANGE [2, 3, 4, 5, 6, 7]

Sub-Saharan Africa. Patas are found from Senegal in the West to S. and W. Sudan in the East; the genus extends as far N. as Aïr (*E.p. villiersi*)[8] and further E. to the Ennedi plateau. Its southern limit in the West is the edge of the rain forest. From Sudan southwards, the eastern limit is approximately 36° E. Doubtfully reported from N. Tanzania (*E.p. baumstarki*). Common in Uganda. LATITUDINAL LIMITS: 18° N. to 2–3° S. in the East; 18° N. to 6° N. in the West, where it extends into Cameroun.

ECOLOGY

HABITAT: Ground-living. Inhabitants of woodland savanna, wooded steppes, open savanna and sometimes subdesert; generally seem to prefer flat open arid country with long grass; seldom known to penetrate into forest. Patas in Aïr Massif (*E.p. villiersi*) live in rocky country.[8] Avoid riverbanks and riverine vegetation in Uganda.[7] ACTIVITY RHYTHM: Diurnal. DIET: Grasses, fruits, beans and seeds, also insects; occasionally mushrooms, small lizards, birds' eggs, and pieces of red mud.[7] PREDATORS: Cheetah and Cape Hunting Dog.

MORPHOLOGY

External Characters[9, 10, 11]

Large animals with slender bodies, long limbs and moderately long tail. Hair is soft and silky in the young, changing in adults to a coarse and shaggy texture. Colour tones and patterns vary considerably from locality to locality,[11] but dominant colour of adults is red-brown; this colour extends from crown to neck, back, outer side of thighs and proximal tail. Underparts of body and outer forelimbs are pale. The nose is prominent being covered by a black triangular patch in young of all races; in adults, nose is grey-black in *E. patas patas* or white in *E. patas pyrronotus*. The cheek tufts are always well developed and are yellowish-black in colour. There is a dark superciliary band which broadens out as it extends towards ears. Adults of both sexes show a "military" white moustache which is black in the young of all races. Hands and feet have elongated palmar and plantar portions, short fingers and toes and a very short thumb and big toe. Ischial callosities are small and widely separated in both sexes.[10] Scrotum is bright blue.[7]

Internal Characters

Principal differences from *Cercopithecus* are in external characters and skeletal proportions. Verheyen (1962) has summarized the principal craniological differences. Craniometrically, the patas monkey can be distinguished from all other cercopitheques by the absolutely greater length of the glabella-inion parameter and the greater width of the post-orbital construction.

Weights and Dimensions[1, 6, 7, 8, 11]

	♂	♀	♀ in % ♂
Body weight range (g)	7483–12,600 (3♂♂)	4082–7100 (4♀♀)	54
Head and body length average and range (mm)	655 (575–750)(10♂♂)		—
Tail length average and range (mm)	683 (620–740)(8♂♂)		—

Marked sexual dimorphism in body size. Adult ♂ estimated to be "more than twice the size of adult ♀".[1]

Genetic Biology

CHROMOSOMES:[14, 15] 2n = 54 (5 specimens). HAEMOGLOBINS:[16] Single major band that, on starch gel electrophoresis, moves very little slower than Human A. P.T.C. TASTING:[17] 8 tasters: 5 non-tasters. BLOOD GROUPS:[25] Human blood-type A.

BEHAVIOUR

Locomotor Behaviour

AUTHORS' CLASSIFICATION: Quadrupedalism. Patas is capable of tree-climbing but is not particularly adept.[7, 18] Reputedly they are extremely fast runners, moving in a way reminiscent of cheetahs (bounding gait). Assume an "alert posture" of bipedalism when alarmed; observed to assume a bipedal gait when carrying food objects in the wild. Tail frequently used as 3rd leg or tripod when standing bipedally. LIMB PROPORTIONS: Compared with Guenons, the fore- and hindlimbs of Patas are longer relative to trunk height. In the forelimbs, greatest length increase occurs in radius and, in the hindlimbs, in the tibia.[12] For Indices, see Part III, p. 394.

Hand Function

Hand prehensile, thumb fully opposable. Precision and power grip fully differentiated.[19] In spite of short thumb (see Hand Indices in Part III), there is a high degree of opposability between thumb and index finger.[19, 20] In the wild, show finger-thumb grass plucking behaviour. Posture of hand during locomotion is digitigrade. Hand preference is not consistent.[20] Patas uses its hand to scoop up water or as a "sponge" from which the water is licked.

Resting Posture

Relaxed posture with body bent forward and feet raised; tense posture is with back straight and head raised.

Social Behaviour

The genus has been the subject of one major field study (Hall, 1966). Laboratory studies have been carried out by Hall and his colleagues.[18, 20, 21] HOME RANGE: Home range varies considerably, but may be as much as 32 sq miles (82 sq km); there are no "core areas" (cf. Papio) and little overlap between groups. DAILY RANGE: 500–1200 m.* Group is dispersed during movement but always within visual range. RESTING BEHAVIOUR: Night-resting takes place in trees at sites which vary from night to night. During night-resting animals are

---

PLATE 40. Patas or Military monkey, *Erythrocebus patas*, adult ♂ (Eric Kirkland)

widely dispersed but during day-resting they form a compact group. GROUP SIZE: Mean size: 15, range: 5–31 (9 groups). Group consists of one adult ♂, several adult ♀♀, and immatures. Lone males or all-male bands have been seen but no males peripheral to the group (cf. *Macaca mulatta*). ADULT SEX RATIO: 1♂ : 4♀♀ to 1♂ : 12♀♀. SOCIAL ORGANIZATION: One-male group. ♂ acts as vanguard and lookout, often remote from group. Enters new terrain ahead of group. ♂♂ lack intragroup and intraspecific aggressiveness owing largely to spacing of groups and of individuals within group (cf. Hamadryas baboons). ♂ being separate from group acts to divert attack from ♀♀. ♀♀ show structured status relationships and, due to dispersal of ♂♂, "lead" groups while retaining visual contact with ♂. COMMUNICATION:[18] Under naturalistic conditions, Patas are remarkably silent; only 4 out of the short repertoire of 9 vocalizations recorded in laboratory, heard in the wild; only the bark of adult ♂ is audible at long range. GROOMING:[18] Principally a ♀ activity towards other ♀♀, and linked to status structure; lip-smacking component is inconspicuous. Grooming by adult ♂ is part of sexual behaviour. SEXUAL BEHAVIOUR:[7, 18] Infrequently observed in the wild. "Soliciting" behaviour of adult ♀ seen in the wild but described in detail from captivity observations; "soliciting" differs markedly from "presenting" of baboons. Copulation behaviour of ♂ and ♀ differs from that seen in *Papio*, e.g. ♂ keeps hindlegs on ground during mounting, and ♀ does not run away from ♂ after copulation.

REPRODUCTION AND DEVELOPMENT

As in closely related cercopitheques, sexual skin is absent. ♀ shows regular 30-day cycle.[22] Discrete birth season, December to February, seems probable.[7*] GESTATION PERIOD: not known; estimated at 170 days.[22*] LABOUR: for full record, see Goswell and Gartlan (1965). INFANT DEVELOPMENT:[22] Grasp reflex present from moment of birth; infant not observed to ride on mother's back but carried ventro-ventrally. Variation in maternal and infant behaviour in 2 cases described, but considerable independence from mother by 2 weeks.

CAPTIVITY

BIRTHS IN CAPTIVITY: Between 1959–1963, 24 births were recorded in World Zoos. LONGEVITY RECORD:[24] 20 years 2 months, Philadelphia Zoo.

REFERENCES

1. Hill, W. C. Osman (1966)
2. Tappen, N. C. (1960)
3. Bigourdan, J. and Prunier, R. (1937)
4. Schouteden, H. (1947)
5. Allen, G. M. (1939)
6. Jeannin, A. (1936)
7. Hall, K. R. L. (1966)
8. Dekeyser, P. L. (1950)
9. Rode, P. (1937)
10. Pocock, R. I. (1925a)
11. Allen, J. A. (1925)
12. Jolly, C. J. (1964)
13. Verheyen, W. N. (1962)
14. Chu, E. H. Y. and Giles, N. H. (1957)
15. Bender, M. A. and Chu, E. H. Y. (1963)
16. Buettner-Janusch, J. and Buettner-Janusch, V. (1964)
17. Chiarelli, B. (1963b)
18. Hall, K. R. L., Boelkins, R. C. and Goswell, M. J. (1965)
19. Bishop, Alison (1964)
20. Hall, K. R. L. and Mayer, B. (1966)
21. Hall, K. R. L. and Goswell, Marilyn J. (in press)
22. Goswell, Marilyn J. and Gartlan, J. S. (1965)
23. International Zoo Year Book, Vols. I–V (1959–1965)
24. Jones, M. L. (1962)
25. Wiener, A. S., Moor-Jankowki, J., and Gordon, E. B. (1966).

PLATE 41. *Erythrocebus patas*, juvenile in bipedal stance, using tail to form tripod (by courtesy of Bernard W. Kenicki)

F

GALAGO†   E. Geoffroy, 1796   Galagos

3 subgenera: 6 species: 28 subspecies

SUBGENUS: *Galago*   Typical Galagos

3 species: 19 subspecies[1, 2, 3]

G. senegalensis (Type species)	Bushbabies	9 subsp.
G. crassicaudatus	Thick-tailed Galago	10 subsp.
C. alleni	Allen's Galago	0 subsp.

GEOGRAPHICAL RANGE [2, 3, 4, 5, 6, 7, 8]

Africa. Galagos are found over most of the forested and woodland savannah areas of Africa between Latitudes 13° N. and 27° S. *G. crassicaudatus*: Angola and south central Africa down E. coast from equator to Natal. *G. senegalensis*: Senegal, Guinea coast, throughout the Guinea savannah and Sudan savannah zones in W. Africa, sub-Saharan savannahs N. of the R. Congo, Ethiopia, eastern uplands of Uganda, Kenya, Tanzania, Zambia[4] and S. Angola. South central savannahs as far as Orange R. in S.W., and Limpopo R. in S.E. *G. alleni*: Tropical forests of Cameroun and Gabon as far N. as the Cross R.[5] and as far E. as the Congo-Ubangi; also found in Fernando Póo I. (Type locality).[3]

ECOLOGY

HABITAT: Tropical rain forest and secondary forest (*G. alleni*); open and mixed forest and woodland savannah (*G. crassicaudatus* and *G. senegalensis*). All species are arboreal; *G. senegalensis* in S.W. Africa builds well-concealed nests and may also nest in hollow trees.[9] ACTIVITY RHYTHM: Nocturnal. DIET: Insectivorous but relish *Acacia* gum; in captivity eat small mammals, fruit, cereals and vegetables.[9] "More or less omnivorous."[4]

MORPHOLOGY

External Characters[2, 3, 10, 11]

Subgenus contains medium sized (*G. crassicaudatus*) and small sized (*G. alleni, G. senegalensis*) species. Fur is soft and woolly and the colour varies from grey through brown to russet. Rusty tinge of outerside of limbs, characteristic of *G. crassicaudatus* and *G. alleni*, is lacking in *G. senegalensis*. Flashes, stripes, etc. are generally absent, but in *G. senegalensis* there is a distinct light-coloured interocular stripe extending down nose. Underparts are yellowish white or greyish (*G. alleni*).[11] Dark circumocular patches are present in the two smaller species. Melanistic forms common in *G.c.argentatus*.

    The muzzle is long and robust in *G. crassicaudatus* but short in other species; ears are large, naked, membranous and mobile. Tail is long in all species; it is thick and bushy in *G. crassicaudatus* and *G. alleni*, but more thinly haired in *G. senegalensis*.[11] Hands and feet are pentadactyl, the digits bear nails except for a toilet claw on the 2nd pedal digit; hands bear 6 well-defined palmar pads.[12] Hindlimbs are very long relative to forelimbs. Foot is elongated in its posterior tarsal segment. MAMMAE: Variable; 2 or 3 pairs.[39, 33]

---

† *See* Taxonomic Notes, Part III, p. 373.

Weights and Dimensions

	♂	♀	♀ in % ♂
Average body weight[13] (g)			
G. crassicaudatus panganiensis	1241 (10♂♂)	1034 (13♀♀)	83
G. senegalensis braccatus	300 (10♂♂)	229 (9♀♀)	76
Head and body length			
average and range[40] (mm)			
G. crassicaudatus	335 (319–373)(4♂♂)	315 (297–336)(4♀♀)	94
G. senegalensis	164 (151–173)(10♂♂)	158 (150–163)(10♀♀)	96
Tail length			
average and range[40] (mm)			
G. crassicaudatus	458 (439–473)(4♂♂)	421 (415–426)(4♀♀)	92
G. senegalensis	236 (217–250)(10♂♂)	229 (205–248)(10♀♀)	97

Dimensions of *G. alleni* are similar to those of *G. senegalensis*.[8]

Internal Characters

For more detailed account of anatomy, *see* Murie and Mivart (1872), Hill (1953), Clark (1959), Nayak (1933); for detailed anatomy of hindlimb musculature and biomechanics, see Hall-Craggs (1965a and b). SKULL: Neurocranium globular, sagittal crest present in *G. crassicaudatus*. Facial region shows moderate prognathism. Orbits large with thin post-orbital bar but no posterior closure; orbits directed somewhat laterally and only slightly upwards; ethmoid forms large part of medial wall of orbit (cf. lemurs); on the base, mastoid region and auditory bulla inflated; foramen magnum well forward. Tympanic ring forms lateral wall of auditory bulla. Body of mandible is slender with blunt angular process and long sharply pointed coronoid. POST-CRANIAL SKELETON; VERTEBRAL COLUMN: C.7, T.13, L.6, S.3, C.23. Axis vert. bears short spinous process but spines are absent from other cervicals. UPPER LIMB: Humerus is short and bowed with large supinator flange and entepicondylar foramen; ulna has long olecranon and head articulates with carpus. Os centrale present between capitate and lunate; hamate very large. LOWER LIMB: Femur has a 3rd trochanter; head is cylindrical with large fovea. In the tarsus, navicular and calcaneum are strikingly elongated. MYOLOGY: Gluteus maximus and quadratus femoris are both well developed, comprising 11% (approx.) of total body weight (cf. *Perodicticus* 1·8% approx.).[17] DENTITION: D.F.: $\frac{2}{2}\frac{1}{1}\frac{3}{3}\frac{3}{3}=36$. INCISORS: In upper jaw they are peglike, subequal in size; in lower jaw, they are very compressed and form dental comb with canine. PREMOLARS: Upper anterior premolar is not caniniform, posterior premolars are molariform; in lower jaw anterior two premolars are procumbent and caniniform. MOLARS: Upper molars are tritubercular with a prominent hypocone except M.$\frac{3}{}$ which is small. Lower molars are quadricuspid; M.$\frac{}{3}$ bears a hypoconulid. ALIMENTARY TRACT: Well-developed sublingua with serrated upper surface. Stomach is simple and globular in shape; caecum is sacculated in *G. senegalensis* and *G. alleni* and the colon is in the form of a double loop. GENITO-URINARY: Vagina believed to be imperforate except during breeding and birth season.[18] Clitoris tunnelled by urethra. Penis contains a baculum; glans covered in small spines which vary interspecifically. VASCULAR: Retia mirabilia absent (cf. *Loris*). VISUAL SYSTEM: Pure rod retina and no true macula.[19]

Genetic Biology

CHROMOSOMES:[20, 21] *G. crassicaudatus*: 2n = 62, *G. senegalensis*: 2n = 38. Marked difference in karyotype between these two species. HAEMOGLOBINS:[22] Electrophoretograms show two major components of equal mobility in *G. crassicaudatus* and *G. senegalensis*; an extra component occurs in the former species. SERUM PROTEINS: (*G. crassicaudatus*): *See* Williams (1964). P.T.C. TASTING:[24*] *G. crassicaudatus* shows polymorphism; *G. senegalensis* shows 100% tasters.

BEHAVIOUR

Locomotor Behaviour

AUTHORS' CLASSIFICATION: Vertical clinging and leaping. Movement in trees is principally by means of leaping; highest measured leap in *G. senegalensis* has been recorded at 7 ft 4¾ in (2·3 m).[17] *G. alleni* reputed to be a prodigious leaper in natural habitat.[25*] On the ground when moving slowly, galagos are quadrupedal but, under pressure, resort to saltatory bipedalism.[26] LIMB PROPORTIONS: Hindlimbs considerably longer than forelimbs, forearms longer than upper arms and femur longer than tibia. *See* Part III, p. 394, for Indices.

Hand Function

Hand prehensile, thumb pseudo-opposable. Palmar pads prominent. Skin between pads is granular in *G. crassicaudatus* but smooth in *G. senegalensis*.[12] Index finger function is uncommitted and variable.[9] During locomotion, digits are hyperextended at metacarpo-phalangeal joints and acutely flexed at proximal interphalangeal joints, the digital pads being pressed squarely to the surface.[9, 27, 28] Prehensive pattern is stereotyped;[27] contact with object is first made with palmar pads, the spread digits then fold at distal two joints and clasp object between proximal phalanges and palmar pads. *G. senegalensis* uses the hand in this way when grabbing at an insect.[27] Hand is also used in grooming, feeding, sparring, and olfactory marking. Fingers are flexed over thumb when hand is inactive. HAND PROPORTIONS: Hand is relatively long, phalanges are very elongated relative to metacarpals. *See* Part III, p. 401, for Indices.

Resting Posture

Extremely varied when sleeping, see Sauer and Sauer (1963). Trunk held vertically when awake.

Social Behaviour

The solitary field-study of any degree of comprehensiveness is of *G. senegalensis* by Sauer and Sauer (1963); the following summary derives from this study unless otherwise stated. MARKING BEHAVIOUR: Urine "marking" in which hand or foot is moistened·with urine has been noted in the wild and captivity in both *G. crassicaudatus* and *G. senegalensis*;[2, 29, 30] some interspecific variation in this behaviour has been noted.[31] It is performed by both sexes, and is assumed to have a territorial function.[9, 30] GROUP SIZE: Sleeping groups in one nest vary in number according to season and may be quite large, i.e. 7–9. Mothers with infants may nest separately. Several families can be maintained in captivity given adequate space. INTRA-GROUP BEHAVIOUR: Galagos are quite sociable animals. Male dominance behaviour exerted during nocturnal activity period but does not operate (in terms of spacing) during sleeping periods in the nest. Mutual grooming occurs between sleeping groups.[9, 30]

PLATE 42. *Galago* (*Galago*) *senegalensis* (by courtesy of H. Butler)

Aggressive behaviour, including fighting, between males apparent; non-dominance gestures include depression of tail. Aggressive posture is bipedal with mouth open (grin face) and hands held in front of body, and is accompanied by a hissing vocalization. PLAY: Conspicuous in infants and juveniles from 5 weeks of age. SEXUAL BEHAVIOUR: Courtship initiated by ♀. Pre-copulatory behaviour involves mutual grooming, ano-genital tongue and nose contacts, interspersed with chases.

REPRODUCTION AND DEVELOPMENT

G. crassicaudatus: In Zambia birth season is August–September.[4] In northern hemisphere (University of Yale, U.S.A.) births occurred March–October.[32] *G. senegalensis*: Butler (1967) in the Sudan concluded that there were restricted breeding seasons, oestrus occurring in December and August, with births in April and December. In London (Zuckerman, 1953) births were reported in April, May and October; recent observations in London indicate regular recurring oestrous cycles of 19–39 days (average: 31·7 days).[35] *See also* Lowther (1940) and Petter-Rousseaux (1962) for lengths of cycle. GESTATION PERIOD: *G. crassicaudatus*: 130 and 135 days (Buettner-Janusch, 1964). *G. senegalensis*: 120 days (Lowther, 1940); 144–146 days (4 observations) (Manley, 1966a). NO. OF YOUNG: Twinning occurs in *G. crassicaudatus*[4] but is apparently uncommon in *G. senegalensis*.[33, 35] Triplets recorded in *G. crassicaudatus*.[32] *See also* Schultz (1948). BIRTH WEIGHT:[50] *G. crassicaudatus* 41 g, *G. senegalensis* 12 g. INFANT DEVELOPMENT:[9] Infant *G. senegalensis* carried by mother during locomotion; infant gripped by mother's canines at "scruff" of neck; infant adopts relaxed "carrying posture". At rest in cage, infant *G. crassicaudatus* clings to fur of mother's belly. Mother may grip skin of belly or neck of infant with hands in protective reflex.[32] BEHAVIOURAL DEVELOPMENT (*G. senegalensis*) IN CAPTIVITY:[9] 2 weeks: some independent activity. $3\frac{1}{2}$–4 weeks: leaping commences. 4 weeks: weaning begins. 5 weeks: individual play commences. 7 weeks: complete independence. 52 weeks: sexual behaviour patterns shown. Sexual maturity in ♀ at approx. 52 weeks. (*See also* Lowther, 1940; Buettner-Janusch, 1964).

CAPTIVITY

Births in captivity are quite common for the two better-known species. Between 1959–63, the following live births have been reported in World Zoos:[37] *G. senegalensis* 25, *G. crassicaudatus* 11, *G. alleni* 2. LONGEVITY RECORDS:[38] *G.s. moholi*, 10 years 5 months, London, Zoological Society; *G.s. senegalensis*, 3 years 3 months, London, Zoological Society; *G. alleni*, 5 years 2 months, London, Zoological Society; *G. crassicaudatus*, 14 years, Bronx Zoo, New York.

(For References, *see* p. 159)

PLATE 43. *Galago (Galago) crassicaudatus*, showing stereotyped prehensive pattern

GALAGO[†]   E. Geoffroy, 1796   Galagos

SUBGENUS: *Euoticus* Gray, 1863.   Needle-nailed Galagos

2 species: 2 subspecies[2]

Galago elegantulus (Type species)   2 subsp.
Galago inustus[†]   0 subsp.

GEOGRAPHICAL RANGE [2, 5]

Africa. *G. elegantulus*: Western rain forest between the Congo and Cross rivers. Fernando Póo. Hill (1953) extends the range to the Niger R., following Schwarz (1931). *G. inustus*: Lake Albert to the headwaters of Kagera R.

ECOLOGY *

HABITAT: Tropical rain forest. Found high in large trees in coffee plantations in Rio Muni.[41]
ACTIVITY RHYTHM: Nocturnal. DIET: Insects.[41]

MORPHOLOGY

External Characters[3, 41]

Small animals approximately the same size as *G. senegalensis*. Fur is dense and woolly and of a reddish brown (*G.e.elegantulus*) to pale cinnamon colour (*G.e.pallidus*) on the back where there is a dark dorsal median stripe. Underparts are pale grey. Tail is long and bushy, grey in colour with a white tip (*G.e.elegantulus*); other subspecies lacks white tip to tail. Ears are smaller than in *G. (Galago)*, oval in shape and membranous. Nails are specialized and bear a central keel ending in a sharp point (*G. elegantulus*); in *G. inustus*, the keel and sharp-pointed nail is present, but less strongly marked than in *G. elegantulus*.[43] Needle-nails are present on all digits except thumb and big toe; second pedal digit bears toilet claw as in *Galago (Galago)*. DIGITAL FORMULA: 4.3.5.2.1. Fingertip pads are club-shaped; palmar pads are 6 in number and fill the palm. Hindlimbs are longer than forelimbs.

Weights and Dimensions

Head and body length range (mm)	215–235 (No. and sex not stated)[2]	187 (1♂)[44]
Tail length range (mm)	280–320 (No. and sex not stated)[2]	332 (1♂)[44]

[†] *See* Taxonomic Notes, Part III, p. 373.

PLATE 44. *Galago (Euoticus) elegantulus*: above left: male (Zoological Society of London); above right: needle-nail on 3rd digit of hand × 12·5; below, palmar and dorsal surfaces of hand

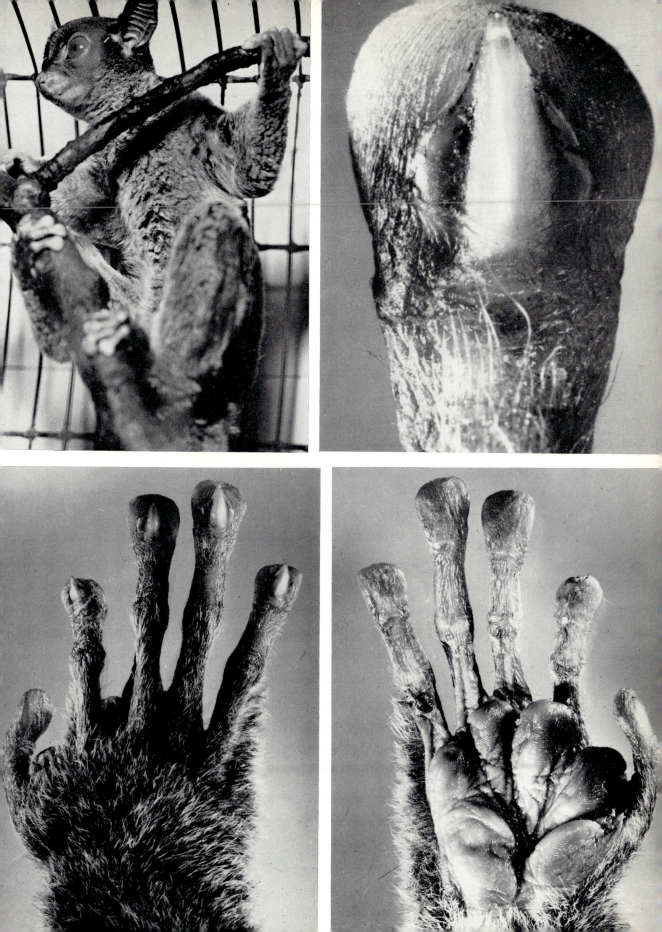

Internal Characters

See *Galago*. Principal differences only noted here. SKULL: Tympanic and mastoid bullae markedly inflated. DENTITION: $\frac{2}{2}\frac{1}{1}\frac{3}{3}\frac{3}{3}=36$. Anterior upper premolar strongly caniniform. ALIMENTARY TRACT: Caecum is long and shows much folding; colon possesses an ansa, is sacculated and is provided with taeniae.

BEHAVIOUR

Locomotor Behaviour

See *Galago*. Downward leaps of up to 150 ft (45 m) reported.[25] Hops bipedally on the ground.[25] LIMB PROPORTIONS: *See* Part III, p. 394, for Indices.

Hand Function

See *Galago* (*Galago*).

Social Behaviour

Not known.

CAPTIVITY

Said to be somewhat aggressive.[42] Specimens have been exhibited in Berlin (1900), Antwerp (1947)[38] and London for a brief period in 1966.

(For References, *see* p. 159)

GALAGO[†] E. Geoffroy 1796, Galagos

SUBGENUS: *Galagoides* A. Smith, 1833 Dwarf Galagos

1 species: 7 subspecies[2]

Galago demidovii Fischer, 1806 Demidoff's Dwarf Galago 7 subsp.

GEOGRAPHICAL RANGE

Africa. Distributed throughout tropical forests of Fernando Póo, the Guinea Coast as far south as the Congo R. and eastwards within the rain forest belt to the Rift Valley.

ECOLOGY

HABITAT:[45, 46] Arboreal; tropical deciduous forest of W. Africa and rain forest of the Congo where it lives in low tangled bush seldom more than 30 ft (9 m) above ground;[6] not found in gallery forest or forest outliers. Nest building noted.[51] ACTIVITY RHYTHM: Nocturnal, but *see* Sanderson (1940) who propounded reasons for regarding the dwarf galago as diurnal in Cameroun. DIET:[45, 46*] Insectivorous in wild state (from stomach contents analysis). Omnivorous in captivity.[46, 47]

MORPHOLOGY

External Characters

The smallest of the Galaginae. Coat colour is extremely variable, predominantly brown to yellowish brown on the back and the underparts yellowish. One race (*G.d. murinus*) is described as having brilliant green back and limbs and saffron-yellow underparts, colours which fade a few hours after death.[6] Eyes are large and forwardly facing and, between them, running down the nose, is a pale streak. Ears are membranous, oval in shape and relatively smaller than in the typical galago.

Weights and Dimensions[8, 48*]

Head and body length range (mm)	125–160
Tail length range (mm)	182–199

Internal Characters

See *G.* (*Galago*). Only principal differences are noted here. SKULL: Premaxillaries long, forming a projecting keel of bone above incisors. POST-CRANIAL SKELETON: Rudimentary spinous processes on cervicals. No true anticlinal vertebrae. DENTITION: $\frac{2}{2}\frac{1}{1}\frac{3}{3}\frac{3}{3}=36$. Canine of upper jaw rather prominent. Anterior upper premolar is not caniniform [cf. *G.* (*Euoticus*)]. ALIMENTARY TRACT: Caecum incipiently sacculated; colon non-sacculated.

[†] *See* Taxonomic Notes, Part III, p. 373.

PLATE 45. *Galago (Galagoides) demidovii*, ♂ (by courtesy of Alan C. Walker)

BEHAVIOUR

Locomotor Behaviour

AUTHORS' CLASSIFICATION: Vertical clinging and leaping. Locomotor behaviour is similar to *G. (Galago)*. Dwarf galagos are capable of a horizontal standing jump of 6 ft (1·8 m).[46] Reputed to be extremely swift and active animals; sometimes run quadrupedally when in trees.[6]

Hand Function

Single prehensive action of the hand as described for *G. (Galago)*.[46]

Social Behaviour

Dwarf galagos are not often seen in their natural habitat, but *see* Sanderson (1940) and Durrell (1954). MARKING BEHAVIOUR: Foot and hand washing as in *G. (Galago)* has been observed.[46] VOCALIZATION has been described by Cansdale (1944). In captivity, they are social animals.[30]

REPRODUCTION AND DEVELOPMENT

Little available information on breeding cycle. Gravid ♀♀ have been captured in December and July in Cameroun[6] and in October and April in Ghana.[46] Infants are able to hold food in the hands at 2 weeks and weaning begins at 5 weeks.[46*] Mother carries infant in her mouth, gripping it at the point of balance; she is able to jump 2–3 ft when so encumbered.

CAPTIVITY

There are no records of births in World Zoos between 1959–63.[37] LONGEVITY RECORD[38] (up to 1962): 2 years 10 months, National Zoological Park, Washington.

REFERENCES

1. Ellerman, J. R., Morrison-Scott, T. C. S. and Hayman, R. W. (1953)
2. Hill, W. C. Osman (1953)
3. Schwarz, E. (1931a)
4. Ansell, W. F. H. (1960)
5. Booth, A. H. (1958)
6. Sanderson, I. T. (1940)
7. Malbrant, R. and Maclatchy, A. (1949)
8. Rode, P. (1937)
9. Sauer, E. G. F. and Sauer, Eleonore M. (1963)
10. Forbes, H. O. (1897)
11. Rosevear, D. R. (1935a)
12. Biegert, J. (1961)
13. Manley, G. H. (1966b)
14. Murie, J. and Mivart, St. G. (1872)
15. Clark, W. E. Le Gros (1959)
16. Nayak, U. V. (1933)
17. Hall-Craggs, E. C. B. (1965a and b)
18. Cooper, R. W. (Personal communication)
19. Polyak, S. (1957)
20. Chu, E. H. Y. and Bender, M. A. (1962)
21. Bender, M. A. and Chu, E. H. Y. (1963)
22. Buettner-Janusch, J. and Buettner-Janusch, V. (1963)
23. Williams, C. A. (1964)
24. Chiarelli, B. (1963b)
25. Sanderson, I. T. (1937)
26. Napier, J. R. and Walker, A. C. (1967)
27. Bishop, A. (1964)
28. Lowther, F. de L. (1939, 1940)
29. Boulenger, E. G. (1936)
30. Andrew, R. J. (1964)
31. Eibl-Eibesfeldt, I. (1953)
32. Buettner-Janusch, J. (1964)
33. Butler, H. (1967)
34. Zuckerman, S. (1953)
35. Manley, G. H. (1966a)
36. Petter-Rousseaux, A. (1962)
37. International Zoo Year Book, Vols. I–V (1959–1965)
38. Jones, M. L. (1962)
39. Schultz, A. H. (1948)
40. Hill, J. E. and Carter, T. D. (1941)
41. Oates, J. (1966)
42. Sanderson, I. T. (1957)
43. Hayman, R. W. (1937)
44. Authors' measurements
45. Booth, A. H. (1956b)
46. Cansdale, G. S. (1944)
47. Crandall, L. S. (1964)
48. Cabrera, A. and Ruxton, A. E. (1926)
49. Durrell, G. (1954)
50. Evans, C. S. (Personal communication).
51. Walker, A. C. (In press)

GORILLA†   I. Geoffroy, 1852   Gorillas

1 species: 3 subspecies[1, 2]

Gorilla gorilla gorilla (Savage and Wyman, 1847)   Western Lowland Gorilla
Gorilla gorilla beringei   Eastern Highland Gorilla
Gorilla gorilla manyema   Eastern Lowland Gorilla

GEOGRAPHICAL RANGE [2, 3, 4]

Equatorial Africa: a discontinuous distribution. The western gorilla range extends from the extreme S.E. of Nigeria (Cross River district) through Cameroun, Spanish Guinea,[48] Gabon, Congo (Brazzaville) and the Central African Republic, south to the mouth of the R. Congo and east to the valley of its tributary, the R. Sangha.

    The eastern gorilla is widely scattered in isolated population units over an area of 35,000 sq miles: *G.g. manyema* from the lowlands east of the Upper Congo (Lualaba) R. to the mountains west of L. Edward and west of the northern tip of L. Tanganyika; *G.g. beringei* in the Virunga Volcanoes and Mt. Kahuzi district, the high mountains to the north and east of L. Kivu. There are also gorillas in the Kayonza forest of S.W. Uganda: these probably belong to *G.g. manyema*. *Latitudinal range*: 0°–4° 20′ S. (eastern), 6° N.–5° 30′ S. (western). *Longitudinal range*: 26° 30′ E.–29° 45′ E. (eastern), 9° 30′ E.–17° 60′ E. (western).

ECOLOGY

HABITAT:[3, 5] Lowland rain forest and montane rain forest up to 8000 ft (2438 m), also bamboo forest up to 10,000 ft (3048 m). In the Virunga Volcanoes area gorillas are found in *Hagenia* woodland where trees are low and there is a dense herbaceous understorey, and also on the open slopes above, up to an altitude of 13,500 ft (4115 m). Gorillas have been seen 50 m below summit of Mt. Muhavura (4127 m).[6] Life is largely (90%) spent on the ground during the day;[6,7] brief forays into trees by both sexes but principally by ♀♀ and juveniles. DIET:[3, 5, 6, 7] wholly vegetarian. Lowland gorillas are said to eat some fruit[8*] but highland gorillas apparently eat little. Principal items of diet of highland gorillas are bulk foods and include pith, stalks, vines, bark, leaves, bamboo shoots and roots. Donisthorpe (1958), Schaller (1963, 1965) and Kawai and Mizuhara (1959) supply lists of food items. Lowland gorillas raid native plantations of bananas and sugar cane.[8*] ACTIVITY RHYTHM: Diurnal. PREDATORS: Leopards,* Man. Merfield (1956) and Donisthorpe (1958) report fear of dogs.

MORPHOLOGY

External Characters

Mature ♂♂ commonly reach 6 ft in bipedal standing height, weigh 300–400 lb and have an arm span of well over 8 ft. Mature ♀♀ are approximately half the weight of the males.

    The face is bare and jetblack in colour, the nostrils are flared and surrounded by prominent alar folds; the appearance of the nose has been likened to a "squashed tomato". The eyes are wide-set and deeply sunk under prominent supra-orbital ridges; the ears are small and set flat against the head. The head is conically elongated in adult ♂♂ due to the prominent nuchal and sagittal crests surmounting the skull. The arms are long (particularly in the lowland forms)

---

† *See* Taxonomic Notes, p. 373.

and the hands broad. The thumb is relatively shorter than man's and is less well muscled. The legs are short and outwardly rotated at the hip; the foot is plantigrade and the heel long. In the western gorilla the big toe is stout, short and well abducted; in the eastern highland form it is proportionately somewhat longer and is less abducted;[9] the remaining toes are syndactylous, markedly so in the eastern gorilla.

Coat and skin colour in all races is black or blackish. The western form may show a brownish or russet colouration to the crown of the head;[10] the eastern form is usually jet-black all over with occasional white streak between ears. Mature males of all three races show a saddle of white or silvery hair across the lumbar region, most pronounced in Eastern race (*G.g. beringei*). Adults of *G.g. beringei* may have only a grey spinal stripe[7] (? young ♂♂). Hair of coat is short, dense, bristly and coarse in lowland gorilla but longer and thicker, especially on the arms and forearms, in the eastern highland form. The face and upper part of the chest are bare. Western gorilla has a distinct "lip" to the nose overhanging the septum, which is absent in the Eastern races. (*See* Plates 46, 47.)

Weights and Dimensions

BODY WEIGHT RANGE: In the wild: ♂ 140–180 kg (300–400 lb); ♀ 75–110 kg (165–240 lb). In captivity, body weight may be as much as 636 lb for a ♂ eastern gorilla ("Ngagi", San Diego Zoo) and 578 lb for a ♂ western gorilla ("Bobby", Berlin Zoo).[11] "Guy", a western form, living in the London Zoo, at present weighs over 450 lb. Heaviest ♀ weight: "Oka" of Bronx Zoo weighed 280 lb when 13 years old.

External Measurements ♂ Gorilla[2]

Race	Weight	Height	Girth	Arm-span	Arm Length	Leg Length	Foot Length
G.g. gorilla	307·3(6)	168·5(25)	143 (19)	233·7(17)	111·6(8)	76·8(8)	28·8(9)
G.g. manyema	360·3(2)	175 (4)	152·3(3)	259·5(2)	114·0(2)	79·0(2)	32·5(1)
G.g. beringei	342·9(13)	172·5(6)	146·7(13)	227·5(10)	106·0(4)	76·3(3)	29·7(11)

Linear measurements in centimetres; weight in pounds.

Internal Characters

For detailed anatomical studies *see* Keith (1896), Duckworth (1915), Sonntag (1924), Schultz (1927), Raven (1950), Steiner (1954). For structural differences between *G.g. gorilla* and *G.g. beringei*, *see* Schultz (1934). The following characters are selected principally on the basis of their known functional importance or for their value for identification. SKULL: Neuro-cranium, facial skeleton large. Cranial capacity 340–685 cc in adult ♂;[12] largest cranial capacity recorded 752 cc.[13] Calvarium surmounted by large bony flanges; in nearly all adult ♂♂ there is a sagittal crest and, in all, a nuchal crest is present. ♀♀ show some cresting in 30%. Mastoid process is very variable in size; sometimes large and sometimes absent; this process continues to grow throughout adult life.[14] Face is markedly prognathic; orbits are rectangular and widely separated by fused nasal bones which are pinched up to form a sharp median crest; supra-orbital ridge strongly developed and deeply excavated by frontal air sinus.[13] Hard

palate is very long and extends well beyond 3rd molar, particularly in *G.g. beringei*.[1] Mandible is very stout and lacks a "chin"; the R and L halves of the mandible are braced by a shelf of bone, so-called "simian" shelf. VERTEBRAL COLUMN: 3rd to 7th cervical spines long, very stout and non-bifid; Thoracic vertebrae: 13, Lumbar vertebrae: 3–4 (commonly 17 thoraco-lumbar vertebrae in lowland form and 16 in highland form).[15] Sacral vertebrae: 5–6. STERNUM: broad but elements remain separate (cf. *Pan*). SCAPULA: Sinuous vertebral border in *G.g. beringei*—straight border in other two races. HAND: os centrale fused with scaphoid. Phalanges stout, heavily buttressed and only slightly curved. Skin on back of middle phalanges is typically modified to form knuckle pads.[16, 17] FOOT: tarsus length and heel length are greater than in any primate except man.[18] DENTITION: D.F. $=\frac{2}{2}\frac{1}{1}\frac{2}{2}\frac{3}{3}=32$. Dental characters are very like *Pan*: in *Gorilla* however the molar cusps are sharply defined and "crystalline" in appearance and the lower molar series increases in size from $M_{\overline{1}}$ to $M_{\overline{3}}$; in upper jaw $M^{\underline{3}}$ is often slightly smaller than $M^{\underline{2}}$. Supernumerary molars occasionally present (4%) but supernumerary premolars very rare (*see* Schultz, 1964). ALIMENTARY SYSTEM:[19, 20, 21] caecum and colon very large. Appendix present. Liver lobes variable in number, up to 6 lobes reported. VASCULAR SYSTEM: coronary vessels (*see* Hall-Craggs, 1961). THORACIC VISCERA (*see* Washburn, 1950). GENITO-URINARY SYSTEM (*see* Steiner, 1954 and Koch, 1937). LARYNX: laryngeal air-sacs present.

Genetic Biology

CHROMOSOMES:[24] *G. g. gorilla* 2n=48 (1♂, 2♀). IMMUNO-CHEMISTRY: See the studies of Goodman (1962, 1963a and b, 1964), Williams *et al.* (1961) and Williams (1964). Serum precipitin data demonstrates close phyletic affinity of *Gorilla*, *Pan* and *Homo*. HAEMOGLOBINS: Human and gorilla Hbs differ insignificantly in amino-acid composition. P.T.C. TASTING:[31] tasters: non-tasters as 14: 4. BLOOD GROUPS: *Gorilla* shows ABO polymorphism, although "O" phenotype is lacking (Franks, 1963). *See also* Wiener *et al.* (1966).

BEHAVIOUR

Locomotor Behaviour

AUTHORS' CLASSIFICATION: Brachiation. Subtype: Modified Brachiation. When on the ground the gait is quadrupedal, the weight of the body being taken on the plantigrade feet and the backs of the middle phalanges of the fingers. Bipedal locomotion rare in the wild.[3] Erect standing occurs during chest-beating display. True brachiation (*see* Part III, p. 388) never seen in adults or juveniles. Tree-climbing more common in infants and ♀♀ than in ♂♂ and is particularly common in Kayonza gorillas according to Pitman (1935) where night-nests are built high in trees. LIMB PROPORTIONS: For Indices, *see* Part III, p. 394.

Hand Function

Hand prehensile, thumb opposable. Hands are used extensively in plucking and manipulating food objects and in nest-building. No evidence of tool-using or tool-making.[3, 7] Thumb plays a relatively larger role in manipulation than in chimpanzees but less than in man. HAND PROPORTIONS: *see* Part III, p. 401.

PLATE 46. Western Gorilla, *Gorilla gorilla gorilla*, adult ♂ aged 15 years (by courtesy of Duane M. Rumbaugh and San Diego Zoo)

Resting Posture

Gorillas make ground- or tree-nests of simple construction; nests are never used two nights consecutively. Siting of nests is clearly related to habitat;[3, 7, 33] in *Hagenia* woodland 97% nests are on ground; in eastern lowland rain forest only 22% are on the ground, these being nests of silverback males. Day-nesting[5] apparently more common among eastern than western gorillas.[33, 34] Eastern gorillas invariably foul their nests during the night.

Social Behaviour

A number of field studies of Eastern highland gorillas have been carried out since 1921, notably by Akeley (1922), Coolidge (1929), Bingham (1932), Pitman (1935), Donisthorpe (1958), Kawai and Mizuhara (1959), Emlen and Schaller (1960), Osborn (1963), and Schaller (1963, 1965). Western gorillas have not been extensively studied. For captivity studies, *see* principally Yerkes and Yerkes (1929).

The following account is derived principally from the field work of Schaller (1963, 1965) and relates to *G.g. beringei* unless otherwise stated. GROUP STRUCTURE: Eastern gorillas live in groups consisting of between 5 and 30 members; average size of groups varies from region to region. Groups are cohesive and relatively stable. Change in group composition limited to birth of infants, and comings and goings of individual adult males. GROUP COMPOSITION: Adult sex ratio: 1♂ : 2♀♀. Each group contains at least one silverback ♂, one or more black-back ♂♂, several ♀♀, juveniles and infants. This composition holds true also for western gorillas.[8] Lone ♂♂, usually young adults, are quite common, briefly attaching themselves to existing groups [*see also* Merfield and Miller (1956); Kawai and Mizuhara (1959)].

Intra-group Behaviour

Generally peaceful. DOMINANCE: Group activity determined by dominant ♂ who acts as leader and protector; there is little overt dominance activity. Among subordinate ♂♂ there is some evidence of a linear hierarchy; among ♀♀, hierarchy may relate to infant-carrying; among juveniles, it appears to be based on size. GROOMING: Infrequent and never reciprocal; principally seen between mother and infant. Grooming appears to have a low social valency. COMMUNICATION: by means of posture, facial expression and vocalization. Vocalization is agreed by all observers to be unobtrusive. Schaller has listed 21 distinct sounds. PLAY: Infants play frequently on their own or in juvenile-infant play groups, but play is not obtrusive. CHEST-BEATING DISPLAY: Ritualized sequence of 9 discrete acts culminating in chest-beating with cupped hands. Excitement producing a build-up of tension is stimulus to display, and its function is probably intimidation. HOME RANGE AND TERRITORIALITY: 10–15 sq miles. Group ranges may overlap but there is no aggression or "defence" of territory. Daily range is very small and seldom exceeds 1 mile although Donisthorpe's (1958) study indicates somewhat greater distances on occasions in Virunga Volcanoes area. POPULATION DENSITY: Variable. Highest density in Virunga Volcanoes area: 6·6 per sq mile.

Sexual Behaviour*

Copulation seen only twice in 12-month study period in the wild. In captivity, among western gorillas, copulation is both *more canum* and *more hominum*.[38*]

REPRODUCTION AND DEVELOPMENT

Field evidence does not indicate any fixed breeding season.[3] SEXUAL CYCLE;* in captivity lasts for 30–31 days; periodic genital swelling is present (Raven, 1936) and menstrual bleeding is minimal. GESTATION PERIOD:* 251–289 days (records from 5 captive births).

PLATE 47. Above: Eastern Highland Gorilla, *Gorilla gorilla beringei* (Eric Kirkland); below: *Gorilla gorilla gorilla*, young aged 2 years (by courtesy of Doris M. Sorby)

LABOUR: Unrecorded in detail, but *see* Lang (1962). INFANT DEVELOPMENT:* In the wild,[3] infant remains with mother for first 3 years, being partly weaned by 1 year. At 1/12 infant can hold on to mother; at 3/12 it rides prone on her back and at 6–7/12 infants are walking and climbing unaided. For the development of the captive infant, *see* Lang (1960, 1962), Carmichael, Kraus and Reed (1962), Rumbaugh (1965c).

CAPTIVITY

LONGEVITY: (in wild)* 25–30 years. LONGEVITY RECORD:[42] Western Lowland Gorilla: 33 years 5 months, Philadelphia Zoo. BIRTHS IN CAPTIVITY:[43] to date, 8 births (*G.g. gorilla*) have taken place in captivity. Only recorded case of twins: Frankfurt, May 1967 to Makulla. Birth Weights, 1·7 kg and 1·8 kg.

Zoo	Date	Name and sex	Parent	Parent	Weight at birth (kg)
Columbus Zoo U.S.A.	Dec. 22nd 1956	Colo ♀	The Baron	Christina	1·87
Basle Zoo Switzerland	Sept. 23rd 1958	Goma ♀	Stephi	Achilla	1·82
Basle Zoo Switzerland	April 17th 1961	Jambo ♂	Stephi	Achilla	2·7 (9 weeks)
National Zoo Washington	Sept. 9th 1961	Tomako ♂	Nikumba	Moka	2·27
National Zoo Washington	Jan. 10th 1964	Leonard ♂	Nikumba	Moka	Not weighed
Basle Zoo Switzerland	June 1st 1964	Migger ♂	Stephi	Achilla	3·95 (11 weeks)
San Diego Zoo U.S.A.	June 3rd 1965	Alvila ♀	Albert	Vila	2·14
Frankfurt Zoo W. Germany	June 22nd 1965	Max ♂	Abraham	Makulla	2·1

REFERENCES

1. Vogel, C. (1961)
2. Groves, C. P. (1966)
3. Schaller, G. B. (1963, 1965)
4. Booth, A. H. (1958)
5. Bingham, H. C. (1932)
6. Kawai, M. and Mizuhara, H. (1959)
7. Donisthorpe, J. (1958)
8. Merfield, F. G. and Miller, H. (1956)
9. Schultz, A. H. (1934b)
10. Rothschild, W. (1923)
11. Crandall, L. S. (1964)
12. Straus, W. L. (1963)
13. Schultz, A. H. (1962)
14. Ashton, E. H. and Zuckerman, S. (1952)
15. Schultz, A. H. (1930, 1961)
16. Ellis, R. A. and Montagna, W. (1962)
17. Montagna, W. (1965)
18. Schultz, A. H. (1963a)
19. Steiner, P. E. (1954)
20. Koch, W. (1937)
21. Elftman, H. and Atkinson, W. B. (1950)

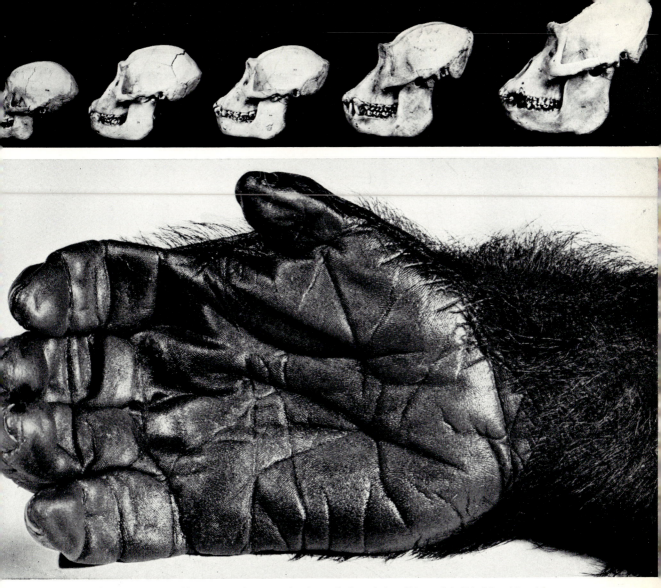

PLATE 48. *Gorilla gorilla beringei*; Above: growth series of male skulls from infant (L.) to adult (R.). (Naturhistoriska Riksmuseet, Stockholm). Below: hand of young ♂.

References (cont. from p. 166)

22. Hall-Craggs, E. C. B. (1961)
23. Washburn, S. L. (1950)
24. Hamerton, J. L. *et al.* (1961)
25. Goodman, M. (1962)
26. Goodman, M. (1963a)
27. Goodman, M. (1963b)
28. Goodman, M. (1964)
29. Williams, C. A. and Wemyss, C. T. (1961)
30. Williams, C. A. (1964)
31. Chiarelli, B. (1963b)
32. Pitman, C. R. S. (1935)
33. Osborn, Rosalie M. (1963)
34. Merfield, F. G. (quoted by Osborn, 1963)
35. Akeley, C. E. (1922)
36. Emlen, J. T. and Schaller, G. B. (1960)
37. Yerkes, R. M. and Yerkes, A. W. (1929)
38. Lang, E. M. (1960)
39. Lang, E. M. (1962)
40. Carmichael, L., Kraus, M. B. and Reed, T. (1962)
41. Rumbaugh, D. M. (1965c)
42. Jones, M. L. (1962)
43. Pournelle, G. H. (1965)
44. International Zoo Year Book, Vols. 1–5 (1959–63)
45. Franks, D. (1963)
46. Raven, H. C. (1936)
47. Schultz, A. H. (1964)
48. Sabater Pi, J. (1964)
49. Smith, L. G. (Personal communication)
50. Wiener *et. al.* (1966)
51. Coolidge, H. J. (1929)

HAPALEMUR   I. Geoffroy, 1851   Gentle Lemurs

2 species: 2 subspecies[1]

H. griseus (Type species)	Grey gentle lemur	2 subsp.
H. simus	Broad-nosed gentle lemur	0 subsp.

GEOGRAPHICAL RANGE [2, 18]

H. grisens: Only seen in recent years in the Lac Alaotra region and the eastern rain forest; however many museum specimens bear labels with west coast localities; thus, range given by other authors may differ. *H. simus* is now thought to be extinct.

ECOLOGY [1]

HABITAT: Arboreal. Found in rain forest being most frequently observed on thick and medium-sized horizontal branches. Seldom seen on the ground. Rand (1935) states that they occupy crowns of lower storey trees and bamboo thickets. On Lake Alaotra *H. griseus* lives among the papyrus reed beds. ACTIVITY RHYTHM: Diurnal. DIET: Fruit, leaves and flowers, also reeds.[1, 4]

MORPHOLOGY

External Characters[5, 6]

Rather small animals ranging in total length from 700 mm (*H. griseus*) to 900 mm (*H. simus*) of which half the length is tail. Fur is greenish-grey washed with red and with a speckling of black; limbs and tail are sooty grey. Head is rounded with a short tapering muzzle and short rounded hairy ears. Face skin is pink in *H.g. griseus*, black in *H.g. olivaceus*. Ante-brachial gland in *H. griseus*. Hindlimbs longer than forelimbs. Hallux is large in both species, but larger in *H. simus*.[18]

Weights and Dimensions[5, 8]

Body weight (g)	2625 (1♂)	2550 (1♀)
Head and body length range (mm)	365, 370 (2♂)	260–330 (3♀)
Tail length range (mm)	365 (1♂)	240–350 (3♀)

Internal Characters

For fuller account of principle features of skull, postcranial skeleton, soft tissue anatomy, see *Lemur*: only notable distinctions recorded here. SKULL: Muzzle blunt and shorter than in *Lepilemur* or *Lemur*; post-glenoid process and auditory bullae large. Angular process of mandible greatly expanded inferiorly and posteriorly. VERTEBRAL COLUMN:[9] Lacking cervical specializations of *Lepilemur*. Transverse diameter of thorax less than antero-posterior diameter. ALIMENTARY TRACT:[8] Stomach globular and unspecialized; caecum is small, compact and thick-walled (as in Cheirogaleinae). Spleen is small and of a shape unique in Prosimians. GENITALIA:[10] Clitoris of unique form bearing a terminal hairy tuft and enclosing

PLATE 49. *Hapalemur griseus ? griseus* (by courtesy of Doris M. Sorby)

the urethra; phallus contains incipiently bifid os penis. CUTANEOUS GLANDS: antebrachial pad covered with epithelial spines overlying glandular structure studied by Affolter (1938) present in *H. griseus*, absent in *H. simus*.[11, 12] Axillary glands also present in ♂. DENTITION: D.F.: $\frac{2}{2}\frac{1}{1}\frac{3}{3}\frac{3}{3}=36$.

Genetic Biology

CHROMOSOMES:[13, 19] *H. griseus* from Lac Alaotra region shows polymorphism. 2n = 54 (1♂, 2♀♀). KARYOTYPE: 4M, 6S, 42A, X = A, Y = A; 2n = 58 (1♀). KARYOTYPE: 2M, 4S, 52A. P.T.C. TASTING:[14] Non-taster (single specimen). HAEMOGLOBINS:[15] Alkali-resistant Hb; two major components on starch-gel electrophoresis.

PLATE 50. *Hapalemur griseus*. Young ♀ from Lake Alaotra (by courtesy of Alan C. Walker)

BEHAVIOUR

Locomotor Behaviour[1]

AUTHORS' CLASSIFICATION: Quadrupedalism. (*H. griseus* shows many of the behavioural characters of Vertical Clinging and Leaping).[18] Relatively unspecialized gait; *Hapalemur* runs or walks along horizontal branches using tail for leaping and for balancing in a small branch milieu. LIMB PROPORTIONS: *See* Part III, p. 394, for Indices.

Hand Function

Hand prehensile; thumb pseudo-opposable. Simple prehensive pattern in which fingers are flexed against palm, wholly or partly enclosing object; thumb not differentiated in manipulation.[16]

Resting Posture

Frequently observed in sitting position leaning against vertical branch.[1]

Social Behaviour[1]

Little is known of social behaviour in the wild. GROUP SIZE: 3–6 individuals. HOME-RANGE: Said to have well-defined home ranges. MARKING BEHAVIOUR: Intensive marking associated with axillary and antebrachial glands; tail used in marking after wiping against forearm as in *L. catta*. VOCALIZATION: short, low grunts—single or double—may be emitted in rapid succession when animals are excited; similar to grunts of *Lemur*. Grooming not reported.

REPRODUCTION AND DEVELOPMENT

Breeding and reproduction unknown.

CAPTIVITY

Rarely seen in captivity outside Madagascar. LONGEVITY RECORD:[17] *H. griseus*, 12 years 1 month, London, Zoological Gardens; *H. simus*, 0 years 6 months, London, Zoological Gardens.

REFERENCES

1. Petter, J. J. (1962c)
2. Petter, J. J. (1965) Personal communication
3. Rand, A. L. (1935)
4. Webb, C. S. (1960) quoted in Hill, W. C. Osman (1953)
5. Hill, W. C. Osman (1953)
6. Schwarz, E. (1931c)
7. Affolter, M. (1938)
8. Davies, D. V. and Hill, W. C. Osman (1954a)
9. Mivart, St. G. (1873)
10. Davies, D. V. and Hill, W. C. Osman (1954b)
11. Beddard, F. (1884)
12. Pocock, R. I. (1917a)
13. Bender, M. A. and Chu, E. H. Y. (1963)
14. Chiarelli, B. (1963b)
15. Buettner-Janusch, J. and Buettner-Janusch, V. (1964)
16. Bishop, Alison (1964)
17. Jones, M. L. (1962)
18. Walker, A. C. (Personal communication)
19. Faed, M. J. W. and Walker, A. C. (In press)

HYLOBATES† Illiger, 1811   Gibbons

6 species: 15 subspecies[1,2,3,4,5,6,7]

H. lar (Type species)	White-handed gibbon	3 subsp.
H. agilis	Dark-handed gibbon	o subsp.
H. moloch	Silvery gibbon	6 subsp.
H. hoolock	Hoolock gibbon	o subsp.
H. concolor	Black gibbon	6 subsp.
H. klossii	Kloss's gibbon	o subsp.

GEOGRAPHICAL RANGE [5,8]

Southeast Asia. Gibbons are confined to areas of primary forest. *H. lar* is found in Indo-China and Thailand to the west of the R. Mekong, in Tenasserim, the Malay peninsula and Sumatra. *H. hoolock* is found in Assam, Burma and West Yunnan; *H. concolor* in Vietnam and Laos, E. of the R. Mekong, and Hainan island. *H. agilis* is sympatric with *H. lar* in Malaya and Sumatra; *H. moloch* is the only species found in Java and Borneo. *H. klossii* is confined to the Mentawai islands, off the W. coast of Sumatra. Limits of genus: 29° N.–9° S. 90–120° E.

ECOLOGY

HABITAT:[9] Arboreal. Tropical rain forest, semi-deciduous forest and montane forest up to about 2000 m. Gibbons prefer the closed canopy but during feeding they may climb to the highest emergent crowns or descend to clumps of bamboo and low bushes; or to the ground to drink. Do not build nests, but sleep amongst dense foliage. ACTIVITY RHYTHM: Diurnal. DIET:[9] 80% fruit, 20% leaves, buds and flowers; sometimes birds' eggs, young birds and insects. Fluid largely acquired from fruit but also obtained from licking bark and leaves after rain; occasionally drink from springs.

MORPHOLOGY

External Characters[1,5]

Hylobates are small tailless apes with long dense shaggy fur varying from black or dark brown to pale fawn or silver grey. Face is bare and deeply pigmented, as are the palms and soles. Arms and hands are extraordinarily elongated, legs and feet less so. Moderate-sized ischial callosities are widely separated.

    The 6 species of *Hylobates* are difficult to distinguish from one another as they are individually variable; 4 of the 6 species have colour phases that vary with age and sex. *H. concolor*, for instance, is born fawn-coloured but becomes black after about 6 months and remains so until, on reaching maturity at about 5–7 years, the ♀ again becomes fawn, a small patch on the crown remaining black; the ♂ remains black all over, sometimes with white or fawn cheek patches. *H. hoolock*, the largest species, shows similar phases; grey at birth, both sexes gradually change to black. At puberty, the ♀ becomes brown, the ♂ remaining black with white "eyebrows" and a large preputial tuft. Apart from *H. lar pileatus* from S.E. Thailand and Cambodia (*see* Plate 51 for ♀ and infant: ♂ is mainly black), *H. lar* and *H. agilis* show no sexual dimorphism; ♂ and ♀ may be black *or* buff. In black specimens, the white hands and feet of *H. lar* contrast with its black limbs ("white-handed"); the contrast is less apparent in buff specimens. These can be confused with buff specimens of *H. agilis* in which the extremities

† *See* Taxonomic Notes, Part III, p. 374.

are always the same colour as the coat; dark specimens of *H. agilis* are thus "dark-handed". Both species have a pale brow-band which often extends round the face to form a complete ring of white hairs.

H. concolor[10] is distinguishable by having a crest of erect hairs on the crown (elongated at the middle of the crown in ♂, at the sides of the crown in ♀) and no pale brow-band. In the other 5 species, the crown hairs are directed smoothly backwards. Small throat-sac present in ♂ *H. concolor*.[10]

H. moloch shows extreme variability in colour from black to silvery grey[11] but is generally grey-brown with pale brow-band and darker shading on crown and chest. Neither *H. moloch* nor *H. klossii* show colour phases; the latter is entirely black and the coat much less dense than that of the other species. In this character *H. klossii* resembles *Symphalangus*.[19]

Weights and Dimensions[8, 12, 13, 14, 15, 16]

Body weight range (g)	4300–7928 (41♂)	4110–6800 (30♀)
Head and body length range (mm)	403–635 (62♂)	408–622 (38♀)

Schultz (1956) gives 93·5% (♀ weight in % of ♂ weight) on 94 specimens.

Internal Characters

For fuller account of anatomy *see* Bischoff (1870); Kohlbrügge (1890); Keith (1891, 1896); Sonntag (1924); Schultz (1930, 1933b, 1944); and, for anatomy of hand *see* Jouffroy and Lessertisseur (1960). SKULL: Ovoid neurocranium, moderately large nuchal area and moderate to slight prognathism. Sagittal crests usually lacking but occasionally seen in both sexes of *H. lar*,[20] associated with below average cranial capacity and high palatal index. Cranial capacity ranges between 82–125 cc (*H. lar*),[20] being lowest in *H. klossii*.[19] Bony palate long (50–54% skull length).[19] Orbits very large,[47] frontally directed, having a prominent, well-buttressed, lateral margin; buttressing of superior border produces strong brow ridges (relatively reduced in *H. concolor*) which are *not* continuous across midline. Mastoid process absent; occipital condyles lie well behind external auditory meatus in adult. VERTEBRAL COLUMN: Intermediate between Old World monkeys and Pongidae in thoraco-lumbo-sacral vertebra number.[18] UPPER LIMB: Bones of upper limb extremely long and slender (*see* LIMB PROPORTIONS, Part III, p. 394); hand is long and narrow with deep cleft between index and thumb. An os centrale is usually present as separate element in carpus; trapezio-metacarpal joint surface is of unique shape among catarrhine primates, the saddle articulation being absent.[21] The thenar muscles are aberrant, deep head of F.P.B. is absent as is oblique head of A.P.[22] For the many muscular specializations of upper limb, *see* Straus (1949).[23] LOWER LIMB: Webbing between 2nd, 3rd and 4th toes frequently present in *H. klossii* and occasionally present in other species (cf. *Symphalangus*).[19] GENITALIA: Sexual skin absent. Penis short and inconspicuous; scrotum absent except in *H. concolor*;[10] long, grooved clitoris in *H. concolor* and *H. hoolock*.[24, 51] DENTITION: D.F. $\frac{2}{2}\frac{1}{1}\frac{2}{2}\frac{3}{3}=32$. INCISORS: small and slightly procumbent. CANINES: long and sabre-like, there being slight dimorphism in size between the sexes;[20, 25] diastema in upper jaw for lower canine. PREMOLARS: upper and lower—bicuspid. 1st lower premolar—sectorial. MOLARS: Upper—quadricuspid showing typical hominoid pattern. Lower—quinquecuspid. $M\frac{3}{3}$ show a marked tendency to reduction;[19] *see also* Eckardt (1930).

Genetic Biology

CHROMOSOMES:[27] 2n=44. (*H. lar*, *H. hoolock* and *H. agilis*). Karyotypes of *H. lar* and *H. hoolock* are identical: 38 metacentrics; 6 subterminals; 0 acrocentrics. X sex-chromosome is a metacentric; Y sex-chromosome is a minute indeterminate structure (*H. lar*).[28] P.T.C. TASTING:[30] 46% tasters (26 specimens—*H. lar*). HAEMOGLOBINS:[31] Hb pattern appears to be slightly different from human A. Haemoglobin polymorphism noted. IMMUNO-CHEMISTRY: *See* Goodman (1962, 1963). BLOOD GROUPS: A, B and AB groups identified. Sex-linked Xg^a antigen as in man.[29]

BEHAVIOUR

Locomotor Behaviour[9]

AUTHORS' CLASSIFICATION: Brachiation. Arm swinging (in *H. lar*) constitutes major (90%), but not sole, means of arboreal locomotion; other patterns include climbing, bipedal walking on branches with or without support by arms. During brachiation, legs are flexed under the body and the arms move alternately; leaps in a downward direction up to 15 m. (Fractured limbs are commonly found in wild-shot specimens.) Bipedal walking on the ground and very occasional quadrupedalism. *See also* Straus (1941), Avis (1962), Napier (1963). Unable to swim.[9] LIMB PROPORTIONS: *See* Part III, p. 394, for Indices.

Hand Function

Hand—prehensile. Thumb—opposable. During brachiating locomotion, thumb is not used but is employed during climbing trunks of trees and thick branches; also used for manipulation of food and grooming. HAND PROPORTIONS: For Indices, *see* Part III, p. 401.

Resting Posture[9]

Hylobates sleep with the knees bent up to the chin, the hands folded on the knees and the face buried between the knees and chest. The thick fur is impenetrable by rain and the hunched position retains body heat. They sometimes lie supine on a broad branch.

Social Behaviour

Observations are largely those of Carpenter on *H. lar* (1940). GROUP SIZE:[9] from 2 to 6 individuals, consisting of an adult ♂ and ♀ and up to 4 young. Occasionally an old senile ♂ may be retained within the group. Solitary animals can be old isolates or young adult animals splitting away from the parent group, exploring for a suitable mate. RANGE AND TERRI-TORIALITY:[9] *Hylobates* occupy and defend sections of the forest which must be considered three-dimensionally: the acreage required by a group depends on the height of the forest as well as on the number in the group; Ellefson (in press) estimates this to be about 250–300 acres per group. *Hylobates* range freely within their territory, often encroaching on to common land between two territories, but migration is restricted. VOCALIZATION: (*H. lar*): A hooting call of rising inflection, rising pitch and increasing tempo is heard most often in the early morning and again less frequently in the afternoon. Other calls include a loud discrete, high-pitched note which operates as an alarm call; a number of intra-group calls have been recognized associated with greeting behaviour, play and group movement. There is very considerable variation in calls between species. FACIAL EXPRESSION: In friendly

PLATE 51. *Hylobates lar pileatus*, ♀ and infant (by courtesy of Twycross Zoo Park; photo by John Doidge)

greeting, the corners of the mouth are drawn back, revealing the teeth, and the tongue is sometimes protruded. In anger, the mouth is opened and closed repeatedly, smacking the lips and snapping the teeth together. Snarling, which is also exhibited, is interpreted as an intention movement of biting.[37] INTER-GROUP BEHAVIOUR: Policing of territorial boundaries and the common land between territories leads to almost daily conflicts in which vocalization, confrontation and chasing by the adult males are the main components. Actual fighting has only rarely been observed.[9, 25, 48] INTRA-GROUP BEHAVIOUR: Male dominance does not exist within the group; ♀ is equally dominant in vocalization and intra-group control, also in sexual behaviour (correlated with lack of sexual dimorphism). Strong antagonism exists between two adults of the same sex. GROOMING: Mutual grooming is important as a social activity and as a hygienic function, keeping the fur clean and free from ecto-parasites. The "service" of grooming is frequently alternated between two animals. Hands and feet may be used to part the dense woolly hair and the teeth are sometimes used to remove particles from the skin. SEXUAL BEHAVIOUR: Copulation of *H. lar* in the wild has been described by Carpenter. Observations on captive pairs include *H. concolor*[38] and *H. moloch*;[39] in the latter, copulation was observed throughout the menstrual cycle and even during pregnancy.

REPRODUCTION AND DEVELOPMENT

REPRODUCTIVE CYCLE:[40, 41]

Species	Duration of cycle in days		Duration of bleeding		No. of cycles observed
	Extremes	Mean	Extremes	Mean	
H. lar	21–43	29.76 ± 4.12	2–5	2.38 ± 0.54	17
H. hoolock	20–33	27.83 ± 4.07	2–4	2.6	6

There are no sexual skin changes, but there are some changes in the colour, degree of eversion and turgidity of the labia. GESTATION PERIOD: circa 210 days.[17] There is no discrete birth season. *Hylobates* give birth to one young, usually at two-yearly intervals. The eyes are open at birth and the body and limbs are bare. The infant is therefore very dependent on the mother for warmth and she holds it between her flexed thighs and abdomen, forming a furry nest.[9] From the first day, it can cling to her unaided.[42] DURATION OF LACTATION is not precisely known; infant is dependent on the mother for about 2 years.[43] First deciduous teeth are cut at about 5 weeks; last permanent teeth at $8\frac{1}{2}$ years.[17] Sexual maturity is reached between 5–7 years (*H. concolor*);[5, 44] between 8–10 years (*H. lar*);[9] *H. hoolock*—about 7 years.[41] The growth and development of an infant ♀ hybrid gibbon (*H. lar × H. moloch*) has been described by Rumbaugh (1965a).

CAPTIVITY

The lifespan is thought to be about 33 years.[45] LONGEVITY RECORD:[46] 31 years 6 months,

---

PLATE 52. *Hylobates lar* in Malaya; above: adult ♀ "Classic" brachiation; below: adult ♂ in commonly adopted feeding posture (by courtesy of John O. Ellefson)

H. lar, Philadelphia Zoological Garden. BIRTHS IN CAPTIVITY: 66 births were recorded in World Zoos between 1959–63.[50] Although, when young, *Hylobates* can make gentle affectionate pets, they develop strong antagonisms on reaching maturity—also long canine teeth—which make them in adult life extremely dangerous.

REFERENCES

1. Kloss, C. Boden (1929)
2. Ellerman, J. R. and Morrison-Scott, T. C. S. (1951)
3. Chasen, F. N. (1940)
4. Sody, H. J. V. (1949)
5. Delacour, J. (1951)
6. Simonetta, A. (1957)
7. Schultz, A. H. (1932)
8. Pocock, R. I. (1927)
9. Carpenter, C. R. (1940)
10. Miller, G. S. (1933)
11. Hose, C. (1893)
12. Miller, G. S. (1903)
13. Lyon, M. W. (1908a)
14. Lyon, M. W. (1908b)
15. Davis, D. Dwight (1962)
16. Lyon, M. W. (1911)
17. Schultz, A. H. (1956)
18. Schultz, A. H. (1930, 1961)
19. Schultz, A. H. (1933b)
20. Schultz, A. H. (1944)
21. Jouffroy, F. K. and Lessertisseur, J. (1960)
22. Day, M. H. and Napier, J. R. (1963)
23. Straus, W. L. (1949)
24. Pocock, R. I. (1925a)
25. Frisch, J. E. (1963)
26. Eckardt, H. (1930)
27. Bender, M. A. and Chu, E. H. Y. (1963)
28. Hamerton, J. L. (1963)
29. Gavin J. *et al.* (1964)
30. Chiarelli, A. B. (1963b)
31. Buettner-Janusch, J. and Buettner-Janusch, V. (1964)
32. Goodman, M. (1962a and b)
33. Goodman, M. (1963)
34. Straus, W. L. (1941)
35. Avis, V. (1962)
36. Napier, J. R. (1963)
37. Andrew, R. J. (1963)
38. Coolidge, H. J. (1933a)
39. Benchley, B. (1942)
40. Carpenter, C. R. (1941)
41. Matthews, L. H. (1946)
42. Benchley, B. (1938)
43. Ogilvie, A. W. (1923)
44. Pocock, R. I. (1905)
45. Harms, J. W. (1956)
46. Jones, M. L. (1962)
47. Schultz, A. H. (1940a)
48. Ellefson, J. O. (In press)
49. Rumbaugh, D. M. (1965a)
50. International Zoo Year Book, Vols. I–V (1959–1965)
51. McCann, C. (1933)

INDRI   E. Geoffroy and G. Cuvier, 1795   Indrises

1 species: 0 subspecies[1]

Indri indri Gmelin, 1788

GEOGRAPHICAL RANGE [2, 3]

Madagascar. Eastern rain forest between Lat. 14°–20° S.; range extends from sea-level to 5900 ft (1800 m).

ECOLOGY *

HABITAT: Wholly arboreal. Becoming increasingly rare as forest habitats diminish. Found on trunks, larger vertical branches and in the forks of trees. ACTIVITY RHYTHM: Diurnal. DIET: Unknown in the wild but assumed to be largely leaves and fruits.

MORPHOLOGY

External Characters

Largest of Indriidae. Stumpy tail. Fur dense and silky; much individual variation in coat colour which is predominantly black and white. Face, ears, crown of head, shoulders, upper arms, back, front of thighs, hands and feet are usually black; remainder white, grey or pale rufous. Head rounded and muzzle prominent; eyes large and yellow-brown in colour with circular pupils. Hindlimbs considerably longer than forelimbs; hands and feet elongated, 3rd, 4th and 5th digits webbed to proximal interphalangeal joints in hand and foot. Big toe very large. No sexual dimorphism apparent in size or colouration. ♀♀ have a single pair of pectoral mammae.

Weights and Dimensions[4]*

Body weight—no information	
Head and body length (mm)	700 (1 specimen)
Tail length (mm)	30 (1 specimen)

Internal Characters[4]

For anatomical details of family, see *Propithecus*. Distinctive differences only noted here. SKULL: Facial region relatively prognathous; auditory bullae extremely prominent; post-glenoid tubercle stouter and wider than in *Propithecus* and *Avahi*. LOWER JAW: Horizontal ramus long and narrow compared to *Propithecus*. LARYNX: A large laryngeal sac is found lying posterior to the trachea and opening into it just below cricoid (*see* VOCALIZATION). HAND: Os centrale absent as in *Avahi*; palmar pads scarcely differentiated.[5] D.F.: 4.3.5.2.1. DENTITION: D.F.: $\frac{2}{2}\frac{1}{0}\frac{2}{2}\frac{3}{3} = 30$. For dental peculiarities, see *Propithecus*.

Genetic Biology

No information available at present.

G

PLATE 53. *Indri indri* ♂ (by courtesy of David Attenborough)

BEHAVIOUR

Locomotor Behaviour

AUTHORS' CLASSIFICATION: Vertical Clinging and Leaping.[7] Locomotion is very similar to that of *Propithecus*[2] in spite of difference in tail length. Although the body is horizontal during major leaps from trunk to trunk, it is held vertically during short leaps.[6] Indrises climb tree trunks by spanning them with their hands and ascending by a series of rapid hops or runs, legs moving together[6] or separately. LIMB PROPORTIONS: Legs extremely long compared with arms. For Indices *see* Part III, p. 394.

Hand Function

Hand is prehensile; thumb pseudo-opposable. Hands are extremely long with a wide span and capable of grasping tree trunks up to 50 cm diameter.[2] HAND PROPORTIONS: Exceptionally long hands; for Indices *see* Part III, p. 401.

Resting Posture

Similar to that of *Propithecus*, but the day-resting posture appears to depend more on some support under the rump.

Social Behaviour

Little is known of behaviour in the wild or in captivity; in the wild indrises are "more often heard than seen".[4] GROUP SIZE: Small family units comprising 2–4 individuals.[2, 3] VOCALIZATION: Their most characteristic calls are loud dog-like howls that are uttered in chorus and taken up by other groups in the forest.[2, 6] Other sounds include a loud sonorous "*coup de klaxon*" and simple grunts.[2]

REPRODUCTION AND GROWTH

Thought to produce single young. Gestation period and growth rate are unknown.

CAPTIVITY

Seldom survive in captivity even in Madagascar. *Indri* has never been exhibited in Zoos outside Madagascar except for a very brief period in Paris in 1939.[4]

REFERENCES

1. Schwarz, E. (1931c)
2. Petter, J. J. (1962b, c)
3. Rand, A. L. (1935)
4. Hill, W. C. Osman (1953)
5. Biegert, J. (1961)
6. Attenborough, D. (1963) (Film—B.B.C.)
7. Napier, J. R. and Walker, A. C. (1967)

LAGOTHRIX E. Geoffroy, 1812 Woolly Monkeys

2 species: 4 subspecies[1]

L. *lagothricha*   Humboldt's Woolly Monkey   4 subsp.
L. *flavicauda* [= *hendeei*]†   Hendee's Woolly Monkey   0 subsp.

GEOGRAPHICAL RANGE [1]

South America. Found extensively throughout whole of Amazon basin W. of R. Negro and R. Tapajos; Andean headwaters of R. Orinoco and R. Magdalena. Latitudinal limits: 8° N.–14° S. Longitudinal limits: 55°–79° W. *L. flavicauda*: restricted to pocket on E. slope of Cordillera Central, approx. 77° W. and 6° S.

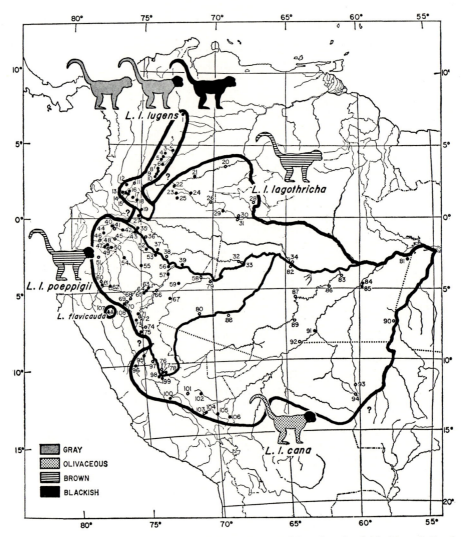

Map showing distribution and colour characters of the four races of *Lagothrix lagothricha* [From J. Fooden (1963) *J. Mammal.* **44**: 213–247]

---

† *See* Taxonomic Notes, Part III, p. 374.

ECOLOGY

HABITAT: Equatorial and montane rain forest up to 3000 metres. Found in the canopy, generally among the emergents;[2, 3] sometimes among slender branches in shrub layer of swampy areas.[4] Frequently killed for food by natives.[3, 5] ACTIVITY RHYTHM: Diurnal. DIET: Avid feeders, principally (in the wild) on leaves and fruit which may be hard-shelled according to Cruz Lima's (1945) analysis of tooth wear; animal protein probably additional.[7]

MORPHOLOGY

External Characters

Large monkeys with muscular bodies, robust limbs and prehensile tails. The coat is composed of dense and woolly—usually dark—fur with longer and more tufted hair on prominent belly. Coat colour, which is subject to seasonal variation,[7] varies from pale brown or grey to blackish in *L. lagothricha*; in *L. flavicauda*, it is deep mahogany with a sharply defined yellow band on distal half of underside of tail; a long yellow genital tuft is present in the ♂.[1] There is no sexual dimorphism in coat colour. Face is black or brownish but *L. flavicauda* has buffy patch around nose. The tail is long and very muscular, thick at the base and gradually narrowing towards the end where there is naked skin on the underside. LIMBS are long and subequal. HANDS: Thumb moderately long but not divergent. FEET: Big toe widely divergent. MAMMAE: Single pair located in axilla.

Weights and Dimensions[1]

	♂	♀	♀ in % of ♂
Body weight range (g)	3600–10,000 (7♂)	5000–6500 (7♀)	85
Head and body length range (mm)	414–568 (58♂)	390–580 (51♀)	99
Tail length range (mm)	560–690 (58♂)	597–730 (51♀)	106

Note sexual dimorphism (♀>♂) in tail length. (♀ in percentage of ♂, based on midpoint of range.)

Internal Characters

SKULL:[1] Rounded; face orthognathous; foramen magnum rather far back; well-developed temporal ridges in adult ♂. POSTCRANIAL:[8] Usually 4 lumbar vertebrae; length of lumbar col. 60% of thoracic. Brachiating adaptations of thorax, scapula and humerus not so marked as in *Ateles*.[8] Os penis absent. TAIL: Naked area on distal third of ventral surface showing papillary ridges, flexure creases, dermatoglyphics and eccrine sweat glands.[10] DENTITION: D.F.: $\frac{2}{2}\frac{1}{1}\frac{3}{3}\frac{3}{3} = 36$. Upper incisors broad and usually undershot.[1] CANINES: Marked sexual dimorphism—♀ 66% of ♂ length. PREMOLARS: Bicuspid. MOLARS: Quadricuspid, M$\frac{3}{3}$ smallest of series. ALIMENTARY TRACT:[14] Salivary glands large; stomach simple; colon is unsacculated for the most part and lacks taeniae coli.

PLATE 54. *Lagothrix lagothricha* adult ♀ (by courtesy of Doris M. Sorby), *see* p. 184

Genetic Biology

CHROMOSOMES:[11] 2n=62 (1♂ L. *lagothricha*). P.T.C. TASTING:[12] 100% non-tasters (15 individuals). HAEMOGLOBINS:[13] L. *lagothricha* generally shows a fast and a slow Hb on starch gels.

BEHAVIOUR

Locomotor Behaviour

AUTHORS' CLASSIFICATION: Quadrupedalism. Subtype: New World Semibrachiation. (Erikson's category: Brachiator.) Basically quadrupedal in gait but move freely and frequently (though not nearly as frequently as *Ateles*) in suspended position using arms and/or tail.[8] Leaping not common; gaps usually crossed by vertical dropping,[4] but *see* Hill (1962a). Frequently bipedal on the ground in captivity.[15] When walking quadrupedally on the ground, fingers are flexed at interphalangeal joints.[8] LIMB PROPORTIONS: Limbs less elongated relative to vertebral column than in *Ateles*;[8] forelimbs slightly shorter than hindlimbs. For Indices *see* Part III, p. 394.

Hand Function

Hand, prehensile; thumb, pseudo-opposable. Retain primitive grasp between 2nd and 3rd digits but thumb may be used discretely in seizing very small objects.[16, 17] HAND PROPORTIONS: For Indices *see* Part III, p. 401.

Resting Posture

Sleep, lying horizontally, limbs flexed, and tail wrapped around body.[14] Rest in upright sitting position. May occasionally rest for short periods hanging by the tail.

Social Behaviour*

No extensive field studies available. GROUP SIZE: Band of 15–25 (excluding young). INTER-GENERIC BEHAVIOUR: Mix freely with other genera, e.g. *Alouatta, Cebus, Ateles*.[7] TOILET BEHAVIOUR: Self-anointing behaviour reported.[18] VOCALIZATION: No extensive study but *see* Andrew (1962, 1964).

REPRODUCTION AND DEVELOPMENT *

Breeding season, if any, is not known. GESTATION PERIOD: 225 days approx.*[20] LACTATION prolonged, lasting 12 months or more.[14] Puberty at 4 years.[14] For information on reproduction in a captive colony, *see* Williams (1967).

PLATE 55. *Lagothrix lagothricha*, adult ♂ (by courtesy of Twycross Zoo Park; photo by John Doidge), *see* p. 185

CAPTIVITY

Placid and friendly animals that are easily tamed; unlike Old World monkeys, old adults may remain reliable, but are potentially dangerous. For observations on the care of woolly monkeys in captivity, *see* Williams (1965). ZOO LONGEVITY RECORD:[21] (*L. lagothricha*) 13 years. Twycross Zoo Park, England. Lifespan has been estimated at 20–25 years.[23] BREEDING RECORD:[22] Very rare. No births were recorded in World Zoos from 1959–63.

REFERENCES

1. Fooden, J. (1963)
2. Bartlett, E. (1871)
3. Lehmann, F. C., quoted in Fooden, J. (1963)
4. Miller, L. E. (1916)
5. Bates, H. W. (1863)
6. Cruz Lima, E. da (1945)
7. Sanderson, I. T. (1957)
8. Erikson, G. E. (1963)
9. Schultz, A. H. (1956)
10. Montagna, W. and Ellis, R. A. (1963)
11. Bender, M. A. and Chu, E. H. Y. (1963)
12. Chiarelli, B. (1963b)
13. Buettner-Janusch, J. and Buettner-Janusch, V. (1964)
14. Hill, W. C. Osman (1962a)
15. Humboldt, A. de and Bonpland, A. (1812)
16. Pocock, R. I. (1920)
17. Bishop, Alison (1964)
18. Ullrich, W. (1954)
19. Andrew, R. J. (1962, 1964)
20. Williams, L. (Personal communication)
21. Badham, M. (Personal communication)
22. International Zoo Year Book, Vols. I–V (1959–1965)
23. Williams, L. (1965)
24. Williams, L. (1967)

LEMUR†   Linnaeus, 1758   True Lemurs

5 species: 13 subspecies[1, 2, 3]

L. *catta* (Type species)	Ring-tailed lemur	o subsp.
L. *variegatus*	Ruffed lemur	3 subsp.
L. *macaco*	Black lemur	8 subsp.
L. *mongoz*	Mongoose lemur	2 subsp.
L. *rubriventer*	Red-bellied lemur	o subsp.

RANGE [1, 4, 5]

Madagascar and Comoro islands. The genus occupies all remaining major forest zones including: (*a*) Tropical rain forest of the E. and extreme N.W. (L. *variegatus*, L. *macaco*, L. *rubriventer*); (*b*) the drier mixed deciduous forest of the W. (L. *catta*, L. *macaco*, L. *mongoz*) and (*c*) temperate woodlands (gallery type) of the S. and S.W. (L. *catta*). L. *variegatus* is found in a relatively small area of rain forest on the E. coast between latitudes 13°–18° S. L. *macaco* is found in all forested areas except in South.

ECOLOGY

HABITAT:[1] All arboreal but L. *catta* tends, more frequently than other true lemurs, to adopt terrestrial habitat; estimated by Jolly (1967) to spend 15% daylight hours on ground. All true lemurs prefer large horizontal branches to a small branch milieu where they appear relatively clumsy compared with monkeys. ACTIVITY RHYTHM: Crepuscular or diurnal. DIET: Fruits primarily, also flowers and leaves; no insects.[3] PREDATORS: Hawks.

MORPHOLOGY

External Characters[3, 6, 7, 8]

Medium to large-sized animals; ruffed lemurs largest and mongoose lemurs smallest of genus. Muzzle moderately elongated and tapering; moist rhinarium; ears rounded, tufted (L. *macaco*, L. *variegatus*), prominent. Eyes have a striking "staring" quality but are somewhat laterally directed; iris golden. Legs longer than arms; tail longer than body (except L. *variegatus*), and often carried erect in an S-curve. L. *catta*: Back is grey, tinged with pink, lighter grey on limbs, extremities white. Top of head, circumocular rings and muzzle are black. Tail is banded black and white. L. *variegatus*: 3 colour varieties have been described.[3] Predominantly black and white or black and red. (i) Back more white than black (L.v. *variegatus*); (ii) Black back with white transverse bands (L.v. *subcinctus*); (iii) White areas replaced by red, black areas reduced (L.v. *ruber*). All have ruffs around head and neck; ruff is reddish in L.v. *ruber* and white in other subspecies. Tail is black in all. L. *macaco*: Sexual dichromatism in this species. Colour varies from black (♂ L.m. *macaco*, ♂ L.m. *flavifrons*) to reddish brown (♀ L.m. *macaco* and ♀ L.m. *flavifrons*) and all-over olive-brown (L.m. *fulvus*). Intraspecific variation extremely marked and complex. *See* Hill (1953), Schwarz (1931c) and Petter (1965). L. *mongoz*: Sexual dichromatism present but not extreme. Predominant colour is dark grey-brown with reddish tinge on cheeks (particularly ♂ L.m. *mongoz*) and underparts; ♀ L.m. *mongoz* has white cheeks. L. *rubriventer*: Coat colour is predominantly brown but underparts are red; according to Hill (1953), can be distinguished from brown varieties of L. *macaco* by presence of furry,

---

PLATE 56. *Lemur catta*, ♂, showing antebrachial gland (by courtesy of R. E. Greed, Bristol Zoo and Bristol Evening Post)

PLATE 57. Ring-tail Lemurs (by courtesy of Doris M. Sorby)

concealed ears. Hindlimbs longer than forelimbs. Big toe large and widely divergent. Full complement of tactile vibrissae.

Weights and Dimensions[6]

Mean body weight (g)	2103 (3 ♂ captive *L. catta*)
Head and body length range (mm)	303–456 (11 ♂ and ♀)
Tail length range (mm)	370–560 (11 ♂ and ♀)

L. variegatus (1 specimen) Head and body length 612 mm, tail length 611 mm

Internal Characters

For detailed accounts of osteology and anatomy, *see* Murie and Mivart (1872), Duckworth (1915); Wood Jones (1929) and Hill (1953). Principal features only noted here. SKULL: Muzzle moderately long, skull rounded in occipital region; tympanic bullae large and

PLATE 58. Above: *Lemur variegatus* (by courtesy of David Attenborough)   Below: *Lemur macaco*, adult ♂ (by courtesy of John Buettner-Janusch)

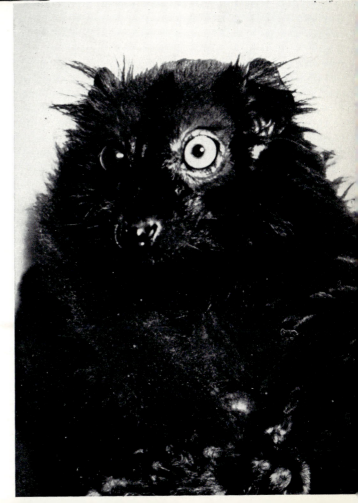

tympanic ring contained within bulla; complex turbinal system much as in treeshrews. ORBITS: Post-orbital bar but no posterior closure. Mandible with sloping symphysis; angular process projected backwards but not downwards (cf. *Hapalemur*). POST-CRANIAL SKELETON: Cervical vertebrae elongated, transverse process of atlas very large. Thoracic vertebrae: 12, lumbar vertebrae: 6–7. HAND: Os centrale present in carpus, hamate large. Digital formula: 4.3.5.2.1. FOOT:[9] Tarsus of medium length (37% foot length, cf. *Lepilemur* 39%, *Tarsius* 49%, *Macaca* 32%). ALIMENTARY TRACT: Colon elongated forming a simple ansa coli; caecum has a well-differentiated conical appendix. SPECIAL SENSES: Retina rich in cones, an "incipient" fovea present.[10] CUTANEOUS GLANDS:[11] (i) Antebrachial glands and horny spur found in *L. catta* only, connected to palmar skin by a narrow hairless strip; gland contains apocrine glands and interstitial cells of unknown function; gland is larger in $\male$ than $\female$. (ii) Brachial gland (sebaceous). DENTITION:[6, 12] D.F.: $\frac{2}{2}\frac{1}{1}\frac{3}{3}\frac{3}{3}=36$. INCISORS: Central incisors separated by wide diastema; lower incisors form part of dental comb with lower canines. CANINES: Upper are large, curved, laterally compressed projecting teeth, longer in $\male$ than $\female$.[13] PREMOLARS: Lower teeth are all somewhat caniniform, particularly $PM.\overline{1}$ which shears against back of upper canine ("sectorial"). MOLARS: $M.^{\underline{123}}$ tricuspid with internal cingulum and styles; some indication of hypocone. $M._{\overline{123}}$ quadricuspid, somewhat bilophodont in appearance.

Genetic Biology

CHROMOSOMES:[14]

L. catta	(2$\male$)	2n = 56	6 M. 4 S. 44 A.	X = A.	Y = A.
L. variegatus	(1$\male$)	2n = 46	14 M. 4 S. 26 A.	X = M.	Y = A.
L.m. macaco	(1$\male$, 1$\female$)	2n = 44	12 M. 8 S. 22 A.	X = A.	Y = A.
L.m. fulvus	(1$\male$, 1$\female$)	2n = 48	10 M. 6 S. 30 A.	X = A.	Y = A.
L.m. rufus	(2$\female$)	2n = 60	0 M. 4 S. 54 A.	X = A.	Y = A.
L.m. albifrons	(1$\female$)	2n = 60	0 M. 4 S. 54 A.	X = A.	Y = A.

BLOOD GROUPS:[15] R.B.C.s (*L. mongoz*, *L. macaco*) are not agglutinated by rabbit anti-sheep sera which agglutinates Group A Human. IMMUNOCHEMISTRY:[16] *L.m. fulvus*, *L. variegatus*, *L. catta* show distinctive protein patterns on two-dimensional starch-gel electrophoresis which are divergent from those of other prosimian groups. P.T.C. TASTING:[17] 56% tasters (16 *Lemur sp.*). HAEMOGLOBINS: Pigment shows high level of alkali resistance;[18] marked polymorphism in Hb structure (*L. catta*);[19] other lemurs show single Hb component.[20]

BEHAVIOUR

Locomotor Behaviour

AUTHORS' CLASSIFICATION: Quadrupedalism. Gait contains some elements approaching that of Vertical Clingers and Leapers (*see* Locomotion in Primates, Part III, p. 387). All forms use the tail in balancing as they move among horizontal branches of trees or horizontally disposed lianes.[1] Lemurs (particularly *L. catta*) are not particularly agile in small branch settings. Leaping ability varies, being least in *L. catta* and greatest (5–6 m) in *L. macaco*.[3] *L. catta* has been observed to walk bipedally for a few steps in captivity, also to hop bipedally.[1,28] *L.m. fulvus* reported to leap vertically from trunk to trunk on occasions.[21] LIMB PROPORTIONS: Low Intermembral Index due to long hindlimbs. For Indices *see* Part III, p. 394.

PLATE 59. *Lemur macaco*, $\female$ (by courtesy of John Buettner-Janusch)

Hand Function

Hand prehensile, thumb pseudo-opposable; thumb capable of wide abduction in plane of palm. Hands show a simple prehensive pattern which consists basically of a hook grip which is used to pull on branches and to pick up objects; grip is between finger tips and proximal pads; lemurs are rather inaccurate with small objects, e.g. raisins.[22] Hands are employed for feeding, for grasping partner's fur during dental and lingual grooming, for agonistic behaviour and for scent-marking.[13, 22] HAND PROPORTIONS: For Indices *see* Part III, p. 401.

Resting Behaviour[1]

Lemurs, particularly *L. catta*, adopt a sitting posture at rest with back supported. Sleeping posture is semi-erect, head resting between knees, hands gripping branch and tail wrapped round body. *L. macaco* frequently lies on abdomen along branch with legs dangling.

Social Behaviour[1, 3]

GROUP SIZE: Gregarious. Social groups are complex consisting of several ♂ and ♀ adults and several young (up to 20 in group); sex ratio usually in favour of ♂♂. Groups of *L. variegatus* are usually smaller, 2–5 in number. *L. macaco*: groups of 10 led by adult ♀. TERRITORIAL: Clearly defined territorial behaviour, e.g. *L. macaco*.

Marking Behaviour[3]

Highly developed in *L. catta* associated with cutaneous arm glands (*see* Internal Characters); tail frequently used to distribute secretions from antebrachial gland. In other species, forearm of ♂ used (though lacking specialized gland); also genito-urinary marking observed in both sexes. No specific marking behaviour in *L. variegatus*. VOCALIZATION: Large variety of grunts and sharp calls; in *L. variegatus*, repertoire less varied but cries extremely powerful and intense.

Sexual Behaviour[23]

Some evidence of consort pairing, probably only of a temporary nature. Sexual behaviour is seasonal, mating occurring April–June and is associated with intensive marking behaviour by ♂.

REPRODUCTION AND DEVELOPMENT

BIRTH SEASON: In captivity: March–June (N. hemisphere) and in the wild (*L. macaco*) Sept.–Nov.[23] GESTATION PERIOD: 120–135 days. Single young, though multiple births not uncommon (8 in 65 recorded).[24] BIRTH WEIGHT: 78 g (*L.m. fulvus*, 1 spec.).[25] Young are carried on mother's abdomen at right angles to its long axis;[21] at 2 weeks, it begins to cling to her back. Completely independent at 6 months; ♂ sexually mature at 18 months.[23] Young of *L. macaco* are black at birth irrespective of sex; dichromatism developed by 6 months.

PLATE 60. *Lemur mongoz mongoz* ♂ (by courtesy of Alan C. Walker)

CAPTIVITY

Most lemurs (*sensu stricto*) can be successfully kept and bred in captivity. Average lifespan: 7 years.[26] LONGEVITY RECORD:[27] 27 years, 1 month (*L. macaco*) London, Zoological Gardens. BIRTHS IN CAPTIVITY:[26] Between 1959–63, 78 lemurs were born in World Zoos: (*L. catta* 51; *L. variegatus* 2; *L. macaco macaco* 4; *L.m. fulvus* 17; *L. mongoz* 4).

Since this book was sent to the printers Alison Jolly has brought out her monograph "Lemur Behaviour" (University of Chicago Press, 1967) which contains many new and detailed observations of *L. catta* and *L. macaco*.

REFERENCES

1. Petter, J. J. (1962c)
2. Schwarz, E. (1936)
3. Petter, J. J. (1965)
4. Schwarz, E. (1931c)
5. Perrier de la Bathie, H. (1921)
6. Hill, W. C. Osman (1953)
7. Forbes, H. O. (1897)
8. Sanderson, I. T. (1957)
9. Schultz, A. H. (1963a)
10. Polyak, S. (1957)
11. Montagna, W. (1962)
12. Clark, W. E. Le Gros (1959)
13. Shaw, G. A. (1879)
14. Bender, M. A. and Chu, E. H. Y. (1963)
15. Dahr, P. (1937) quoted in Franks, D. (1963)
16. Goodman, M. (1962a, b)
17. Chiarelli, B. (1963b)
18. Buettner-Janusch, J. and Twickell, J. B. (1961)
19. Buettner-Janusch, J. (1962)
20. Buettner-Janusch, J. and Buettner-Janusch, V. (1964)
21. Rand, A. L. (1935)
22. Bishop, Alison (1964)
23. Petter-Rousseaux, A. (1964)
24. Schultz, A. H. (1948)
25. Evans, C. S. (Personal communication)
26. International Zoo Year Book, Vols. I–V (1959–1965)
27. Jones, M. L. (1962)
28. Walker, A. C. (Personal communication)
29. Jolly, Alison (1967)

LEONTIDEUS† Cabrera, 1956   Golden Lion Tamarins

3 species: 0 subspecies[1, 2]

L. rosalia (Type species)   Golden Lion Tamarin (or Marmoset)
L. chrysomelas
L. chrysopygus

GEOGRAPHICAL RANGE [3]

South America. Mountainous forests of E. littoral of Brazil. Serra do Mar $23\frac{1}{2}°$ S. (*L. rosalia*); Serra do Periperi, $15°$ S. (*L. chrysomelas*); and in the mountainous region between R. Tiete and R. Panapanema, $23°$ S. $49°$ W. (*L. chrysopygus*).

ECOLOGY *

HABITAT: Arboreal. Tropical rain forest at altitudes of 1640–3280 ft (500–1000 m). Little is known of minor habitat but *L. rosalia* is said to live in a small-branch setting high in the canopy.[4] ACTIVITY RHYTHM: Diurnal. DIET: Insects, fruits and small lizards.

MORPHOLOGY

External Characters[3]

Small monkeys but largest members of Callitrichidae. Long silky coat which may be: (i) Reddish gold all over (*L. rosalia*). (ii) Generally black with golden mane, arms and upper tail (*L. chrysomelas*). (iii) Wholly black except for golden forehead and inner sides of hindlimbs (*L. chrysopygus*). All species have dark, almost hairless, faces and long swept-back manes which conceal the ears. Nostrils typically platyrrhine. Tail relatively short for Callitrichidae. Narrow hands and feet. All digits bear modified claws, except big toe which has a flat nail. HAND: Digital formula: 3.4.2.5.1.; 2nd, 3rd and 4th digits are webbed.

Weights and Dimensions[3, 5]

Body weight (g)	553 (1♂)	480 (1♀)
Head and body length range (mm)	227–370 (6♂ + ♀)	
Tail length range (mm)	300–360 (6♂ + ♀)	

Internal Characters

Characters as in *Callithrix*; only major differences noted here. SKULL:[13] More robust than in other Callitrichidae; facial portion is raised relative to the neurocranium. Heavy brow ridges, flattish cranial vault and elongation of whole skull. Zygoma robust. Pterygoid plates much expanded and pterygoid fossae exceptionally deep, associated with complex internasal air-spaces. DENTITION: $\frac{2}{2} \frac{1}{1} \frac{3}{3} \frac{2}{2} = 32$. Lower incisors are short relative to canines (cf. *Callithrix*); this is the "long-tusked" condition. Premolars and molars as in *Callithrix* although $M\frac{2}{2}$ are even more reduced. Dental arcade less V-shaped than in *Callithrix*. HANDS: Reputed to be

---

† *See* Taxonomic Notes, *Saguinus*, Part III, p. 376.

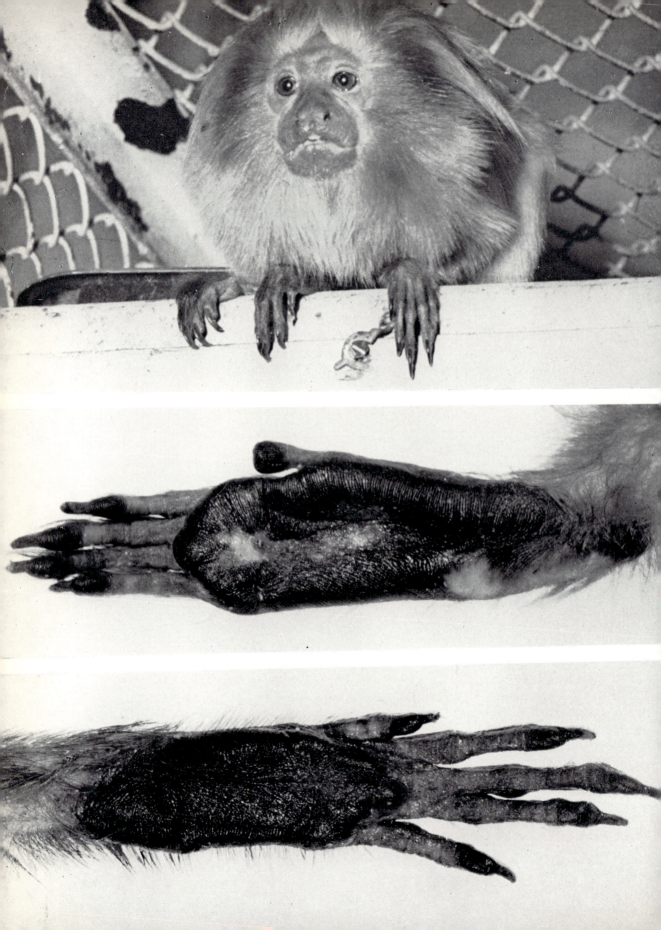

exceptionally long[3, 6] but Hand Length Index (*see* Part III, p. 401) does not bear this out; however their narrowness is unquestionable, and the thumb is considerably shorter than in *Callithrix* or *Saguinus*. FEET: Elongated but not exceptionally; there is no syndactyly.

Genetic Biology

CHROMOSOMES:[7*] 2n = 46 (1♀ *L. rosalia*). KARYOTYPE: Y sex-chromosome is a small metacentric.

BEHAVIOUR

Locomotor Behaviour

AUTHORS' CLASSIFICATION: Quadrupedalism. (Erikson's category: Springer.) Adaptive significance of slender hands and feet not understood, but *see* Pocock (1920).

Hand Function

Hand prehensile, thumb non-opposable. Hands are used for feeding when food is clasped one-handed between flexed digits and palm; also for social grooming during which activity thumb is not differentiated.[9]

Social Behaviour*

Believed to live in small groups.[4]

REPRODUCTION AND DEVELOPMENT

GESTATION PERIOD: Not known. Twin births usual. Young cling to mother for first week or so, then are taken over by father and transferred to mother for feeding which continues for 3 months. At 4 months, young are independent of father. Adult size achieved at 1 year.[10]

CAPTIVITY

Breeding in captivity is not uncommon. Between 1959–63, 12 births were recorded in World Zoos.[12] LONGEVITY RECORD:[11] *L. rosalia* 10 years 4 months, New York: Bronx Zoo. Alvila-Pires (1966) draws attention to the unsuitability of *L. rosalia* as a laboratory animal; it is one of the rarest tamarins with a very limited range. Owing to its diminishing numbers in nature, it is now protected by law from capture and export.

REFERENCES

1. Cabrera, A. (1956)
2. Cabrera, A. (1957)
3. Hill, W. C. Osman (1957)
4. Forbes, H. O. (1897)
5. Authors' observation
6. Pocock, R. I. (1917b, 1920)
7. Benirschke, K., Anderson, J. M. and Brownhill, L. E. (1962)
8. Erikson, G. E. (1963)
9. Bishop, Alison (1964)
10. Ditmars, R. L. (1933)
11. Jones, M. L. (1962)
12. International Zoo Year Book, Vols. I–V (1959–1965)
13. Du Brul, E. L. (1965)
14. Avila-Pires, F. D. de (1966)

PLATE 61. *Leontideus rosalia* ♂; plate also shows right foot (above), left hand (below) × 2·3

LEPILEMUR† I. Geoffroy, 1851   Sportive Lemurs

1 species: 5 subspecies[1]

L. mustelinus (I. Geoffroy, 1851)

GEOGRAPHICAL RANGE [1, 2, 3]

Madagascar. Widely distributed throughout all forested regions of Madagascar and the island of Nosy Bé off the N.W. coast where a distinct subspecies *L.m. dorsalis* is found. *L.m. leucopus* lives in the S.W. Euphorbia forest region.

ECOLOGY

HABITAT:[2, 3, 4] Inhabitant of tropical forest, particularly of the gallery type,[5] where it frequents the trunks of trees and vertical branches 3–10 m above the ground. Sleeps during the day in a hole in a tree trunk. On island of Nosy Bé, where predators are absent, *Lepilemur* sleeps on exposed branches. ACTIVITY RHYTHM: Nocturnal. DIET: Leaves, fruit and bark.

MORPHOLOGY

External Characters[6, 7]

Medium-sized lemur with shortish blunt face and prominent oval ears; fur is soft and woolly. Colour varies slightly with subspecies but dominant colour of dorsal region, head and tail is red, combined with brown (*L.m. mustelinus*) or grey (*L.m. ruficaudatus*). There may be a darker, median spinal stripe extending from head to root of tail. The underparts and sometimes the hindlimbs are pale grey or yellowish white. The feet are wholly white in *L.m. leucopus*. Tail reddish brown with white terminal hairs (*L.m. ruficaudatus*) or pale grey tinged with rufous (*L.m. leucopus*). Tail is never longer than body. HAND: D.F.: 4.3.2.5.1.

Weights and Dimensions[7]

Head and body length range (mm)	280–356 (3 specimens ♂ and ♀)
Tail length range (mm)	254–280 (3 specimens ♂ and ♀)

Internal Characters

For fuller account of principal features of skull, post-cranial skeleton and soft tissue anatomy, see *Lemur*; only notable distinctions recorded here. SKULL: Muzzle projecting, but blunt and square-cut. Orbits rather large. Bullae are large and inflated; post-glenoid tubercle large. Angle of mandible is larger, rounder and more backwardly projecting than in *Lemur*. VERTEBRAL COLUMN: Neural laminae C_{3-7} notched posteriorly and anterior hypopophyseal ridge in cervical region as in Indriidae. Lumbar Vertebrae: 8–9, with very large transverse processes.[15] THORAX: Transverse diameter greater than antero-posterior; scapula narrow cranio-caudally. HANDS: Exceptionally long (cf. *Lemur*). Os centrale absent—*see* Indriidae. FOOT: Tarsus is relatively elongated compared with other Lemurinae.[8] ALIMENTARY SYSTEM: Parotid glands much enlarged; stomach characterized by lengthening of pylorus

---

† *See* Taxonomic Notes, Part III, p. 374.

PLATE 62. *Lepilemur mustelinus ruficaudatus* (by courtesy of Jean Jacques Petter)

and thickening and differentiation of circular and longitudinal coats.[9] Caecum and colon very large but caecum is a long thin-walled tapering organ (cf. *Hapalemur*).[9] Ansa coli forms a simple loop. CUTANEOUS GLANDS: Glandular area on scrotum. DENTITION: D.F.: $\frac{0}{2} \frac{1}{1} \frac{3}{3} \frac{3}{3} = 32$. Upper incisors absent in permanent dentition.

N.B. Mivart (1873) was the first to draw attention to the many post-cranial similarities between *Lepilemur* and the Indriidae (*see* Locomotor Behaviour and Limb Proportions).

BEHAVIOUR

Locomotor Behaviour[4, 5]

AUTHORS' CLASSIFICATION: Vertical Clinging and Leaping. Principal locomotor pattern is a rapid series of leaps from trunk to trunk with body vertical and tail inactive—as in Indriidae. Very occasionally quadrupedal in trees and on ground. When on the ground, usually moves by a series of hops. LIMB PROPORTIONS: Hindlimbs much longer than forelimbs; forearm longer than arm. For Indices *see* Part III, p. 394.

Hand Function[4]

Hand is prehensile; thumb pseudo-opposable; hand is adapted for gripping large vertical branches rather than fine, horizontal ones, thumb being somewhat shorter than in *Lemur*. Prehensive pattern is simple, showing no fine movements. Hand is sometimes employed in agonistic behaviour by "slapping" at adversary. HAND PROPORTIONS: For Indices, *see* Part III, p. 402.

Resting Posture[4]

Sleeps rolled up in a ball, either in a tree-hole or in thick foliage. During periods of inactivity, rests in vertical position gripping upright branch.

Social Behaviour[4, 11]

GROUP SIZE: Solitary animals that live in population centres ("noyaux de peuplement"); the largest social group appears to be mother and infant. Home range very limited, not exceeding 50 m from nesting hole. VOCALIZATION: Extremely vocal animals with wide range of calls which have been studied by spectrographic analysis by Petter (1962c). TERRITORIAL BEHAVIOUR: Assumed to be present from vocalization behaviour. MARKING BEHAVIOUR: Not apparently very highly evolved, but marking with urine and circumanal secretions has been observed.

REPRODUCTION AND DEVELOPMENT [12]

MATING SEASON: May–August in Madagascar, associated with marked increase in size and volume of all glands associated with ♂ genital tract. GESTATION PERIOD: 120–150 days. BIRTH: Single young; infants are relatively mature and active at birth. Infant may be left in nest, or grasping a branch, while mother forages, or it may be carried in her mouth while she leaps; locomotor independence from approx. 30 days; infant is fully weaned at 75 days. SEXUAL MATURITY: approx. 18 months.

CAPTIVITY

Rarely exhibited in Zoos. LONGEVITY RECORD:[13] 3 months, Philadelphia Zoo. No births were recorded in World Zoos between 1959–63.[14] A specimen was kept for more than 12 months at Le Jardin des Plantes, Paris.[16]

REFERENCES

1. Petter, J. J. (1960)
2. Petter, J. J. (1962a)
3. Petter, J. J. (1962b)
4. Petter, J. J. (1962c)
5. Rand, A. L. (1935)
6. Schwarz, E. (1931c)
7. Hill, W. C. Osman (1953)
8. Jouffroy, F.-K. (1962)
9. Davies, D. V. and Hill, W. C. Osman (1954a)

10. Mivart, St. George (1873)
11. Petter, J. J. (1965)
12. Petter-Rousseaux, A. (1964)
13. Jones, M. L. (1962)
14. International Zoo Year Book, Vols. I–V (1959–1965)
15. Schultz, A. H. (1961)
16. Letellier, F. and Petter, J. J. (1961)

LORIS   E. Geoffroy, 1796   Slender Lorises

1 species: 6 subspecies[1]

Loris tardigradus Linnaeus, 1758   6 subsp.

GEOGRAPHICAL RANGE [1, 2, 3]

Ceylon and southern India. From sea level to 6000 ft (1850 m) altitude. Northern limits of genus are not known; possibly as far N. as Tapti R. (W. coast).

ECOLOGY

HABITAT:[2, 4] Arboreal. Tropical rain forest, swampy coastal forest; also woodland in the dry zones of southern India and Ceylon. ACTIVITY RHYTHM: Nocturnal. Sometimes sleep in hollow trees or in the leafy extremities of branches.[2, 5] DIET: Mainly insects, also small lizards and birds.[3, 4]

MORPHOLOGY

External Characters

Very small animals with well-furred bodies and etiolated limbs which become less furred distally, the wrists and hands being almost bare, though heels are furred as in other Lorisinae. Eyes are very large and directed forwards; iris orange-brown, the pupil narrowing to a vertical slit. Projecting pointed muzzle with naked rhinarium; ears larger and more membranous than those of *Nycticebus*. Limbs subequal in length, hands considerably smaller than feet. Small flat nails on all digits except 2nd toe which is much reduced and bears a toilet claw; 2nd finger also reduced. Thumb and big toe widely divergent; no interdigital webbing. No tail.

Soft short woolly fur is pale grey, brown or red brown with white or buff underparts. Distinct markings are a white stripe between eyes from muzzle to forehead separating dark pear-shaped patches around eyes. Dark median dorsal stripe sometimes present. A thickly-furred short-limbed race (*L.t. nycticeboides*) inhabits high ground 6000 ft (1850 m) in Ceylon. Little sexual dimorphism in colour and size; considerable variation in size between subspecies. MAMMAE: 2 pairs.[2]

Weights and Dimensions[3]

	♂	♀	♀ in % of ♂
Body weight range (g)	85–348 (16♂♂)	85–270 (7♀♀)	82
Head and body length range (mm)	186–264 (11♂♂)	198–249 (9♀♀)	100

(♀ in % of ♂ based on midpoint of ranges)

Internal Characters

For more detailed accounts of anatomy, *see* Hill (1953), Nayak (1933), Murie and Mivart (1872). SKULL: Globular form of neurocranium with little protrusion of facial region as in all Lorisidae. Foramen magnum more rostral than in *Nycticebus*. Tympanic bulla markedly inflated; short, bony external auditory meatus. Orbits are very large, directed forwards with no laterality; exceptionally broad orbital margin; no supraorbital notch or foramen; ethmoid forms major element of medial orbital wall. Premaxillaries protrude in front of incisors to form support for sharp protruding nose. POST-CRANIAL SKELETON: Relatively long thoraco-lumbar region as in all Lorisinae. Vertebrae: C.7, T.14–15, L.8–9, S.3, C.5. No anticlinal vertebrae;[8] lumbar vertebrae elongated. LIMBS are long and slender. Foot is extremely long with elongate phalanges, remarkably short heel and a long hallux.[9] The shortness of the heel can be correlated with the total lack of "propulsive" elements to the hindlimb activity (cf. *Nycticebus*). The intrinsic musculature of the hand has been studied by Kanagasuntheram and Jayawardene (1957) and by Day and Napier (1963), and that of the forelimb by Miller (1943). DENTITION:[13] D.F.: $\frac{2}{2}\frac{1}{1}\frac{3}{3}\frac{3}{3}=36$. Fairly typical of Lorisidae. INCISORS: Peglike in upper jaw, in lower jaw they are procumbent and form a dental comb with the canine. Upper canine is long and sharp. PREMOLARS: Upper anterior premolar is somewhat caniniform and PM.$\frac{2.3}{}$ are molariform; lower anterior premolar is large, semi-procumbent and caniniform. MOLARS: Upper are tritubercular with additional moderate-sized hypocone; lower are quadritubercular with a hypoconulid on M.$\frac{}{3}$. Diastemata not marked. ALIMENTARY TRACT: Long and narrow sublingua with lateral denticles. Stomach simple; neither caecum nor colon are sacculated, the ansa coli has a simple arrangement in *Loris*. VASCULAR SYSTEM: Retia mirabilia form vascular leashes associated with main limb arteries.[14] SKIN: Dendritic cells of epidermis found in African lorisoids absent in *Loris*.[15] A brachial organ containing a large group of apocrine sweat glands present on medial side of arm[16] (*see also* Hill, 1956a).

BEHAVIOUR

Locomotor Behaviour

AUTHORS' CLASSIFICATION: Quadrupedalism, slow-climbing sub-type. Slow, deliberate progression that depends upon prehensile grasp of extremities, and in which legs play the most important rôle. Frequently suspends itself by legs alone to reach next handhold. Hip and ankle joint show extreme mobility allowing Loris to adopt many extraordinary postures.[5] Movement is more rapid than that of *Nycticebus*.[3] LIMB PROPORTIONS: Forelimbs and hindlimbs approx. $1\frac{1}{2}$ times trunk height.[18] Legs slightly longer than arms; forearm longer than arm. For Indices, *see* Part III, p. 394.

Hand Function

Hand prehensile, thumb pseudo-opposable and widely divergent as in e.g. *Perodicticus*. Single prehensile pattern in which thumb opposes 4th digit.[19] Hand used in locomotion, grasping of food (living insects), grooming and fighting.[5, 19] During locomotion, small diameter branches are preferred, which can be enclosed by the hand.[5] HAND PROPORTIONS: Hands are short relative to total arm length; phalanges are moderately long, though relatively shorter than *Nycticebus*; thumb stout and long. For Indices, *see* Part III, p. 402.

PLATE 63. *Loris tardigradus*

Resting Posture

Usually sleep at a bifurcation of branches with the body rolled in a ball, head and hands tucked between thighs, feet gripping the branch; sometimes hands also grasp branch.[5] During sleep hands and feet are cold to the touch.

Social Behaviour

RANGE: Nothing is known of the territorial range of *Loris*. GROUP SIZE: Thought to be solitary.[3] VOCALIZATION: Six types of vocalization have been described including a low growl and a faint chatter. MARKING BEHAVIOUR:[20] Two types of marking behaviour have been observed: firstly, rhythmic micturition which occurs when moving along a branch so that the whole surface is sprinkled with urine; secondly, urine-washing of hands and feet. First description of urine-washing in Lorisidae is by Hill (1938a). Both behaviours are interpreted as olfactory marking of territory.[20] GROOMING: Self-grooming common but social (mutual) grooming has only been noted in captivity.[2]

REPRODUCTION AND DEVELOPMENT

Oestrous cycle of captive *Loris* occurred twice in 12-month period separated by $5\frac{1}{2}$ month anoestrous phase; each full oestrus was preceded by two episodes of lesser oestrus with incomplete genital changes (based on careful observations of a single animal).[22] Twice annual oestrous episodes, separated by anoestrous period, reported by Narayan Rao (1927), Hill (1953) and Ramiswami and Anand Kumar (1962).* Birth season in Ceylon: April–May and November–December.[2, 23] GESTATION PERIOD: 160 days (Manley, 1966a); 174 days (Nicholls, 1939). Single offspring common and twinning occasional.[26]

CAPTIVITY

The Slender Loris is not a particularly successful animal in captivity owing to delicacy and irascible temper.[27] For accounts of captive *Loris*, see Crandall (1964), Phillips (1931) and Hill (1937b). LONGEVITY RECORD:[30] 7 years 20 days, Bronx Zoo, New York. BIRTHS IN CAPTIVITY: Relatively few births have been recorded in private ownership, e.g. Nicholls (1939). Between 1959–63, only a single birth was reported from World Zoos (London, Wellcome Institute).[31]

REFERENCES

1. Ellerman, J. R. and Morrison-Scott, T. C. S. (1951)
2. Hill, W. C. Osman (1953)
3. Pocock, R. I. (1939)
4. Sanderson, I. T. (1957)
5. Subramoniam, S. (1956)
6. Nayak, U. V. (1933)
7. Murie, J. and Mivart, St. G. (1872)
8. Straus, W. L. and Wislocki, G. B. (1932)
9. Schultz, A. H. (1963a)
10. Kanagasuntheram, R. and Jayawardene, F. L. W. (1957)
11. Day, M. H. and Napier, J. R. (1963)
12. Miller, R. A. (1943)
13. James, W. Warwick (1960)
14. Wislocki, G. B. and Straus, W. L. (1933)
15. Montagna, W. and Ellis, R. A. (1963)
16. Ellis, R. A. and Montagna, W. (1963)
17. Hill, W. C. Osman (1956a)
18. Schultz, A. H. (1956)
19. Bishop, Alison (1964)
20. Ilse, D. R. (1955)
21. Hill, W. C. Osman (1938a)
22. Manley, G. H. (1966a)
23. Narayan Rao, C. R. (1927)
24. Ramiswami, L. S. and Anand Kumar, T. C. (1962)
25. Nicholls, L. (1939)
26. Schultz, A. H. (1948)
27. Crandall, L. S. (1964)
28. Phillips, W. W. A. (1931)
29. Hill, W. C. Osman (1937b)
30. Jones, M. L. (1962)
31. International Zoo Year Book, Vols. I–V (1959–65)

MACACA† Lacépède, 1799   Macaques

12 species: 46 subspecies[1, 2, 3, 4]

M. sylvana (Type species)	Barbary ape	0 subsp.
M. sinica	Toque monkey	3 subsp.
M. radiata	Bonnet monkey	2 subsp.
M. silenus	Lion-tailed macaque	0 subsp.
M. nemestrina	Pig-tailed macaque	4 subsp.
M. fascicularis [= *M. irus*]†	Crab-eating monkey	21 subsp.
M. mulatta	Rhesus monkey	4 subsp.
M. assamensis	Assamese macaque	2 subsp.
M. cyclopis	Formosan rock macaque	0 subsp.
M. speciosa†	Stump-tailed macaque	4 subsp.
M. fuscata	Japanese macaque	2 subsp.
M. maurus	Celebes or Moor macaque	4 subsp.

GEOGRAPHICAL RANGE

North Africa; Gibraltar (introduced); Asia from E. Afghanistan and Tibet to China, Japan and Formosa, south to India and Ceylon; throughout S.E. Asia including Sumatra, Java, Borneo, Philippines and Celebes, and many offshore islands. Limits of genus: 41° 20′ N.–11° S.: 10° W.–128° E. From sea-level to 13,000 ft (4000 m).[5] *M. fascicularis* has been introduced into Mauritius,[6] and *M. mulatta* into Cayo Santiago, West Indies.[7] *See* p. 403 for range of species.

ECOLOGY

HABITAT: From tropical rain forest, monsoon forest and mangrove swamps to montane forest of the Himalayas and temperate forests of China and Japan; also grassland and dry areas of scrub and cactus in India and Ceylon. *Macaca* are partly arboreal and partly terrestrial, usually sleeping in trees to avoid predators, but also frequenting cliffs and rocky places. *M. cyclopis* prefers cliffs and rocks by the seashore to the forest.[8] *M. fascicularis* typically lives near the coast in tidal creeks and mangrove swamps. In India, *M. mulatta* traditionally inhabits temples and villages.[9] In common with most species, *M. mulatta* raids plantations and cultivated fields for food; *M. silenus* is relatively shy, inhabiting secluded parts of monsoon forest of the Western Ghats.[10] ACTIVITY RHYTHM: Diurnal. DIET: Fruit, roots and young leaves; insects, grubs; crops such as rice, maize, potatoes and sugar-cane; molluscs and crustaceans (*M. fascicularis*, *M. cyclopis*).

MORPHOLOGY

External Characters

Medium to large, heavily-built, monkeys with robust limbs of almost equal length. Coat is of various shades of brown, or black. Low brow ridges are continuous over nose in ♂♂. Muzzle moderately prognathous and rounded. Nose does not extend beyond upper lip; nostrils, separated by a narrow septum, are directed obliquely outwards and downwards. Ears typically

---

† *See* Taxonomic Notes, Part III, p. 375.

PLATE 64. *Macaca nemestrina*, adult ♂, showing prominent canines and opening to left cheek pouch (by courtesy of Doris M. Sorby). *See* p. 208.

bare; upper posterior margin of pinna is angled. Ischial callosities conspicuous and not fused across midline except in *M. maurus* ♂ where they are almost confluent. Considerable sexual dimorphism in body size. In colder climates, the fur grows very long and thick. Cheek pouches are visible when full of food (*see* Plate 69, Adult ♀).

Colour and texture of coat, colour of face, characters of tail and external genitalia show considerable variability within the genus; for full details of inter-specific variation in external characters *see* Part III, Data on Macaques, p. 405.

Weights and Dimensions

Body weight range[6, 10–22] (g)	3500–18,000 (82♂♂)	2500–16,300 (63♀♀)

According to available records, *M. fascicularis* is the lightest species and *M. fuscata* the heaviest. Body weight of ♀ in % body weight of ♂: *M. fascicularis* 63·9%; *M. mulatta* 69%.[23] *See* Part III, p. 406 for detailed weights and dimensions of all species.

Internal Characters

For details of the anatomy of *Macaca*, reference should be made to works of Pocock (particularly 1925a) and to Hartman and Straus (1933). Only characters of special interest are noted here. SKULL: Facial and jaw regions are relatively heavy compared with calvarium but prognathism is only moderate. Orbits are frontally facing and in ♂ surmounted by a low supra-orbital torus. Lacrimal bone extends slightly on to face as in *Papio*. Paranasal depressions are lacking (cf. *Cercocebus*, *Papio*). External auditory meatus long as in all Old World monkeys. VERTEBRAL COLUMN: C.7/T.12/L.7/S.3. Manubrium and sternum, rodlike; five sternebrae united by cartilage. FORELIMB: Os centrale present; paired sesamoids opposite each metacarpo-phalangeal joint. Thenar muscles well developed including a deep head of flexor pollicis brevis; flexor pollicis longus not discrete from deep flexor group. D.F.: 3.4.2.5.1. HINDLIMB: Pelvis long and narrow with broad flat ischial tuberosities, widely splayed in the ♀. Femur bears a long, prominent greater trochanter; third trochanter absent and linea aspera poorly defined. Foot has digital formula 3.4.2.5.1., the hallux is abducted and of medium length as in all Old World monkeys (but particularly large in *M. nemestrina*).[24] DIGESTIVE SYSTEM: Cheek pouches well developed as in all Cercopithecinae; they form discrete muscular mucous-lined pockets extending under mandibular rami; pouch musculature contracts to propel food back into mouth; over-distension of pouches leads to ineffectiveness of voluntary musculature and pouches must be emptied manually by external pressure.[26] Stomach is a simple sac (cf. Colobinae); caecum is conical in form and lacks appendix; colon is long, mobile, tortuous, sacculated and has a mesentery throughout its length. GENITALIA: Pendulous scrotum and penis situated anteriorly over symphysis pubis;[27] typically glans penis is short and rounded with a short thick baculum. Glans is longest in *M. mulatta* and shortest in *M. fascicularis*. In *M. radiata* and *M. sinica*, penis is large and has specializations of the glans; in *M. speciosa*, the glans is particularly long and tapering, supported throughout its length by a long thin baculum.[24, 28] NERVOUS SYSTEM: Brain is large and shows similar fissural pattern to certain New World monkeys, e.g. *Cebus*. Cerebellum is large with expanded lateral lobes, floccular lobes are distinct and occupy a pit in petrous temporal bone, the subarcuate fossa. DENTITION:[29] D.F.: $\frac{2}{2}\frac{1}{1}\frac{2}{2}\frac{3}{3}=32$. INCISORS: Upper central incisors broader than laterals. CANINES show sexual dimorphism being strongly developed in ♂ and barely projecting in ♀. PREMOLARS: Bicuspid with relatively large buccal cusp; $PM._{\overline{1}}$ is adapted for shearing against upper canine ("sectorial"). MOLARS: All molars are

PLATE 65. *Macaca fascicularis*, adult and juvenile (Eric Kirkland). *See* p. 209.

quadricuspid except $M._{\overline{3}}$ which bears an extra cusp on talonid; anterior and posterior cusps united by transverse crests ("bilophodonty"). DECIDUOUS DENTITION: D.F.: $\frac{2}{2}\frac{1}{1}\frac{2}{2} = 20$. Central incisors appear at 2–3 weeks, canines and 1st milk molars at 12–14 weeks; 2nd milk molars at 23–25 weeks.[12]

Genetic Biology

CHROMOSOMES:[30, 88] 2n=42. KARYOTYPE of *M. mulatta*: 0 acrocentrics, 18 metacentrics, 22 subterminals, X=M, Y=M or A. Chiarelli (1962b) has analysed the chromosomes of all species of *Macaca* (except *M. cyclopis*) and compares the karyotypes with those of *Cynopithecus*, *Papio*, *Theropithecus* and *Cercocebus*, all of which have a diploid number of 42. In *Macaca* the X chromosome shows a great deal of variation; the Y is always very small and the centromere cannot be distinguished. BLOOD GROUPS: For MN and Rh factors, *see* Franks (1963), and for recent investigations on A–B–H and Lewis substances, *see* Wiener, Moor-Jankowski and Gordon (1966); also Owen and Anderson (1962). HAEMOGLOBINS: *M. mulatta* show transferrin type B.B. and Haptoglobin type 1–1.[35] Mobility on starch gel electrophoresis of *M. mulatta* and *M. nemestrina* is similar to that of man.[36] *M. fascicularis*: 13% have fast component P^{mi}; 24% showed occurrence of another variant Q^{mi}.[86] SERUM PROTEINS: Marked similarity in reactions between genera of Cercopithecinae (particularly *Macaca* and *Cercopithecus*) on basis of immuno-precipitin data.[37] P.T.C. TASTING:[38] Tasters : non-tasters—80 : 11.

BEHAVIOUR

Locomotor Behaviour

AUTHORS' CLASSIFICATION: Quadrupedalism. Macaques move freely on the ground as well as in the trees. Proportionate time spent in trees and on ground varies intra- as well as interspecifically. The most arboreal species include *silenus* and *nemestrina*; the most terrestrial are *sylvana*, *cyclopis* and *mulatta*. During branch-walking the hand is plantigrade but when on the ground, it is usually digitigrade.[39] Bipedalism is common when hands are carrying food objects (Hewes, 1961). LIMB PROPORTIONS: For Indices, *see* Part III, p. 394.

Hand Function

Hand prehensile, thumb fully opposable. Precision grip between thumb and index finger well-developed. Hand used in feeding and grooming. HAND PROPORTIONS: For Indices, *see* Part III, p. 402.

Social Behaviour

A considerable amount of work has been done on the behaviour of the macaque both in the laboratory and in the field. For principal references to behaviour studies, see the following:

	Laboratory	*Field*	*Captivity*
M. mulatta	40–48	7, 9, 19, 57–60	51–53, 55, 56
M. fuscata	—	61–69	—
M. nemestrina	49	—	50
M. radiata	—	70, 71	—
General	—	72	54

PLATE 66. *Macaca silenus*, young ♂ aged 3 years (by courtesy of Doris M. Sorby). *See* p. 211.

PLATE 67. Above: *Macaca fuscata*, adult ♂ (by courtesy of Masao Kawai); Below: *Macaca sylvana*

The following is an abstract of some of the above-mentioned field studies. Social behaviour in macaques is subject to many interspecific variations; intraspecific differences are generally associated with differences in habitat. *Macaca* live in large groups in which there is usually more than one adult ♂.

AVERAGE GROUP SIZE:

M. mulatta	N = 17·6	(399 groups). Temple and forest-dwelling macaques have on the average larger groups (41·9, 49·8) than railside, roadside and village dwellers (11·4, 15·1, 17·4).[60]
M. radiata	N = 34·5	Range: 6–58 (4 groups).[71]
M. fuscata	N = 194	Range: 26–570 (10 observations). Since the provisioning of *M. fuscata*, begun in 1952, group size has tended to increase.[67]
M. assamensis	N = 12, 26	(2 observations).[73]
M. fascicularis	N = 6–10	in tropical rain forest: 30 in nipa-mangrove swamp.[74, 75]

COMPOSITION OF GROUPS:

	Adult ♂	Adult ♀	Juvenile	Infant	Total	Adult sex ratio	N
M. mulatta	3·7	7·7	1·5	4·5	17·6	1♂ : 2·1♀	399 groups[60]
M. radiata	12	10·25	5·75	6·5	34·5	1♂ : 0·85♀	4 groups[71]
M. assamensis	2 4	6 10	2 8	2 4	12 26	1♂ : 2·7♀	2 groups[73]
M. fuscata						1♂ : 1·4♀	10 observ.[67]

DOMINANCE: Clearcut dominance hierarchies are formed among ♂♂, and more obscurely among ♀♀. Relationships may be friendly or antagonistic according to individual personality and/or kinship.[65, 68] Subgroups are formed within the group; central area is occupied by dominant ♂♂, plus ♀♀ and infants; in *M. mulatta*[58] and *M. fuscata*,[61] subordinate ♂♂ live in a peripheral area, or outside the group as solitary ♂♂. In *M. radiata* no ♂♂ were excluded from the central area, neither were solitary ♂♂ nor subgroups observed.[71] HOME RANGE AND TERRITORIALITY: Home ranges of up to about 3 sq miles (8 sq km) may overlap those of other groups (*M. fuscata, M. mulatta*). Inter-group behaviour is antagonistic but subordinate groups tend to avoid dominant groups so inter-group fighting is relatively rare. In an urban area however 24 severe fights were seen in 85 days observation (*M. mulatta*: 4 groups).[60] *Macaca* do not defend precise territories; sleeping trees and sites may be within the range of other groups (*M. mulatta*).

PLATE 68. *Macaca radiata*, adult ♂ and adult ♀ with twins (by courtesy of Phyllis Jay)

Macaca live in the same habitat as *Presbytis* and, in interactions, *Macaca* are dominant, usually without conflict.[71, 75] COMMUNICATION: Consistent with their complex social life, *Macaca* are capable of communicating a wide range of emotions; over 30 vocal sounds have been described by Itani (1963) for *M. fuscata*. Facial expressions have been described by van Hooff (1962) among them eyebrow-raising associated with retraction of the scalp, lip-smacking, and the "*flehmen*" face. Subordination in *Macaca* is indicated by directing the hindquarters towards a dominant animal ("presenting"); mounting the hindquarters so presented and carrying the tail erect are dominance gestures. Branch- or tree-shaking is an aggressive gesture seen in *M. fuscata*[66], *M. mulatta*[19] and *M. radiata*.[70] SOCIAL GROOMING: Incidence varies seasonally. Most common patterns are ♂–♀ grooming during consort relationships, and mother–young grooming (*M. fuscata*,[65] *M. mulatta*).[60] In *M. radiata*[71] (and in *M. fuscata*[65] during the non-breeding season) ♂–♂ and ♀–♀ grooming are more common than heterosexual grooming.

PLATE 69. *Macaca sinica*, L. to R. Adult ♀ with infant, young ♂, adult dominant ♂ (by courtesy of Phyllis Jay)

PLAY: *M. mulatta*: infants and juveniles play in their respective age groups.[60] *M. fuscata*: from 8 months, infants and juveniles play with others of the same sex.[61] *M. radiata*: play continues into adult life in ♂♂ only.[71] Play is usually preadaptive and consists of mounting, wrestling, biting and chasing, but *M. mulatta* invent apparently non-functional games, i.e. 20–30 ft jumps from trees into pools of water.[58] SEXUAL BEHAVIOUR of *M. mulatta* has been described by Carpenter (1942); that of *M. fuscata* by Tokuda (1961–62); and that of *M. radiata* by Simonds (1965). In *M. mulatta* and *M. fuscata*, consort relationships are formed; copulation consists of several mountings before ejaculation. (For comparative behaviour, *see* Tokuda, 1961–62). In *M. radiata*, however, consort relationships are not formed and copulation consists of only one mounting;[71] similar copulatory behaviour has been observed in *M. fascicularis*.[76] Incidence of copulation varies seasonally;[77] in *M. fuscata* it is restricted to October–April, with peak

PLATE 70. *Macaca fuscata*; above: 8-year old ♀ running bipedally; below: erect posture and bipedal walking in the (by courtesy of Masao Kawai)

frequency January and February; in *M. radiata*, copulation was observed throughout the year, with peak frequency October and November. Copulation between mother and son has never been observed in *M. fuscata*.[78]

Macaca are highly social animals. Male role is to lead, organize progression, settle quarrels—in fact to impose discipline on the group. Female role is to produce and rear young—usually once a year—and to continue a relationship with them after weaning, thus providing continuity and bonds of kinship within the group (cf. *Presbytis*). Paternity is not recognized in macaque society, but ♂♂ occasionally show "paternal" care towards infants (*M. fuscata*,[63] *M. sylvana*[79] and, in the laboratory, *M. radiata*).[42]

REPRODUCTION AND DEVELOPMENT

For comparative date on reproduction in Macaque species, see Table 4, p. 406, Part III. Menstrual cycles occur throughout the year; where data are available, oestrus appears to be seasonal. Typical manifestations of oestrus have been described in Table 2, showing specific variation of adult macaques (*see* Part III, p. 405); there is great variability between individuals but sexual skin changes are usually more pronounced in adolescent than in older ♀♀. Sexual skin of *M. sinica* and *M. radiata* shows no change during oestrus; a copious discharge of clear strong-smelling mucus from the vagina occurs not only during periods of sexual receptivity but also frequently throughout the cycle.[80, 82]

Seasonal enlargement of the testes of *M. mulatta*, accompanied by increased reddening of the sexual skin of the ♂, has been observed to correspond with peak frequency of copulation.[83]

Spiegel (1954) has described the birth of *M. fascicularis*. Hartman (1928) reported the birth of *M. mulatta*; at birth, eyes closed, but open within 2 hours; no teeth visible.[84] For age estimation from dentition (*M. mulatta*), *see* Schultz (1933a). *Complete deciduous dentition* at 6 months; *1st permanent molars* erupt at 1 year 8–9 months; *complete permanent dentition*: 7–8 years or later. Although sexual maturity is reached at about 4 years, full growth is not complete until 10th year in ♂♂, 6th year in ♀♀ (*M. fascicularis*).[21]

CAPTIVITY

Macaca are very adaptable and have proved relatively easy to keep and breed in captivity. All 12 species have been kept successfully in Zoos. LONGEVITY RECORD:[85] Longevity for the genus: *M. sinica*, 29 years 4 months, Colombo Zoo. For longevity records of species, *see* Macaque section, Part III, p. 407.

REFERENCES

1. Allen, G. M. (1939)
2. Ellerman, J. R. and Morrison-Scott, T. C. S. (1951)
3. Chasen, F. N. (1940)
4. Laurie, E. M. O. and Hill, J. E. (1954)
5. Elliot, D. G. (1913)
6. British Museum (Natural History) Records
7. Carpenter, C. R. (1942a)
8. Swinhoe, R. (1862)
9. Southwick, C. H., Beg, M. A. and Siddiqi, M. R. (1961)
10. Pocock, R. I. (1939)
11. Hazama, N. (1964)
12. Schultz, A. H. (1933a)

13. Schultz, A. H. (1941a)

14. Davis, D. Dwight (1962)

15. Washburn, S. L. (1942)

16. Miller, G. S. (1907a)

17. Lyon, M. W. (1907b)

18. Lyon, M. W. (1908b)

19. Altmann, S. A. (1962)

20. Hartman, C. G. (1938)

21. Spiegel, A. (1956)

22. Veterinary Officer's Reports, London Zoo

23. Schultz, A. H. (1956)

24. Pocock, R. I. (1925a)

25. Hartman, C. G. and Straus, W. L. (1933)

26. Huber, E. (1933)

27. Wislocki, G. B. (1933)

28. Pocock, R. I. (1921)

29. James, W. Warwick (1960)

30. Bender, M. A. and Chu, E. R. Y. (1963)

31. Chiarelli, B. (1962b)

32. Franks, D. (1963)

33. Wiener, A. S., Moor-Jankowski, J. and Gordon, E. B. (1966)

34. Owen, R. D. and Anderson, D. R. (1962)

35. Lange, V. and Schmitt, J. (1963)

36. Buettner-Janusch, J. and Buettner-Janusch, V. (1964)

37. Goodman, M., Maisel, H. and Syner, F. N. (In press)

38. Chiarelli, B. (1963b)

39. Jolly, C. J. (1965)

40. Harlow, H. F. and Harlow, M. K. (1961)

41. Harlow, H. F. and Harlow, M. K. (1962)

42. Harlow, H. F. and Harlow, M. K. (1965)

43. Harlow, H. F., Harlow, M. K. and Hansen, E. W. (1963)

44. Harlow, H. F. and Zimmerman, R. R. (1959)

45. Hines, M. (1942)

46. Mason, W. A. (1960)

47. Mason, W. A. (1961a)

48. Mason, W. A. (1961b)

49. Cole, J. (1963)

50. Corner, E. J. H. (1955)

51. Chance, M. R. A. (1956)

52. Hinde, R. A. and Rowell, T. E. (1962)

53. Rowell, T. E. and Hinde, R. A. (1962)

54. Hooff, J. A. R. A. M. van (1962)

55. Bernstein, I. S. and Mason, W. A. (1963)

56. Bernstein, I. S. (1964)

57. Southwick, C. H. (1962)

58. Koford, C. B. (1963)

59. Koford, C. B. (1965)

60. Southwick, C. H., Beg, M. A. and Siddiqi, M. R. (1965)

61. Imanishi, K. (1957)

62. Frisch, J. E. (1959)

63. Itani, J. (1959)

64. Kawamura, S. (1959)

65. Tokuda, K. (1961–62)

66. Itani, J. (1963)

67. Itani, J., Tokuda, K., Furuya, Y., Kano, K. and Shin, Y. (1963)

68. Yamada, M. (1963)

69. Mizuhara, H. (1964)

70. Nolte, Angela (1955)

71. Simonds, P. E. (1965)

72. Washburn, S. L., Jay, Phyllis C. and Lancaster, Jane B. (1965)

73. Carpenter, C. R. (1958) quoted in Altmann, S. A. (1962)

74. Banks, E. (1949)

75. Furuya, Y. (1961–62a)

76. Furuya, Y. (1961–62b)

77. Lancaster, Jane B. and Lee, R. B. (1965)

78. Kawai, M. and Mizuhara, H. (1959)

79. MacRoberts, M. (1965) quoted in Washburn, S. L., Jay, Phyllis C. and Lancaster, Jane B. (1965)

80. Zuckerman, S. (1930)

81. Spiegel, A. (1954)

82. Hill, W. C. Osman (1939b)

83. Sade, D. S. (1964)

84. Hartman, C. G. (1928)

85. Jones, M. L. (1962)

86. Barnicot, N. A., Huehns, E. R. and Jolly, C. J. (In press)

87. Hewes, G. W. (1961)

88. Chiarelli, B. (1966b)

MANDRILLUS† Ritgen, 1824 Drills and Mandrills

2 species: 2 subspecies

M. sphinx (Type species)	Mandrill	0 subsp.
M. leucophaeus	Drill	2 subsp.

GEOGRAPHICAL RANGE [1]

Africa. Range of both species is relatively limited and is confined to high forest regions between the Cross R. in S.E. Nigeria and the R. Congo. Both species are found in Cameroun, S. of Sanaga R., Gabon, Congo (Brazza) and Spanish Guinea. Drills, alone, extend westward to the Cross R.; also Fernando Póo.[23]

ECOLOGY

HABITAT:[2] Inhabitants of rain forest but also of mountainous regions of Cameroun. Usually seen in rocky clearings of forest floor. Principally ground-living but feed and sleep in trees. ACTIVITY RHYTHM: Diurnal. DIET:* Omnivorous.

MORPHOLOGY

External Characters[3, 4]

Large animals showing well-marked sexual dimorphism. Both sexes of both species have massive muzzles with prominent, longitudinal, fusiform, rugose swellings on either side of nose; these swellings are smaller in drills than in mandrills. Eyes are deepset, ears flesh-coloured in *M. sphinx*, black in *M. leucophaeus*. The coat of ♂ mandrill is long and thick, dark brown to charcoal grey in colour, with fringes of yellow and orange. The nose and nostrils of the ♂ are lacquer-red and the longitudinal paranasal swellings are a brilliant electric blue. Cheek tufts are white and the beard yellow to orange; hair rises from ridge on brow to crest on top of head; the ♀ mandrill lacks bicoloured mask of the ♂. The genitalia of the ♂ mandrill correspond, broadly speaking, to the colour combination of the face.[5] The circumanal region is red; lateral to the callosities there is a blue patch fading peripherally to lilac; posterior scrotum lilac, anterior pink; pubic region scarlet and glans penis pink. Perineal colouration is not developed in ♀.[6]

The coat of the drill is olivegreen and the mask is jet black. Beard and cheek tufts white. The perineal area of the ♂ drill shows even more vivid colouration than that of the mandrill, and of a somewhat metallic nature. Sexual swelling of the ♀ drill resembles that of *Cercocebus* and is relatively unpigmented.[6] Both species have moderate ischial callosities, pink in colour, which, in ♂♂, are fused across the midline as in *Papio*. The tail in both species is stumpy and the forelimbs appear longer and stronger than the hindlimbs giving the trunk a backward-sloping inclination.

Weights and Dimensions

Body weight (g)	*M. sphinx*	19,522 (♂)		
Head and body length (mm)	*M. sphinx*	810 (♂)	*M. leucophaeus*	700 (♂)
Tail length (mm)	*M. sphinx*	70 (♂)	*M. leucophaeus*	120 (♂)

---

† *See* Taxonomic Notes, p. 375.

Internal Characters

For principal anatomical characters, see *Papio*. Distinguishing features are noted here. SKULL: Massively constructed, markedly prognathic, heavy bony swellings on maxilla. In the ♂ a supra-orbital torus and a sagittal crest are present. Mandible is long, stout and curved along its lower border and almost wholly lacking an angle. Palate is wide in front and narrow at the back, thus the premolar tooth series converge posteriorly; this pattern is quite unlike the parallel tooth-rows of *Papio*. HANDS: Unlike those of *Papio*; the length of the hand relative to the length of the arm is greater, the palm is broader and the fingers and thumb are longer (*see* Hand Proportions, Part III, p. 402). FEET:[7] Differ from those of *Papio* in the relatively greater length of the digits especially the big toe which is strikingly enlarged. Clearly the characters of the hand and foot are adaptations to bring about a greater span in the extremities in relation to branch-walking habits.[11] DENTITION: D.F.: $\frac{2}{2}\frac{1}{1}\frac{2}{2}\frac{3}{3} = 32$. Incisors are rather small in both upper and lower jaws. Wide diastema between upper incisors and canine. Molars are similar in form to those of *Papio* but differ in the curvature of the tooth-rows. Size increases from M.1–3 in both jaws.

Genetic Biology

CHROMOSOMES:[9, 22] 2n = 42 (♂ + ♀ *M. sphinx*, ♂ + ♀ *M. leucophaeus*). P.T.C. TASTING:[10] Tasters: non-tasters = 48 : 8 (86%). BLOOD GROUPS:[25] Drill shows human A. Lewis substance absent in saliva.

BEHAVIOUR

Locomotor Behaviour

AUTHORS' CLASSIFICATION: Quadrupedalism. Mandrills show a digitigrade gait of forelimbs both on the ground and in trees when branch-walking.[11] LIMB PROPORTIONS: For Indices, *see* Part III, p. 394.

Hand Function

Hand prehensile, thumb opposable. High "opposability" index (*see* Hand Proportions in Part III) indicating well-developed index-finger to thumb precision grip as in *Papio*. Precision and power grip well differentiated.

Social Behaviour

At present no field studies are available and information on drills and mandrills in the wild is wholly anecdotal.[12, 13, 14]

Psychobiology

Darwin (1872) and Elliot (1913) state that colour of facial and perineal skin of mandrill is intensified when animal becomes excited. These observations have not been confirmed by Hill (1955).

REPRODUCTION AND DEVELOPMENT

Little is known of the reproductive cycle; mean menstrual cycle length: 32·6 days ± 0·9 days (*M. leucophaeus*).[24] Swelling of the sexual skin observed in both species.[24] GESTATION PERIOD: 245 days.[17] HYBRIDS:[18, 19] A number of ♀ *Mandrillus* crosses with *Cercocebus*, *Macaca* and *Papio* reported in captivity; fewer ♂ *Mandrillus* crosses recorded.

PLATE 72. Drill, *Mandrillus leucophaeus*, ♂ aged 7 years (by courtesy of Doris M. Sorby)

CAPTIVITY

Births in captivity are now very common.[20] LONGEVITY RECORD (up to 1962):[21] *M. leucophaeus*, 28 years 6 months, Milwaukee Zoo, U.S.A.; *M. sphinx*, 27 years 3 months, National Zoological Park, Washington.

REFERENCES

1. Booth, A. H. (1958)
2. Jeannin, A. (1936)
3. Forbes, H. O. (1897)
4. Sanderson, I. T. (1957)
5. Morris, R. and Morris, D. (1966)
6. Hill, W. C. Osman (1955b)
7. Pocock, R. I. (1925a)
8. Wiener, A. S., *et. al.* (1964)
9. Bender, M. A. and Chu, E. H. Y. (1963)
10. Chiarelli, B. (1963b)
11. Jolly, C. J. (1965)
12. Lydekker, R. (1893–94)
13. Avon, F. (1963)
14. Bates, G. L. (1905)
15. Darwin, C. (1872)
16. Elliot, D. G. (1913)
17. International Zoo Year Book, Vol. I (1959)
18. Chiarelli, B. (1963c)
19. Gray, Annie P. (1954)
20. International Zoo Year Book, Vols. I–V (1959–1965)
21. Jones, M. L. (1962)
22. Chiarelli, B. (1962b)
23. Zukowsky, L. (1922)
24. Zuckerman, S. (1937)

PLATE 71. Mandrill, *Mandrillus sphinx*, young ♂ aged 3 years (by courtesy of Doris M. Sorby)

MICROCEBUS E. Geoffroy, 1828   Mouse Lemurs

2 species: 2 subspecies[1]

M. murinus (Type species)	Lesser Mouse Lemur	2 subsp.
M. coquereli	Coquerel's Mouse Lemur	0 subsp.

GEOGRAPHICAL RANGE [2]

Madagascar. *M. murinus* is found in all forested areas on E. and W. coasts, though it is probably less common on W. coast south of Bombétoka Bay. *M. coquereli* has a more limited distribution in extreme N.W. in the region of Ampasindava Bay. Schwarz (1931c) states that the type locality of *M. coquereli* is Morondava in S.W. Madagascar.

ECOLOGY

HABITAT: Arboreal. Denizen of tropical forest. Nests in bushes and holes in trees; nests are lined with dry leaves.[2, 3] According to Shaw (1879) *M. m. smithii* is seen in the tops of the highest trees amongst small branches. Petter (1962c) states that *M. murinus* is seen on branches of all sizes. ACTIVITY RHYTHM:[2] Nocturnal. Some evidence of seasonal lethargy, but not nearly as marked as in *Cheirogaleus*[20]. DIET:[2, 3] Principally insectivorous and possibly carnivorous, also fruits. PREDATORS:[16] Goshawks (*Astur henstii*).

MORPHOLOGY

External Characters[4]

Very small animals weighing approximately 60 g. Fur is soft, generally brown or grey in colour with a reddish tinge grading to white or yellowish-grey on underparts; dorsal stripe generally darker than body. Face is marked by white median nasal stripe that is absent in *M. coquereli*. Face has shortish muzzle; ears large, mobile, rounded and membranous. Tail is generally longer than body. Limbs short; legs longer than arms. HANDS: Palmar pads are sharply defined and show typical lemurine arrangement. D.F.: 4.3.5.2.1. MAMMAE: 2 pectoral and 2 abdominal.[5] Carpal vibrissae present.

Weights and Dimensions[4]*

	M. murinus	*M. coquereli*
Head and body length (mm)	130	250
Tail length (mm)	170	280

Internal Characters[4, 6, 7]

For general characters of Lemuridae, see *Lemur*. Principal differences only noted here. SKULL: Remarkably similar in general form to *Tupaia*.[7] Bony palate very long and often

PLATE 73. *Microcebus murinus* (by courtesy of Gilbert H. Manley)

fenestrated; large premaxillary element in face. Ethmoid exposed on orbital wall (as in Lorisiformes). POST-CRANIAL: Tarsus elongated (43% foot length)[8] in cuboid and navicular elements. HANDS: Papillary ridges of simple type, thumb not markedly divergent. ALIMENTARY TRACT:[9, 10] Colon primitive in form, lacking ansa coli; caecum simple and globular. RESPIRATORY: Accessory vocal sac extending on to back and flanks. GENITO-URINARY: Penis has a horny pad on its apex with urethral opening dorsal to it. VISUAL SYSTEM: Retina contains rods only.[7] C.N.S.: Most primitive brain among primates, still showing piriform lobe separated from temporal by a faint rhinal sulcus; see Clark (1931). DENTITION: D.F.: $\frac{2}{2}\frac{1}{1}\frac{3}{3}\frac{3}{3}=36$. Incisors: Upper central incisors larger than lateral pair; diastema lacking between centrals. Premolars: PM.$^{\underline{1}}$ small (cf. Cheirogaleus); PM.$^{\underline{3}}$ bicuspid; PM.$_{\overline{1}}$ somewhat caniniform but not as in Lemur. Molars as in Lemur but less evidence of hypocones.

Genetic Biology

CHROMOSOMES:[12] 2n = 66 (♂♂ + ♀♀ M. murinus murinus). Karyotype shows all but two (subterminals) to be acrocentric.

BEHAVIOUR

Locomotor Behaviour[2]

AUTHORS' CLASSIFICATION: Quadrupedalism. Microcebus show a type of scurrying gait; that is, they progress in a series of short runs (Fr. par saccades) like a rodent. Capable of quite considerable leaping (better than Cheirogaleus) using the tail for balance.

Hand Function

Hand—prehensile; thumb—pseudo-opposable. Digits at rest on a flat surface are widely divergent and hyper-extended at metacarpo-phalangeal and distal inter-phalangeal joints (as in Galago). Prehensive pattern however is like that of lemurs rather than lorises.[13]

Resting Behaviour[2]

Rests in normal quadrupedal position but assumes sitting posture when eating. Sleeps rolled in a ball. Tail is sometimes twisted round a support.[3]

Social Behaviour

GROUP SIZE:[2] Solitary but may be gregarious during sleep in nests. Gregarious in captivity. Range and territoriality unknown. GROOMING: Not observed in captivity.[14] VOCALIZA-TION:[2, 14] Not particularly vocal; cries are high-pitched, verging on the supersonic. SEXUAL BEHAVIOUR: Genital and anal marking behaviour by ♂ observed before copulation.

REPRODUCTION AND DEVELOPMENT [15]

(M. murinus): Polyoestrous. OESTROUS CYCLE: Usually between 45 and 55 days. During anoestrous phase vaginal orifice is completely closed over by fur-bearing skin (see also Cheirogaleus and Galago). At the beginning of cycle, area at base of clitoris swells up and vaginal opening appears. OESTRUS: 2–5 days. GESTATION: 59–62 days. NO. OF YOUNG: 1–3.

BIRTH SEASON: (In the wild) December to March; (Northern Hemisphere) May–September.
GROWTH OF INFANT: At birth, Head & Body 37–50 mm: Tail 25–32 mm: Weight 2·7–4·3 g
(approx. 6% adult ♀ weight). Infants climb at 15 days, walk at 20 days, are fully independent
at 60 days. Sexual maturity at 7–10 months. Lactation lasts 45 days.

CAPTIVITY

Aggressive in captivity, although Petter (1965) states that there is an intra-specific difference
in this character. LONGEVITY RECORD:[17] *M. coquereli*, 15 years 5 months, London, Zoological
Gardens. BREEDING RECORDS: Relatively easy to breed in captivity; successful breeding in
London Zoo and in a laboratory at the Faculty of Medicine in Paris since 1957.[18] *See* Manley
(1966b) for review of laboratory suitability.

REFERENCES

1. Schwarz, E. (1931c)
2. Petter, J. J. (1962c)
3. Shaw, G. A. (1879)
4. Hill, W. C. Osman (1953)
5. Schultz, A. H. (1948)
6. Mivart, St. George (1873)
7. Clark, W. E. Le Gros (1959)
8. Schultz, A. H. (1963a)
9. Mitchell, P. Chalmers (1905)
10. Mitchell, P. Chalmers (1916)
11. Clark, W. E. Le Gros (1931)
12. Chu, E. H. Y. and Bender, M. A. (1962)
13. Bishop, Alison (1962, 1964)
14. Andrew, R. J. (1964)
15. Petter-Rousseaux, A. (1964)
16. Petter, J. J. (1965)
17. Jones, M. L. (1962)
18. Bourlière, F., Petter-Rousseaux, A. and Petter, J. J. (1962)
19. Manley, G. H. (1966b)
20. Bourlière, F. and Petter-Rousseaux, A. (1966)

NASALIS   E. Geoffroy, 1812   Proboscis Monkeys

1 species: 0 subspecies[1]

Nasalis larvatus Wurmb, 1781

GEOGRAPHICAL RANGE [1, 2, 3]

Borneo. *Nasalis* have been reported from North Borneo (Sabah), Brunei, S., E., and W. Borneo (Kalimantan) and from Sarawak.

ECOLOGY [1, 3]

HABITAT: Forest and mangrove swamp. Arboreal. Usually found near rivers, or in nipa palm and mangrove swamps along the coast and tidal creeks. Prefer the shadier mangrove in the day, retiring to the taller pedada trees at night.[3] ACTIVITY RHYTHM: Diurnal. DIET: Young leaves and growing tips of mangrove and pedada trees; about 5% fruits and flowers.[3] PREDATORS: Clouded leopard.[1]

MORPHOLOGY

External Characters

Medium to large monkeys with brick-red fur on head, shoulders, back, upper arms and thighs, blending to pale grey on arms and legs but sharply differentiated from pale grey of rump patch and tail. Hands and feet well-furred, pale grey, with dark palms and soles. Redbrown fur is darkest on crown with a dark stripe continuing down back of neck on to shoulders, contrasting with cream-coloured cheeks and ruff. Face bare and pinkish-brown; nose of adult ♂ is long, bulbous and drooping; ♀ nose is less developed and slightly upturned. In the young infant, the face is a deep blue, the nose slightly upturned.[4] Large, separated ischial callosities present. Toes II and III frequently webbed as far as middle, or distal end, of middle phalanx.[5] Sexual dimorphism in body weight is marked.

Weights and Dimensions[1, 2, 5]

	♂	♀	♀ in % ♂
Body weight range (g)	11,700–23,608 (21♂♂)	8165–11,794 (18♀♀)	57
Head and body length range (mm)	555–723 (11♂♂)	540–605 (4♀♀)	90
Tail length range (mm)	660–745 (11♀♀)	570–620 (4♀♀)	84

Adult ♂♂ are almost twice as heavy as adult ♀♀; ♀ tails are relatively shorter than ♂ tails. (♀ % of ♂ based on midpoint of range.)

PLATE 74. Opposite. *Nasalis larvatus*, young ♂ (San Diego Zoo; photo by R. Van Nostrand)

PLATE 75. *Nasalis larvatus*, ♀ and infant (San Diego Zoo), see p. 230

Internal Characters

Anatomy is in most respects typical of Asiatic Colobinae (*see* Ayer on the Anatomy of *Semnopithecus entellus*, also profile on *Presbytis*). SKULL:[7] Facial region is orthognathous with a straight profile and heavy jaws. Nasal bones are long and straight (cf. *Presbytis* where the nasal bones are short). Interorbital width is relatively narrow compared with other Colobinae except *Simias*. DENTITION: D.F.: $\frac{2}{2} \frac{1}{1} \frac{2}{2} \frac{3}{3} = 32$. According to James (1960) the sectorial anterior lower premolar is particularly large in *Nasalis*.*

BEHAVIOUR

Locomotor Behaviour[1, 3]

AUTHORS' CLASSIFICATION: Quadrupedalism. Subtype, Old World Semibrachiation. The proboscis monkey hangs for short periods, and sometimes moves for short distances, using the arms alone. Characteristically leaps with arms outstretched using the whip of slender branches to provide a springboard effect for take-off; also prone to drop considerable distances into a mass of small branches; and to leap into streams from heights of 50 ft (15 m). [It is to be noted that healed fractures are common, being found in 7 adults in a series of 25.][5] Large heavy ♂♂ are said to move with considerable circumspection.[1] Proboscis monkeys swim often and freely,[3] even swimming underwater for a recorded distance of 30–40 ft (9–12 m).[9] LIMB PROPORTIONS: *See* Indices (Part III, p. 394). Forelimb (Radius + Humerus) is considerably longer in proportion to trunk length than in *Presbytis* or *Colobus*. Hindlimb (Femur + Tibia) is only slightly longer proportionately than in *Presbytis*;[10] thus, the Intermembral Index in *Nasalis* is high.

Hand Function*

Hand prehensile, thumb opposable. Hand is used in feeding to pluck leaves and to stuff large quantities of leaves into the mouth.[1, 3]

Social Behaviour[3]

Loosely cohesive groups of about 20 in number (Range: 12–27: 8 observations) inhabiting a territory with flexible boundaries; no defence of territory has been observed. Larger groups have been reported; this is thought to be due to the peaceful mingling of 2 groups.* A group may contain several adult ♂♂; solitary ♂♂ have also been observed. HOME RANGE: About $\frac{1}{2}$ sq mile or more per group. VOCALIZATION: Apart from shrieks of excitement or fear, which are the most common sounds, old ♂♂ produce a long nasal snort which appears to discipline the group; in warning, ♂♂ give loud "honks" in which the long drooping nose rigidly straightens out with each "honk". Except for mothers and young, *Nasalis* sleep separately and in trees as much as 1000 ft (300 m) apart.

PLATE 76. *Nasalis larvatus*, subadult ♀ (by courtesy of Sarawak Museum), *see* p. 231

REPRODUCTION AND DEVELOPMENT [5]

There appears to be no restricted breeding season. *Nasalis* seem not to become pregnant until the permanent dentition is complete. Gestation is thought to be about 166 days. WEIGHT OF NEWBORN: 450 g. Infant is carried on the mother's chest; face, which is deep blue at birth, becomes slate-grey at about 3 months.

CAPTIVITY

Until recently Proboscis monkeys have not been successfully kept in Zoos outside Borneo. The first breeding success in captivity, at San Diego Zoo, has recently been reported.[4] For captivity problems, *see* Pournelle (1960) and Hill (1964b). LONGEVITY RECORD:[4] $4\frac{1}{2}$ years at San Diego Zoo.

REFERENCES

1. Davis, D. Dwight (1962)
2. Chasen, F. N. (1940)
3. Kern, J. A. (1964)
4. Pournelle, G. H. (1966)
5. Schultz, A. H. (1942)
6. Ayer, A. A. (1948)

7. Verheyen, W. N. (1962)
8. James, W. Warwick (1960)
9. Harrisson, B. (Personal communication)
10. Schultz, A. H. (1953)
11. Pournelle, G. H. (1960)
12. Hill, W. C. Osman (1964b)

NYCTICEBUS[†] E. Geoffroy, 1812   Slow Lorises

2 species: 9 subspecies[1, 2]

N. coucang (Type species)	Slow Loris	9 subsp.
N. pygmaeus	Lesser slow loris	0 subsp.

GEOGRAPHICAL RANGE [1, 2, 3]

South-East Asia. From Assam in India, southwards and eastwards into Burma—possibly Yunnan—Thailand, Vietnam, Laos, Cambodia, Malaya, Sumatra, Java, Borneo and many adjacent islands including Tioman I., Natuna Besar (Bunguran), and Bangka. *See also* Banks (1961). Its presence in the Philippines is doubtful except on Tawitawi and some other islands in the Sulu Archipelago.[4] LIMITS OF GENUS: Latitudes: 28° N.–9° S.: Longitudes: 90°–122° E. Sea level to 4000 ft (1220 m).[5]

ECOLOGY

HABITAT: Arboreal. Tropical rain forest; logged forest.[6] High branches of trees, also low shrubs.[7] ACTIVITY RHYTHM: Nocturnal. DIET:[6, 8, 9] Insects, fruit, leaves, seeds, birds, lizards, birds' eggs.

MORPHOLOGY

External Characters[7]

Small compact animals with short very dense woolly fur, mainly brown, reddish-brown or grey, sometimes with a frosted appearance due to long scanty white-tipped hairs. Short rounded muzzle with naked rhinarium; large, forwardly-directed eyes with pupil which narrows to a vertical slit; ears small and inconspicuous. Distinctive markings are a white line between eyes from forehead to muzzle, dark markings around eyes, and a dark median dorsal stripe extending on to the crown whence it may diverge to ears and to join the dark eye markings as in *N. coucang coucang*; in *N. coucang bengalensis* the head is pale and dorsal stripe does not extend beyond the crown. In *N. pygmaeus*, the stripe is redbrown anteriorly, becoming brownish-black posteriorly; *N. pygmaeus* is only about half the size of *N. coucang* (*see* Weights and Dimensions). No sexual dimorphism in colour and little in size.

Limbs subequal in length, but legs more powerful; hands are broad with short, widely-divergent thumb, index finger reduced but less so than in *Perodicticus*. Nails on all digits except short 2nd toe which bears a toilet claw; big toe opposes other digits at 180°. Heels are haired; no webbing of digits as in *Arctocebus*. Short tail generally concealed in fur. MAMMAE: 2 or 3 pairs.[10]

[†] *See* Taxonomic Notes, Part III, p. 375.

PLATE 77. *Nycticebus coucang*

Weights and Dimensions[6, 12, 13, 14, 15, 16]

	♂	♀	♀ in % of ♂
Body weight range (g)	1012–1675 (9♂♂)	1105–1370 (3♀♀)	92
Head and body length range (mm)	265–380 (15♂♂)	268–335 (14♀♀)	94
N. pygmaeus	190 (1♂)		—

Nycticebus coucang is said to weigh up to 2 kg (Manley, 1966b). (♀ in % of ♂ is based on midpoint of ranges.)

Internal Characters

See *Loris*: only principal differences noted here. SKULL:[7] Cranium more globular than *Loris* but broader from side to side. Foramen magnum lies relatively far back. Well-marked sagittal crest in some adult ♂ and ♀ (Seth, 1964). Orbits smaller than in *Loris*. Premaxillaries do not project in front of incisive alveolar margin. Ascending ramus of mandible stouter than in *Loris* with more rounded angular process and thicker coronoid process. POST-CRANIAL SKELETON: Vertebral column:[17] Increase in thoracic and sacral vertebrae but reduction in lumbar series (*Loris*: T.13–15, L.8–9, S.2–5; *Nycticebus*: T.15–17, L.7–8, S.5–9). In this character, *Nycticebus* is like the African Lorisinae. Limb bones more robust than in *Loris*. FOOT: Posterior projection of calcaneum, forming the heel, more pronounced but whole foot relatively shorter; pedal phalanges relatively longer than in *Loris*. Joints of foot extremely mobile allowing a large range of adaptability for the foot in prehension.[15] DENTITION: $\frac{2}{2}\frac{1}{1}\frac{3}{3}\frac{3}{3}=36$. Upper lateral incisors may be absent.[7, 12] Upper molars are more primitive than in *Loris* having less pronounced hypocones. M.$\underline{3}$ much reduced (as in *Perodicticus*). ALIMENTARY SYSTEM: Caecum is longer and the ansa coli more complicated than in *Loris*. VASCULAR SYSTEM: Cardio-vascular system has been studied in detail by Davies (1947) who discusses functional significance of retia mirabilia.

Genetic Biology

CHROMOSOMES:[19, 20] 2n=50 (1♂ and 1♀ *N. coucang*); 2n=50 (1♂ *N. pygmaeus*). In ♂ *N. coucang* examined by Klinger (1963) all chromosomes were metacentric.

BEHAVIOUR

Locomotor Behaviour

AUTHORS' CLASSIFICATION: Quadrupedalism. Slow-climbing sub-type. Prehensive adaptations of hands and feet are very marked.[15] Slow deliberate progress consists of un-clamping the digits from one support and clamping on to another, moving the body smoothly forward. Limbs are used in any direction and any sequence. No leaping. Travel quadrupedally on top of branch, or beneath, sometimes moving spirally to avoid projecting branches. Frequently hang by feet, leaving both hands free for grasping food which is eaten in this position. Erect or semi-erect trunk can be supported by hindlimbs alone. LIMB PROPORTIONS: Limbs are much shorter, relative to trunk height, than in *Loris*.[22] Hindlimbs are slightly longer than forelimbs, and forearms are equal in length to upper arms; in this last character, *Nycticebus* is more like *Perodicticus* than *Loris*. *See* Part III, p. 394, for Indices.

Hand Function

Hand is prehensile and thumb is pseudo-opposable. Function is very similar to that of *Loris* and *Perodicticus*.[23] HAND PROPORTIONS: As in *Loris*, *see* Part III, p. 402.

Resting Posture

Sleeps rolled up in a ball with head and arms buried between the thighs.[6]

Social Behaviour

Nothing is known of the range and territoriality of *Nycticebus*; they are found singly or in pairs. VOCALIZATION: Several types of call have been observed; a low growl and high-pitched chatter, both expressing disapproval; a greeting call; and a high clear whistle made frequently by the ♀ during oestrus.[24] GROOMING: Careful and complete self-grooming, including the ears, takes place at least once a day, using the dental comb, sub-lingua and the toilet claws.[24] MARKING BEHAVIOUR: Urine marking observed in captivity.[5]

REPRODUCTION AND DEVELOPMENT

Continuously polyoestrous. OESTROUS CYCLE:[26] 42·3 days (Average of 17 cycles of 2♀♀). RANGE: 37–54 days. EXTERNAL SIGNS: Reddening and turgidity of the genitalia and enlargement of the vaginal opening. GESTATION PERIOD:[26] 193 days.* Zuckerman (1932b) suggested absence of discrete breeding period. NO. OF YOUNG: Single births but twinning recorded.[28] Young is born with eyes open; it is immediately able to cling to the mother's underside.[7] Before 24 hours old, it may be left hanging on its own under a branch for a short period. Independent locomotion begins at about 2 weeks. Infant is also carried by ♂ or earlier offspring, and may be found clinging to ♂ during sleep.[28] LACTATION: 3–6 months approximately, supplemented by solid food from about the 10th day.[29] Young may remain dependent on mother for 9 months in captivity even though almost fully grown.[28]

CAPTIVITY

BIRTHS IN CAPTIVITY: 3 births were recorded in World Zoos between 1959–1963;[30] 10 births were recorded at Bronx Zoo between 1949–1955.[28] LONGEVITY RECORD:[31] 12 years 8 months (*N. coucang*), Bronx Zoo, New York. DIET:[28] Large quantities of fruit; also dog-food, bone-meal, raw horseflesh in small quantities; fortified by cod liver oil. As pointed out by Hediger (1950), *N. coucang* prefers its cage to smell of urine; whenever the cage is cleaned, *N. coucang* will drink quantities of water "and sprinkle the nice clean floor systematically, just like a watering cart." *Nycticebus* must be protected from overexposure to light.

REFERENCES

1. Ellerman, J. R. and Morrison-Scott, T. C. S. (1951)
2. Chasen, F. N. (1940)
3. Allen, G. M. (1938)
4. Taylor, E. H. (1934)
5. Thomas, O. (1927c)
6. Davis, D. Dwight (1962)
7. Hill, W. C. Osman (1953)
8. Harrison, J. L. (1962)
9. Pocock, R. I. (1939)
10. Schultz, A. H. (1948)
11. Banks, E. (1961)
12. Lyon, M. W. (1907a)
13. Bonhote, J. L. (1907)
14. Zoological Society of London: Veterinary Officer's Reports
15. Grand, T. I. (1967)
16. Manley, G. H. (1966b)
17. Schultz, A. H. (1961)
18. Schultz, A. H. (1963a)
19. Chu, E. H. Y. and Bender, M. A. (1962)
20. Bender, M. A. and Chu, E. H. Y. (1963)
21. Klinger, H. P. (1963)
22. Schultz, A. H. (1956)
23. Bishop, Alison (1964)
24. Butterfield, R. S. (1954)
25. Hediger, H. (1950)
26. Manley, G. H. (1966a)
27. Zuckerman, S. (1932b)
28. Crandall, L. S. (1964)
29. Hill, W. C. Osman (1937a)
30. International Zoo Year Book, Vols. I–V (1959–65)
31. Jones, M. L. (1962)
32. Davies, D. V. (1947)
33. Seth, P. K. (1964)

2 species: 3 subspecies [1, 2, 3]

P. troglodytes troglodytes	Tschego
P. troglodytes verus	Common or masked chimpanzee
P. troglodytes schweinfurthii	Eastern or long-haired chimpanzee
P. paniscus	Pygmy chimpanzee

N.B. The "common chimpanzee" in Great Britain is the familiar name for *P.t. verus*; in Europe, *P.t. troglodytes* is regarded as the "common chimpanzee".

GEOGRAPHICAL RANGE [1, 3, 4, 5, 6, 7]

P.t. verus: W. Africa. Forest regions from Sierra Leone and French Guinea eastward to R. Niger. Latitudinal limit: 10° N. *P.t. troglodytes*: Central Africa. E. of R. Niger to R. Congo where it is limited to the W. bank. *P.t. schweinfurthii*: Central and E. Africa. Extends from the E. bank of the R. Lualaba and S. of R. Ubangi, as far E. as Lake Victoria in northern part of range and Lake Tanganyika in southern part. *P. paniscus*: Limited to enclave formed by Congo and Lualaba Rivers. TYPE LOCALITY: Befalé, S. of Maringa River.

ECOLOGY

HABITAT:[7, 8, 9] Tropical rain forest, forest savannah mosaic and deciduous woodland in hilly country; also found in montane forest up to 10,000 ft (3048 m). Secondary forest in Sierra Leone. Habitat is arboreal for approximately 50–75% daylight hours; sleeping hours are spent in tree-nests, newly built every night and seldom less than 15 ft from the ground. DIET: Primarily vegetarian, consisting of fruits, leaves, palm-nuts, bark, seeds and stems.[8, 9, 10] Less common components include galls, termites and ants,[9, 11] native-cultivated fruits,[12, 13] e.g. paw-paw, meat[9–11] and fish.[13]* ACTIVITY RHYTHM: Diurnal.

MORPHOLOGY

Weights and Dimensions

	♂	♀	♀ in % of ♂
Body weight[14] (Average) (*P. troglodytes*)	48·9 kg (2♂)	40·6 kg (5♀)	90†
Head and body length[1] (mm) (*P. troglodytes*)	770–925 (7♂)	700–850 (4)	94

† Schultz (1956) states adult ♀ weighs 87·9% adult ♂ (28 specimens).

N.B. Information on wild-shot weights is very inadequate. One authority (L. G. Smith—private communication) estimates maximum weights of ♂ and ♀ in wild to be approximately 54·6 kg. Maximum weights recorded in Zoo animals: ♂ 90 kg, ♀ 80 kg. (♀ in % ♂ based on midpoint of ranges.)

---

† *See* Taxonomic Notes, p. 375.

PLATE 78. *Pan troglodytes schweinfurthii*, young ♀

External Characters

Except for *P. paniscus*, which is of lighter build, chimpanzees are large, robust animals with pale, mottled or darkly pigmented faces, prominent ears and protrusive lips; arms are longer than legs; hand long but thumb short. Tail-less. Coat is predominantly black in colour. Juveniles are black with white tuft of hairs in anal region; mature adults have grey hairs mingling with black on lumbar region and thighs; white hairs grow on the chin in adults of both sexes. Both sexes prone to baldness in early maturity; in the ♀ the bald patch extends back as far as the vertex, in the ♂ baldness is usually limited to triangular patch on forehead. Skin of body is white, but skin of face varies with species and race, as follows:

Species	*Skin colour of face*
P.t. verus	Black pigmentation forming butterfly-shaped mask. Whole face darkens with age.
P.t. troglodytes	Freckled on white but may become muddy colour with age and heavily mottled.
P.t. schweinfurthii	White passing into a dark muddy colour with age.
P. paniscus	Black.

Internal Characters

For details of anatomy *see* Elliot-Smith (1902), Sonntag (1924), Schultz (1930, 1940b), Clark (1959). The following characters are selected principally for their known functional importance or for their value for identification. SKULL: Calvarium rounded, facial skeleton moderately prognathic; orbits frontally directed and surmounted by prominent and confluent supra-orbital crests. Small sagittal crest very occasionally seen in large ♂♂ and ♀♀; nuchal crest absent. Cranial capacity[14] 290–500 cc (94 adults). Foramen magnum situated well posteriorly on basis cranii. VERTEBRAL COLUMN:[18] Thoraco-lumbar vertebrae very variable in number, commonly 17: T.13, L.4. THORAX: Greatest diameter is transverse; body of sternum long and slender, sternebrae frequently fused. ARM: Humerus longer than radius. Humeral head medially directed; trochlear and capitulum separated by a prominent keel (as in all Hominoidea). Olecranon process short, head of radius rounded and shaft well bowed. HAND: Os centrale usually fused to scaphoid in adults; carpal tunnel deep, metacarpals long, slender with rounded heads. Phalanges curved and ventrally grooved. Pollex short. Deep head flexor pollicis brevis absent.[21] LEG: Femur robust with antero-posterior curvature; sometimes longer than humerus (cf. *Gorilla*, *Pongo*). FOOT:[20] Relatively short compared to trunk length but big toe is long and stout (as in all Hominoidea except *Pongo*). DENTITION: D.F.: $\frac{2}{2}\frac{1}{1}\frac{2}{2}\frac{3}{3}=32$. INCISORS: Central upper pair broad, spatulate. CANINES: Long, powerful, conical teeth in ♂, somewhat shorter in ♀. Upper canine separated from lateral incisor by diastema in adults. PRE-MOLARS: Upper: homodont and bicuspid. Lower: heterodont; anterior p.m. is unicuspid and sectorial; posterior p.m. is bicuspid. MOLARS: Decrease in size 1–3 (cf. *Gorilla*, *Pongo*). Upper molars are quadricuspid; lower molars bear 5 cusps (Y or "Dryopithecus" pattern), including a hypoconulid but lacking the talonid heel of catarrhine monkeys. Cusps of molars are conical. For range of variation in chimpanzee dentition.[22, 23] ALIMENTARY SYSTEM:[24] Stomach simple and capacious; caecum as in man, with appendix. Liver is essentially a simple bilobular structure (cf. *Gorilla*) and its peritoneal attachments to diaphragm are as in man. VASCULAR SYSTEM: Great vessels arise from aortic arch from 2 branches, usually R and L innominate. RESPIRATORY SYSTEM: Extensive laryngeal air sacs are present.

PLATE 79. Above: *Pan troglodytes troglodytes*, subadult (photo by Marcel Langer); Below: *Pan troglodytes verus* (Basle Zoo)

Genetic Biology

CHROMOSOMES: *P. troglodytes* (11♂, 9♀): 2n=48[25, 26, 27, 28, 29]; *P. paniscus* (1♂, 2♀): 2n=48[25]; IMMUNOCHEMISTRY: *See* the studies of Goodman (1962a, b; 1963), Williams and Wemyss (1961) and Williams (1964). Serological evidence demonstrates close phyletic affinity of *Pan*, *Gorilla* and *Homo*. HAEMOGLOBINS: Serum proteins have been studied by starch gel electrophoresis by Lange and Schmitt (1963) and Buettner-Janusch and Buettner-Janusch (1964). *Pan* has Hb pattern that closely resembles that of *Gorilla* and *Homo*. BLOOD GROUPS: Groups A and O identified.[37] A antigen of *Pan* is not identical with either A_1 or A_2 antigens of man.[38] Polymorphic for MN blood factors which have been extensively studied.[38, 39, 40] P.T.C. TASTING:[41] *P. troglodytes*: 53 tasters: 17 non-tasters; *P. paniscus*: 8 tasters: 3 non-tasters.

BEHAVIOUR

Locomotor Behaviour[8, 9, 12]

AUTHORS' CLASSIFICATION: Modified brachiation. Brachiation is quite common for short distances but frequently the feet and hands are used with the body held in upright position. On the ground (25–30% daylight hours) chimpanzees walk quadrupedally using the backs of the middle phalanges and the flat of the feet. BIPEDALISM: Bipedal standing frequently occurs to improve visual range but bipedal walking and running is relatively rare, and appears to be used in long grass, when the hands are occupied with a load or during display activities. For bio-mechanical analysis of bipedal walking, *see* Preuschoft (1963) and Elftman (1964), and for characteristics of gait, *see* Hildebrand (1967). LIMB PROPORTIONS: For Indices, *see* Part III, p. 394.

Hand Function

Hand prehensile, thumb opposable. Fingers disproportionately long compared with thumb which prevents precision grip between tips of thumb and index finger.[45] Power grip specially modified to grasp slender twigs and lianas.[45] Principal grip during locomotion is "hook-grip". Manipulative activity includes self-grooming, nest-building,[46] tool-using,[11] and in captivity action-painting,[47] etc. For dermatoglyphics, *see* Cummins and Spragg (1938). HAND PROPORTIONS: For Indices, *see* Part III, p. 402.

Resting Posture[9, 46]

Sleep in nests on their side with knees drawn up, sometimes on back with legs extended and occasionally on stomach. Day-nesting takes place either on ground or in trees; posture is either lying on side or sitting and sprawling in relaxed postures.

Social Behaviour

The following brief account of the social behaviour of *P. troglodytes* is an abstract of a number of field studies to which reference should be made.[8, 9, 12, 49] Principal sources are those of Kortlandt (1962), the Reynolds (Budongo Forest) and Goodall (Gombe Stream Reserve). As in the case of baboons, evidence is accumulating that behaviour of chimpanzees is subject to considerable inter- and intraspecific variation that appears to be closely related to the nature of the habitat. The literature concerning behaviour of chimpanzees in captivity is extensive;

PLATE 80. *Pan paniscus*, young ♂ (San Diego Zoo)

PLATE 81. *Pan troglodytes schweinfurthii* (by courtesy of Jane Goodall and the National Geographic Society)

reference should be made to the studies of Nissen, Kohler (1925) and Yerkes (1943, 1929); for laboratory studies and for studies in zoological gardens, *see* Benchley (1942), Hediger (1950, 1955), Morris (1963), and Rempe (1961) (*P. paniscus*). DENSITY OF POPULATION: Approx. 3/sq mile (Gombe Stream Reserve) and 7/sq mile (Budongo rain forest). GROUP STRUCTURE AND BEHAVIOUR: NUMBERS: No stable groups. Temporary association groups in Gombe population vary in number from 2–23; in Budongo, fruit-ripening in certain trees may lead to temporary associations of small bands to form mixed groups of maximum 46. Commonest group size in Gombe and Budongo is less than 9. Largest group seen by Kortlandt was 48. COMPOSITION: Unstable. Four group "types" are recognizable: (i) adult bands composed of both sexes. (ii) male bands. (iii) Mother bands with infants. (iv) Mixed bands. Solitary ♂♂ are seen.[8, 9] DOMINANCE: No evidence of linear hierarchy within groups but some evidence of dominance reactions between individuals; these are relatively rare and usually between mature ♂♂. Goodall observed marked tolerance between adult ♂♂ and younger animals. The Reynolds also note infrequency of quarrelling and aggressive displays. SOCIAL GROOMING:[9] Grooming is an important activity of adults. COMMUNICATION: Chimpanzees express themselves by means of vocalizations, facial expression, hand gesture and body posture. Goodall describes greeting and submissive gestures in detail. Both the Reynolds and Goodall describe "drumming" on tree-trunks and buttress roots. HOME RANGE AND TERRITORIALITY: In hilly woodland habitat of Gombe, range is 6–20 sq miles; smaller range (approx. 10 sq miles) in Budongo forest habitat. INTER-GROUP RELATIONS: Notable for lack of aggressiveness; groups communicate by means of loud calls; for vocalizations of chimpanzees, *see* Goodall (1965). PLAY: Individual play activity becomes social play during juvenile phase (3 to 8 years) and tapers off after puberty, being "replaced" by social grooming. SEXUAL BEHAVIOUR:[9] Copulation may be initiated by ♂ or ♀; it usually takes place in trees with the ♀ in a crouched position, the ♂ squatting behind her. Relationships are promiscuous (polyandrous and polygamous); an oestrous ♀ may be mounted by as many as 7♂♂ in one session.

REPRODUCTION AND DEVELOPMENT

Insufficient evidence for fixed mating season although copulations occur predominantly from August to November in Tanzania.[9] In Zoos, births occur throughout the year.[57] GESTATION PERIOD: 225 days.[58] BIRTH:[59] Usually single young; labour is short and foetus is relatively small compared with both pelvic dimensions and weight of mother.[15] INFANT DEVELOPMENT: Growth and development have been studied by Kellogg and Kellogg (1933), Schultz (1940b), Nissen and Riesen (1945, 1949), Hayes and Hayes (1951) and Gavan (1953) and Riopelle (1963); for observations on infant and juvenile behaviour in the wild, *see* Goodall (1965). PUBERTY: In ♀, 6–10 years (average 8·8 years); in ♂, 7–8 years.[6, 58] SEXUAL CYCLE: Averages 35 days; characterized by swelling and turgescence in ano-genital region, and menstrual bleeding.

CAPTIVITY

LONGEVITY: 30–38 years. (Potential life-span has been estimated at 60 years).[58] LONGEVITY RECORD: *P.t. troglodytes*, 41 years (Philadelphia Zoo);[58] *P.t. schweinfurthii*, 11 years (Bronx Zoo, New York).[64] *P. troglodytes*: births in captivity are common.[65] *P. paniscus*: 2 births in World Zoos (1959–63).[65] For information on husbandry and welfare, *see* Crandall[66] and International Zoo Year Books.[65] For discussion of conservation of free-ranging chimpanzees, *see* Kortlandt (1966).

REFERENCES

1. Allen, G. M. (1939)
2. Fiedler, W. (1956)
3. Schwarz, E. (1934)
4. Rode, P. (1937)
5. Coolidge, H. J. (1933b)
6. Yerkes, R. M. (1943)
7. Booth, A. H. (1958)
8. Reynolds, V. and Reynolds, F. (1965)
9. Goodall, J. (1965)
10. Jones, T. S. and Cave, A. J. E. (1960)
11. Goodall, J. (1963)
12. Kortlandt, A. (1962)
13. Stanley, W. B. (1919)
14. Schultz, A. H. (1941a)
15. Schultz, A. H. (1956)
16. Elliot-Smith, G. (1902)
17. Sonntag, C. F. (1924)
18. Schultz, A. H. (1930)
19. Schultz, A. H. (1940b)
20. Clark, W. E. Le Gros (1959)
21. Day, M. H. and Napier, J. R. (1963)
22. Ashton, E. H. and Zuckerman, S. (1950b)
23. Schuman, E. L. and Brace, C. L. (1954)
24. Straus, W. L. (1936)
25. Klinger, H. P., Hamerton, J. L., Mutton, D. and Lang, E. M. (1963)
26. Chu, E. H. Y. and Bender, M. A. (1961)
27. Bender, M. A. and Chu, E. H. Y. (1963)
28. Young, W. J., Merz, T., Ferguson-Smith, M. A. and Johnston, A. W. (1960)
29. Yeager, C. H., Painter, T. S. and Yerkes, R. M. (1940)
30. Goodman, M. (1962a)
31. Goodman, M. (1962b)
32. Goodman, M. (1963)
33. Williams, C. A. and Wemyss, C. T. (1961)
34. Williams, C. A. (1964)
35. Lange, V. and Schmitt, J. (1963)
36. Buettner-Janusch, J. and Buettner-Janusch, V. (1964)
37. Franks, D. (1963)
38. Wiener, A. S. and Gordon, E. B. (1960)
39. Wiener, A. S., Baldwin, M. and Gordon, E. B. (1963)
40. Moor-Jankowski, J., Wiener, A. S. and Gordon, E. B. (1964)
41. Chiarelli, B. (1963b)
42. Preuschoft, H. (1963)
43. Elftman, H. (1944)
44. Hildebrand, Milton (1967)
45. Napier, J. R. (1960)
46. Goodall, J. (1962)
47. Morris, D. (1963)
48. Cummins, H. and Spragg, S. D. S. (1938)
49. Nissen, H. W. (1931)
50. Nissen, H. W. (1951, 1956)
51. Kohler, W. (1925)
52. Yerkes, R. M. and Yerkes, A. W. (1929)
53. Benchley, Belle J. (1942)
54. Hediger, H. (1950)
55. Hediger, H. (1955)
56. Rempe, U. (1961)
57. International Zoo Year Book, Vol. 3 (1961)
58. Riopelle, A. J. (1963)
59. Harms, J. W. (1956)
60. Kellogg, W. N. and Kellogg, L. A. (1933)
61. Nissen, H. W. and Riesen, A. H. (1945, 1949)
62. Hayes, K. J. and Hayes, C. (1951)
63. Gavan, J. A. (1953)
64. Jones, M. L. (1962)
65. International Zoo Year Book, Vols. 1–5 (1959–1965)
66. Crandall, L. S. (1964)
67. Kortlandt, A. (1966)

PAPIO†   Erxleben, 1777   Baboons

2 species groups: 5 species: 11 subspecies[1]

Papio cynocephalus group:

Species:		
P. anubis	Olive baboon	4 subsp.
P. cynocephalus	Yellow baboon	3 subsp.
P. papio (Type species)	Guinea baboon	0 subsp.
P. ursinus	Chacma baboon	4 subsp.

Papio hamadryas group:

Species:		
P. hamadryas	Sacred baboon	0 subsp.

GEOGRAPHICAL RANGE [2–8]

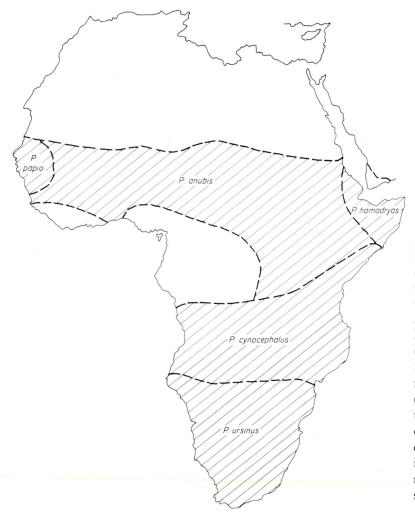

The distribution of the 5 species of the genus *Papio* (after Jolly, 1965).

Africa and Asia (extreme W.). Throughout whole of sub-Saharan Africa except for southern coastal regions of Ivory Coast, Ghana and Nigeria; Congo basin, S.W. of Congo and Lualaba Rivers. Most northerly range is Tibesti plateau (*P. anubis*) and most easterly in Africa is E. Abyssinia and N. Somalia (*P. hamadryas*); this species extends into Asia to the Yemen and Aden Protectorate. Most westerly form (*P. papio*) found in Sierra Leone. The most southerly form (*P. ursinus*) extends to the Cape. All species of *Papio* replace each other geographically[1] (*see* range map and key to species).

---

† *See* Taxonomic Notes, p. 376.

ECOLOGY

HABITAT:[9, 10, 11] Occupy a wide range of major vegetational zones including sub-desert, savannah, Acacia thornveld, forest-savannah mosaic and rain forest. Minor habitats include rocky cliffs and gorges (*P. hamadryas*) and sea-side cliffs (*P. ursinus*). All baboons with the exception of *P. hamadryas* and some *P. ursinus*, sleep in trees. *P. cynocephalus* is the most arboreal species.[12*] DIET: Omnivorous, including fruits, grasses, roots, lizards, insects; occasional meat-eating.[10, 13, 14, 34] ACTIVITY RHYTHM: Diurnal. Retire to sleep from before nightfall until after dawn.

MORPHOLOGY

External Characters[15]

Large animals with marked sexual dimorphism in size (♂ is approx. twice the size of ♀). Largest species is *P. ursinus* and smallest *P. cynocephalus kindae*. Coat is of dense texture showing a well-developed mane in ♂ especially *P. hamadryas*[16] (for Coat Colour, *see* Key to species). Face is long with prominent muzzle and jaws. Nares are open widely and point forwards. In *P. hamadryas*, nose is somewhat tip-tilted. Limbs are long and equal in length (particularly long in *P. cynocephalus*); tail is moderately long, generally tufted and held in characteristic U-curve (marked kink in *P. cynocephalus*). Prominent ischial callosities which are bright red in *P. papio*; they form a continuous straight transverse pad in ♂♂ being fused across midline, but are separate in ♀♀.[15] Hands are rather stubby with well-marked palmar pads; fingers short and thumb relatively long.

Key to Species of *Papio*[44]

1.a. Skin of face flesh-pink. Pelage in ♀♀ and immatures plain greyish; adult ♂♂ with copious mane of waved light-coloured hair. HABITAT: E. Ethiopia, northern Somalia, S.W. Arabia - - - - - - - - - - - - *P. hamadryas*
  b. Skin of face black - - - - - - - - *P. cynocephalus* Superspecies 2.
2.a. Longest hairs of back with many rings, alternating reddish and black. General colour of animal reddish, underside as back. ♂ develops mane over shoulders. HABITAT: Senegal to Guinea - - - - - - - - - - - - *P. papio*
  b. Longest hairs of back with at most two light and two dark bands. General colour greyish, yellowish or brownish - - - - - - - - - 3.
3.a. Underside coloured as back; individual hairs brown at base, with one or two light rings, black tip. Hair of paws often black. Both sexes develop ruff round cheeks giving rounded outline to face from front. ♂ develops shoulder mane. HABITAT: Sierra Leone, eastwards to central Ethiopia, southwards to northern Tanzania - - - - *P. anubis*
  b. Underside lighter than back. Hairs of cheek not forming ruff - - - - 4.
4.a. Cheeks contrastingly lighter than crown, hair of paws not black. Long silky yellow hairs form fringes along back and limbs in adults. Build lanky. HABITAT: N. Angola to N. Mozambique, northwards to eastern Kenya, S.E. Somalia - - *P. cynocephalus*
  b. Cheeks not contrastingly lighter than crown, paws often deep brown or black. Long silky *black* hairs form fringes along back and limbs in adults. Build stocky. HABITAT: S. Africa, northwards to southern Zambia, central Angola to S. Mozambique *P. ursinus*

PLATE 82. *Papio cynocephalus*, adult ♀ grooming mother with infant (by courtesy of Sherwood L. Washburn)

PLATE 84. *Papio ursinus*, adult ♀♀ and infants (Photos by Stephen Peet)

Left:
PLATE 83. *Papio cynocephalus*. Ischial callosities form sitting pads for night or day resting in trees (by courtesy of Sherwood L. Washburn)

Weights and Dimensions

Body weight range[17] (g)	*P. anubis* 22,000–30,000 (♂♂)	*P. anubis* 11,000–15,000 (♀♀)
Head and body length[18] (*Average and Range* mm)	*P. anubis* 760 (735–785) (5♂♂)	612 (562–660) (4♀♀)
Tail length range[18] (mm) *Average and Range*	*P. anubis* 556 (520–600) (5♂♂)	462 (415–530) (4♀♀)

Body weight: ♀ 50% of ♂; Head and Body length: ♀ 81% of ♂; Tail length: ♀ 83% of ♂.

Internal Characters

The special features of the anatomy of *Papio* are as follows: SKULL: Muzzle is elongated, in profile contour of face is flattened, nasal bones are very long. Sub-orbital depression present in paranasal region. Supra-orbital ridges continuous across midline. Calvarium relatively small and flattened; sagittal crest present. MANDIBLE: Mandibular torus and simian shelf well-developed and extending as far as 1st molars. Hollow on body of mandible below anterior cheek teeth. Angle of mandible obtuse and rounded. VERTEBRAL COLUMN:[19] C.7, T.12 or 13, L.6 or 7, S.3. Slight lumbar lordosis and well-marked promontory between L.6 and S.1 (*P. hamadryas*). FORELIMBS: Scapula is longer and narrower than that of *Cercopithecus* and *Mandrillus*. Humerus is stout, anteriorly convex and strongly marked with muscular impressions; head points backwards and is somewhat flattened; greater tuberosity very prominent. Long, sharply defined medial lip to trochlear. Ulna has a long, backwardly tilted olecranon process. HAND: Metacarpals are robust with deep sesamoid gutters impressed on their heads. Trapezium bears a well-developed saddle articulation. DENTITION: D.F.: $\frac{2}{2}\frac{1}{1}\frac{2}{2}\frac{3}{3}=32$. Canines exceptionally long and sharp in ♂. Premolars: $PM.\overline{1}$ long sloping tooth (sectorial) which is more exaggerated than in most Cercopithecinae. Molars: $M.\frac{3}{3}$ largest of molar series; in this character *Papio* is more striking than other Cercopithecinae. $M.\overline{3}$ bears 5th cusp as in all Cercopithecidae except *Cercopithecus*.

Genetic Biology

CHROMOSOMES:[20, 21] 2n = 42 (*P. anubis, P. cynocephalus, P. papio* and *P. hamadryas*). Karyotypes of *Papio, Theropithecus, Cercocebus* and *Macaca* have been analysed and compared by Chiarelli (1962b). P.T.C. TASTING:[23] 72% tasters (all species—50 specimens). *P. hamadryas* contains a higher % of non-tasters than other species. SEROLOGICAL REACTIONS:[24] High degrees of antigenic correspondence with other genera of Cercopithecinae, using immunodiffusion and electrophoretic techniques on serum and lens proteins. HAEMOGLOBINS AND TRANS-FERRINS: *See* Buettner-Janusch (1963b). BLOOD GROUPS: For A.B.O. and Lewis blood factors, *see* Moor-Jankowski *et al.* (1964) and Wiener *et al.* (1966). HAEMATOLOGY: *See* Moor-Jankowski *et al.* (1965).

PLATE 85. *Papio hamadryas*, adult ♂ (by courtesy of Doris M. Sorby)

BEHAVIOUR

Locomotor Behaviour

AUTHORS' CLASSIFICATION: Quadrupedalism. Forelimb stance is digitigrade. Baboons move freely on the ground and in trees where at least 30% time is spent, except for *P. hamadryas* which is much less arboreal. Agile in climbing cliffs and rocks (e.g. *P. ursinus*). Capable of facultative bipedalism particularly during play. LIMB PROPORTIONS: Hindlimb very slightly longer than forelimb; radius longer than humerus giving a high Brachial Index. For Indices, *see* Part III, p. 395.

Hand Function

Fingers short and thumb relatively long and fully opposable; index finger used with thumb independently of other digits. Precision grip employed, e.g. during grass-plucking activity that is part of feeding repertoire. HAND PROPORTIONS: For Indices, *see* Part III, p. 402.

Resting Posture

Frequently sleep sitting upright on slender branches, bearing weight on ischial callosities.[26] Sitting posture adopted during day when resting and feeding, etc.

Social Behaviour

Evidence is accumulating that social behaviour is subject to a great deal of inter- and even intra-specific variation which appears to be closely related to the nature of habitat; recent evidence indicates, for instance, that forest-living troops of *P. anubis* in southern Uganda show a much looser social organization than populations of the same species living in open sparsely wooded country.[34] The following description is an abstract of a number of field studies, referring to *P. anubis*, *P. cynocephalus* and *P. ursinus*, to which reference should be made.[27-34] The social structure of the sacred baboon (*P. hamadryas*), being apparently unique among true baboons, is described separately. Troop structure consists of adults, subadults, juveniles and infants of both sexes. ADULT SEX RATIO (range): $1\male : 4\female\female$ to $1\male : 12\female\female$. Group size varies from 8–200, commonly 40–80. Dominance hierarchies of both sexes are apparent and stable; role of adult $\male\male$ is to lead troop, prevent intra-group fighting, protect troop from predators, protect young and inseminate $\female\female$. In defensive formation, subdominant and sub-adult $\male\male$ are located on periphery of group where high selection pressure on survival operates; dominant males alongside females with infants. Home range has a maximum of 15 sq miles and overlaps that of other troops; core areas, exclusive to troop, include feeding and sleeping trees and/or rocks. Inter-troop relations are generally amicable; little fighting observed in or outside troop though tension may be high. Social gestures include "presentation" of sexual area by lower animal towards one higher in social scale. Mock "mounting" by dominant animal may follow. Grooming is an important source of group stability and is freely indulged in, particularly as a prelude to, or interlude in, sexual relationships; it also occurs between females and is particularly centred on mothers with newborn infants. Play is an important activity of juveniles. Play group activity is thought to set patterns of adult social structure. VOCALIZATION:[35, 36] Principal vocalization is by a series of grunting calls of varying length but other calls include a loud bark associated with alarm and a high-pitched shrieking associated with fear. SOCIAL ORGANIZATION OF *P. hamadryas*:[33, 37, 38, 39] SOCIAL GROUP: One-male group is characteristic in captivity and in

---

PLATE 86. *Papio hamadryas*. Feeding party (above) splits into component one-male groups (below) (by courtesy of Hans Kummer and F. Kurt)

PLATE 87. *Papio ursinus*, black infant, about 6 weeks old (by courtesy of C. K. Brain)

wild populations studied so far; harem consists of a single male and 1–4 or more females, plus offspring. One-male groups foregather at night at sleeping cliffs. This grouping in *P. hamadryas* is also observed in captivity.[39] Male enforces following-reaction of females by means of bite in the nape of the neck (*see* Simonds (1965): neck-chewing by ♂ *Macaca radiata* establishes dominance among males).

Sexual Behaviour

Sexual system of *P. cynocephalus* group is promiscuous, more or less based on dominance relationships.[14] Exclusive copulation by dominant ♂ takes place only when sexual swelling of ♀ is maximal; females may copulate with subdominant males prior to this. Consort-pairing

Resting Posture

Pottos may adopt a horizontal or vertical clinging posture during rest, the body being rolled into a ball, a position which exposes the prominent cervical and upper thoracic spines. The function of the prominent spinous processes is equivocal.

Social Behaviour

MARKING BEHAVIOUR: Scent marking from specialized cutaneous glands in anal region has been observed but there is no evidence of urine washing as in other Lorisidae.[22] COMMUNICATION: Vocalization has not been studied in pottos. Threat movements of mouth-opening and head-lowering ("lunging") have been observed.[22] AGGRESSIVE BEHAVIOUR: Functional significance of prominent cervical-thoracic spines is equivocal, but evidence is in favour of aggressive rather than purely defensive function.[21] INTRA-GROUP BEHAVIOUR: Inferred to be relatively solitary animals but under laboratory conditions two adults will indulge in mutual grooming and seek close contact.[22]

REPRODUCTION AND DEVELOPMENT [8]

Evidence suggests that pottos are polyoestrous in captivity. Oestrous changes in external genitalia are overt. Cycles are recurrent and show a range of 34–47 days (mean: 39 days). Births in captivity[23] (N. Hemisphere) occurred in February, April (2), July, September, October and November. GESTATION PERIOD: Not known. NO. OF YOUNG: 1 only; twinning not recorded.[9, 23] INFANT DEVELOPMENT:[26] Rate of growth is rapid and linear with time, lacking any noticeable "spurts"; projecting vertebral spines are not present at birth but appear at 30 days.

CAPTIVITY

Common zoo animals having a zoo life span of $3\frac{3}{4}$ years up to a maximum of 9 years.[24] LONGEVITY RECORD:[25] 8 years 11 months (*P.p. ibeanus*), Bronx Zoo, New York. Between 1959–1963, only 2 births were reported in World Zoos (Jersey and Washington).[24]

REFERENCES

1. Schwarz, E. (1931b)
2. Hayman, R. W. (1935)
3. Booth, A. H. (1958)
4. Cansdale, G. S. (1946)
5. Booth, A. H. (1956b)
6. Rosevear, D. R. (1935a)
7. Sanderson, I. T. (1940)
8. Manley, G. H. (1966a)
9. Schultz, A. H. (1948)
10. Malbrant, R. and Maclatchy, A. (1949)
11. Murie, J. and Mivart, St. G. (1872)
12. Nayak, U. V. (1933)
13. Hill, W. C. Osman (1953)
14. Clark, W. E. Le Gros (1959)
15. Wislocki, G. B. and Straus, W. L. (1933)
16. Montagna, W. and Yun, J. S. (1962)
17. Bender, M. A. and Chu, E. H. Y. (1963)
18. Buettner-Janusch, J. and Buettner-Janusch, V. (1964)
19. Hofer, H. (1957)
20. Bishop, Alison (1964)
21. Walker, A. C. Personal communication
22. Andrew, R. J. (1964)
23. Crandall, L. S. (1964)
24. International Zoo Year Books, Vols. I–V (1959–1965)
25. Jones, M. L. (1962)
26. Grand, T., Duro, E. and Montagna, W. (1964)

PLATE 88. *Perodicticus potto*

PHANER Gray, 1870   Fork-marked Dwarf Lemurs

1 species: 0 subspecies[1]

Phaner furcifer Blainville, 1841

GEOGRAPHICAL RANGE

Madagascar. Precise distribution unknown. Seen by Rand (1935) at foot of Mt. D'Ambre; in the western dry forest in the region of Morondava by Webb (1953); and as far S. as Tulear by Petter (1962); also found in the N.W. rain forest region.[4] Type locality: Baie D'Antongil.

ECOLOGY

HABITAT: Inhabitant of rain forest where it moves on large to medium-sized branches[4] at all levels but particularly in the closed canopy and in the shrub layer; also seen by Rand in gallery forest and in low dry bush in savannah country.[2] Nests in holes in trees. ACTIVITY RHYTHM: Nocturnal. DIET:[4] Insects, fruits.

MORPHOLOGY

External Characters[5]

Considerably larger than *Microcebus* and *Cheirogaleus*. Fur is brownish-grey with light-coloured underparts. Dark, well-defined spinal stripe bifurcates on the crown, the two stripes becoming continuous with the dark eye rings. Head round; face rather blunt with large, dark, forward-looking eyes. Ears large and pointed. Tail, which is bushy, is longer than body. Legs longer than arms.

Weights and Dimensions[5]*

Body weight—no information	
Head and body length (mm)	250–275
Tail length (mm)	325–350

Internal Characters

For general characters of Lemuridae, see *Lemur*, and for Cheirogaleinae, see *Microcebus*. Only principal differences noted here. DENTITION:[1, 6] $\frac{2}{2} \frac{1}{1} \frac{3}{3} \frac{3}{3} = 36$. INCISORS: Upper central incisors very long with a marked median slope; lateral incisor is very small. Lower incisors and canine (dental comb) are unusually long. PREMOLARS: $PM.^{1}$ large and markedly projecting, caniniform tooth; $PM._{\overline{1}}$ also large and caniniform. MOLARS: $M.^{1-2}$ show a hypocone.

BEHAVIOUR [4]*

Locomotor Behaviour

AUTHORS' CLASSIFICATION: Quadrupedalism. Moves quadrupedally at most times with tail held in a typical lemuroid posture. Leaps frequently.

Hand Function

Hands are broad and prehensile, and the nails, except for thumb, are slightly keeled [as in *G. (Euoticus)* and *Cheirogaleus*]; the hands are used freely during feeding.

Resting Posture[4]

Rests in a squatting or sitting position, frequently with the back supported as in *Lemur*; during sleep they remain in a sitting position with the head tucked well down between forelimbs.

PLATE 89. *Phaner furcifer* (by courtesy of Jean Jacques Petter)

Social Behaviour

Little is known. Rand (1935) states that they are often found in pairs but Petter (1962c) reports that they are solitary. Sexual behaviour, reproduction and development are unknown.

CAPTIVITY

The single record of a specimen on exhibition is from Berlin Zoo in 1908.[7]

REFERENCES

1. Schwarz, E. (1931c)
2. Rand, A. L. (1935)
3. Webb, C. S. (1953)
4. Petter, J. J. (1962c)
5. Hill, W. C. Osman (1953)
6. James, W. Warwick (1960)
7. Jones, M. L. (1962)

PITHECIA Desmarest, 1804 Sakis

2 species: 2 subspecies[1]

P. *pithecia* (Type species)	Pale-headed Saki	o subsp.
P. *monachus*	Monk Saki	2 subsp.

GEOGRAPHICAL RANGE [2, 3]

South America. Sakis are found south of the R. Orinoco and eastwards to the Guiana coast; south of the R. Amazon, their eastern range is limited by the R. Tapajos. They extend westwards to the foothills of the Andes and southwards to the limits of tropical forest on latitude 13° S.

ECOLOGY

HABITAT: Tropical rain forest. In Suriname, they are found only in forest that borders on open savannah, sometimes descending from canopy to shrub layer for feeding purposes.[3, 4] They seem to prefer unflooded areas and are found up to 2300 ft (770 m). Webb[12] (quoted by Hill) avers that in the Guianas they are inhabitants of the shrub layers of gallery forests rather than of the canopy. ACTIVITY RHYTHM: Diurnal. DIET: Wholly frugivorous (based on stomach contents in 3 specimens).[5] Sanderson (1957) states that berries are principal articles of diet but birds and small mammals are also eaten.

MORPHOLOGY

External Characters[2]

Coat is thick, coarse and untidy and predominantly black (P. *pithecia*) or dark grey in colour and brindled (P. *monachus*). The face of P. *monachus* is dark with pale-coloured oblique stripes on either side of nose. The long hair of the head grows forward from a central whorl on the occiput or between the shoulders, forming a hood. There is a remarkable degree of sexual dichromatism and dimorphism in P. *pithecia*; the ♂ has a black muzzle surrounded by creamy-white hairs like a "white-face clown" make-up; the ♀ has the lightly-coloured oblique para-nasal streaks of P. *monachus* in an otherwise dark face. Beards are absent (cf. *Chiropotes*). The nose is flask-shaped with widely separated nostrils. Tail is thick, bushy, non-prehensile but tapers to a point (cf. *Chiropotes*). LIMBS: Legs considerably longer than arms. HANDS: D.F. 4.3.2.5.1. or 4=3.2.5.1. Mammae are axillary.

Weights and Dimensions[2, 4, 5, 6, 7]

	♂	♀	♀ in % of ♂
Average body weight (g)	1578 (6♂)	1406 (5♀)	89
Head and body length range (mm)	355–480 (11♂)	300–425 (12♀)	87
Tail length range (mm)	315–510 (11♂)	255–545 (12♀)	99

Sexual dimorphism in weights and dimensions not marked. (♀ in % ♂ based on midpoint of ranges.)

PLATE 90. *Pithecia pithecia*. Left: ♀ with ♀ infant, right: ♂, showing sexual dimorphism in coat colour (San Diego Zoo)

Internal Characters

CUTANEOUS GLANDS:[4] In *P. pithecia* there is a large glandular area on throat extending on to chest in some ♂; area surrounded by naked skin. Histologically, "gland" is composed of sebaceous and sweat glands interspersed with large lobulated, coiled glands.[2] ALIMENTARY TRACT:[5] Relatively long small intestine; caecum and colon long and unsacculated. LARYNX:[8] Hyoid and thyroid cartilages expanded. DENTITION:[9] D.F.: $\frac{2}{2} \frac{1}{1} \frac{3}{3} \frac{3}{3} = 36$. Upper incisors projecting; lower incisors semi-procumbent, somewhat resembling "dental comb" of lemurs; canines strong with well-marked diastemata, particularly in upper jaw. Molars quadricuspid with transversely concave wear pattern.

Genetic Biology

CHROMOSOMES:[10]* $2n = 46$ ($1♀$ *P. pithecia*). No karyotype.

BEHAVIOUR

Locomotor Behaviour*

AUTHORS' CLASSIFICATION: Quadrupedalism. (Erikson's category: Climber). Capable of rapid travel through the trees when alarmed.[4] Leaping ability somewhat equivocal.[4, 12] Reported to be bipedal in the trees on occasions.[4] LIMB PROPORTIONS: For Indices, *see* Part III, p. 395.

Hand Function*

Hand prehensile, thumb pseudo-opposable. Functional axis lies between digits 2 and 3. HAND PROPORTIONS: Thumb and fingers elongated relative to hand length. For Indices, *see* Part III, p. 402.

Resting Posture

Sleep coiled "like a cat" on open branches.[4]

Social Behaviour*

Group size does not exceed 5 but they are customarily seen in pairs.[4] VOCALIZATION: Infrequent in the wild but, when used, is said to be "loud and penetrating".

REPRODUCTION AND DEVELOPMENT

Single young. Infants cling to mother's belly[4] but later shift to her back. Hill (1960) points out that abdominal carrying position is unusual among platyrrhines, but see *Ateles*.

CAPTIVITY

Gentle disposition, but seldom survive long in captivity. LONGEVITY RECORD:[14] *P. pithecia*, 13 years 8 months, San Diego Zoo. Births in captivity are very rare.

REFERENCES

1. Cabrera, A. (1957)
2. Hill, W. C. Osman (1960)
3. Sanderson, I. T. (1957)
4. Sanderson, I. T. (1949)
5. Fooden, J. (1964b)
6. Lönnberg, E. (1938)
7. Cruz Lima, E. da (1945)
8. Lampert, H. (1926)
9. James, W. Warwick (1960)
10. Bender, M. A. and Chu, E. H. Y. (1963)
11. Erikson, G. E. (1963)
12. Webb, C. S., quoted in Hill, W. C. Osman (1960)
13. Bode, N. (1952) (1953)
14. Jones, M. L. (1962)

PONGO Linnaeus, 1760 Orang-utans

1 species: 2 subspecies[1]

Pongo pygmaeus pygmaeus   Bornean orang
Pongo pygmaeus abelii   Sumatran orang

GEOGRAPHICAL RANGE [2-5]

Sumatra and Borneo. Probable range in N. Sumatra is Atjeh, N. of the Wampoe R. Centres of population in 1938 said to be along the Simpang-Kanan and the Peureulak Rivers and in forested regions of E. coast between Menlaboh and Singkel. In North Borneo (Sabah, Malaysia), orangs are found in lowland primary forest particularly in the Sandakan district. In Sarawak the diminishing orang populations are found in the forests of W. Sarawak between the Sadong and the Butang Lupar Rivers. Isolated pockets reported (1961) S. of Rajang and Balek Rivers, and around the headwaters of Balui and Baram Rivers. Distribution in Indonesian Borneo (Kalimantan) is not known.

ECOLOGY

HABITAT:[3-6] Arboreal. Tropical rain forest. Peatswamp and Dipterocarp forest in Sarawak; Dipterocarp in Sabah (N. Borneo). In peatswamp forest, open canopy trees reach 120–150 ft (37–46 m); ground cover is absent and forest floor usually swampy. Orangs are found at all levels feeding among smaller branches.* Night nests in closed canopy 20–80 ft (6–24 m) above ground.[4, 6] DIET: Predominantly frugivorous; (Durian, rambutans, etc. Durian "season": August–December); also leaves, bark and birds' eggs.* *See* Schaller (1961) for food list. PREDATORS: Man, indirectly, through reduction of forests for agriculture and, directly, for sale to zoos. No other known predators. ACTIVITY RHYTHM: Diurnal.

MORPHOLOGY

External Characters

Large size with marked sexual dimorphism: Sumatran forms probably larger than Bornean.[7] Coat is rather coarse and long especially over shoulders and arms (but *see* Hill, 1938b). Colour in various shades of reddish-brown which becomes darker (purplish) with age. Sumatran orang is generally lighter-coloured than Bornean variety. Face is bare except for orange beard; hairy skin is bluish-black in colour and somewhat papillated. Some adult ♂♂ develop enormous cheek flanges of fat and fibrous tissue which are placed at the sides of the face like blinkers. A large dependent gular pouch is a prominent feature of adult ♂♂. Ears are small and adpressed. Face is somewhat concave ("dished"), and markedly prognathic in adults. The arms are extremely long, the hands broad and long and the thumb very small. The legs are relatively short. The foot which, at rest, is held in a curled position has long toes and a short hallux.

PLATE 92. *Pongo pygmaeus* in Sarawak, juvenile (by courtesy of Barbara Harrisson)

PLATE 91. *Pongo pygmaeus*, young adult ♂ (by courtesy of Doris M. Sorby)

Weights and Dimensions[8, 9]

	♂	♀	♀ in % of ♂
Bornean Orang:			
Mean body weight (kg)	189* (4♂♂)	81* (6♀♀)	43
Mean height (mm)	1370 (3♂♂)	1150 (4♀♀)	84
Mean head and body length (mm)	965 (3♂♂)	785 (6♀♀)	81
Arm span range (mm)	2150–2400		
Sumatran Orang:			
Mean body weight (kg)	69 (4♂♂)	37 (5♀♀)	54
Mean height (mm)	1364 (4♂♂)	1148 (3♀♀)	83·4
Mean head and body length (mm)	944 (4♂♂)	768 (5♀♀)	81·3

Note that sexual dimorphism is more apparent in weight than in body dimensions. Hill (1938) describes a single specimen of Sumatran ♂ as having a stature of 1581 mm.

    * Discrepancy between weights of Bornean and Sumatran forms in spite of similarity of body size is noted with dubiety, and is probably due to a miscalculation by Lyon (1911) of the collector's figures for Bornean specimens.

Internal Characters

For details of anatomy, *see* Fick (1895), Milne-Edwards (1895), Hartmann (1885), Owen (1831, etc.), Temminck (1841), Sonntag (1924), Schultz (1930, 1941b), and Hill (1938b). The following adult characters are selected principally for their known functional importance or their value for identification. SKULL: The skull is domed and, in 7 out of 10 adult ♂♂, bears a sagittal crest which may be as much as 12 mm high; a nuchal crest is present in all. The orbits are usually elliptical with the longest axis vertical and the inter-orbital distance is less than in *Pan* and *Gorilla*; supra-orbital crests are not confluent. The facial skeleton is prognathous, the profile being straight or slightly concave[18] (simognathic condition). The mandible is massive with a broad ascending ramus and simian shelf. On the base, the foramen magnum is placed far back, the glenoid cavities are shallow, and the mastoid process is not usually well-developed. CRANIAL CAPACITY:[19] 405–540 cc (11♂♂): 320–400 cc (9♀♀)—*see also* Selenka (1898). VERTEBRAL COLUMN:[16] Commonest formula: C.7, T.12, L.4, S.5 or 6. RIBS: 12 pairs. UPPER LIMB: Scapula shows the characteristic cranio-caudal elongation of brachiating apes[21] and is sited on back of thorax. Humerus has a supra-trochlear foramen present in 80% ♂♂ and ♀♀. Radius is strongly curved; ulnar styloid does not abut against proximal carpal row even in 90° forced adduction[22] (cf. *Pan* and *Gorilla*). CARPUS: Os centrale usually separate but shows tendency to fusion in old age. Pollex is relatively shorter than in other Pongidae but thenar muscles are remarkably specialized.[23] Metacarpals and phalanges are extremely bowed. DIGITAL FORMULA:[7] 3.4.5.2.1. LOWER LIMB: Relatively short compared to trunk height and upper limb length (*see* Limb Proportions). PELVIS: Marked expansion of ilium as in *Pan* and *Gorilla*. FEMUR: Fossa for ligamentum teres frequently absent. FOOT: Hallux is relatively the shortest among all primates;[24] distal phalanx 5th digit absent in 60%[17] when nail is also absent (*see also* Lyon, 1908a, 1911; Tuttle and Rogers, 1966). Flexor hallucis longus absent or rudimentary.[25] There appears to be a higher frequency of absence in Sumatran Orang (*P. p. abelii*).[7, 9] DENTITION: D.F.: $\frac{2}{2}\frac{1}{1}\frac{2}{2}\frac{3}{3}=32$. The dentition shows a typical pongid pattern as described under *Pan*. The main cusps of molar teeth show secondary wrinklings of the enamel by which they can be distinguished from *Pan* and *Gorilla*. The lower 3rd molar in

Pongo is often the longest of the series. Supernumerary molars are common in the orang.[26] Roots of teeth are extraordinarily long. ALIMENTARY TRACT: Intestinal tract very long; stomach similar to *Pan*.[27] DUCTLESS GLANDS: *See* Hill (1938b). VASCULAR: Coronary arteries; *see* Chase and De Garis (1938).

Genetic Biology

CHROMOSOMES:[29, 30] 2n = 48 (2♂♂, 2♀♀). Karyotype suggests a less close relationship between orang and man than between chimpanzee and gorilla and man. For comparative study of the karyotypes of *Pongo*, *Pan* and *Homo*, see Chiarelli (1962a). IMMUNOCHEMISTRY:[32] Serological evidence suggests evolutionary divergence of orang from man, gorilla and chimpanzee. P.T.C. TASTING:[33] 2 tasters : 37 non-tasters. BLOOD GROUPS:[34] Show ABO polymorphism, "O" phenotype being absent. Polymorphic for ABH secretor status.[50] HAEMOGLOBINS: A_2 variant ($2\frac{1}{2}\%$ frequency in *Homo*) found in this genus. *See* Barnicot and Jolly (1966).

BEHAVIOUR

Locomotor Behaviour[4, 5, 36, 37]

AUTHORS' CLASSIFICATION: Modified Brachiation. Habitat is arboreal and they are only occasionally seen on ground. Arboreal progress is cautious,[5, 37] and includes occasional true brachiation especially by young animals;[5] movement is by climbing, walking quadrupedally along branches or bipedally with arms holding on above. Stability depends largely on grasping power of feet.[4, 5, 37] All observers deny regular leaping or jumping. On the ground in captivity, bipedalism is commonly adopted;[36, 38] normal ground gait is quadrupedal, weight being borne by the clenched fists and inverted, clenched feet (cf. *Gorilla*, *Pan*); other variations of hand posture during walking are seen in captivity, such as a palmigrade posture.[22] LIMB PROPORTIONS: For Indices, *see* Part III, p. 395.

Hand Function[39]

Hand is prehensile, thumb is short but fully opposable against proximal phalanx of index digit. The power grip is exceedingly strong and adapted for grasping slender branches. Interdigital grip frequently employed for picking up small objects. Principal grip employed in locomotion is "hook-grip" (for functional terms relating to hand use, *see* Part III, p. 396). Manipulative activities include feeding, drinking, nest-building;[5, 36] also handling and eventual destruction of mechanical objects in captivity.[36] No evidence of tool-using in wild state but digging sticks are used in captivity.[36*] HAND PROPORTIONS: *See* Part III, p. 402, for Indices.

Resting Behaviour

Nesting behaviour has been studied by Schaller (1961), Davenport (1967) and Harrisson (1960). Nests are of simple construction and do not involve interweaving or knotting. New nests are constructed every night; ground nests are not seen. Animals do not defaecate in nests[5] (cf. *Gorilla*). Night-sleep may exceed 12 hours and frequent periods of rest, somnolence or sleep are observed during day.[5]

Social Behaviour

Reports on behaviour in wild populations are relatively few: *see* Schaller (1961), Davenport (1967) and Harrisson (1960). Ecological surveys have been carried out by Carpenter (1938), Yoshiba (1964) and Stott and Selsor (1961a). For general captivity studies, *see* Yerkes and

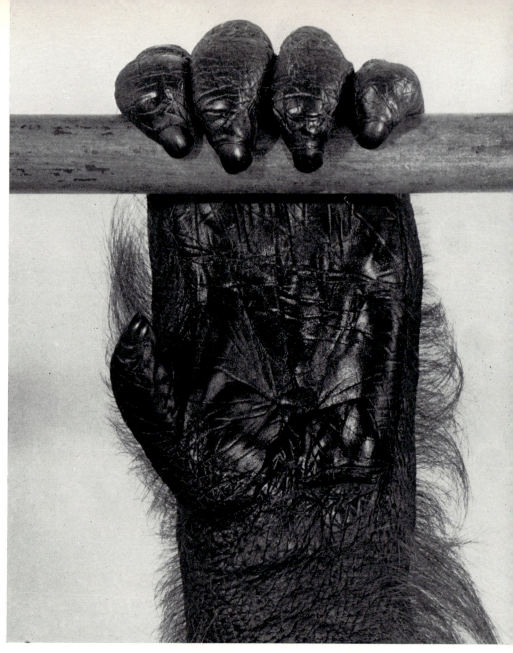

PLATE 93. *Pongo pygmaeus*. Hand of adult ♂ in brachiating posture

Yerkes (1929) and Harrisson (1960). RANGE AND TERRITORIALITY: Unknown. GROUP SIZE:[4, 5] Habitually 2, 3 or 4; lone ♂♂ common. GROUP COMPOSITION: (i) pairs with or without infant; (ii) ♀ with infant or juvenile; (iii) 2 or 3 subadults. POPULATION DENSITY: Sarawak:[4] 1 per 2 sq mile (5 sq km): N. Borneo:[6] 1 per 1 sq mile (2·5 sq km) to 1 per 2 sq miles (5 sq km). Sumatra (in 1938): two or three per 10 sq miles (25 sq km). INTRA-GROUP BEHAVIOUR: No information. VOCALIZATION:* Orangs are silent animals with apparently a small repertoire of calls. AGONISTIC BEHAVIOUR: Throwing or dropping of branches in relation to observer reported by many workers.[4, 5, 42, 43] SEXUAL BEHAVIOUR: Copulation is *more hominum*.[44]

REPRODUCTION AND DEVELOPMENT

MENSTRUAL CYCLE: 29 days; characterized by slight menstrual flow lasting 3–4 days; periodic sexual swelling absent. GESTATION: 275 days;[45] genital swelling occurs during pregnancy[46] and mammae become prominent. BIRTH WEIGHTS: 1265–1600 g (3 infants).[46]

CAPTIVITY

Births in captivity are now quite common, e.g. between 1959–63, 33 orangs were born in world zoos;[47] until 1928 (Berlin Zoo and Philadelphia Zoo) no births had been recorded.[48] LONGEVITY IN CAPTIVITY: Between 1930–1960, average life-span in London Zoo was approximately 10 years;[47] the record longevity during this period was 24 years 6 months. LONGEVITY RECORD[49] (up to 1962): 31 years 8 months—Philadelphia Zoo.

CONSERVATION [2]

Up until June, 1964, the estimated number of free-ranging orangs totalled 3800, distributed in the following manner: North Borneo (Sabah, Malaysia) 2000; Sarawak 700; Indonesian Borneo (Kalimantan) 1000; Sumatra 100.

REFERENCES

1. Chasen, F. N. (1940)
2. Survival Service Commission of the I.U.C.N. (1964)
3. Carpenter, C. R. (1938)
4. Schaller, G. B. (1961)
5. Davenport, R. K. (1967)
6. Yoshiba, K. (1964)
7. Hill, W. C. Osman (1938b)
8. Lyon, M. W. (1911)
9. Lyon, M. W. (1908b)
10. Fick, R. (1895)
11. Milne-Edwards, A. (1895)
12. Hartmann, R. (1885)
13. Owen, R. (1831, 1837, 1844)
14. Temminck, C. J. (1835–41)
15. Sonntag, C. F. (1924)
16. Schultz, A. H. (1930)
17. Schultz, A. H. (1941b)
18. Fitzinger, L. J. (1853)
19. Hrdlicka, A. (1907)
20. Selenka, E. (1898)
21. Ashton, E. H. and Oxnard, C. E. (1963)
22. Tuttle, R. H. (1967)
23. Day, M. H. and Napier, J. R. (1963)
24. Schultz, A. H. (1963a)
25. Straus, W. L. (1942)
26. Colyer, F. (1936)
27. Straus, W. L. (1936)
28. Chase, R. E. and De Garis, C. F. (1938)
29. Chiarelli, B. (1961)
30. Klinger, H. P. et al. (1963)
31. Chiarelli, B. (1962a)
32. Goodman, M. (1962b)
33. Chiarelli, B. (1961)
34. Franks, D. (1963)
35. Barnicot, N. A. and Jolly, C. J. (1966)
36. Harrisson, Barbara (1960)
37. Schlegel, H. and Müller, S. (1839–44)
38. Napier, J. R. (1965)
39. Napier, J. R. (1960)
40. Stott, K. and Selsor, G. J. (1961a)
41. Yerkes, R. M. and Yerkes, A. W. (1929)
42. Wallace, A. R. (1856)
43. Attenborough, D. (1957)
44. Fox, H. (1929)
45. Aulmann, G. (1932)
46. Schultz, A. H. (1938)
47. International Zoo Year Book, Vols. I–V (1959–1965)
48. Ulmer, F. A. (1957)
49. Jones, M. L. (1962)
50. Wiener, A. S. et al. (1965)

PRESBYTIS† Eschscholtz, 1821   Langurs

4 species groups: 14 species: 84 subspecies[1-6, 49]

P. entellus Group	*P. entellus*	Hanuman langur, Entellus langur	15 subsp.
P. senex Group	*P. senex*	Purple-faced leaf-monkey	5 subsp.
	P. johnii	John's langur	0 subsp.
P. aygula Group	*P. aygula* (Type species)	Sunda Island leaf-monkey	8 subsp.
	P. melalophos	Banded leaf-monkey	19 subsp.
	P. frontatus	White-fronted leaf-monkey	2 subsp.
	P. rubicundus	Maroon leaf-monkey	5 subsp.
P. cristatus Group	*P. cristatus*	Silvered leaf-monkey	8 subsp.
	P. obscurus	Dusky leaf-monkey	7 subsp.
	P. phayrei	Phayre's leaf-monkey	4 subsp.
	P. francoisi	François' leaf-monkey	4 subsp.
	P. potenziani	Mentawai leaf-monkey	2 subsp.
	P. pileatus	Capped langur	5 subsp.
	P. geei	Golden langur	0 subsp.

GEOGRAPHICAL RANGE [1, 2, 7]

P. entellus group: India and Pakistan; from Kashmir, Nepal, S. Tibet, Sikkim and Assam southwards to Ceylon. *P. senex group*: Extreme S.W. India and Ceylon. *P. aygula group*: Tenasserim, S. Thailand, Malaya, Sumatra, Java, Borneo and many offshore islands. *P. cristatus group*: Assam, Bhutan border, Burma, S.W. China, Thailand, Indo-china, Malaya, Sumatra, Java, Borneo and many offshore islands. The genus does not cross Wallace's Line, except in Lombok I. where it was probably introduced by man. LIMITS OF GENUS: Latitudes: 33° N.–9° S. Longitudes: 70°–120° E.

ECOLOGY [8-12]

HABITAT: *Presbytis* have a wide range of habitat: found at high altitudes, 12,000 ft (3658 m) in the Himalayas, in dry zones of S. India and Ceylon, in rain forests of Assam and Indo-china, and among tidal mangrove swamps in Malaya and Borneo. *P. entellus* sometimes inhabit towns and villages in India where they are considered sacred and are not molested although they raid cultivated fields.[12] *Presbytis* are basically arboreal. *P. pileatus* from dense rain forests of the Naga Hills does not come to the ground;[8] *P. senex* and *P. johnii* are more arboreal than *P. entellus* which may spend up to 80% of day on the ground, though always within a safe distance of trees.[12] *P. rubicundus* (Borneo) occupy middle and sub-canopy levels in primary forest, and the tops of medium-height trees in secondary forest.[13] ACTIVITY RHYTHM: Diurnal. DIET: Bulk diet of leaves, also fruit, buds, shoots and bark. Langurs have not been observed to eat insects or dig for roots; many groups live through a dry season without drinking water.[14] Licking of earth has been observed.[9, 19] For list of food trees of *P. entellus* see McCann (1934) and Sugiyama (1964); for general ecology of *P. entellus*, see Oboussier and Maydell (1959).

---

† *See* Taxonomic Notes, p. 376.   PLATE 94. *Presbytis pileatus*, ♀ aged 20 years (San Diego Zoo)

Erratum

Pages 249 and 251

In legends for Plates 82 and 83, for *Papio cynocephalus* read *Papio ursinus*

A Handbook of Living Primates

J. R. NAPIER and P. H. NAPIER

MORPHOLOGY
External Characters[8, 16–19]

Presbytis are medium to large monkeys with round heads, short muzzles, long slender limbs, prominent abdomens and long tails of uniform thickness. Fur is rather long; crown hairs often form a crest or cap, and eyebrows are bristly and forward-projecting, particularly in *P. entellus*. Face is generally black, also palms and soles; hands and feet are long, slender and well-furred. Typically, the newborn young has a distinctive colour. *P. entellus* GROUP: Natal colour is blackish brown; at 3–5 months this changes to light grey; later to brown, slate-grey or buff. Brows are prominent, brow hairs are directed forward and crown hairs backward by a whorl on forepart of crown. *P. senex* GROUP: In *P. senex* newborn is grey with white cheeks; adult colour is black or grey with a tendency to partial albinism; brown crown hairs and whitish whiskers. *P. johnii* is black at birth, developing long brown crown hairs and whiskers in adult life. Both species usually have a shorthaired grizzled patch on rump. *P. aygula* GROUP: In *P. aygula* and *P. melalophos*, newborn is white with a dark stripe from head to tailtip, extending on to shoulders forming a cross ("cruciger" pattern). With age, the dark area gradually extends until only the underparts remain white, or just the inside of the thigh with a white stripe continuing down the leg to the ankle. Adult colour: black, grey or brown, with black and red races and white mutants. *P. rubicundus* is all-white at birth, soon changing to redbrown with bright blue facial skin.[13] *P. frontatus* has a naked white patch low on the forehead; colour of newborn is unknown. *P. aygula* group have prominent nasal bones and a variety of crests on the crown (*see* Pocock, 1934). *P. cristatus* GROUP: Bright yellow or orange-red at birth; by about 6 months coat colour changes to black, brown or grey. *P. cristatus* is black with grey-tipped hairs giving a silvered appearance; ♀ has a patch of paler hairs beneath callosities. *P. obscurus* and *P. phayrei* have conspicuous white circles round the eyes and a white patch on lips; hindlimbs, tail and crown of *P. obscurus* are lighter in colour than the back. *P. potenziani* is black with some white on the head, neck and chest and a relatively short tail. *P. francoisi* is black with variable amounts of white on the head; *P. f. delacouri* has white rump and thighs, and a black tail. *P. pileatus* is grey or blackish-grey with a thick mat of dark erect hairs on the crown, typically contrasting with the long whiskers and underparts which are whitish, buff or rust-red. *P. geei* is cream or golden, the newborn almost white.[20]

Weights and Dimensions[5, 6, 8, 18, 21, 22]

	♂	♀	♀ in % ♂
Body weight range (g)			
P. entellus group	9534–20,884 (11♂♂)	3178–17,706 (13♀♀)	68
P. senex group	3859–13,166 (11♂♂)	4313–11,350 (10♀♀)	92
P. aygula group	5500–7037 (27♂♂)	5500–7000 (21♀♀)	99
P. cristatus group	3650–13,620 (27♂♂)	4767–11,350 (35♀♀)	93
Head and body length range (mm)			
All groups	415–787 (163♂♂)	432–695 (131♀♀)	94
Tail length range (mm)			
All groups	495–1092 (163♂♂)	599–1016 (131♀♀)	102

Races from high altitudes in the Himalayas are larger and heavier than those from southern India and the Malaysian Region. The female of these races is appreciably smaller than the male. (♀ in % ♂ based on midpoint of range.)

Internal Characters

For an account of the anatomy of *P. entellus*, see Ayer (1948). For the osteology of the cranial and post-cranial skeleton of the *P. cristatus* group, see papers of Olivier *et al.* (1952–1964). SKULL: Markedly orthognathous having a facial angle of 110°.[24] Glenoid fossa is shallow and post-glenoid tubercle moderate (cf. *Papio*). Interorbital space wide as in all Colobinae. POST-CRANIAL: Vertebral column is typical of generalized catarrhines, C.7, T.12, L.7, S.3. Thorax shows relative broadening from side-to-side as in *Colobus* in distinction to Cercopithecinae.[24] Pelvis has long ischium and relatively short ilium.[25] Foot is relatively long particularly the phalangeal segment and the big toe is short. ALIMENTARY TRACT:[24] Cheek pouches are absent; salivary glands are larger than in Cercopithecinae. Stomach is sacculated and tripartite with marked dilatations; the gastro-intestinal tract is of normal catarrhine length and large intestine is not unduly dilated. RESPIRATORY: R. lung shows 5 lobes and 2 extra lobules as in *Colobus* though not in *P.e. priam*.[26] LARYNX: Described and discussed by Hill (1952, 1957); laryngeal saccules and sub-hyoid air sac are present.[28] DENTITION: D.F.: $\frac{2}{2}\frac{1}{1}\frac{2}{2}\frac{3}{3} = 32$. Canines in ♂♂ are large and broad; considerably smaller in ♀♀.[29] Molars: $M.\overline{3}$ bears a 5th cusp which is said to be absent in *P. melalophos*. ISCHIAL CALLOSITIES: Present but well separated.[30]

Genetic Biology

CHROMOSOMES: Makino (1952) gives 2n = 50 for *P. entellus* (1♂); Chiarelli (1963a) gives 2n = 44 for *P. obscurus* (1♂); the karyotype is compared with those of *Colobus* and *Hylobates*.

BEHAVIOUR

Locomotor Behaviour

AUTHORS' CLASSIFICATION: Quadrupedalism. Subtype: Old World Semibrachiation. Essentially arboreal animals though some species, e.g. *P. entellus* spend 50–80% of their day on the ground. On the ground and in large branches of trees, langurs run or walk quadrupedally. Among small peripheral branches they walk or clamber. Movement from tree-to-tree is by leaping, involving strong propulsive push-off with hindlimbs and stretching out of the arms ahead of the body.[8, 9, 33] Longest leaps are between 35–40 ft (10–12 m) obliquely and 12–15 ft (4 m approx.) horizontally (*P. entellus*).[33] Leaps of *P. melalophos* in Malaya have been described by Harrisson (1962). *See also* Napier (1963). Arm-swinging has been described by Tennent (1861) and by Hill (personal communication) in *P. senex*. For detailed account of locomotor behaviour of *P. entellus*, see Ripley (1967). LIMB PROPORTIONS: For indices relating to *Presbytis* collectively, *see* Part III, p. 395. There are however considerable interspecific differences which are noted here:

	No. of specimens	Rel. upper limb length	Rel. lower limb length	Brachial index	Crural index	Intermembral index
P. entellus group	3	—	—	101	88	79
P. senex group	3	—	—	100	92	78
P. aygula group	36	83	109	114	91	76
P. cristatus group	34	76	92	94	90	82

Indices from Washburn (1942) and Gabis (1960). Note particularly the differences between *P. cristatus* group and remainder in Brachial and Intermembral Indices. The relative femoro-humeral length in *P. entellus* is close to that of man, i.e. 1·4 : 1.[24]

PLATE 96. *Presbytis entellus*, subadult (San Diego Zoo)

Resting Posture

Sleep and feed in sitting position at extremities of branches. Tail hangs straight down and acts as stabilizer.[34] Langurs may occasionally lie on stomach or side when on the ground[33] but sitting is more common.

Hand Function[6, 34, 37]

Hand prehensile, thumb opposable. Leaves plucked by thumb acting against side of hand. Fine manipulative movements absent. In captivity, *P. entellus* and *P. obscurus* have been observed to use one hand in facewashing movements, licking the palm and passing the hand slowly downwards over the face.[38] HAND PROPORTIONS: Hand elongated especially in phalangeal portion; thumb very short. *See* Part III, p. 402, for Indices.

PLATE 95. *Presbytis obscurus*, adult ♀ (by courtesy of Doris M. Sorby)

surface. VERTEBRAL COLUMN: Cervical region elongated; Lumbar vertebrae: 8; lumbar column long, thoracic short. SHOULDER REGION: Scapula "human"-like having a long and straight vertebral border (cf. *Lemur* where this border is short and convex). HUMERUS: Short, stout, S-curved with prominent tuberosities and supinator crest. RADIUS: Long (high brachial index) and markedly bowed. HAND: Exceptionally long (*see* Part III, p. 402, for hand indices); thumb short; os centrale present (cf. *Avahi*). D.F.: 4.3.5.2.1. FEMUR: Very long bone with large greater trochanter; 3rd trochanter present. Deep and narrow intercondylar notch with elongated patella (typical characters of Vertical Clinging locomotor category). Tarsus short, and metatarsals and phalanges elongated. ALIMENTARY CANAL: Salivary glands hypertrophied. VISCERA: Bulky, especially stomach and colon, no sacculations of stomach. Colon is characteristically coiled in loops and sited in R. hypochondrium. GALL BLADDER: Present and very large (cf. *Avahi*). CUTANEOUS GLANDS: Small oval paired glands on front of neck in ♂.[3] DENTITION: D.F.: $\frac{2}{2}\frac{1}{0}\frac{2}{2}\frac{3}{3}=30$. INCISORS: Small and somewhat protrusive, upper central pair separated by diastema; lower incisors procumbent forming a dental comb. CANINES: Upper, prominent and trenchant; lower, absent. PREMOLARS: P.$\frac{1.2}{}$ pointed and laterally compressed; P.$_{\overline{1}}$ caniniform. MOLARS: Cusps arranged in selodont pattern. M.$\frac{3}{}$ much reduced. M.$_{\overline{123}}$ quadricuspid and elongated. M.$_{\overline{3}}$ bears a hypoconulid.

Genetic Biology

CHROMOSOMES:[5] 2n=48 (2♂ and 2♀ *P. verreauxi*). HAEMOGLOBINS:[6] On starch gel electrophoresis, single Hb band seen with mobility equivalent to human A. SERUM PROTEINS: Immuno-electrophoretic analysis (*P. verreauxi*): *see* Goodman (1962b) and Williams (1964).

BEHAVIOUR

Locomotor Behaviour[3, 9, 10, 11]

AUTHORS' CLASSIFICATION: Vertical Clinging and Leaping.[12] Travels through forest by means of leaps from vertical support to vertical support (cf. *Tarsius*, *Lepilemur*). Body held horizontally during long leaps, arms extended, hindlimbs make contact before forelimbs. Tail trails inertly during leaping.[3] When on ground (rarely), sifakas progressing by hopping or slow bipedal walking.[12] LIMB PROPORTIONS: Hindlimbs much longer than forelimbs; for Indices, *see* Part III, p. 395.

Hand Function

Hand prehensile, thumb is pseudo-opposable. Prehension is of a typical lemuriform pattern, thumb is not employed in precision grip,[13] but only in coarse grasping movements during locomotion. HAND PROPORTIONS: For Indices, *see* Part III, p. 402.

Resting Posture

During the day the resting posture is almost exclusively vertical; tail may be coiled like a watchspring. During sleep, they adopt an upright sitting posture, the hands and feet grasping a vertical trunk with the head between the knees and the tail rolled under the body.

PLATE 99. *Propithecus verreauxi*, leaping in *Alaouadia* forest (by courtesy of David Attenborough)

Social Behaviour

GROUP SIZE: (*P. verreauxi*) Based on family units consisting of 3–5 individuals including young. Petter (1962a) has observed groups up to 7. Rand observed (1935) groups of 5–9. HOME RANGE AND TERRITORIALITY: Well-defined home range which is vigorously defended; groups travel approx. 500 m daily in search of food. VOCALIZATION: For descriptive account and spectrographic analysis, *see* Petter (1962c). MARKING BEHAVIOUR: Neck-rubbing behaviour observed in males (*see* Internal Characters), never in females; urine marking particularly by females.

REPRODUCTION AND DEVELOPMENT [15]

Probably a single mating season as in *Avahi*. GESTATION PERIOD: 5 months approx. Births occur in Madagascar in June to July. Single young. Infant is carried across belly of mother up to 30 days, then starts clinging to mother's back. The birth of an infant has been recorded on film.[17] Independence of infant begins at 45 days, but close maternal contact continues for 6–7 months. Fully grown at 21 months. Sexual maturity of ♂ attained at $2\frac{1}{2}$ years.

CAPTIVITY

Gentle and tractable in captivity. LONGEVITY RECORD: 7 years. Madagascar: Tananarive.[2] Specimens have been exhibited in London, Breslau and Berlin but have not survived beyond a few weeks;[16] a laboratory colony has been maintained at Yale University and later at Duke University in the United States.

REFERENCES

1. Schwarz, E. (1931c)
2. Hill, W. C. Osman (1953)
3. Petter, J. J. (1962a)
4. Webb, C. S. Quoted in Hill, W. C. Osman (1953)
5. Chu, E. H. Y. and Bender, M. A. (1962)
6. Buettner-Janusch, J. and Buettner-Janusch, V. (1964)
7. Goodman, M. (1962b)
8. Williams, C. A. (1964)
9. Attenborough, D. (1961)
10. Rand, A. L. (1935)
11. Attenborough, D. (1963) B.B.C. film
12. Napier, J. R. and Walker, A. C. (1967)
13. Bishop, Alison (1964)
14. Petter, J. J. (1962a)
15. Petter-Rousseaux, A. (1964)
16. Jones, M. L. (1962)
17. Film: Les Lémuriens de Madagascar

N.B. Since this book was written Alison Jolly has published her book "Lemur Behavior" (University of Chicago Press, 1967) which contains many new observations on the behaviour of *P. verreauxi verreauxi*.

PTILOCERCUS Gray, 1848 — Feather-tailed Treeshrews

1 species: 2 subspecies[1]

Ptilocercus lowii Gray, 1848

GEOGRAPHICAL RANGE [2]

South-East Asia. Southern Malaya, northern Sumatra, Kundur I. (Riau Archipelago), Pini I. (W. Sumatra), Bangka I., N.W. Borneo including Labuan I., and Serasan I. (Natuna Selatan). LIMITS OF GENUS: Latitudes: 6° N.–3° S. Longitudes: 97°–117° E.

ECOLOGY

HABITAT: Tropical rain forest. Arboreal.* Found in the canopy of primary forest,[12] also in low trees and undergrowth, and on the ground. *Ptilocercus* are sometimes found in or near human habitations; the type specimen was caught in the Rajah of Sarawak's House by Mr. Hugh Low after whom the species is named.[5] Nest in hollow tree trunks or branches, sometimes 40 ft above ground.[12] ACTIVITY RHYTHM: Nocturnal or crepuscular.[3, 6] DIET: Principally insects, some lizards.[12]

MORPHOLOGY

External Characters[1]

Approximately the size of a small rat with soft, short grey fur and a dark, scaly tail, the terminal portion of which is tufted on either side like a feather (hence "pen-tail" or "feather-tail"). Proximal hairs of the tuft (about 10 mm) are black; distal portion (about 80 mm) is white. The ears, large and bare but furry at base, stand away from the head and are mobile. Well-developed vibrissae on muzzle; also carpal and calcaneal vibrissae.[6] An ill-defined dark stripe runs from the nose to a little beyond the eye. Hands and feet relatively slightly larger than in Tupaiinae; hallux much reduced in size. All digits are clawed. Conspicuous spherical scrotum.[6] MAMMAE: 2 pairs.[1]

Weights and Dimensions[1, 6, 7, 8]

	♂	♀	♀ in % ♂
Body weight (g)	46·4 (average of 4♂♂)	40 (1♂) : 34 (1♀)	85
Head and body length average and range (mm)	134 (120–143) (6♂♂)	127 (120–140) (4♀♀)	95
Tail length average and range (mm)	172 (165–180) (6♂♂)	176 (170–180) (4♀♀)	102

Internal Characters

For an account of anatomy, *see* Clark (1926). The following summary is concerned with principal differences from *Tupaia*. SKULL: Lyon (1913) provides a list of differences between *Tupaia* and *Ptilocercus*. These differences include the large size of the orbits which are facing relatively further forward (orbital axes subtend an angle of 100° in *Ptilocercus* and 140° in *Tupaia*); the bi-zygomatic diameter which is relatively greater owing to the large size of the temporal fossa; also presumably correlated with this last character, are the prominence and parallel arrangement of temporal lines on the skull, and the bifid arrangement of the lambdoid crest. DENTITION:[1] D.F.: $\frac{2}{3} \frac{1}{1} \frac{3}{3} \frac{3}{3} = 38$. INCISORS: $I.^{\underline{1}}$ larger than $I.^{\underline{2}}$ which bears a posterior cusp. In lower jaw $I.\overline{2}$ larger than $I.\overline{1}$ or $I.\overline{3}$. MOLARS: Upper molars lack a mesostyle and are surrounded by a cingulum; $M.^{\underline{3}}$ is markedly compressed antero-posteriorly; in the lower jaw, molars have an external cingulum. POST-CRANIAL: Carpal bones separate (cf. scapho-lunate of *Tupaia*).[6] C.N.S.: Visual pathway relatively poorly developed.[6] Retina consists of rods only.[9] Tail thought to have specialized tactile function.[*4] MYOLOGY: Ear musculature better developed than in *Tupaia*[6] (correlated with large mobile ears and nocturnal habit).

Genetic Biology

No information.

BEHAVIOUR

Locomotor Behaviour*

Very few observations have been made of the locomotion of *Ptilocercus*; it has been described as an excellent climber,[12] able to climb vertically with ease; it uses the tail for balancing and it leans it against the trunk of a tree as a prop when stationary. The fingers and toes spread out widely to give a good grip; the digits are flexed so that the claws are always in contact with the branch. On the ground, it progresses in a series of hops with the tail held up at an angle of 30°, the tuft being almost vertical.[10] LIMB PROPORTIONS: For Indices, *see* Part III, p. 395.

Hand Function*

Hand is convergent but probably non-prehensile. Thumb is non-opposable but is divergent and mobile. Insects can be grasped one-handed.[6] HAND PROPORTIONS: Digits of hand are longer than in *Tupaia*, the thumb is also rather long. For Indices, *see* Part III, p. 402.

Resting Posture

In captivity, sleeps on one side covering the snout and face with the tufted tail,[10] or rolled in a ball.[12]

Social Behaviour*

Observations of *Ptilocercus* in the wild and in captivity are few; *see* Schneider (1905), Lyon (1913) and Banks (1926). COMMUNICATION: When annoyed, gives a snarling hiss with the mouth open.[11] GROUP SIZE: Found in pairs; sometimes 4 in one nest hole.[12]

PLATE 100. *Ptilocercus lowii* (by courtesy of Lim Boo Liat)

REPRODUCTION AND DEVELOPMENT*

Nothing is known of the reproductive cycle or growth periods.

CAPTIVITY

A specimen has been kept in captivity for 2 years, 8 months in Malaysia.[12]

REFERENCES

1. Lyon, M. W. (1913)
2. Chasen, F. N. (1940)
3. Davis, D. Dwight (1962)
4. Schneider, G. (1905)
5. Gray, J. E. (1848)
6. Clark, W. E. Le Gros (1926)
7. British Museum (Natural History) Records

8. Hill, J. E. (1960)
9. Clark, W. E. Le Gros (1959)
10. Banks, E. (1926) quoted in Clark, W. E. Le Gros (1926)
11. Harrison, J. L. and Lim, B. L. (1950)
12. Lim, B. L. (In press)

PYGATHRIX   E. Geoffroy, 1812   Douc Langurs

1 species: 2 subspecies[1]

Pygathrix nemaeus nemaeus Linnaeus, 1771
Pygathrix nemaeus nigripes Milne-Edwards, 1871

GEOGRAPHICAL RANGE [1]

Laos, Vietnam and the island of Hainan. From sea level to 6500 ft (2000 m). LIMITS OF GENUS: Latitudes: 8°–23° N. Longitudes: 100°–111° E.

ECOLOGY

HABITAT: Tropical rain forest. ACTIVITY RHYTHM: Diurnal. DIET: No information.

MORPHOLOGY

External Characters

Large monkeys with arms only slightly shorter than legs; tail approximately equal to head and body length. Fur is short; no crest on crown, hairs of which are directly smoothly backward. *P. nemaeus nemaeus* is grey with black ticking, except for white cheeks, neck and forearms; short-haired white triangular rump patch and tail. Semi-circular red band on upper part of chest is outlined with black and extends on to the shoulders. Thighs, hands and feet are black; legs are red. *P. nemaeus nigripes* is similar, except that the forearm is grey, like the upper arm, and the whole leg is black. No sexual dimorphism in colour. Ischial callosities are present. Two pectoral mammae.

Weights and Dimensions[2, 3]

	♂	♀	♀ in % ♂
Head and body length *average and range* (mm)	644 (550–820) (6♂♂)	614 (597–630) (2♀♀)	95
Tail length *average and range* (mm)	693 (600–769) (6♂♂)	631 (597–665) (2♀♀)	91

Internal Characters

Relatively orthognathous as in all Colobinae with interorbital widening characteristic of subfamily. Posterior nares are wide and deep and *P. nemaeus* can be distinguished from *Presbytis cristatus* in this respect.[3] Temporal crests well separated on skull vault. DENTITION: D.F.: $\frac{2}{2}\frac{1}{1}\frac{2}{2}\frac{3}{3} = 32$. Extremely short canines, particularly in *P. nemaeus nemaeus*; 6 cusps on 3rd lower molar in 3 out of 4 specimens;[4] but *see* James (1960, Fig. 57c) where $M.\overline{3}$ has extremely reduced talonid cusp. POST-CRANIAL:[4] Long axillary border to scapula and very short sternum.

BEHAVIOUR

Locomotor Behaviour*

Unknown in the wild state. LIMB PROPORTIONS: (*See* Part III, p. 395). These indices suggest similar locomotor behavioural pattern to *Nasalis*.

Hand Function*

Not known. HAND PROPORTIONS:[6] Digital formula: 3.4.2 = 5.1. Fingers are relatively short and stubby compared with the palm and are unlike *Presbytis* in this respect. The thumb extends as far as the metacarpo-phalangeal flexion line of the index finger.

Social Behaviour*

Pygathrix are said to live in large groups.[7]

REPRODUCTION AND DEVELOPMENT

No information.

CAPTIVITY

Pygathrix has very rarely been exhibited in Zoos.[8]

REFERENCES

1. Ellerman, J. R. and Morrison-Scott, T. C. S. (1951)
2. British Museum (Natural History) Records
3. Pocock, R. I. (1934)
4. Washburn, S. L. (1944)
5. James, W. Warwick (1960)
6. Biegert, J. (1961)
7. Forbes, H. O. (1897)
8. Jones, M. L. (1962)

RHINOPITHECUS   Milne-Edwards, 1872

Snub-nosed
Langurs

2 species: 3 subspecies[1]

Rhinopithecus roxellanae roxellanae	Golden monkey
Rhinopithecus roxellanae bieti	
Rhinopithecus roxellanae brelichi	
Rhinopithecus avunculus	Tonkin snub-nosed monkey

GEOGRAPHICAL RANGE [2, 3]

R. roxellanae: Western China, possibly entering Tibet. *R. avunculus*: North Vietnam. LIMITS OF GENUS: Latitudes: 21°–35° N. Longitudes: 100°–109° E. Sea level to 10,000 ft (3000 m) approx. *Rhinopithecus roxellanae roxellanae* was discovered by Père Armand David in central Szechwan, China.

ECOLOGY [2, 3]

HABITAT: *R. avunculus*: tropical rain forest. *R. roxellanae*: high mountains of western China among coniferous forests, bamboo jungle and rhododendron thickets; terrain is snow-covered for more than half the year, when *R. roxellanae* descends to lower cultivated valleys. Chiefly arboreal, descending to the ground for water. ACTIVITY RHYTHM: Diurnal. DIET: Fruit, buds, leaves and young shoots of bamboo. PREDATORS: Fur of *R. roxellanae roxellanae* is much prized by the Chinese; formerly it was extensively hunted, but is now protected.

MORPHOLOGY

External Characters

Large snub-nosed monkeys with robust bodies and limbs; arms only slightly shorter than legs. Face around eyes and nose is bare and pale green-blue in colour. Nose is very upturned, the tip forming two little follicles which approach the forehead in adult life. Fur is long and thick, becoming longer, thicker and more brightly coloured with age. Tail is shorter than combined head and body length in *R. r. roxellanae* and *R. r. bieti*; it is considerably longer than head and body length in *R. r. brelichi* and *R. avunculus*. Digits of hands and feet are longer and more slender in *R. avunculus*.[4] Ischial callosities are present. Two pectoral mammae.

Weights and Dimensions[5, 6, 8, 9, 10]

	♂	♀	♀ in % ♂
Head and body length range (mm)	703 (560–830) (7♂♂)	600 (500–740) (5♀♀)	85
Tail length range (mm)	766 (610–920) (7♂♂)	726 (510–1040) (5♀♀)	95

COLOUR KEY

	Back and outer sides of limbs	Inner sides of limbs and back of thighs	Forehead, cheeks, whiskers and throat	Hands and feet	Tail
R. r. roxellanae	Chocolate brownish-grey with long (100 mm) golden hairs on back	Variable: buff to golden-orange in ♂: pale yellow in ♀	Variable: buff to golden-orange in ♂: pale yellow in ♀	Variable: buff to golden-orange in ♂: pale yellow in ♀	Dark yellow-grey, slightly tufted
R. r. bieti	Black with long grey hairs	White: long white fringes on back of thighs in adult ♂	White with black forehead	Black	Black, curly in adult ♂
R. r. brelichi	Dark grey: White patch between shoulders	Upper arms buff; back of thighs yellow	Yellow and grey with black tips to hairs	Dark (missing on Type)	V. long. Black with white tip
R. avunculus	Black	Yellowish-buff. White patches either side of tail	White with orange throat patch	Black	Long. Dark with buff tufted tip

Internal Characters

For general anatomy of Asiatic Colobinae, *see* Ayer (1948). The myology of *Rhinopithecus* has been described, on a single specimen, by Patterson (1942). Milne-Edwards (1872) gives an account of skull and teeth in a small number of individuals. SKULL:[5] Nasal bones are reduced, and interorbital space is broad; the face is moderately prognathic, though not so much as in *Nasalis*. Temporal lines are widely separated. DENTITION:[13] D.F.: $\frac{2}{2}\frac{1}{1}\frac{2}{2}\frac{3}{3} = 32$. Canines of adult ♂ are extremely long and sharp while those of ♀ are barely longer than incisors and premolars.[5] M.$\overline{3}$ has prominent 5th cusp on talonid. ALIMENTARY TRACT:[5] Cheek pouches absent; the presence of a sacculated stomach inferred from diet.

BEHAVIOUR

Locomotor Behaviour

Not known. LIMB PROPORTIONS: (*See* Part III, p. 395). Short limbs relative to body length;[5] humerus longer than radius (cf. *Presbytis*). Foot of R. *roxellanae* is long, also the metatarsals, but the phalanges are rather short and curved.[5] Pocock (1924) separates R. *avunculus* from R. *roxellanae*, placing the former in the genus *Presbytiscus*, on the grounds that the digits of hands and feet are longer in R. *avunculus* than in R. *roxellanae*.

PLATE 101. *Rhinopithecus roxellanae*. Above: Family
group at Pekin Zoo; *Rhinopithecus roxellanae*,
Below: adult ♂ at Shanghai Zoo (by courtesy of
Caroline Jarvis, and the Pekin and Shanghai zoos)

Hand Function

Not known. HAND PROPORTIONS:[5] Hand of *R. roxellanae* is short and broad compared with *Presbytis*. Thumb is also short. Hands of *R. avunculus* are more slender and have longer digits.[4]

Social Behaviour

Unknown; said to be found in large groups of 100 or more.[2]

REPRODUCTION AND DEVELOPMENT

No information.

CAPTIVITY

Rarely exhibited in Zoos outside China; in 1964, there were 13 individuals of *R. roxellanae* in Chinese Zoos and 3 births have been recorded there.[15]

REFERENCES

1. Ellerman, J. R. and Morrison-Scott, T. C. S. (1951)
2. Allen, G. M. (1938)
3. Osgood, W. H. (1932)
4. Pocock, R. I. (1925a)
5. Milne-Edwards, A. (1872)
6. Dollman, G. (1912)
7. Thomas, O. (1928a)
8. Thomas, O. (1903)
9. Milne-Edwards, A. and Pousargues, E. de (1898)
10. British Museum (Natural History) Records
11. Ayer, A. A. (1948)
12. Patterson, E. L. (1942)
13. James, W. Warwick (1960)
14. Pocock, R. I. (1924)
15. Jarvis, C. (1965)

SAGUINUS†   Hoffmannsegg, 1807   Tamarins

[= *Leontocebus* Wagner, 1840]†   3 subgenera: 22 species: 4 subspecies

SUBGENUS: *Saguinus*[1] Hoffmannsegg, 1807.   Hairy-faced tamarins

16 species: 4 subspecies[2]

S. tamarin (Type species)	Negro tamarin	
S. nigricollis	Black and red tamarin	
S. fuscicollis	Brown-headed tamarin	
S. fuscus		
S. graellsi	Rio Napo tamarin	
S. illigeri	Red-mantled tamarin	
S. imperator	Emperor tamarin	2 subsp.
S. melanoleucus	White tamarin	
S. midas	Red-handed tamarin	
S. labiatus	Red-bellied tamarin	2 subsp.
S. mystax	Moustached tamarin	
S. pileatus	Red-capped tamarin	
S. pluto	Lönnberg's tamarin	
S. weddelli	Weddell's tamarin	
S. lagonotus	Hare-lipped tamarin	
S. devillei	Deville's tamarin	

GEOGRAPHICAL RANGE [3, 4, 5]

South America. (i) North of the R. Amazon between the R. Negro-Branco and the east coast. (ii) S. of the R. Amazon; the range extends as far as the southern limits of the tropical rain forest bounded to W. by R. Xingu and to E. by R. Gurupi. (iii) Extensive range in the region of the headwaters of the upper Amazon; range limited in E. by R. Madiera and in the W. by High Andes; northern range does not extend beyond the R. Putumayo.

ECOLOGY

Tropical and montane forest up to 1000 m, where they inhabit the larger branches of open and closed canopy. ACTIVITY RHYTHM: Diurnal. DIET: (*S. midas*) fruit only, found in stomach contents of 3 specimens.[7]

MORPHOLOGY

External Characters

Small animals with long, non-prehensile tails with no annulations. All species are generally black, brown or dark red, except *S. melanoleucus* which has white body fur and a blackish-grey face; *S. tamarin* and *S. midas* are black with rust-coloured marbling on the back; *S. midas* is distinguished by its orange or yellow hands and feet. All other species have conspicuous white moustaches and may be divided into two groups: (i) Face wholly blackish, the muzzle (except the nose) being covered with short white hairs, i.e. *S. nigricollis*, *S. graellsi*, *S. fuscicollis*,

---

† *See* Taxonomic Notes, Part III, p. 376.

S. devillei, S. fuscus, S. weddelli, S. illigeri, S. lagonotus (*see* Plate 102). (ii) Face blackish with an unpigmented area, covered with longer white hairs, on the muzzle, generally including the nostrils. Of these, *S. imperator* is grey with reddish tail and long drooping white moustache. *S. mystax* and *S. pluto* are mainly black with conspicuous white moustache in the shape of a clover-leaf; *S. pluto* has a white patch on the inguinal and anal region. *S. pileatus* has the tip of nose, nostrils and mouth outlined with white; forehead and crown chestnut-red, contrasting with marbled back, darkbrown limbs and black tail. *S. labiatus* has a narrow white area around lips (not including nostrils), blackish-brown back, black limbs and tail; underparts and inner sides of limbs orange-red. (*See* Cruz Lima, 1945, and Hill, 1957.)

Ears are conspicuous and generally notched below postero-superior angle. LIMBS: Legs longer than arms; hands bear claws at ends of digits and are broad (cf. *Leontideus*); foot has a short divergent big toe with flattened nail.

Weights and Dimensions[4, 5, 8]

	♂	♀	♀ in % of ♂
Body weights average and range (g)	312 (264–341) (3♂)	320 (264–395) (4♀)	102
Head and body length range (mm)	170–310 (23♂)	155–280 (25♀)	91
Tail length range (mm)	275–420 (23♂)	325–425 (25♀)	108

Length of tail in ♀ may be absolutely longer than in ♂ (♀ in % of ♂ for head-body and tail length based on midpoint of ranges).

Internal Characters

SKULL:[4] Long and ovoid in shape have a high vaulted neurocranium and a bulging occiput; orbits frontally facing separated by a narrow septum (cf. *Leontideus*); face orthognathous. Nuchal area and crest often strongly marked; mandible is somewhat V-shaped, associated with "long-tusked" dental characters; ascending ramus is broad and high. POSTCRANIAL:[4, 9] Vertebral formula: C.7, T.13, L.6, S.3, C.25; lumbar vertebrae laterally compressed with a ventro-median keel increasing in length and width from L.1 to L.6. ARM: Entepicondylar foramen absent from humerus which is a robust bone with a prominent deltoid tuberosity. HANDS: Palmar pads relatively inconspicuous; modified claws (tegulae) at ends of digits.[10] THENAR MUSCLES: See *Callithrix*. LEG: 3rd trochanter present on femur. C.N.S.: Cerebral hemispheres show few convolutions. CUTANEOUS GLANDS[11]: Large fields of mixed sebaceous and apocrine glands in inguinal region and around genitalia. DENTITION:[4] D.F.: $\frac{2.1.3.2.}{2.1.3.2.}=32$. *Saguinus* shows "long-tusked" condition in which canines project well beyond incisor crowns. MOLARS: M.$\underline{^2}$ very small. M.$\overline{_{1.2}}$ quadricuspid.

Genetic Biology

CHROMOSOMES:[12, 13] 2n = 46 (2♂, 2♀ *S. illigeri*). KARYOTYPE: 10 acrocentrics, 4 metacentrics, 30 subterminals. X = subterminal: In *S. illigeri*, the Y chromosome is a small metacentric; in *S. nigricollis*, the Y chromosome is a small acrocentric. P.T.C. TASTING:[14] 100% non-tasters (7 specimens).

PLATE 102. *Saguinus* (*Saguinus*) sp. ♂ and ♀ with infant aged 7 weeks (by courtesy of John K. Hampton)

BEHAVIOUR

Locomotor Behaviour

AUTHORS' CLASSIFICATION: Quadrupedalism. (Erikson's category: Springer). Loco-motion as in *Callithrix* as far as is known. Springing or jumping over considerable distances is a prominent feature in the wild in *S. oedipus*[15] and is therefore likely, in view of similar postcranial morphology, to apply equally to *Saguinus* (*Saguinus*). LIMB PROPORTIONS: Hindlimbs considerably longer than forelimbs: for Indices *see* Part III, p. 395.

Hand Function

Hand prehensile, thumb non-opposable. Hand has limited range of manipulative function other than feeding which is usually carried out one-handed, although food is sometimes taken by mouth and transferred to hand. HAND PROPORTIONS: For Indices *see* Part III, p. 40 2.

Social Behaviour

No extensive study has yet been reported of these animals in their natural habitat. Information is derived principally from captive specimens and will be described under sub-genus *Oedipomidas*.

REPRODUCTION AND GROWTH

Described under sub-genus *Oedipomidas*.

CAPTIVITY

For biological baseline data *see* Deinhardt and Deinhardt (1966). BREEDING RECORDS:[16] Between 1959–63, 14 live births were recorded in World Zoos. LONGEVITY RECORD:[17] *Saguinus weddelli*: 7 years 6 months, San Diego Zoo.

For References, *see* p. 308.

SAGUINUS Hoffmannsegg, 1807 Tamarins

SUBGENUS: *Oedipomidas* Reichenbach, 1862   Crested Bare-faced Tamarins, Pinchés

2 species: o subspecies[2, 3]

S. oedipus (Type species)	Pinché, Cotton-top
S. geoffroyi	Geoffroy's tamarin

GEOGRAPHICAL RANGE [3]

Found E. of Panama Canal Zone, extending southwards throughout Panama into the Choco between Cordillera Occidentale and the Pacific (*S. geoffroyi*). *S. oedipus* is found in northern Colombia as far E. as the R. Magdalena. Latitudinal limits (approx.): 4°–11° N. Longitudinal limits (approx.): 74°–80° W.

ECOLOGY

Tropical rain forest where they are found high up in larger trees.[15] ACTIVITY RHYTHM: Diurnal. DIET: Omnivorous. Enders (1930) states that stomach contents contain seeds.[18]

MORPHOLOGY

External Characters

Dark brown back contrasting with white underparts and limbs; back in *S. geoffroyi* is marbled with buff. Face is black and sparsely haired, and lacks a moustache (cf. sub-genus *Saguinus*). Head bears a crest of white hairs which is long and flowing in *S. oedipus* ("cotton-top") but short in *S. geoffroyi* becoming reddish on back of head. Proximal third of tail reddish brown; terminal two-thirds dark brown or black. Ears relatively small but prominent; notched at postero-superior angle; lamina of lower posterior margin of pinna obsolete.[3] HANDS: Digital formula. 3.2 = 4.5.1. Thumb long and big toe extremely short.

Weights and Dimensions

	♂	♀	♀ in % of ♂
Body weight range[4] (g)	300–510 (5♂)	337–567 (3♀)	112
Mean body weight[15] (g)	417 (28♂)	394 (30♀)	94
Head and body length range[3, 8] (mm)	219–245 (5♂)	250 (1♀)	—
Tail length range[3, 8] (mm)	362–382 (5♂)	370 (1♀)	—

Schultz (1956) states adult ♀ 104% weight of adult ♂ (♀ in % of ♂ weights based on midpoint of range).

Internal Characters

See *S. (Saguinus)* for morphological characters. SKULL: Hershkovitz (1949a) states that there are no essential differences between skulls of the 3 subgenera of *Saguinus*.

Genetic Biology

BLOOD GROUPS:[20*] (Tentative results). Only a weak B-like antigen identified. HAEMO-

GLOBINS:[20] Serum samples (25 specimens) show Hb corresponding to Human A. CHROMO-
SOMES:[12*] 2n=46. Karyotype shows subterminal X chromosome; Y=small metacentric
(*S. oedipus*).

BEHAVIOUR

Locomotor Behaviour

Climbing activity is squirrel-like and tail is used to maintain balance when moving. Springing
or jumping over considerable distances are prominent features in the wild. Move rapidly
when pursued. When excited rises from a sitting to a modified bipedal standing posture.[15]

Hand Function

See *S. (Saguinus)*.

Resting Behaviour[15]

A typical resting posture is to stretch along branch with fore- and hindlimbs dangling on
either side, particularly in warm weather. Tail at rest is characteristically rolled in under the
body. Sleep in curled-up position with tail tightly rolled under the body. Sleeping animals
are hard to wake.

Social Behaviour

Knowledge of social behaviour is derived almost entirely from captive studies, particularly
that of Hampton *et al.* (1963). GROUP ORGANIZATION:[15] It is believed that family groups,
consisting of two parents, a late juvenile and an early juvenile or infant, constitute basic unit
in the wild. The ♀ is much more aggressive and competitive than ♂. MARKING BEHAVIOUR:
Predominantly by ♀ by means of secretions from genital and perineal glands, reinforced by
urine. VOCALIZATION: Reported to emit sounds in ultrasonic range, i.e. 10,000–50,000
cycles/second of varying pattern. GROOMING: Mutual grooming is prominent in Pinchés
including a form of dental grooming using the tongue; self-grooming by scratching is also
common. SEXUAL BEHAVIOUR: Marking behaviour (see above) may be part of ♀ sexual
repertoire. Copulation is rarely seen but lacks any typical pre-coital and post-coital activities.
In-and-out movements of tongue observed during copulation (cf. *Alouatta*).

REPRODUCTION AND DEVELOPMENT

External evidence of seasonal or menstrual cycling has not been observed. GESTATION
PERIOD:* 140–145 days.[20] PREGNANCY: Weight loss apparent in early pregnancy, followed
by a weight gain of as much as 100 g. NUMBER OF YOUNG: Twin births usual in the wild but
in captive conditions, single young are common. As in *Callithrix*, ♂ parent takes dominant
role in bringing up young.

CAPTIVITY

For accounts of husbandry and breeding records in laboratory colonies, *see* Hampton (1964),
Deinhardt and Deinhardt (1966). LONGEVITY RECORD:[17] *Saguinus (Oedipomidas) oedipus*:
7 years 8 months, San Diego Zoo.

For References, *see* p. 308   PLATE 103. *Saguinus (Oedipomidas) oedipus* (San Diego Zoo)

SAGUINUS Hoffmannsegg, 1807   Tamarins

SUBGENUS: *Marikina* Lesson, 1840   True Bare-faced Tamarins

4 species: 0 subspecies[2, 3, 21]

S. bicolor (Type species)	Pied tamarin
S. martinsi	Martin's tamarin
S. leucopus	White-footed tamarin
S. inustus	

GEOGRAPHICAL RANGE [3, 4, 24]

South America. (i) N. bank of R. Amazon between R. Paru and R. Negro (*S. bicolor*, *S. martinsi*); (ii) between R. Negro and R. Japura and extending as far N. as Rio Guaviare (*S. inustus*); (iii) Colombia, between R. Cauca and R. Magdalena up to 1000 m altitude (*S. leucopus*).

ECOLOGY

Assumed to be similar to other subgenera of *Saguinus*.

MORPHOLOGY

External Characters[3, 4]

Coat colour is generally brown, with yellow, or rusty red underparts. Extreme dichromatism in *S. bicolor* with sharply defined white chest and forelimbs in contrast to yellowish-brown hindparts ("pied" effect). Forearms and hands of *S. martinsi* are yellowish, those of *S. leucopus* are whitish. Face is bare and black as far as vertex except *S. leucopus* in which there are long silvery hairs on cheeks and forehead. Ears are large, bare and obtrusive. *S. inustus* is mainly black, with brown on back and flanks, and some unpigmented areas on the bare face.

Weights and Dimensions[3, 4]

	♂	♀	♀ in % of ♂
Head and body length (mm)	240 (219–292) (4♂)	236 (210–250) (6♀)	98
Tail length (mm)	359 (349–368) (4♂)	358 (235–420) (6♀)	100

BEHAVIOUR

See *Saguinus* (*Oedipomidas*); but, according to Bates (1863), *S. bicolor* do not make the long leaps and jumps of *S.* (*Oedipomidas*).

PLATE 104. Above: *Saguinus* (*Saguinus*) *mystax*, adult ♂ and ♀ (by courtesy of John K. Hampton). Below: *Saguinus* (*Marikina*) *leucopus* (by courtesy of John K. Hampton)

CAPTIVITY

LONGEVITY RECORD:[17] *Saguinus (Marikina) martinsi*: 9 years 10 months. New York: Bronx Zoo.

REFERENCES

1. Hershkovitz, P. (1958)
2. Cabrera, A. (1957)
3. Hershkovitz, P. (1949a)
4. Hill, W. C. Osman (1957)
5. Lönnberg, E. (1940a)
6. Sanderson, I. T. (1949)
7. Fooden, J. (1964b)
8. Authors' Observations
9. Erikson, G. E. (1963)
10. Clark, W. E. Le Gros (1936)
11. Montagna, W. and Ellis, R. A. (1963)
12. Bender, M. A. and Chu, E. H. Y. (1963)
13. Benirschke, K., Anderson, J. M. and Brownhill, L. E. (1962)
14. Chiarelli, B. (1963b)
15. Hampton *et al.* (1966)
16. International Zoo Year Book, Vols. 1-5 (1959–65)
17. Jones, M. L. (1962)
18. Enders, R. K. (1930)
19. Bates, H. W. (1863)
20. Hampton, J. K. (Personal communication)
21. Hershkovitz, P. (1964)
22. Schultz, A. H. (1956)
23. Deinhardt, F. and Deinhardt, J. (1966)
24. Hershkovitz, P. (1966a)
25. Hampton, J. K. (1964)
26. Du Brul, E. Lloyd (1966)
27. Cruz Lima, E. da (1945)

SAIMIRI†   Voigt, 1831   Squirrel Monkeys

2 species: 8 subspecies[1, 2]

S. sciureus	Common Squirrel Monkeys	6 subsp.
S. oerstedii	Red-backed Squirrel Monkeys	2 subsp.

GEOGRAPHICAL RANGE [1, 2, 3]

Central and South America. In C. America they are found on Pacific coastal strip, Lat. 81°–85° W. (*S. oerstedii*) at sea level and up to 4920 ft (1500 m). In S. America, *S. sciureus* is found S. and E. of R. Orinoco, in the Guianas, throughout the Amazon basin, into the Mato Grosso as far as Lat. 11° S. Further west, they extend further southwards to Lat. 17° in the Llanos de Guarayos; also northwestwards to the foothills of the Andes in Bolivia, Peru, Ecuador and Colombia.

ECOLOGY

HABITAT: Tropical rain forest, but mainly gallery forest and forest edges.[4] They are to be found in a small branch setting in the closed canopy and also in emergents of open canopy, in the shrub layer[5] and on the ground.[4] ACTIVITY RHYTHM: Diurnal. DIET: Fruit and insects (stomach contents of 12 specimens);[6] but *see* Sanderson (1949). In captivity, require animal protein and Vit. D additives.[7]

MORPHOLOGY

External Characters[3, 4]

Amongst the smallest of the Cebidae. Fur is short and dense and of various shades of grey-green to olive on back, flanks and back of the head; undersides and limbs are generally white yellowish or orange; the end of the tail is jet black. The colour of the crown hair distinguishes the two species, being black in *S. oerstedii* and olive green to grey-blue in *S. sciureus*. (N.B. Two races of *S. sciureus* (*S. s. boliviensis* and *S. s. nigriceps*) also have a black or blackish crown but they can be distinguished from *S. oerstedii* by having less red or orange colouration on the back.) The dark hair of the crown in both species forms a well-defined peak in contrast to the white circumocular mask; the muzzle is always dark. Tail is non-prehensile, thick at the base and frequently tufted at the tip. Head is long and oval in profile and face is orthognathous. Nostrils typically platyrrhine; ears large and very often tufted. LIMBS: Legs are markedly longer than arms. Some sexual dimorphism ($\male > \female$) in body weight, and head and body length.

Weights and Dimensions

	♂	♀	♀ in % of ♂
Body weight range[4, 6, 9] (g)	550–1135 (14♂)	365–750 (5♀)	—†
Head and body length range[3, 6, 10] (mm)	249–370 (34♂)	225–295 (12♀)	84
Tail length range[3, 10] (mm)	367–465 (27♂)	370–445 (7♀)	98

♀ tails are relatively longer than ♂ tails. (♀ in % ♂ based on midpoint of range.)
† Schultz (1956) states adult ♀ weighs 92% adult ♂ (*S. oerstedii*: 30 specimens).

---

† *See* Taxonomic Notes, Part III, p. 377.

Internal Characters

SKULL:[3] Large, oval with bulging occiput and horizontally placed foramen magnum. Orbits are large, frontally directed and close together, the interorbital septum being incomplete postero-medially.[8] MANDIBLE: Dental arch U-shaped; simian shelf present. C.N.S.:[3] Backward extension of occipital lobes concealing cerebellum (as in man). Union of sylvian fissure and intraparietal sulcus produces a complete fissure which runs obliquely across cerebral hemisphere. Cerebellum morphologically specialized. VISION: Colour vision deficient at red end of spectrum.[12] ALIMENTARY CANAL: Remarkably short small intestine, caecum and colon;[6] colon is straight and caecum is of equal length and directed cranially.[13] CUTANEOUS GLANDS: Small, presternal gland, presumably sebaceous. EXTERNAL GENITALIA: Clitoris is prominent and tip is "claw-like" being pigmented and covered with horny denticles.[4] DENTITION: D.F.: $\frac{2}{2}\frac{1}{1}\frac{3}{3}\frac{3}{3}=36$. INCISORS: I.$\underline{1}$ spatulate and large relative to I.$\underline{2}$. CANINES: Long and pointed. PREMOLARS: PM.$\underline{1}$ caniniform, PM.$\overline{1}$ large and unicuspid. MOLARS: M.$\underline{123}$ trigonal cusps well-marked, hypocones very small, M.$\underline{3}$ vestigial. M.$\overline{123}$ quadricuspid; Carabelli cusps frequently present on lower molars.[14]

Genetic Biology

CHROMOSOMES:[15] 2n = 44 (*S. sciureus*: 1♂, 2♀). KARYOTYPE: 12 acrocentrics, 16 metacentrics, 14 subterminals, X = subterminal, Y = acrocentric. P.T.C. TASTING:[17] Tasters : non-tasters = 13 : 1. HAEMOGLOBINS: *See* Buettner-Janusch, J., and Buettner-Janusch, V. (1964). BLOOD GROUPS: Four specimens of *S. sciureus* have been tested for Human-type ABO groups; three were Group A and one was Group O.[16]

BEHAVIOUR

Locomotor Behaviour

AUTHORS' CLASSIFICATION: Quadrupedalism (Erikson's category: Climber). Sanderson (1949) observed that squirrel monkeys seldom leap; the tail plays a major part as an accessory locomotor organ, being used for balance and even as a third leg of the tripod in bipedal standing (see *Erythrocebus*). Bipedal walking, while carrying a helpless infant, has also been observed.[34] LIMB PROPORTIONS: For Indices *see* Part III, p. 395.

Hand Function

Hand, prehensile; thumb, pseudo-opposable. Little evidence of selective use of thumb, the whole hand being used in manipulation;[20] in grooming, however, some selectivity observed. Squirrel monkeys show behavioural evidence of well-developed tactile discrimination in finger tips.[3, 20] HAND PROPORTIONS: For Indices, *see* Part III, p. 402.

Resting Posture

Tail used to wrap round the body at rest and during sleep. Squirrel monkeys huddle together in sleep, the head being tucked between the knees.[4]

PLATE 105. *Saimiri sciureus*, with juvenile (San Diego Zoo)

PLATE 106. *Saimiri sciureus* (by courtesy of Frank Dumond, Monkey Jungle, Florida)

Social Behaviour

GROUP SIZE: Live in large bands which are said, on occasions, to exceed 500 individuals.[21]
IN CAPTIVITY:[9] Ranking order apparent in captive colony but this varies with different behavioural situations. Self-grooming is of rather low intensity and mutual grooming is

rare and quite unconnected with sexual behaviour. Penile display, associated with thigh spreading, constitutes a social gesture with respect to dominance activity.[9] SEXUAL BEHAVIOUR: Copulation observed in captivity.[9]

GROWTH AND DEVELOPMENT

There is some evidence in favour of a restricted birth season;[22, 23] but *see* Husson (1957). GESTATION PERIOD: 168–182 days, approx.[35] Parturition has been observed, *see* Takeshita (1961–62) and Bowden *et al.* (1967). Twinning is rare. Infant may be carried on the back of either parent.[26] Female gives minimum care to the infant which clings to her fur unaided, even when asleep. It is carried on her back, moving round to the front to feed.[34]

CAPTIVITY

Breeding in captivity is fairly common. Between the years 1959–63, 58 births were recorded in World Zoos.[27] LONGEVITY RECORDS:[27] 10 years 10 months (*S. sciureus*). London: Zoological Gardens. Under laboratory conditions a ♀ squirrel monkey lived for 21 years.[7] LABORATORY SUITABILITY:[28] Squirrel monkeys are popular as laboratory animals having a number of advantages such as size, tractability, cheapness (in U.S.A.) and physiological suitability especially for neurophysiological operations; they have however disadvantages in terms of maintenance and establishment of breeding colonies. Studies on observational learning and learning-set formation have been carried out.[29, 30, 31, 32] For laboratory husbandry, *see* Hanson (1963), Furry *et al.* (1963), Rumbaugh (1963) and Brooks (1963).

REFERENCES

1. Cabrera, A. (1957)
2. Hall, E. R. and Kelson, K. R. (1959)
3. Hill, W. C. Osman (1960)
4. Sanderson, I. T. (1949)
5. Carpenter, C. R. (1935)
6. Fooden, J. (1964b)
7. Hume, E. M. (1957)
8. Du Brul, E. Lloyd (1965)
9. Ploog, D. W., Blitz, J. and Ploog, F. (1963)
10. Lönnberg, E. (1940b)
11. Schultz, A. H. (1956)
12. Miles, R. C. (1958)
13. Clark, W. E. Le Gros (1959)
14. Bolk, L. (1914)
15. Bender, M. A. and Chu, E. H. Y. (1963)
16. Wiener, A. S., Moor-Jankowski, J. and Gordon, E. B. (1966)
17. Chiarelli, B. (1963b)
18. Buettner-Janusch, J. and Buettner-Janusch, V. (1964)
19. Erikson, G. E. (1963)
20. Bishop, Alison (1964)
21. Sanderson, I. T. (1957)
22. Schultz, A. H. (1934) *in* Hill, W. C. Osman (1960)
23. Wislocki, G. B. (1930) *in* Hill, W. C. Osman (1960)
24. Husson, A. M. (1957)
25. Takeshita, H. (1961–62)
26. Zuckerman, S. (1932a)
27. International Zoo Year Book, Vols. 1–5 (1959–1965)
28. Woodburne, L. S. (1963)
29. Mahan, J. L. and Rumbaugh, D. M. (1963)
30. Rumbaugh, D. M. and McQueeney, J. A. (1963)
31. Miles, R. C. (1957)
32. Shell, W. F. and Riopelle, A. J. (1958)
33. Hanson, H. M. (1963)
34. Rumbaugh, D. M. (1965b)
35. Bowden, D. *et. al.* (1967)
36. Furry, D. E., Lowery, R. T. and Beischer, D. E. (1963)
37. Rumbaugh, D. M. (1963)
38. Brooks, Barbara, A. (1963)

SIMIAS   Miller, 1903   Pagai Island Langurs

1 species: 2 subspecies[1]

Simias concolor Miller, 1903

GEOGRAPHICAL RANGE [1, 2]

Islands of Siberut, Sipora and South Pagai (Mentawai Islands) off W. coast of Sumatra.
LIMITS OF GENUS: Latitudes: 0°–4° S. Longitudes: 98°–101° E.

ECOLOGY [2, 3]

HABITAT: Tropical rain forest which is frequently flooded and swampy. Hills of Mentawai
Islands do not exceed 1500 ft (450 m). ACTIVITY RHYTHM: Diurnal. DIET: No information.

MORPHOLOGY [4]

External Characters

Medium-sized monkeys with limbs of almost equal length. Dusky dark brown fur, longer and
paler on crown, head and shoulders; shorter and darker on rump, underparts and limbs.
Hands and feet almost black. Cream-buff variants have been recorded.[1] Face is black with
snub-nose similar to *Rhinopithecus* but less developed. Tail is short, about one-third as long as
head and body length, and bare except for an inconspicuous tuft at the tip. *Simias* is very
similar in build to *Macaca nemestrina*. Ischial callosities are large, black and conspicuous; in the
♂ they are joined on the median line but, in the ♀, narrowly separated. Two pectoral mammae.

Weights and Dimensions[2, 4, 5]

	♂	♀	♀ in % ♂
Body weight (g)	—	7150·5 (1♀)	—
Head and body length average and range (mm)	518 (490–550) (3♂♂)	503 (460–550) (3♀♀)	97
Tail length average and range (mm)	158 (130–190) (3♂♂)	130 (100–150) (3♀♀)	82

Internal Characters

SKULL: Similar to *Nasalis* but considerably smaller.[4] Differs from that of *Presbytis* in the
character of the nasal bones, which are long and straight, and the interorbital space which is
relatively narrow. Compared with *Nasalis* the nasal bones are narrower and less prominent,[4]
and the face less prognathic. DENTITION: D.F.: $\frac{2}{2}\frac{1}{1}\frac{2}{2}\frac{3}{3} = 32$. Teeth similar to *Presbytis*.
ALIMENTARY TRACT: Cheek pouches absent.

BEHAVIOUR

Locomotor Behaviour*

Unknown, assumed to be arboreal, but morphological convergence with *Macaca* suggests a partly ground-living habit. Arms are proportionately similar to *M. nemestrina* but not so robust.

Hand Function

Unknown. HAND PROPORTIONS:* Short hands with long fingers.[3] Small, short thumb.

Social Behaviour

No information.

REPRODUCTION AND DEVELOPMENT

Nothing known.

CAPTIVITY

As far as is known, the Pagai Island Langur has never been exhibited in a Zoo.

REFERENCES

1. Chasen, F. N. (1940)
2. Chasen, F. N. and Kloss, C. Boden (1927)
3. Sanderson, I. T. (1957)
4. Miller, G. S. (1903)
5. British Museum (Natural History) Records

SYMPHALANGUS† Gloger, 1841 Siamangs

1 species: 2 subspecies[1]

Symphalangus syndactylus Raffles, 1821

GEOGRAPHICAL RANGE [1]

Sumatra and the Malay peninsula. In Sumatra they are found up to 9000 ft (2800 m) and the continental subspecies is found in the mountainous areas of Malaya between Negri Sembilan, Pahang and Perak, from 2000–6000 ft (600–1850 m). LIMITS OF GENUS: 7° N.–6° S.; 95°–106° E.

ECOLOGY

HABITAT: Tropical rain forest and montane forest. Minor habitat is assumed to be similar to *Hylobates* in preferring the middle canopy but climbing to the crowns of trees or into low bushes to obtain food. Sympatric in Malaya with *Hylobates lar*.[16, 17] ACTIVITY RHYTHM: Diurnal. DIET: Probably similar to *Hylobates*—80% fruit; seen to eat young leaves.[16*]

MORPHOLOGY

External Characters[1, 2]

The Siamang is heavily-built compared with *Hylobates*. The coat is long and shaggy, and black all over except for some pale hairs around the mouth and chin. There is no pale brow-band and the fur is much less dense than in *Hylobates* (except for *H. klossii*), though this varies with climatic conditions, being denser and less silky in forms that live at high altitudes. The arms are longer than in *Hylobates*, the hands and feet are broader and the whole body is heavier. There is a naked air-sac beneath the chin in both ♂ and ♀. The ♂ has a prominent preputal tuft of black hairs 150 mm in length and can thus be distinguished from the all-black *H. concolor*. Webbing of the 2nd and 3rd toe, which may extend to terminal joint, is a constant feature. HAND: Digital formula: 3.2.4.5.1. or 3.2=4.5.1.

Weights and Dimensions[2, 3, 4, 5]

	♂	♀	♀ in % of ♂
Body weight range[2] (g)	9500–12,700 (5 ♂♂)	9000–11,600 (5 ♀♀)	91·8
Head and body length			
average and range (mm)	533 (468–595) (11 ♂♂)	542 (438–630) (13 ♀♀)	102

The Type specimen (♂) of *S. syndactylus continentis* measures 846 mm, which appears to be exceptional.

Internal Characters

Only morphological distinctions from *Hylobates* are noted below. SKULL:[2] Cranial capacity

---

† *See* Taxonomic Notes, p. 377.

Hand Function

As for *Hylobates*.

Social Behaviour*

There have been few observations of *Symphalangus* in the wild. They have been observed singly or in small family groups up to 5 in number (1 ♂, 1 ♀, infant, 1 or 2 juveniles), but little is known of the territoriality or home range.[11, 16*] VOCALIZATION probably plays an important role in the group life of *Symphalangus*. Heard calling in the early morning and late afternoon. Loud howls and shrill whistles are interspersed with a booming sound of great resonance made by vocalizing into the laryngeal sac while keeping the mouth closed. In captivity, *Symphalangus* have been observed to sit quite still while vocalizing, in contrast to *Hylobates*.[12]

REPRODUCTION AND DEVELOPMENT

GESTATION PERIOD: 230–235 days.[18] For development during first 16 months *see* Rumbaugh (1967.) WEIGHT AT BIRTH: 560 g (1 ♀).[19]

CAPTIVITY

For general account of captivity behaviour, *see* Benchley (1942). LONGEVITY RECORD: 16 years 2 months, National Zoological Park, Washington.[14] BIRTHS IN CAPTIVITY:[13] Between 1959–63, only one birth was recorded in World Zoos. ♀ born at San Diego Zoo (1965).[18]

REFERENCES

1. Kloss, C. Boden (1929)
2. Schultz, A. H. (1933b)
3. Miller, G. S. (1903)
4. Thomas, O. (1908)
5. British Museum (Natural History) Records
6. Pocock, R. I. (1925a)
7. Mott, F. (1924)
8. Klinger, H. P. (1963)
9. Miller, G. S. (1933)
10. Bender, M. A. and Chu, E. H. Y. (1963)
11. Stott, K. (1962)
12. Benchley, B. (1942)
13. International Zoo Year Book, Vols. I–V (1959–1965)
14. Jones, M. L. (1962)
15. Chiarelli, B. (1966a)
16. McClure, H. E. (1964)
17. Ellefson, J. O. (In press)
18. Hill, Clyde A. (1967)
19. Rumbaugh, D.M. (1967)

TARSIUS Storr, 1780   Tarsiers

3 species: 12 subspecies[1]

Tarsius syrichta	Philippine Tarsier	3 subsp.
Tarsius bancanus	Horsfield's Tarsier	4 subsp.
Tarsius spectrum (Type species)	Spectral Tarsier	5 subsp.

GEOGRAPHICAL RANGE [1]

South-East Asia. Found in many islands of the Malay Archipelago. *T. syrichta* is found in the Philippines on Samar, Leyte, Bohol and Mindanao Islands; *T. bancanus* in S.E. Sumatra, Borneo, Bangka I., Belitung I., Karimata Is. and Serasan I. (Natuna Selatan); *T. spectrum* in Celebes, Peleng I., Salajar I., and Sangi I. *T. spectrum* reported in 1890 from Sawu I. between Sumba and Timor,[2] but this has not been confirmed. LIMITS OF GENUS: Latitudes: 13° N.–7° S. Longitudes: 101°–127° E.

ECOLOGY [3–6]

HABITAT: Tropical rain forest, usually in low lying and coastal areas, sometimes in dense bamboo thickets, secondary growth of small trees, or recently cleared primary forest. During the day may occupy dark tangled places or holes in trees. ACTIVITY RHYTHM: Nocturnal. DIET: Insects, lizards, spiders. *Tarsius* are not thought to feed on the ground.[7] PREDATORS: owls.

MORPHOLOGY

External Characters

Tarsiers are about the size of a rat. Body is rather squat with short upper arms, long forearms, extremely long legs and a long tail. Head is broad and dominated by enormous round eyes which are directed forwards; nose is short, nostrils facing laterally (cf. *Aotus*). The membranous ears are large and mobile. The fur is short, dense and greybrown in colour. In *T. syrichta* the grey fur is tinged with redbrown and the tail is naked for about two-thirds of its length, the terminal third bearing a very fine fuzz of short hairs. In *T. bancanus* the grey fur is mottled with golden brown and the terminal third of the tail has a stronger tuft of brown hairs. *T. spectrum* has darker grey fur mottled with brown, small patches of white behind the ears; the tuft of the tail is thicker and darker and extends about halfway along the tail. Hands and feet are almost naked; the terminal pads of the fingers and toes are greatly enlarged to form flat soft discs with small flake-like nails except for digits II and III of the foot which bear toilet claws.[8] Digital formula of hand: 3.4.2.5.1. Foot has an elongated posterior tarsal region; big toe widely divergent and very large. MAMMAE: Vary inter- and even intra-specifically in number—2 or 3 pairs.[7, 9, 10] GLANDULAR ACCRETIONS: Circumanal, epigastric (♂ only) and upper lip.[10, 31]

Weights and Dimensions[1, 3, 5, 7, 11, 12, 13]

	♂	♀	Sexes unknown
Body weight range (g)	95–165 (10♂♂)	87–154 (8♀♀)	—
Head and body length range (mm)	85–159 (9♂♂)	95–160 (14♀♀)	85–162 (44)
Tail length range (mm)	135–274 (9♂♂)	189–239 (14♀♀)	135–274 (44)

PLATE 109. *Tarsius bancanus* (by courtesy of Heinrich Sprankel)

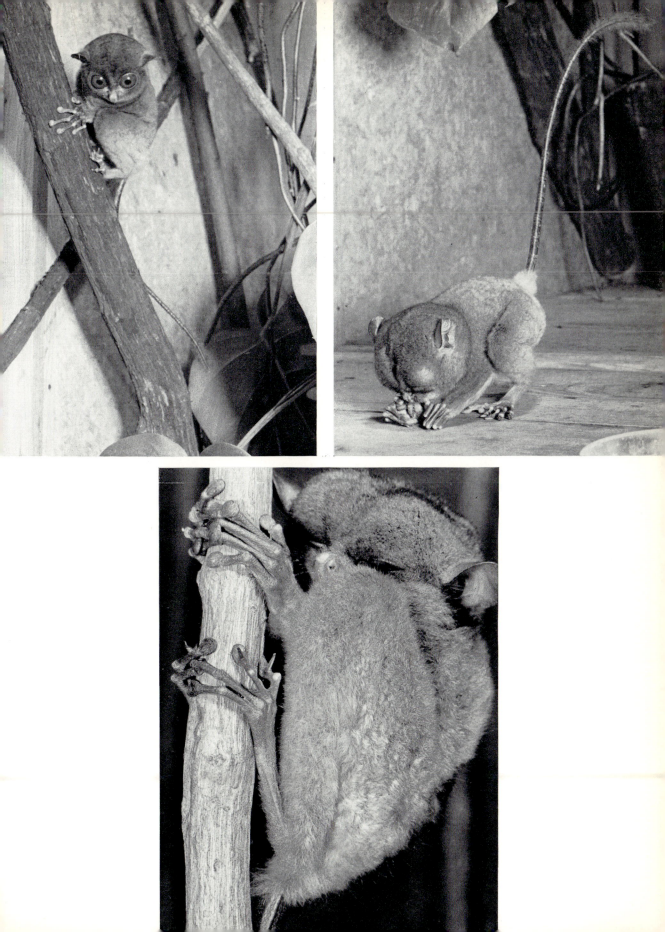

PLATE 110. *Tarsius bancanus*, Stages of the leap photographed on separate occasions (by courtesy of Barbara Harrisson)

Internal Characters

Anatomy of *Tarsius* has been studied by Burmeister (1846) and more recently by Woollard (1925); *see also* Hill (1955a) and Clark (1959). Important and distinguishing aspects of morphology only are listed here. SKULL: Skull is rounded; and moderate prognathism is masked by enormous frontally facing orbits. Post-orbital bar closes orbit laterally but closure incomplete postero-laterally. Brain-case is rounded and foramen magnum is placed well forward. Short tubular external auditory meatus and prominent auditory bulla. Mandible is slender and possesses a short ascending ramus; two halves of lower jaw meet in V-shaped synostosis. VERTEBRAL COLUMN:[15] Cerv. 7, Thor. 12–13, Lum. 6, Sacr. 3, Cocc. 23–30. Atlas vertebra has transverse ligament ossified. FEMUR: Femoral head cylindrical in shape, shaft extremely long; 3rd trochanter prominent. FIBULA: Fused in distal half to shaft of tibia. TARSUS: Calcaneum and navicular markedly elongated. TAIL:[29]* Modified skin, sited ventro-proximally, showing friction pads and dermatoglyphics. GASTRO-INTESTINAL: Stomach is simple and small intestine is arranged in simple loops; caecum and large intestine are approximately equal in length; large intestine lacks flexures or coils. VISUAL SYSTEM: Cornea protuberant, pupil contracts to horizontal slit; retina is composed wholly of rods but a macula and well-formed fovea are present[4] (but *see* Hill, 1955a). Eye movements very limited but visual range achieved by ability to turn the head through 180°. DENTITION: $\frac{2}{1}\frac{1}{1}\frac{3}{3}\frac{3}{3}=34$. INCISORS: Upper central pair large and closely apposed, lateral pair are small. Lower incisors are small and erect. CANINES: Projecting but rather small. PREMOLARS: Show a simple conical form in lower jaw; in upper jaw, P.$^{2.3}$ have a well-developed internal cingulum. MOLARS: Upper molars are tritubercular; in the lower jaw molars are tuberculo-sectorial. M.$_{\overline{1.2}}$ are quadricuspid and M.$_{\overline{3}}$ shows a deep talonid basin with a hypoconulid cusp. GENITO-URINARY: Uterus is bicornuate as in lemuriforms. Placentation is discoidal, deciduate and haemochorial in type (as in Anthropoidea).

Genetic Biology

CHROMOSOMES:[16] 2n=80 (1♀ *T. bancanus*), the highest recorded diploid number for any mammal. Karyotype shows 66 acrocentric, 14 metacentric chromosomes, 2 or 4 micro-chromosomes present.

BEHAVIOUR

Locomotor Behaviour

AUTHORS' CLASSIFICATION: Vertical clinging and leaping.[17] *Tarsius* leap from vertical trunk to vertical trunk with extraordinary rapidity, sometimes as much as 6 ft. The very long flexed legs are suddenly extended, rather like a frog. A turn through 180° may be made in mid-air. Just before landing, the tail is whipped up over the back; the feet touch the trunk first, cushioning the impact. Long hops are occasionally made on the ground when travelling fast but *Tarsius* is clumsily quadrupedal when moving slowly. Biomechanics of leaping[18] appear to be similar to that of *Galago senegalensis* analysed by Hall-Craggs (1965a). LIMB PROPORTIONS: Hindlimbs are remarkably long relative both to trunk length[20] and to forelimb length (*see* Part III, p. 395). Radius is longer than humerus giving a high Brachial Index, and femur and tibia are of equal length.

Hand Function

Hand prehensile; thumb is non-opposable. Divergence and some axial rotation of the thumb take place at the metacarpo-phalangeal joint.[21] Hand has probably only a single prehensive pattern.[22] Hand has somewhat neutral function in locomotion, i.e. neither supportive nor suspensory. Single hand used for feeding.[4] HAND PROPORTIONS: Digits are elongated and metacarpals very short; whole hand is long relative to forelimb length (*see* Part III, p. 402).

Resting Posture

Tarsius cling to upright stems of small trees with all four extremities, the knees tucked under the face. The tail also acts as a support, the basal portion being placed firmly against the tree. *Tarsius* sleep in this position with the head sunk forward between the arms.[3] The basal portion of the tail is also used to help stabilize the upright body and free the hands when feeding or preparing to pounce upon prey.[23]

Social Behaviour

TERRITORIAL: There are very few observations in the wild. Preliminary studies in captivity show that 30% or more of activity is territorial, concerned with the marking and policing of territory. Marking is executed nightly by urinating on specific perches, or by rubbing toepads in urine, and thus distributing it on the perches.[24] COMMUNICATION: VOCALIZATION: Nothing has been recorded of the tarsier's calls in the wild. In captivity, they are almost silent; the young sometimes squeak quietly if left alone.[3] During times of increased sexual activity both ♂ and ♀ may call frequently.[24] FACIAL EXPRESSION: In fear, the mouth is half-opened, revealing the teeth.[25] When resting or drowsy, the closing of only one eye, leaving the other eye almost fully open, is occasionally observed.[4] INTRA-GROUP BEHAVIOUR: GROUP SIZE: Usually found in pairs, but sometimes ♀ and young are found alone; ♀ may have an almost fully-grown juvenile as well as an infant with her.[5] GROOMING: Self-grooming is an important activity and consists of scratching, biting, cat-like licking and rubbing the head and ears against a perch.[24] Scratching is done with the foot flexed in such a way that only the two toilet claws protrude.[3] Grooming is intensified during periods of increased sexual activity.[24] Mutual grooming has rarely been observed.[10] SEXUAL BEHAVIOUR:[24] Tarsiers establish a territory as a basic requirement for mating and breeding. 50% of a Tarsier's activity in captivity is devoted to social encounters between ♂ and ♀. These encounters increase in intensity, culminate in copulation, and decrease again within the period of the cycle which has been described by Harrisson (1963).

REPRODUCTION AND DEVELOPMENT

Tarsius breed continuously with no significant seasonal fluctuations.[26] Sexual cycle lasts 23·5 days [±0·7].[11] There is a period of increased sexual activity during which the ♀ external genitalia become enlarged.[11] Information about periodic bleeding is contradictory.[10, 11] Gestation period is thought to be about 6 months.[27] Tarsiers give birth to a single young; head and body length at birth is 66–72 mm; tail length 114–117 mm; weight 25–27 g (2♂♂). A newborn tarsier is in an advanced state of development, well furred, with eyes open and capable of clinging to branches and scrambling about. It clings to the fur of the mother's abdomen with both hands and feet;[27] the mother may sometimes carry the infant in her mouth.[25] Duration of lactation is not known, neither is the age at which *Tarsius* become sexually mature.

CAPTIVITY

Tarsius has very rarely been exhibited in Zoos. The longevity record is 12 years at the Philadelphia Zoo where a ♀ captured in Mindanao in April, 1947 lived until June 1959.[28] On examination the body was not found to be senile, and the potential longevity may prove to be about 20 years. Two births occurred during this time, but the young did not survive. (*See* Ulmer, 1963.) For maintainence in captivity *see* Evans, C. S. (In press).

REFERENCES

1. Hill, W. C. Osman (1955a)
2. Jentinck, F. A. (1890)
3. Clark, W. E. Le Gros (1924c)
4. Polyak, S. (1957)
5. Wharton, C. H. (1950b)
6. Hoogstraal, H. (1947)
7. Davis, D. Dwight (1962)
8. Clark, W. E. Le Gros (1959)
9. Woollard, H. H. (1925)
10. Hill, W. C. Osman, Porter, A. and Southwick, M. D. (1952)
11. Catchpole, H. R. and Fulton, J. F. (1943)
12. Hill, J. E. (1960)
13. Taylor, E. H. (1934)
14. Burmeister, H. C. C. (1846)
15. Schultz, A. H. (1961)
16. Klinger, H. P. (1963)
17. Napier, J. R. and Walker, A. C. (1967)
18. The Tarsier—16 mm film distributed by British Film Institute (silent)
19. Hall-Craggs, E. C. R. (1965a)
20. Schultz, A. H. (1953)
21. Napier, J. R. (1961)
22. Bishop, Alison (1964)
23. Harrisson, Barbara (1962)
24. Harrisson, Barbara (1963)
25. Cuming, H. (1838)
26. Zuckerman, S. (1933)
27. Ulmer, F. A. (1963)
28. Ulmer, F. A. (1960)
29. Sprankel, H. (1965)
30. Evans, C. S. (In press)
31. Montagna, W. and Machida, H. (1966)

THEROPITHECUS I. Geoffroy, 1843 Geladas

1 species: 2 subspecies[1-4]

Theropithecus gelada gelada Rüppell, 1835 — Common Gelada
Theropithecus gelada obscurus Heuglin, 1863 — Dusky Gelada

GEOGRAPHICAL RANGE [*4]

Ethiopia. Detailed range uncertain. Rocky mountainous regions of central and northern Ethiopia centering around Sea of Tana. *T. g. gelada* found to N. and E. of Lake Tana; *T. g. obscurus* to the E., S.E. and S.W., as far as 70 km north of Addis Ababa. LIMITS OF GENUS: Latitudes: 14°–9° N. Longitudes: 36° 30′ E.–40° E. Altitudinal range: 6500–16,400 ft (2000–5000 m).

ECOLOGY

HABITAT: Grassy mountain slopes at the edges of cliffs and rocky gorges at high altitudes.[5] Probably never climb trees. Sleep on small ledges on vertical rock faces. ACTIVITY RHYTHM: Diurnal. DIET:[5] Grasses, bulbs, some insects.

MORPHOLOGY

External Characters

Large heavily-built animals with rounded muzzles and deep suborbital maxillary hollows giving face a "figure-of-eight" appearance. Nose is tip-tilted, upper lip long and bulbous. Long heavy mane (in ♂♂ only) covering forequarters is dark brown; below the mane the body hair is buffy, also rump, hindlimbs and upper arm. Forearms, hands and feet are almost black. Tail is midbrown and tufted at extremity. Face is dark brown and eyelids white. Pale cheek tufts are directed upwards and backwards, particularly prominent in ♂♂. Coat colour stated to be of little use in distinguishing the two races in the field. CHEST PATCH:[6, 4] On the chest is a heart-shaped livid patch of naked skin sometimes divided into two in males. In females the pectoral patch is hour-glass shaped and is surrounded laterally and inferiorly by caruncles which give the appearance of a necklace; in ♀♀ the patch is subject to change during oestrus. Nipples in the female are close together either side of midline in post-parous individuals. Sexual dimorphism is marked in size, weight, canine development and thickness of mane. Ischial callosities of ♂♂ are dark grey in colour and discrete as in *Cercopithecus*, separated by strip of soft hairless skin; below callosities are paired, tough-skinned, hairless cushions.[7] HAND: Digits as in *Papio*; index finger and thumb very short (*see* Opposability Index under Hand Proportions in Part III). FOOT: Big toe greatly reduced in length.[7] Tail shorter than body.

Weights and Dimensions[8, 14, 15]

Body weight (g)	20,500 (♂ est.)	13,620 (1♀)
Head and body length (mm)	690, 740 (2♂)	500, 650 (2♀)
Tail length (mm)	460, 500 (2♂)	325, 410 (2♀)

PLATE III. *Theropithecus gelada*, ♂ grooming ♀ (San Diego Zoo)

Internal Characters[9]

Only those characters distinctive of the gelada among the Cercopithecinae are given below:
SKULL AND JAW: Skull shows moderate prognathism having a lower Facial Length Index
(Facial L. × 100/calvarium L.) than most baboon species. In the Frankfurt plane, the occlusal
plane of the teeth is horizontal in contrast to *Papio*, *Mandrillus* and *Cercocebus*; this results from
a deepening of the posterior part of the maxilla. Strong sagittal and nuchal crests in ♂♂;
sagittal crest differs from that of *Papio* being placed further anteriorly on vault. Very long
post-glenoid process. DENTITION: D.F.: $\frac{2}{2} \frac{1}{1} \frac{2}{2} \frac{3}{3} = 32$. Upper incisors are relatively small and
do not project, in profile view, beyond the canines (cf. *Papio*); diastema therefore relatively
narrow. Molars: Relatively large teeth show deep invaginations on lingual and buccal
surfaces between bilophs; there are narrow high crests connecting the buccal cusps in lower
jaw and lingual cusps in upper jaw.

Genetic Biology

CHROMOSOMES:[10] 2n = 42 (3 specimens). Similarity of karyotype between *Theropithecus* and *Papio* (especially *P. hamadryas*).

BEHAVIOUR

Locomotor Behaviour

AUTHORS' CLASSIFICATION: Quadrupedalism. Almost entirely ground-living; seldom if ever ascends trees. Digitigrade even in "arboreal" milieu in captivity.[9] LIMB PROPORTIONS: Limbs long and subequal; forearm elongated relative to arm as in all fully ground-adapted Cercopithecinae. *See* Part III, p. 395, for Indices.

Hand Function

Hand prehensile, thumb opposable. High Opposability Index suggests well-developed index finger and thumb dexterity. HAND PROPORTIONS: *See* Part III, p. 402, for Indices.

Social Behaviour

The following summary of the social behaviour of *Theropithecus* in the wild is derived from the fieldwork of Crook (1966), also *see* Starck and Frick (1958). GROUP SIZE AND COMPOSITION: Geladas are normally found in herds which are structured by division into one-male groups, all-male groups and juvenile play-groups. Herd may consist of up to 400 individuals. Size depends largely on food availability and nature of terrain; under arid conditions, break-up of herd into one-male groups is apparent. Crook (1966) stresses that gelada herds and baboon troops are not equivalent. GROUPING OF INDIVIDUALS: Within herd, a formalized structure is apparent when herd is moving, with infants and ♀♀ nearest to cliff edges and males further away. DAILY RANGE: Somewhat "linear" in form owing to tendency to stay within 1 mile of cliff edges. Maximum range does not exceed 5 miles per day. CORE AREAS: No specific sleeping crags but herds appear to centre on particular areas with many sleeping cliffs, i.e. population demes are apparent. ONE-MALE GROUP STRUCTURE: One-male groups are the reproductive units and are intermingled with herd, but separate out sufficiently often to be recognized. Unit consists of adult ♂, adult and young ♀♀, juveniles and infants, and occasional immature ♂. ADULT SEX RATIO: 1♂ : 3·9♀♀ to 1♂ : 8♀♀. SIZE OF UNIT: 5–30 individuals. Membership stable with occasional addition of ♀. Male initiates unit movement and is responsible for unit cohesiveness. NECK-BITING: Absent (cf. *P. hamadryas*). GROOMING: Main period is early morning but it occurs sporadically during rest of day. AGGRESSIVE BEHAVIOUR:[4] No evidence of aggressive behaviour (attack or "traditional" stone-throwing) towards humans. FACIAL EXPRESSION:[13] The "lip-flip" is unique to *Theropithecus*; both teeth and gums are completely bared; upper lip is retracted so far that it covers the nostrils; thought to be a submissive gesture. Rapid retraction of the scalp, which suddenly reveals the white eyelids, is often observed.

REPRODUCTION AND DEVELOPMENT

Perineal region of females shows a rim of caruncles which undergo hypertrophy during oestrus;[6, 14] chest patch also intensifies in colour and caruncles of the "necklace" become more prominent. Occurrence of birth season: February–April in Ethiopia.[5]* GESTATION PERIOD: Unknown.

CAPTIVITY

Breeding in captivity is not uncommon. Between 1959–1963, 11 births were reported in world zoos.[11] LONGEVITY RECORD:[12] (Up to 1962): 10 years 5 months, Philadelphia Zoo.

REFERENCES

1. Rüppell, E. (1835)
2. Heuglin, M. T. v (1863)
3. De Beaux, O. (1925, 1943)
4. Starck, D. and Frick, H. (1958)
5. Crook, J. H. (1966)
6. Appelman, F. J. (1954, 1957)
7. Pocock, R. I. (1925a)
8. Elliot, D. G. (1913)
9. Jolly, C. J. (1965)
10. Chiarelli, B. (1962b)
11. International Zoo Year Book, Vols. I–V (1959–1965)
12. Jones, M. L. (1962)
13. Morris, D. (Personal communication)
14. Matthews, L. H. (1956)
15. Authors' observation.

TUPAIA† Raffles, 1821   Treeshrews

2 subgenera: 12 species: 87 subspecies[1-9]

SUBGENUS: *Tupaia* Raffles, 1821

10 species: 71 subspecies

T. glis (Type species)	Common treeshrew	49 subsp.
T. splendidula		4 subsp.
T. muelleri	Müller's treeshrew	0 subsp.
T. montana	Mountain treeshrew	2 subsp.
T. javanica	Small treeshrew	0 subsp.
T. nicobarica	Nicobar treeshrew	2 subsp.
T. minor	Pygmy treeshrew	5 subsp.
T. gracilis	Slender treeshrew	3 subsp.
T. picta	Painted treeshrew	2 subsp.
T. palawanensis	Palawan treeshrew	4 subsp.

GEOGRAPHICAL RANGE [1, 2, 8, 10]

South-East Asia. India N. of R. Ganges and S. of the Himalayas, Burma, Southern and Western China, Indo-China, Thailand and Malaya; islands of Hainan, Sumatra, Java, Borneo and Bali; many small off-shore islands and more distant groups such as the Mentawai and Batu Is. off the W. coast of Sumatra and the Palawan, Calamian and Cuyo Is., west of the Philippines. Treeshrews reach high altitudes in Nepal, Sikkim and N. Borneo, and between 10,000–11,000 ft (3000–3350 m) in N.W. Yunnan. LIMITS OF SUBGENUS: Latitudes: 28° N.–9° S. Longitudes: 85°–122° E. *Tupaia* are not found S.E. of Wallace's Line.

ECOLOGY

HABITAT: Tropical rain forest and secondary growth, also montane forest. Less arboreal than their common name would suggest. Live and feed on the ground and in thickets and shrubs; *T. nicobarica* and *T. glis longicauda* are the only species thought to be truly arboreal.[11] ACTIVITY RHYTHM: Diurnal. In captivity, peak periods of activity have been observed in the morning and evening.[12, 13] In the wild, nest in holes in fallen timber, hollow bamboos, etc.[14, 15] DIET: Insects and fruit. *T. glis* is thought to forage on the surface of the forest floor.[6]

MORPHOLOGY

External Characters

For detailed key, *see* Lyon (1913); for key to Bornean species, *see* Medway (1965). Squirrel-like primates with small bodies and short arms and legs; the largest species are *T. glis*, *T. nicobarica* and *T. picta*, and the smallest is *T. minor*. The tail is bushy and approximately equal to head and body length; it is distinctly longer than head and body length in some species, e.g. *T. nicobarica* and *T. minor*. Ears are small and bare and set close to the head; treeshrews have short whiskers, elongated shrew-like nose terminating in a naked moist snout which is finely reticulated and cut squarely across; it does not extend backwards on to the furred part of the

---

† *See* Taxonomic Notes, p. 377.

nose as in *T. tana* and *Urogale*. *T. minor* and *T. gracilis* have rather short stubby snouts. Fur is light or dark brown, or dark redbrown, finely speckled with black; an oblique pale shoulder stripe is sometimes present. *T. picta* is distinguished by a narrow black dorsal stripe. The northerly races of *T. glis* on the mainland of Asia are greybrown and paler than the southerly representatives which are dark redbrown. This colour variation is clinal and may be attributed to differences in temperature and humidity.[5] HANDS: Pentadactyl with digital projection formula: 3.4.2.5.1. Six well-marked pads on palm, and claws on ends of digits. Feet bear claws. MAMMAE: 1, 2 or 3 pairs. No sexual dimorphism in size apparent.

Weights and Dimensions

	♂	♀	♀ in % of ♂
Body weight (g)			
T. glis (average)[12]	177 (♂♂)	159 (♀♀)	90
T. glis (range)[6]	150–190 (12♂♂ and ♀♀)		—
T. minor (range)[6]	30–60 (10♂♂ and ♀♀)		—
Head and body length range (mm)[6, 14]			
T. glis	140–230 (158♂♂)	143–225 (164♀♀)	100
T. minor	105–142 (25♂♂)	118–170 (20♀♀)	108
Tail length range (mm)[6, 14]			
T. glis	129–215 (158♂♂)	130–205 (164♀♀)	98
T. minor	142–165 (25♂♂)	130–165 (19♀♀)	96

(♀ in % of ♂ based on midpoint of ranges)

Internal Characters

For account of the myology and brain of *Tupaia*, reference should be made to Clark (1924a and b). *See also* Noback and Moskowitz (1963) for central nervous system. SKULL: Elongated muzzle and small brain case with little or no flexion of basicranial axis. Orbits are laterally directed but show a post-orbital bar, but no post-orbital closure. Foramen magnum placed well back on base of skull; large auditory bulla containing tympanic ring. Zygoma has large oval fenestra.[14] Mandible synostosed at V-shaped symphysis; the horizontal ramus is slender and the ascending ramus is very short bearing an elongated coronoid process and a hook-shaped angular process. HAND: Scaphoid and lunate bones are fused[48] (cf. *Ptilocercus*). DENTITION: D.F.: $\frac{2}{3}\frac{1}{1}\frac{3}{3}\frac{3}{3}=38$. Lower incisors are somewhat procumbent, reminiscent of *Lemur*, but "dental comb" does not include canines; lateral incisors in lower jaw are recessive. Upper incisors are widely spaced. Premolars increase in size from front to back. Molars are tritubercular, the lower series having high pointed cusps; 3rd upper molar is quite small. VISUAL SYSTEM: Retina rich in cones, but fovea centralis absent;[20, 21] no uncrossed fibres in optic chiasma[22] (? correlated with absence of binocular vision); lateral geniculate body has a simple inversion pattern;[23] striate area is small and difficult to localize but has been identified by Clark (1931). ALIMENTARY TRACT: Sublingua present which is relatively unspecialized (cf. *Lemur*). Stomach and small intestine are simple in form; short caecum is present,[14] and colon consists of a simple straight tube. REPRODUCTIVE SYSTEM: Glans penis is elongated (cf. *Ptilocercus*) and a baculum is absent. Uterus is bicornuate. PLACENTATION: Type is in dispute. According to J. P. Hill (1965), placenta is bidiscoidal and endotheliochorial, but *see* Meister and Davis (1956, 1958). CUTANEOUS GLANDS: Glandular area on neck and chest of

♂ and ♀ that secretes oily substance; glands predominantly apocrine.[28] SKIN:[29] Skin unlike that of prosimians; hair follicles arranged in rows (cf. "island" arrangement of prosimians); eccrine sweat glands in hairy skin, on friction surfaces and on rhinarium and scrotum.

Genetic Biology

CHROMOSOMES: $2n = 60$ ($1♂$ and $2♀♀$)[30, 31]; $2n = 62$ ($2♂♂$ and $2♀♀$).[32] Klinger (1963) provides a karyotype: 12 metacentrics, 48 acrocentric autosomes, X = metacentric, Y = acrocentric. Difference in chromosome number may be attributed to polymorphism or to unrecognized speciation. SERUM PROTEINS: *T. glis*: A- and B- Transferrins (A_5 and B_6) present.[33] HAEMOGLOBINS: Electrophoretic analysis indicates degree of slowness of Hb unique among primates.[34]

BEHAVIOUR

Locomotor Behaviour

AUTHORS' CLASSIFICATION: Quadrupedalism. Employs rapid jerky scurrying movements on ground or in trees, rather like a rodent; may jump 4 ft gaps between branches and drop distances of up to 12 ft to the ground.[13] LIMB PROPORTIONS: Hindlimbs are longer than forelimbs and both are short relative to trunk length: Forelimb = 56%, Hindlimb = 78%. For Indices, *see* Part III, p. 395.

Hand Function

Hands convergent but not prehensile; thumb divergent but non-opposable.[35] Hand shows a longitudinal orientation when running on slender branches.[36] Treeshrews normally feed two-handed.[13] HAND PROPORTIONS: Long palm and relatively short digits. For Indices, *see* Part III, p. 402.

Resting Posture

Rest lying on the side or abdomen, with tail alongside the body or curled one half turn around a slender branch.[13]

Social Behaviour

There are very few observations of *Tupaia* in the wild. TERRITORIALITY: Cantor (1846) observed that *Tupaia* lives singly or in pairs and attacks intruders of its own species. In captivity,[13] a large enclosure (50′ by 50′) was not large enough to accommodate more than one mature male *T. glis* for long. Fights resulted in the death of the weaker animal, usually after several encounters. Aggression between ♀♀ was similar but less frequent. No fights were observed between ♂ and ♀. Other studies in smaller cages indicate considerable sociality including the formation of ♂ dominance hierarchies.[38, 40] COMMUNICATION: VOCALIZATION, combined with visual signals, has been described by Sprankel (1961b), Andrew (1964) and Kaufman (1965). Visual signals include tail-flicking; tail is flicked up into a vertical position (sometimes forward over the head) and allowed to fall slowly back to the horizontal. Lunging forward with open mouth, and "presenting" behaviour have also been observed. GROOMING:[40] During self-grooming the coat is licked, scraped with the procumbent lower incisors, scratched with the claws of both fore- and hindfeet, and rubbed along branches. Mutual grooming is relatively rare; ♂ grooms the ♀ at the approach of oestrus. *T. glis* has special behaviour patterns for cleaning the face, first licking the palms and then drawing them down the sides of the muzzle.[39] SCENT-MARKING: *T. glis* marks objects with a secretion from a glandular area on neck and chest.[12, 13, 39] Urine marking has also been observed.[12] Sexual behaviour of *T. glis* has been described by Sprankel (1961b) and Kaufman (1965), and of *T. minor* and other species by Conaway and Sorenson (1966) who found that differences in size, behaviour and mounting postures prevented interspecies copulation.

PLATE 113. *Tupaia glis belangeri* (San Diego Zoo)

REPRODUCTION AND DEVELOPMENT

There is no fixed birth season in captivity; in N. Borneo,[42]* pregnancies have been observed to be associated with the period of low rainfall—June, July and August. OESTRUS CYCLE: *See* Conaway and Sorenson (1966) for discussion of three distinctive types of cycle observed in captivity and the incidence of uterine bleeding. *Tupaia*, in captivity, may exhibit post-partum oestrus, and copulation may take place immediately after birth; after about 2 hours after birth, the ♀ is no longer receptive and repels the ♂. GESTATION PERIOD:[41] 41–50 days. NO. OF YOUNG:[14] 1–4, usually 2. Lactation begins immediately after birth and continues for up to 28 days.[43] GROWTH OF INFANT:[12] *T. glis*: Newborn is hairless and has closed eyes. Head and body length 79 mm: Tail length 46 mm: Weight 11·2 g (average of 8 specimens). 9th day: some teeth are present. 15th day: eyes begin to open; it starts to move around in the nest. 20th day: soft food may be taken. 24th–27th day: leaves nest. 30th day: begins to climb branches. At 6 months, *T. glis* are sexually mature. Martin (1966) describes mother and infants in separate nests and feeding once every 48 hours.

CAPTIVITY

A full description of the behaviour and breeding of *T. glis* is given by Sprankel (1961b). For laboratory maintenance of treeshrews, *see* Draper, W. A. (1963) and Sorenson and Conaway (1964). LONGEVITY RECORD (up to 1962): $5\frac{1}{2}$ years.[43]

See References, p. 336.

TUPAIA   Raffles, 1821   Treeshrews

SUBGENUS: *Lyonogale* Conisbee, 1953†

2 species: 16 subspecies[2, 9]

T. tana (Type species)	Terrestrial treeshrew	16 subsp.
T. dorsalis	Striped treeshrew	0 subsp.

GEOGRAPHICAL RANGE [2]

Islands of the Malay Archipelago. *T. dorsalis*: Borneo only. *T. tana*: Borneo, Sumatra and many smaller islands including Tambelan Is., Banjak and Batu Is. (W. Sumatra), Lingga I. Serasan I., and Banggi I. (N. Borneo). LIMITS OF SUBGENUS: Latitudes: 8° N.–6° S, Longitudes: 97°–119° E.

ECOLOGY

HABITAT: Tropical rain forest, from sea level up to about 4000 ft (1200 m).[14] *T. tana* is reported to be terrestrial rather than arboreal; it has been observed scurrying about the forest floor, and occasionally climbing into low branches.[6] ACTIVITY RHYTHM: Diurnal. DIET: *T. tana*: mostly earthworms and insects, some fruit (based on stomach contents of 10 specimens).[6] This species appears to use the large claws of the forefeet to scratch into the forest floor for food in contrast to other species of *Tupaia* who forage on the surface.[6]

MORPHOLOGY

External Characters

For detailed description, *see* Lyon (1913). Small squirrel-like primates similar to *T. (Tupaia)* but having a relatively short tail and a more elongated snout; the naked rhinarium extends backwards on top into the furred area of the nose. General colour is light brown to dark redbrown with black speckling. *T. tana*, the larger species, has a dark dorsal stripe which extends from nape to lower back where it blends with a dark area or distinct black patch; anteriorly it is bordered by a pale grizzled, sometimes greyish, area and this, with the light shoulder stripe, give a striped effect to the forepart of the body. Underparts orange red to rust red. *T. dorsalis* is dull brown in colour, with black dorsal line from nape to root of tail; shoulder stripe is narrow and whitish. Claws of forefeet of *T. tana* are exceptionally robust.[6] MAMMAE: 2 pairs. Little sexual dimorphism in body size.

Weights and Dimensions

Body weight range:[6] *T. tana*	160–260 g (25 specimens ♂ and ♀)		
T. dorsalis	105 g (1 ♂)		
Head and body length range)[6, 14]	♂	♀	♀ in % ♂
T. tana (mm)	163–240 (30 ♂♂)	177–240 (25 ♀♀)	103
T. dorsalis (mm)	161, 220 (2 ♂♂)	175–210 (3 ♀♀)	100
Tail length range:			
T. tana (mm)	150–196 (30 ♂♂)	145–190 (25 ♀♀)	97
T. dorsalis (mm)	145, 150 (2 ♂♂)	140–150 (3 ♀♀)	98

(♀ in % ♂ based on midpoint of ranges.)

---

† *See* Taxonomic Notes, Part III, p. 377.

Internal Characters[14]

See *T. (Tupaia)*; differences only noted here. SKULL: Rostrum is more elongated with long nasal and premaxillary elements. DENTITION: Owing to elongation of rostrum, anterior teeth show greater spacing. ALIMENTARY TRACT: Caecum present.

BEHAVIOUR

Locomotor Behaviour

AUTHORS' CLASSIFICATION: Quadrupedalism. Similar scurrying gait to *T. (Tupaia)*.

Social Behaviour

Nothing is known of the social behaviour of *T. (Lyonogale)* in the wild. Captivity studies show that copulatory behaviour in *T. tana* differs from that shown by other species; ♂ adopts a bipedal attitude before and during mounting.[41]

REPRODUCTION AND DEVELOPMENT

No information.

CAPTIVITY

T. (Lyonogale) have rarely been exhibited in Zoos. LONGEVITY RECORD: *T. tana*: 2 years 4 months, Zoological Society of London.[46]

REFERENCES

1. Ellerman, J. R. and Morrison-Scott, T. C. S. (1951)
2. Chasen, F. N. (1940)
3. Shamel, H. H. (1930)
4. Medway, Lord (1961)
5. Hill, J. E. (1960)
6. Davis, D. Dwight (1962)
7. Chasen, F. N. (1935)
8. Sanborn, C. C. (1952)
9. Medway, Lord (1965)
10. British Museum (Natural History) Records
11. Kloss, C. Boden (1911)
12. Sprankel, H. (1961b)
13. Vandenbergh, J. G. (1963)
14. Lyon, M. W. (1913)
15. Thomas, O. and Wroughton, R. C. (1911)
16. Chasen, F. N. and Kloss, C. Boden (1931)
17. Clark, W. E. Le Gros (1924a)
18. Clark, W. E. Le Gros (1924b)
19. Noback, C. R. and Moskowitz, N. (1963)
20. Polyak, S. (1957)
21. Clark, W. E. Le Gros (1959)
22. Chacko, L. W. (1954)
23. Chacko, L. W. (1955)
24. Clark, W. E. Le Gros (1931)
25. Hill, J. P. (1965)
26. Meister, W. and Davis, D. Dwight (1956)
27. Meister, W. and Davis, D. Dwight (1958)
28. Sprankel, H. (1961a)
29. Montagna, W., Yun, J. S., Silver, A. F. and Queredo, W. C. (1962)
30. Chu, E. H. Y. and Bender, M. A. (1962)
31. Hsu, T. C. and Johnson, M. L. (1963)
32. Klinger, H. P. (1963)
33. Lange, V. and Schmitt, J. (1963)
34. Buettner-Janusch, J. and Buettner-Janusch, V. (1964)
35. Napier, J. R. (1961)
36. Bishop, Alison (1964)
37. Cantor, T. (1846)
38. Sorenson, M. W. and Conaway, C. H. (1966)
39. Andrew, R. J. (1964)
40. Kaufman, J. H. (1965)
41. Conaway, C. H. and Sorenson, M. W. (1966)
42. Wade, P. (1958)
43. Sprankel, H. (Personal communication)
44. Draper, W. A. (1963)
45. Sorenson, M. W. and Conaway, C. H. (1964)
46. Jones, M. L. (1962)
47. Martin, R. D. (1966)
48. Clark, W. E. Le Gros (1926)

UROGALE   Mearns, 1905   Philippine Treeshrews

1 species: 0 subspecies[1]

Urogale everetti Thomas, 1892

GEOGRAPHICAL RANGE [1, 3]

Philippines. Mindanao I. from sea level up to approximately 6000 ft (1825 m). LIMITS OF GENUS: Latitudes: 5°–10° N. Longitudes: 122°–127° E.

ECOLOGY

HABITAT: Tropical rain forest and montane forest. *Urogale* live in dense jungle or among scattered bushes and trees, sometimes along river gorges. Nest in holes in the ground or in cliffs.[2, 3] ACTIVITY RHYTHM: Diurnal; in captivity, two peaks of activity were observed, early morning and dusk. DIET: Insects, grubs, lizards, young birds and birds' eggs, also fruit; *see* Wharton (1950a) for list of food plants.

MORPHOLOGY

External Characters[1]

One of the larger treeshrews, *Urogale* has dark brown fur with yellowish or rufous underparts; a pale shoulder stripe is present but not conspicuous. *Urogale* has a rather close-haired tail and a very elongated snout, the tip of which is covered with naked moist skin which extends backwards on top of the nose to form a point. Small immobile ears are set close to the head. There are some short vibrissae around eyes and muzzle. Claws particularly long on the forefeet. MAMMAE: 2 pairs.

Weights and Dimensions

	♂	♀	♀ in % ♂
Body weight (g)[5]	355 (1♂)	—	—
Head and body length average and range[1] (mm)	203 (182–235) (5♂♂)	201 (200, 202) (2♀♀)	99
Tail length average and range[1] (mm)	160 (148–170) (5♂♂)	149 (147, 150) (2♀♀)	93

Internal Characters[1]

See *Tupaia* for details. Only principal distinguishing characters noted here. SKULL: Facial skeleton shows greater elongation than in *Tupaia*. Zygomatic fenestra is small and slit-like. Characters of skull (e.g. temporal ridges and stout coronoid) can be correlated with heavier jaw. DENTITION: $\frac{2}{3} \frac{1}{1} \frac{3}{3} \frac{3}{3} = 38$. UPPER JAW: 2nd pair of upper incisors are canine-like and longer than 1st pair. LOWER JAW: I.$\overline{3}$ is rudimentary. Canine well developed, to oppose large lateral incisor of upper jaw.

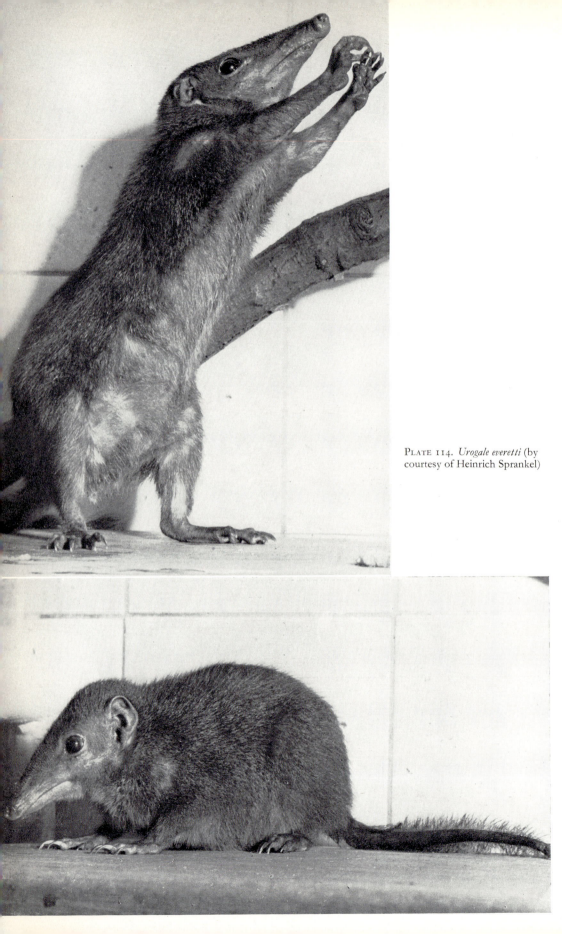

PLATE 114. *Urogale everetti* (by courtesy of Heinrich Sprankel)

Genetic Biology

CHROMOSOMES:[6] 2n=44 (2♀♀); karyotype consists of metacentrics with only 4 pairs of acrocentric autosomes. Diploid number of 26 has also been recorded tentatively.[8]

BEHAVIOUR

Locomotor Behaviour

AUTHORS' CLASSIFICATION: Quadrupedalism. Quadrupedal and plantigrade, *Urogale* move over the ground and along branches in a series of very swift running movements; they are good climbers.[4]

Hand Function

One-handed grasping of mealworms is not always accurate, but is usually achieved after 2 or 3 attempts. Can catch flies one-handed.[2]

Resting Posture

Usually sleep in a tight ball with the top of the head directly underneath the body.[2]

Social Behaviour

Nothing is known of their behaviour in the wild. COMMUNICATION: A variety of different calls has been described, but no definite study has been done.[4] GROOMING: Self-grooming with the claws of both hands and feet has been observed, and some social grooming between ♂ and ♀.[5] Scent marking has been observed.[7]

REPRODUCTION AND DEVELOPMENT *

In captivity, copulation has been observed to take place on several consecutive days;[5] it may also take place immediately after parturition.[4] GESTATION PERIOD: 54–56 days approximately.[4, 5] NO. OF YOUNG: 1 or 2. SIZE OF NEWBORN:* Head and body 66 mm: Tail 35 mm(1♂). Newborn is hairless and has eyes closed. 19th day: eyes open. Young remains in nest for about 30 days, by which time it can climb about almost as well as its parents and can eat solid food.[5]

CAPTIVITY

LONGEVITY RECORD: 7 years, Brookfield Zoo, Chicago.[7]

REFERENCES

1. Lyon, M. W. (1913)
2. Polyak, S. (1957)
3. Wharton, C. H. (1948)
4. Wharton, C. H. (1950a)
5. Snedigar, R. (1949)
6. Chu, E. H. Y. and Bender, M. A. (1962)
7. Rabb, G. B. (Personal communication)
8. Bender, M.A. and Chu, E.H.Y. (1963)

M

PART III

Supplementary and Comparative Data

Taxonomy and Nomenclature

1. SYSTEMATIC LIST OF LIVING PRIMATES

Order **PRIMATES** Linnaeus, 1758
Suborder **PROSIMII** Illiger, 1811
Infraorder **LEMURIFORMES** Gregory, 1915
Superfamily Tupaioidea Dobson, 1882
Family Tupaiidae Mivart, 1868
Subfamily Tupaiinae Lyon, 1913
Genus *Tupaia* Raffles, 1821
Subgenus *Tupaia* Raffles, 1821
Tupaia glis Diard, 1820 (Type species)
 T. g. glis Diard, 1820
 T. g. belangeri Wagner, 1841
 T. g. dissimilis Ellis, 1860
 T. g. chinensis Anderson, 1879
 T. g. modesta Allen, 1906
 T. g. concolor Bonhote, 1907
 T. g. siccata Thomas, 1914
 T. g. laotum Thomas, 1914
 T. g. sinus Kloss, 1916
 T. g. clarissa Thomas, 1917
 T. g. cambodiana Kloss, 1919
 T. g. olivacea Kloss, 1919
 T. g. assamensis Wroughton, 1921
 T. g. cochinchinensis Robinson and Kloss, 1922
 T. g. annamensis Robinson and Kloss, 1922
 T. g. versurae Thomas, 1922
 T. g. lepcha Thomas, 1922
 T. g. brunetta Thomas, 1923
 T. g. kohtauensis Shamel, 1930
 T. g. wilkinsoni Robinson and Kloss, 1911
 T. g. ferruginea Raffles, 1821
 T. g. operosa Robinson and Kloss, 1914
 T. g. ultima Robinson and Kloss, 1914
 T. g. longicauda Kloss, 1911
 T. g. obscura Kloss, 1911
 T. g. sordida Miller, 1900
 T. g. pemangilis Lyon, 1911
 T. g. pulonis Miller, 1903
 T. g. cognata Chasen, 1940

Tupaia glis Diard (continued)
 T. g. umbratilis Chasen, 1940
 T. g. raviana Lyon, 1911
 T. g. lacernata Thomas and Wroughton, 1909
 T. g. demissa Thomas, 1904
 T. g. jacki Robinson and Kloss, 1918
 T. g. siaca Lyon, 1908
 T. g. castanea Miller, 1903
 T. g. batamana Lyon, 1907
 T. g. redacta Robinson, 1916
 T. g. phaeura Miller, 1902
 T. g. discolor Lyon, 1906
 T. g. tephrura Miller, 1903
 T. g. chrysogaster Miller, 1903
 T. g. siberu Chasen and Kloss, 1927
 T. g. chrysomalla Miller, 1900
 T. g. riabus Lyon, 1913
 T. g. anambae Lyon, 1913
 T. g. hypochrysa Thomas, 1895
 T. g. longipes Thomas, 1893
 T. g. salatana Lyon, 1913
Tupaia gracilis Thomas, 1893
 T. g. gracilis Thomas, 1893
 T. g. inflata Lyon, 1906
 T. g. edarata Lyon, 1913
Tupaia javanica Horsfield, 1822
Tupaia minor Günther, 1876
 T. m. minor Günther, 1876
 T. m. malaccana Anderson, 1879
 T. m. sincipis Lyon, 1911
 T. m. caedis Chasen and Kloss, 1931
 T. m. humeralis Robinson and Kloss, 1919
Tupaia montana Thomas, 1892
 T. m. montana Thomas, 1892
 T. m. baluensis Lyon, 1913
Tupaia muelleri Kohlbrugge, 1896
Tupaia nicobarica Zelebor, 1869
 T. n. nicobarica Zelebor, 1869
 T. n. surda Miller, 1902

Tupaia palawanensis Thomas, 1894
  T. p. palawanensis Thomas, 1894
  T. p. cuyonis Miller, 1910
  T. p. moellendorffi Matschie, 1898
  T. p. busuangae Sanborn, 1952
Tupaia picta Thomas, 1892
  T. p. picta Thomas, 1892
  T. p. fuscior Medway, 1965
Tupaia splendidula Gray, 1865
  T. s. splendidula Gray, 1865
  T. s. lucida Thomas and Hartert, 1895
  T. s. natunae Lyon, 1911
  T. s. carimatae Miller, 1906
Subgenus *Lyonogale* Conisbee, 1953
Tupaia tana Raffles, 1821 (Type species)
  T. t. tana Raffles, 1821
  T. t. speciosa Wagner, 1840
  T. t. besara Lyon, 1913
  T. t. nitida Chasen, 1933
  T. t. utara Lyon, 1913
  T. t. chrysura Günther, 1876
  T. t. paitana Lyon, 1913
  T. t. banguei Chasen and Kloss, 1931
  T. t. cervicalis Miller, 1903
  T. t. masae Lyon, 1913
  T. t. tuancus Lyon, 1913
  T. t. lingae Lyon, 1913
  T. t. sirhassenensis Miller, 1901
  T. t. bunoae Miller, 1900
  T. t. kelabit Davis, 1958
  T. t. kretami Davis, 1962
Tupaia dorsalis Schlegel, 1857

Genus *Anathana* Lyon, 1913
Anathana ellioti Waterhouse, 1850
  A. e. ellioti Waterhouse, 1850
  A. e. wroughtoni Lyon, 1913
  A. e. pallida Lyon, 1913

Genus *Urogale* Mearns, 1905
Urogale everetti Thomas, 1892

Genus *Dendrogale* Gray, 1848
Dendrogale murina Schlegel and Müller, 1844
  (Type species)
Dendrogale melanura Thomas, 1892
  D. m. melanura Thomas, 1892
  D. m. baluensis Lyon, 1913

Subfamily Ptilocercinae Lyon, 1913
Genus *Ptilocercus* Gray, 1848
Ptilocercus lowii Gray, 1848
  Pt. l. lowii Gray, 1848
  Pt. l. continentis Thomas, 1910

Superfamily Lemuroidea Mivart, 1864
Family Lemuridae Gray, 1821
Subfamily Lemurinae Mivart, 1864
Genus *Lemur* Linnaeus, 1758
Lemur catta Linnaeus, 1758 (Type species)
Lemur variegatus Kerr, 1792
  L. v. variegatus Kerr, 1792
  L. v. subcinctus A. Smith, 1833
  L. v. ruber E. Geoffroy, 1812
Lemur macaco Linnaeus, 1766
  L. m. macaco Linnaeus, 1766
  L. m. albifrons E. Geoffroy, 1796
  L. m. collaris E. Geoffroy, 1812
  L. m. flavifrons Gray, 1867
  L. m. fulvus E. Geoffroy, 1812
  L. m. mayottensis Schlegel, 1886
  L. m. rufus Audebert, 1800
  L. m. sanfordi Archbold, 1932
Lemur mongoz Linnaeus, 1766
  L. m. mongoz Linnaeus, 1766
  L. m. coronatus Gray, 1842
Lemur rubriventer I. Geoffroy, 1850

Genus *Hapalemur* I. Geoffroy, 1851
Hapalemur griseus Link, 1795 (Type species)
  H. g. griseus Link, 1795
  H. g. olivaceus I. Geoffroy, 1851
Hapalemur simus Gray, 1870

Genus *Lepilemur* I. Geoffroy, 1851
Lepilemur mustelinus I. Geoffroy, 1851
  L. m. mustelinus I. Geoffroy, 1851
  L. m. microdon Forsyth Major, 1894
  L. m. ruficaudatus Grandidier, 1867
  L. m. leucopus Forsyth Major, 1894
  L. m. dorsalis Gray, 1870

Subfamily Cheirogaleinae Gregory, 1915
Genus *Cheirogaleus* E. Geoffroy, 1812

Cheirogaleus major E. Geoffroy, 1812 (Type species)
  Ch. m. major E. Geoffroy, 1812
  Ch. m. crossleyi Grandidier, 1870
Cheirogaleus medius E. Geoffroy, 1812
Cheirogaleus trichotis Günther, 1875

Genus *Microcebus* E. Geoffroy, 1828
Microcebus murinus Miller, 1777 (Type species)
  M. m. murinus Miller, 1777
  M. m. smithii Gray, 1842
Microcebus coquereli Grandidier, 1867

Genus *Phaner* Gray, 1870
Phaner furcifer Blainville, 1841

Family Indriidae Burnett, 1828
Genus *Indri* E. Geoffroy and G. Cuvier, 1795
Indri indri Gmelin, 1788

Genus *Avahi* Jourdan, 1834
Avahi laniger Gmelin, 1788
  A. l. laniger Gmelin, 1788
  A. l. occidentalis Lorenz, 1898

Genus *Propithecus* Bennett, 1832
Propithecus diadema Bennett, 1832 (Type species)
  P. d. diadema Bennett, 1832
  P. d. candidus Grandidier, 1871
  P. d. edwardsi Grandidier, 1871
  P. d. holomelas Günther, 1875
  P. d. perrieri Lavauden, 1931
Propithecus verreauxi Grandidier, 1867
  P. v. verreauxi Grandidier, 1867
  P. v. coquereli Milne-Edwards, 1867
  P. v. coronatus Milne-Edwards, 1871
  P. v. deckenii Peters, 1870
  P. v. majori Rothschild, 1894

Superfamily Daubentonioidea Gill, 1872
Family Daubentoniidae Gray, 1870
Genus *Daubentonia* E. Geoffroy, 1795
Daubentonia madagascariensis Gmelin, 1788

Infraorder **LORISIFORMES** Gregory, 1915
Family Lorisidae Gregory, 1915
Subfamily Lorisinae Flower and Lydekker, 1891
Genus *Loris* E. Geoffroy, 1796
Loris tardigradus Linnaeus, 1758
  L. t. tardigradus Linnaeus, 1758
  L. t. grandis Hill and Phillips, 1932
  L. t. lydekkerianus Cabrera, 1908
  L. t. malabaricus Wroughton, 1917
  L. t. nordicus Hill, 1933
  L. t. nycticeboides Hill, 1942

Genus *Nycticebus* E. Geoffroy, 1812
Nycticebus coucang Boddaert, 1785 (Type species)
  N. c. coucang Boddaert, 1785
  N. c. bengalensis Fischer, 1804
  N. c. tenasserimensis Elliot, 1913
  N. c. insularis Robinson, 1917
  N. c. hilleri Stone and Rehn, 1902
  N. c. bancanus Lyon, 1906
  N. c. borneanus Lyon, 1906
  N. c. natunae Stone and Rehn, 1902
  N. c. javanicus E. Geoffroy, 1812
Nycticebus pygmaeus Bonhote, 1907

Genus *Arctocebus* Gray, 1863
Arctocebus calabarensis J. A. Smith, 1860
  A. c. calabarensis J. A. Smith, 1860
  A. c. aureus de Winton, 1902

Genus *Perodicticus* Bennett, 1831
Perodicticus potto Müller, 1766
  P. p. potto Müller, 1766
  P. p. edwardsi Bouvier, 1879
  P. p. faustus Thomas, 1910
  P. p. ibeanus Thomas, 1910
  P. p. juju Thomas, 1910

Subfamily Galaginae Mivart, 1864
Genus *Galago* E. Geoffroy, 1796
Subgenus *Galago* E. Geoffroy, 1796
Galago senegalensis E. Geoffroy, 1796 (Type species)
  G. s. senegalensis E. Geoffroy, 1796

Galago senegalensis E. Geoffroy (continued)
  G. s. albipes Dollman, 1909
  G. s. braccatus Elliot, 1907
  G. s. dunni Dollman, 1910
  G. s. gallarum Thomas, 1901
  G. s. granti Thomas and Wroughton, 1907
  G. s. moholi A. Smith, 1836
  G. s. sotikae Hollister, 1920
  G. s. zanzibaricus Matschie, 1893
Galago crassicaudatus E. Geoffroy, 1812
  G. c. crassicaudatus E. Geoffroy, 1812
  G. c. agisymbanus Coquerel, 1859
  G. c. argentatus Lönnberg, 1913
  G. c. garnettii Ogilby, 1838
  G. c. kikuyuensis Lönnberg, 1912
  G. c. lasiotis Peters, 1876
  G. c. loennbergi Schwarz, 1930
  G. c. monteiri Gray, 1863
  G. c. panganiensis Matschie, 1906
  G. c. umbrosus Thomas, 1917
Galago alleni Waterhouse, 1837

Subgenus *Euoticus* Gray, 1863
Galago elegantulus Le Conte, 1857 (Type species)
  G. e. elegantulus Le Conte, 1857
  G. e. pallidus Gray, 1863
Galago inustus Schwarz, 1930

Subgenus *Galagoides* A. Smith, 1833
Galago demidovii Fischer, 1806
  G. d. demidovii Fischer, 1806
  G. d. anomurus Pousargues, 1893
  G. d. orinus Lawrence and Washburn, 1936
  G. d. phasma Cabrera and Ruxton, 1926
  G. d. poensis Thomas, 1904
  G. d. murinus Murray, 1859
  G. d. thomasi Elliot, 1907

Infraorder **TARSIIFORMES** Gregory, 1915
Family Tarsiidae Gill, 1872
Genus *Tarsius* Storr, 1780
Tarsius spectrum Pallas, 1779 (Type species)
  T. s. spectrum Pallas, 1779
  T. s. sangirensis Meyer, 1897

Tarsius spectrum Pallas (continued)
  T. s. dentatus Miller and Hollister, 1921
  T. s. pumilis Miller and Hollister, 1921
  T. s. pelengensis Sody, 1949
Tarsius bancanus Horsfield, 1821
  T. b. bancanus Horsfield, 1821
  T. b. saltator Elliot, 1910
  T. b. borneanus Elliot, 1910
  T. b. natunensis Chasen, 1940
Tarsius syrichta Linnaeus, 1758
  T. s. syrichta Linnaeus, 1758
  T. s. fraterculus Miller, 1910
  T. s. carbonarius Heude, 1898

Suborder **ANTHROPOIDEA** Mivart, 1864
Superfamily Ceboidea Simpson, 1931
Family Callitrichidae Thomas, 1903
Subfamily Callitrichinae Thomas, 1903
Genus *Callithrix* Erxleben, 1777
Callithrix jacchus Linnaeus, 1758 (Type species)
Callithrix argentata Linnaeus, 1766
  C. a. argentata Linnaeus, 1766
  C. a. emiliae Thomas, 1920
  C. a. leucippe Thomas, 1922
  C. a. melanura E. Geoffroy, 1812
Callithrix aurita E. Geoffroy, 1812
  C. a. aurita E. Geoffroy, 1812
  C. a. coelestis Ribiero, 1924
Callithrix flaviceps Thomas, 1903
Callithrix geoffroyi Humboldt, 1812
Callithrix penicillata E. Geoffroy, 1812
  C. p. penicillata E. Geoffroy, 1812
  C. p. jordani Thomas, 1904
Callithrix humeralifer E. Geoffroy, 1812
Callithrix chrysoleuca Wagner, 1842

Genus *Cebuella* Gray, 1866
Cebuella pygmaea Spix, 1823
  C. p. pygmaea Spix, 1823
  C. p. niveiventris Lönnberg, 1940

Genus *Saguinus* Hoffmannsegg, 1807
Subgenus *Saguinus* Hoffmannsegg, 1807
Saguinus tamarin Link, 1795 (Type species)

Saguinus devillei I. Geoffroy, 1851
Saguinus fuscicollis Spix, 1823
Saguinus fuscus Lesson, 1840
Saguinus graellsi Espada, 1870
Saguinus illigeri Pucheran, 1845
Saguinus imperator Goeldi, 1907
    S. i. imperator Goeldi, 1907
    S. i. subgrisescens Lönnberg, 1940
Saguinus melanoleucus Ribiero, 1912
Saguinus midas Linnaeus, 1758
Saguinus labiatus E. Geoffroy, 1812
    S. l. labiatus, E. Geoffroy, 1812
    S. l. griseovertex Goeldi, 1907
Saguinus mystax Spix, 1823
Saguinus pileatus I. Geoffroy and Deville, 1848
Saguinus pluto Lönnberg, 1926
Saguinus weddelli Deville, 1849
Saguinus nigricollis Spix, 1823
Saguinus lagonotus Espada, 1870

Subgenus *Oedipomidas* Reichenbach, 1862
Saguinus oedipus Linnaeus, 1758 (Type
    species)
Saguinus geoffroyi Pucheran, 1845

Subgenus *Marikina* Lesson, 1840
Saguinus bicolor Spix, 1823 (Type species)
Saguinus martinsi Thomas, 1912
Saguinus leucopus Günther, 1876
Saguinus inustus Schwarz, 1951

Genus *Leontideus* Cabrera, 1956
Leontideus rosalia Linnaeus, 1766 (Type
    species)
Leontideus chrysomelas Kuhl, 1820
Leontideus chrysopygus Mikan, 1823

Subfamily Callimiconinae Thomas, 1913
Genus *Callimico* Ribiero, 1911
Callimico goeldii Thomas, 1904

Family Cebidae Swainson, 1835
Subfamily Aotinae Elliot, 1913
Genus *Aotus* Illiger, 1811
Aotus trivirgatus Humboldt, 1812
    A. t. trivirgatus Humboldt, 1812

Aotus trivirgatus Humboldt (continued)
    A. t. boliviensis Elliot, 1907
    A. t. griseimembra Elliot, 1912
    A. t. lemurinus I. Geoffroy, 1843
    A. t. microdon Dollman, 1909
    A. t. nigriceps Dollman, 1909
    A. t. roberti Dollman, 1909
    A. t. bipunctatus Bole, 1937
    A. t. azarae Humboldt, 1812

Genus *Callicebus* Thomas, 1903
Callicebus personatus E. Geoffroy, 1812 (Type
    species)
    C. p. personatus E. Geoffroy, 1812
    C. p. brunello Thomas, 1913
    C. p. nigrifrons Spix, 1823
    C. p. melanochir Kuhl, 1820
Callicebus moloch Hoffmannsegg, 1807
    C. m. moloch Hoffmannsegg, 1807
    C. m. donacophilus d'Orbigny, 1836
    C. m. hoffmannsi Thomas 1908
    C. m. brunneus Wagner, 1842
    C. m. cupreus Spix, 1823
    C. m. discolor I. Geoffroy and Deville, 1848
    C. m. ornatus Gray, 1866
Callicebus torquatus Hoffmannsegg, 1807
    C. t. torquatus Hoffmannsegg, 1807
    C. t. lugens Humboldt, 1812
    C. t. medemi Hershkovitz, 1963

Subfamily Pitheciinae Mivart, 1865
Genus *Pithecia* Desmarest, 1804
Pithecia pithecia Linnaeus, 1766 (Type
    species)
Pithecia monachus E. Geoffroy, 1812
    P. m. monachus E. Geoffroy, 1812
    P. m. capillamentosa Spix, 1823

Genus *Chiropotes* Lesson, 1840
Chiropotes satanas Hoffmannsegg, 1807 (Type
    species)
    Ch. s. satanas Hoffmannsegg, 1807
    Ch. s. chiropotes Humboldt, 1812
Chiropotes albinasus I. Geoffroy and Deville,
    1848

Genus *Cacajao* Lesson, 1840

Cacajao melanocephalus Humboldt, 1812 (Type species)

Cacajao calvus I. Geoffroy, 1847

Cacajao rubicundus I. Geoffroy and Deville, 1848

   C. r. rubicundus I. Geoffroy and Deville, 1848

   C. r. ucayalii Thomas, 1928

Subfamily Alouattinae Elliot, 1904

Genus *Alouatta* Lacépède, 1799

Alouatta belzebul Linnaeus, 1766 (Type species)

   A. b. belzebul Linnaeus, 1766

   A. b. discolor Spix, 1823

   A. b. mexianae Hagmann, 1908

   A. b. nigerrima Lönnberg, 1941

   A. b. ululata Elliot, 1912

Alouatta villosa Gray, 1845

   A. v. villosa Gray, 1845

   A. v. aequatorialis Festa, 1903

   A. v. coibensis Thomas, 1902

   A. v. luctuosa Lawrence, 1933

   A. v. mexicana Merriam, 1902

   A. v. palliata Gray, 1849

   A. v. pigra Lawrence, 1933

   A. v. trabeata Lawrence, 1933

Alouatta seniculus Linnaeus, 1766

   A. s. seniculus Linnaeus, 1766

   A. s. sara Elliot, 1910

   A. s. straminea Humboldt, 1812

   A. s. arctoidea Cabrera, 1940

   A. s. insulanus Elliot, 1910

Alouatta caraya Humboldt, 1812

Alouatta fusca E. Geoffroy, 1812

   A. f. fusca E. Geoffroy, 1812

   A. f. beniensis Lönnberg, 1941

   A. f. clamitans Cabrera, 1940

Subfamily Cebinae Mivart, 1865

Genus *Cebus* Erxleben, 1777

Cebus capucinus Linnaeus, 1758 (Type species)

   C. c. capucinus Linnaeus, 1758

   C. c. curtus Bangs, 1905

Cebus capucinus Linnaeus (continued)

   C. c. imitator Thomas, 1903

   C. c. limitaneus Hollister, 1914

   C. c. nigripectus Elliot, 1909

Cebus albifrons Humboldt, 1812

   C. a. albifrons Humboldt, 1812

   C. a. hypoleucus Humboldt, 1812

   C. a. cesarae Hershkovitz, 1949

   C. a. pleei Hershkovitz, 1949

   C. a. versicolor Pucheran, 1845

   C. a. leucocephalus Gray, 1865

   C. a. adustus Hershkovitz, 1949

   C. a. unicolor Spix, 1823

   C. a. yuracus Hershkovitz, 1949

   C. a. cuscinus Thomas, 1901

   C. a. aequatorialis Allen, 1914

   C. a. trinitatis von Pusch, 1941

Cebus nigrivittatus Wagner, 1848

   C. n. nigrivittatus Wagner, 1848

   C. n. apiculatus Elliot, 1907

   C. n. brunneus Allen, 1914

   C. n. castaneus I. Geoffroy, 1851

   C. n. olivaceus Schomburgk, 1848

Cebus apella Linnaeus, 1758

   C. a. apella Linnaeus, 1758

   C. a. margaritae Hollister, 1914

   C. a. macrocephalus Spix, 1823

   C. a. pallidus Gray, 1865

   C. a. libidinosus Spix, 1823

   C. a. xanthosternos Wied, 1820

   C. a. robustus Kuhl, 1820

   C. a. nigritus Goldfuss, 1809

   C. a. cay Illiger, 1815

   C. a. vellerosus I. Geoffroy, 1851

   C. a. versutus Elliot, 1910

Genus *Saimiri* Voigt, 1831

Saimiri sciureus Linnaeus, 1758

   S. s. sciureus Linnaeus, 1758

   S. s. boliviensis d'Orbigny, 1834

   S. s. collinsi Osgood, 1916

   S. s. macrodon Elliot, 1907

   S. s. nigriceps Thomas, 1902

   S. s. ustus I. Geoffroy, 1844

Saimiri oerstedii Reinhardt, 1872

   S. oe. oerstedii Reinhardt, 1872

   S. oe. citrinellus Thomas, 1904

Subfamily Atelinae Miller, 1924
Genus *Ateles* E. Geoffroy, 1806
Ateles paniscus Linnaeus, 1758 (Type species)
    A. p. paniscus Linnaeus, 1758
    A. p. chamek Humboldt, 1812
Ateles belzebuth E. Geoffroy, 1806
    A. b. belzebuth E. Geoffroy, 1806
    A. b. hybridus I. Geoffroy, 1829
    A. b. marginatus E. Geoffroy, 1809
Ateles fusciceps Gray, 1866
    A. f. fusciceps Gray, 1866
    A. f. robustus J. A. Allen, 1914
Ateles geoffroyi Kuhl, 1820
    A. g. geoffroyi Kuhl, 1820
    A. g. vellerosus Gray, 1866
    A. g. yucatanensis Kellogg and Goldman, 1944
    A. g. pan Schlegel, 1876
    A. g. frontatus Gray, 1842
    A. g. ornatus Gray, 1870
    A. g. panamensis Kellogg and Goldman, 1944
    A. g. azuerensis Bole, 1937
    A. g. grisescens Gray, 1866

Genus *Brachyteles* Spix, 1823
Brachyteles arachnoides E. Geoffroy, 1806

Genus *Lagothrix* E. Geoffroy, 1812
Lagothrix lagothricha Humboldt, 1812 (Type species)
    L. l. lagothricha Humboldt, 1812
    L. l. lugens Elliot, 1907
    L. l. poeppigii Schinz, 1844
    L. l. cana E. Geoffroy, 1812
Lagothrix flavicauda Humboldt, 1812

Superfamily Cercopithecoidea Simpson, 1931
Family Cercopithecidae Gray, 1821
Subfamily Cercopithecinae Blanford, 1888
Genus *Macaca* Lacépède, 1799
Macaca sylvana Linnaeus, 1758 (Type species)
Macaca sinica Linnaeus, 1771
    M. s. sinica Linnaeus, 1771
    M. s. aurifrons Pocock, 1931
    M. s. opisthomelas Hill, 1942

Macaca radiata E. Geoffroy, 1812
    M. r. radiata E. Geoffroy, 1812
    M. r. diluta Pocock, 1931
Macaca silenus Linnaeus, 1758
Macaca nemestrina Linnaeus, 1766
    M. n. nemestrina Linnaeus, 1766
    M. n. leonina Blyth, 1863
    M. n. blythii Pocock, 1931
    M. n. pagensis Miller, 1903
Macaca fascicularis Raffles, 1821
    M. f. fascicularis Raffles, 1821
    M. f. aurea E. Geoffroy, 1831
    M. f. umbrosa Miller, 1902
    M. f. valida Elliot, 1909
    M. f. atriceps Kloss, 1919
    M. f. argentimembris Kloss, 1911
    M. f. capitalis Elliot, 1910
    M. f. laeti Elliot, 1909
    M. f. pumila Miller, 1900
    M. f. fusca Miller, 1903
    M. f. lasiae Lyon, 1916
    M. f. phaeura Miller, 1903
    M. f. mordax Thomas and Wroughton, 1909
    M. f. cupida Elliot, 1910
    M. f. baweana Elliot, 1910
    M. f. philippinensis I. Geoffroy, 1843
    M. f. mindanensis Mearns, 1905
    M. f. mindora Hollister, 1913
    M. f. tua Kellogg, 1944
    M. f. limitis Schwarz, 1913
    M. f. sublimitis Sody, 1933
Macaca mulatta Zimmerman, 1780
    M. m. mulatta Zimmerman, 1780
    M. m. vestita Milne-Edwards, 1892
    M. m. villosa True, 1894
    M. m. mcmahoni Pocock, 1932
Macaca assamensis M'Clelland, 1839
    M. a. assamensis M'Clelland, 1839
    M. a. pelops Hodgson, 1840
Macaca cyclopis Swinhoe, 1862
Macaca speciosa F. Cuvier, 1825
    M. s. speciosa F. Cuvier, 1825
    M. s. arctoides I. Geoffroy, 1831
    M. s. melanota Ogilby, 1839
    M. s. thibetana Milne-Edwards, 1870
Macaca fuscata Blyth, 1875

Macaca fuscata Blyth (continued)
  M. f. fuscata Blyth, 1875
  M. f. yakui Kuroda, 1941
Macaca maurus F. Cuvier, 1823
  M. m. maurus F. Cuvier, 1823
  M. m. brunnescens Matschie, 1901
  M. m. togeana Sody, 1949
  M. m. ochreata Ogilby, 1840

Genus *Cynopithecus* I. Geoffroy, 1835
Cynopithecus niger Desmarest, 1822
  C. n. niger Desmarest, 1822
  C. n. lembicus Miller, 1931

Genus *Cercocebus* E. Geoffroy, 1812
Cercocebus albigena group:
Cercocebus albigena Gray, 1850
  C. a. albigena Gray, 1850
  C. a. johnstoni Lydekker, 1900
  C. a. zenkeri Schwarz, 1910
Cercocebus aterrimus Oudemans, 1890
Cercocebus torquatus group:
Cercocebus torquatus Kerr, 1792
Cercocebus atys Audebert, 1797 (Type species)
  C. a. atys Audebert, 1797
  C. a. lunulatus Temminck, 1853
Cercocebus galeritus Peters, 1879
  C. g. galeritus Peters, 1879
  C. g. agilis Rivière, 1886
  C. g. chrysogaster Lydekker, 1900

Genus *Papio* Erxleben, 1777
Papio cynocephalus group:
Papio anubis Lesson, 1827
  P. a. anubis Lesson, 1827
  P. a. tibestianus Dekeyser and Derivot, 1960
  P. a. heuglini Matschie, 1898
  P. a. neumanni Matschie, 1897
Papio cynocephalus Linnaeus, 1766
  P. c. cynocephalus Linnaeus, 1766
  P. c. ibeanus Thomas, 1893
  P. c. kindae Lönnberg, 1919
Papio papio Desmarest, 1820 (Type species)
Papio ursinus Kerr, 1792
  P. u. ursinus Kerr, 1792
  P. u. orientalis Goldblatt, 1926

Papio ursinus Kerr (continued)
  P. u. ruacana Shortridge, 1942
  P. u. griseipes Pocock, 1911
Papio hamadryas group:
Papio hamadryas Linnaeus, 1758

Genus *Mandrillus* Ritgen, 1824
Mandrillus sphinx Linnaeus, 1758 (Type species)
Mandrillus leucophaeus F. Cuvier, 1807
  M. l. leucophaeus F. Cuvier, 1807
  M. l. poensis Zukowsky, 1922

Genus *Theropithecus* I. Geoffroy, 1841
Theropithecus gelada Rüppell, 1835
  Th. g. gelada Rüppell, 1835
  Th. g. obscurus Heuglin, 1863

Genus *Cercopithecus* Linnaeus, 1758
Subgenus *Cercopithecus* Linnaeus, 1758
Cercopithecus aethiops group:
Cercopithecus aethiops Linnaeus, 1758
  C. ae. aethiops Linnaeus, 1758
  C. ae. hilgerti Neumann, 1902
  C. ae. ellenbecki Neumann, 1902
  C. ae. zavattarii de Beaux, 1943
  C. ae. tantalus Ogilby, 1841
  C. ae. budgetti Pocock, 1907
  C. ae. marrensis Thomas and Wroughton, 1923
Cercopithecus pygerythrus F. Cuvier, 1821
  C. p. pygerythrus F. Cuvier, 1821
  C. p. arenarius Heller, 1913
  C. p. centralis Neumann, 1900
  C. p. callidus Hollister, 1912
  C. p. johnstoni Pocock, 1907
  C. p. excubitor Schwarz, 1926
  C. p. nesiotes Schwarz, 1926
  C. p. rufoviridis I. Geoffroy, 1842
  C. p. whytei Pocock, 1907
  C. p. cloeti Roberts, 1931
  C. p. ngamiensis Roberts, 1932
  C. p. marjoriae Bradfield, 1936
  C. p. cynosuros Scopoli, 1786
Cercopithecus sabaeus Linnaeus, 1766
Cercopithecus cephus group:
Cercopithecus cephus Linnaeus, 1766

Cercopithecus cephus Linnaeus (continued)
  C. c. cephus Linnaeus, 1766
  C. c. cephodes Pocock, 1907
Cercopithecus diana group:
Cercopithecus diana Linnaeus, 1758 (Type species)
  C. d. diana Linnaeus, 1758
  C. d. roloway Schreber, 1774
  C. d. dryas Schwarz, 1932
Cercopithecus lhoesti group:
Cercopithecus lhoesti Sclater, 1898
Cercopithecus preussi Matschie, 1898
Cercopithecus hamlyni group:
Cercopithecus hamlyni Pocock, 1907
Cercopithecus mitis group:
Cercopithecus mitis Wolf, 1822
  C. m. mitis Wolf, 1822
  C. m. boutourlinii Giglioli, 1887
  C. m. stuhlmanni Matschie, 1893
  C. m. doggetti Pocock, 1907
  C. m. maesi Lönnberg, 1919
  C. m. kandti Matschie, 1905
  C. m. schoutedeni Schwarz, 1928
  C. m. opisthostictus Sclater, 1893
Cercopithecus albogularis Sykes, 1831
  C. a. albogularis Sykes, 1831
  C. a. albotorquatus Pousargues, 1896
  C. a. monoides I. Geoffroy, 1841
  C. a. phylax Schwarz, 1927
  C. a. kibonotensis Lönnberg, 1910
  C. a. kolbi Neumann, 1902
  C. a. moloneyi Sclater, 1893
  C. a. francescae Thomas, 1902
  C. a. nyasae Schwarz, 1928
  C. a. erythrarchus Peters, 1852
  C. a. schwarzi Roberts, 1931
  C. a. labiatus I. Geoffroy, 1841
Cercopithecus mona group:
Cercopithecus mona Schreber, 1774
Cercopithecus campbelli Waterhouse, 1838
  C. c. campbelli Waterhouse, 1838
  C. c. lowei Thomas, 1923
Cercopithecus wolfi Meyer, 1891
  C. w. wolfi Meyer, 1891
  C. w. pyrogaster Lönnberg, 1919
  C. w. elegans Dubois and Matschie, 1912
Cercopithecus denti Thomas, 1907

Cercopithecus pogonias Bennett, 1833
  C. p. pogonias Bennett, 1833
  C. p. grayi Fraser, 1850
  C. p. nigripes du Chaillu, 1860
  C. p. schwarzianus Schouteden, 1946
Cercopithecus neglectus group:
Cercopithecus neglectus Schlegel, 1876
Cercopithecus nictitans group:
Cercopithecus nictitans Linnaeus, 1766
  C. n. nictitans Linnaeus, 1766
  C. n. martini Waterhouse, 1841
  C. n. stampflii Jentink, 1888
Cercopithecus petaurista Schreber, 1775
  C. p. petaurista Schreber, 1775
  C. p. buettikoferi Jentink, 1886
Cercopithecus ascanius Audebert, 1799
  C. a. ascanius Audebert, 1799
  C. a. katangae Lönnberg, 1919
  C. a. whitesidei Thomas, 1909
  C. a. montanus Lorenz, 1914
  C. a. schmidti Matschie, 1892
Cercopithecus erythrotis Waterhouse, 1838
  C. e. erythrotis Waterhouse, 1838
  C. e. camerunensis Hayman, 1940
  C. e. sclateri Pocock, 1904
Cercopithecus erythrogaster Gray, 1866

Subgenus *Miopithecus* I. Geoffroy, 1842
Cercopithecus talapoin Schreber, 1774
  C. t. talapoin Schreber, 1774
  C. t. ansorgei Pocock, 1907
  C. t. vleeschouwersi Poll, 1940
  C. t. pilettei Lönnberg, 1919

Subgenus *Allenopithecus* Lang, 1923
Cercopithecus nigroviridis Pocock, 1907

Genus *Erythrocebus* Trouessart, 1897
Erythrocebus patas Schreber, 1775
  E. p. patas Schreber, 1775
  E. p. villiersi Dekeyser, 1950
  E. p. pyrronotus Hemprich and Ehrenberg, 1829
  E. p. baumstarki Matschie, 1905

Subfamily Colobinae Elliot, 1913
Genus *Presbytis* Eschscholtz, 1821

Presbytis aygula group:
Presbytis aygula Linnaeus, 1758 (Type species)
  P. a. aygula Linnaeus, 1758
  P. a. fredericae Sody, 1930
  P. a. hosei Thomas, 1889
  P. a. canicrus Miller, 1934
  P. a. nubilus Millar, 1942
  P. a. sabanus Thomas, 1893
  P. a. thomasi Collett, 1892
  P. a. margae Hooijer, 1948
Presbytis melalophos Raffles, 1821
  P. m. melalophos Raffles, 1821
  P. m. femoralis Martin, 1838
  P. m. australis Miller, 1913
  P. m. siamensis Müller and Schlegel, 1841
  P. m. nubigena Elliot, 1909
  P. m. robinsoni Thomas, 1910
  P. m. rhionis Miller, 1903
  P. m. canus Miller, 1906
  P. m. natunae Thomas and Hartert, 1894
  P. m. catemanus Lyon, 1908
  P. m. percura Lyon, 1908
  P. m. paenulatus Chasen, 1940
  P. m. sumatranus Müller and Schlegel, 1841
  P. m. batuanus Miller, 1903
  P. m. ferrugineus Schlegel, 1876
  P. m. fluviatilis Chasen, 1940
  P. m. fuscomurinus Elliot, 1906
  P. m. chrysomelas Müller, 1838
  P. m. cruciger Thomas, 1892
Presbytis frontatus Müller, 1838
  P. f. frontatus Müller, 1838
  P. f. nudifrons Elliot, 1909
Presbytis rubicundus Müller, 1838
  P. r. rubicundus, Müller, 1838
  P. r. rubidus Lyon, 1911
  P. r. ignitus Dollman, 1909
  P. r. carimatae Miller, 1906
  P. r. chryseus Davis, 1962
Presbytis entellus group:
Presbytis entellus Dufresne, 1797
  P. e. entellus Dufresne, 1797
  P. e. schistaceus Hodgson, 1840
  P. e. hypoleucos Blyth, 1841
  P. e. dussumieri I. Geoffroy, 1843
  P. e. anchises Blyth, 1844
  P. e. priam Blyth, 1844

Presbytis entellus Dufresne (continued)
  P. e. thersites Blyth, 1847
  P. e. lania Elliot, 1909
  P. e. achilles Pocock, 1928
  P. e. ajax Pocock, 1928
  P. e. achates Pocock, 1928
  P. e. iulus Pocock, 1928
  P. e. aeneas Pocock, 1928
  P. e. elissa Pocock, 1928
  P. e. priamellus Pocock, 1928
Presbytis senex group:
Presbytis senex Erxleben, 1777
  P. s. senex Erxleben, 1777
  P. s. vetulus Erxleben, 1777
  P. s. nestor Bennett, 1833
  P. s. monticola Kelaart, 1850
  P. s. harti Deraniyagala, 1954
Presbytis johnii Fischer, 1829
Presbytis cristatus group:
Presbytis cristatus Raffles, 1821
  P. c. cristatus Raffles, 1821
  P. c. pyrrhus Horsfield, 1823
  P. c. sondaicus Robinson and Kloss, 1919
  P. c. kohlbruggei Sody, 1931
  P. c. ultimus Elliot, 1910
  P. c. vigilans Miller, 1913
  P. c. germaini Milne-Edwards, 1876
  P. c. atrior Pocock, 1928
Presbytis pileatus Blyth, 1843
  P. p. pileatus Blyth, 1843
  P. p. shortridgei Wroughton, 1915
  P. p. brahma Wroughton, 1916
  P. p. durga Wroughton, 1916
  P. p. tenebricus Hinton, 1923
Presbytis geei Gee, 1956
Presbytis obscurus Reid, 1837
  P. o. obscurus Reid, 1837
  P. o. flavicauda Elliot, 1910
  P. o. halonifer Cantor, 1845
  P. o. carbo Thomas and Wroughton, 1909
  P. o. styx Kloss, 1911
  P. o. seimundi Chasen, 1940
  P. o. sanctorum Elliot, 1910
Presbytis phayrei Blyth, 1847
  P. p. phayrei Blyth, 1847
  P. p. crepusculus Elliot, 1909
  P. p. shanicus Wroughton, 1917

Presbytis phayrei Blyth (continued)
  P. p. rubei Knottnerus-Meyer, 1933
Presbytis francoisi Pousargues, 1898
  P. f. francoisi Pousargues, 1898
  P. f. poliocephalus Trouessart, 1911
  P. f. laotum Thomas, 1921
  P. f. delacouri Osgood, 1932
Presbytis potenziani Bonaparte, 1856
  P. p. potenziani Bonaparte, 1856
  P. p. siberu Chasen and Kloss, 1927

Genus *Rhinopithecus* Milne-Edwards, 1872
Rhinopithecus roxellanae Milne-Edwards, 1870
    (Type species)
  Rh. r. roxellanae Milne-Edwards, 1870
  Rh. r. bieti Milne-Edwards, 1897
  Rh. r. brelichi Thomas, 1903
Rhinopithecus avunculus Dollman, 1912

Genus *Pygathrix* E. Geoffroy, 1812
Pygathrix nemaeus Linnaeus, 1771
  P. n. nemaeus Linnaeus, 1771
  P. n. nigripes Milne-Edwards, 1871

Genus *Nasalis* E. Geoffroy, 1812
Nasalis larvatus Wurmb, 1781

Genus *Simias* Miller, 1903
Simias concolor Miller, 1903
  S. c. concolor Miller, 1903
  S. c. siberu Chasen and Kloss, 1927

Genus *Colobus* Illiger, 1811
Subgenus *Colobus* Illiger, 1811
Colobus polykomos Zimmerman, 1780 (Type
    species)
  C. p. polykomos Zimmerman, 1780
  C. p. adolfifriederici Matschie, 1914
  C. p. angolensis Sclater, 1860
  C. p. cordieri Rahm, 1959
  C. p. cottoni Lydekker, 1905
  C. p. dollmani Schwarz, 1927
  C. p. palliatus Peters, 1868
  C. p. prigoginei Verheyen, 1959
  C. p. ruwenzorii Thomas, 1901
  C. p. satanas Waterhouse, 1838
  C. p. sharpei Thomas, 1902
  C. p. vellerosus I. Geoffroy, 1834

Colobus guereza Rüppell, 1835
  C. g. guereza Rüppell, 1835
  C. g. caudatus Thomas, 1885
  C. g. dodingae Matschie, 1913
  C. g. gallarum Neumann, 1902
  C. g. kikuyuensis Lönnberg, 1912
  C. g. matschiei Neumann, 1899
  C. g. occidentalis Rochebrune, 1886–7
  C. g. percivali Heller, 1913
  C. g. poliurus Thomas, 1901
  C. g. uellensis Matschie, 1913

Subgenus *Procolobus* Rochebrune, 1886–7
Colobus verus van Beneden, 1838

Subgenus *Piliocolobus* Rochebrune, 1886–7
Colobus badius Kerr, 1792 (Type species)
  C. b. badius, Kerr, 1792
  C. b. bouvieri Rochebrune, 1887
  C. b. ellioti Dollman, 1909
  C. b. foai Pousargues, 1899
  C. b. gordonorum Matschie, 1900
  C. b. graueri Dollman, 1909
  C. b. gudoviusi Matschie, 1914
  C. b. langi J. A. Allen, 1925
  C. b. metternichi Krumbiegel, 1942
  C. b. nigrimanus Trouessart, 1906
  C. b. oustaleti Trouessart, 1906
  C. b. pennantii Waterhouse, 1838
  C. b. powelli Matschie, 1913
  C. b. preussi Matschie, 1900
  C. b. rufomitratus Peters, 1879
  C. b. temminckii Kuhl, 1820
  C. b. tephroceles Elliot, 1907
  C. b. tholloni Rivière, 1886
  C. b. waldroni Hayman, 1936
Colobus kirkii Gray, 1868

Superfamily Hominoidea Simpson, 1931
Family Hylobatidae Blyth, 1875
Genus *Hylobates* Illiger, 1811
Hylobates lar Linnaeus, 1771 (Type species)
  H. l. lar Linnaeus, 1771
  H. l. longimanus Schreber, 1775
  H. l. pileatus Gray, 1861
Hylobates moloch Audebert, 1797–8

Hylobates moloch Audebert (continued)
   H. m. moloch Audebert, 1797–8
   H. m. pongoalsoni Sody, 1949
   H. m. muelleri Martin, 1841
   H. m. albibarbis Lyon, 1911
   H. m. abbotti Kloss, 1929
   H. m. funereus I. Geoffroy, 1850
Hylobates agilis F. Cuvier, 1821
Hylobates hoolock Harlan, 1834
Hylobates concolor Harlan 1826
   H. c. concolor Harlan, 1826
   H. c. hainanus Thomas, 1892
   H. c. lu Delacour, 1951
   H. c. leucogenys Ogilby, 1840
   H. c. siki Delacour, 1951
   H. c. gabriellae Thomas, 1909
Hylobates klossii Miller, 1903

Genus *Symphalangus* Gloger, 1841
Symphalangus syndactylus Raffles, 1821
   S. s. syndactylus Raffles, 1821
   S. s. continentis Thomas, 1908

Family Pongidae Elliot, 1913

Genus *Pongo* Lacépède, 1799
Pongo pygmaeus Linnaeus, 1760
   P. p. pygmaeus Linnaeus, 1760
   P. p. abelii Lesson, 1827

Genus *Pan* Oken, 1816
Pan troglodytes Blumenbach, 1779 (Type species)
   P. t. troglodytes Blumenbach, 1779
   P. t. verus Schwarz, 1934
   P. t. schweinfurthii Giglioli, 1872
Pan paniscus Schwarz, 1929

Genus *Gorilla* I. Geoffroy, 1852
Gorilla gorilla Savage and Wyman, 1847
   G. g. gorilla Savage and Wyman, 1847
   G. g. beringei Matschie, 1903
   G. g. manyema Rothschild, 1908

Family Hominidae Gray, 1825
Genus *Homo* Linnaeus, 1758
Homo sapiens Linnaeus, 1758

2. SOME COMMON SYNONYMS

Alouatta guariba	= *Alouatta fusca*	*Inuus*	= *Macaca sylvana*
Alouatta palliata	= *Alouatta villosa*	*Kasi*	= *Presbytis*
Anthropopithecus	= *Pan*	*Lagothrix hendeei*	= *L. flavicauda*
Aotes	= *Aotus*	*Lasiopyga*	= *Cercopithecus*
Ateleus	= *Ateles*	*Leontocebus*	= *Leontideus* and
Bonobo	= *Pan paniscus*		*Saguinus*
Brachitanytes	= *Hylobates klossii*	*Lichanotus*	= *Avahi*
Brachyurus	= *Cacajao*	*Lyssodes*	= *Macaca*
Cebus fatuellus	= *Cebus apella*	*Macaca irus*	= *Macaca fascicularis*
Chaeropithecus	= *Papio*	*Macaca rhesus*	= *Macaca mulatta*
Chrysothrix	= *Saimiri*	*Macaca speciosa*	= *Macaca arctoides*
Colobus abyssinicus	= *Colobus guereza*	*Maimon*	= *Papio*
Comopithecus	= *Papio hamadryas*	*Marikina*	= *Saguinus (Marikina)*
Cynocephalus	= *Papio*	*Mico*	= *Callithrix*
Cynomolgus	= *Macaca fascicularis*	*Midas*	= *Saguinus*
Gymnopyga	= *Macaca maurus*	*Mycetes*	= *Alouatta*
Hapale	= *Callithrix*	*Mystax*	= *Saguinus*
Hemigalago	= *Galago (Galagoides)*	*Nomascus*	= *Hylobates concolor*

Oedipomidas	= *Saguinus (Oedipomidas)*	*Semnopithecus*	= *Presbytis*
Otolemur	= *Galago crassicaudatus*	*Silenus*	= *Macaca*
Papio comatus	= *Papio ursinus*	*Simia satyrus*	= *Pongo pygmaeus* or *Pan*
Papio doguera	= *Papio anubis*		*troglodytes*
Pithecus	= *Presbytis*, etc.	*Simia*	= *Papio. Pan. Macaca*
Presbytis femoralis	= *Presbytis melalophos*		*sylvana. Pongo*
Presbytis maurus	= *Presbytis cristatus*	*Tamarin*	= *Saguinus*
Presbytis pyrrhus	= *Presbytis cristatus*	*Tamarinus*	= *Saguinus*
Presbytiscus	= *Rhinopithecus*	*Tana*	= *Tupaia (Lyonogale)*
	avunculus	*Tarsius carbonarius*	= *Tarsius syrichta*
Prolemur	= *Hapalemur simus*	*Tarsius philippinensis*	= *Tarsius syrichta*
Rhesus	= *Macaca*	*Trachypithecus*	= *Presbytis*
Rhinostigma	= *Cercopithecus hamlyni*	*Troglodytes*	= *Pan*
Saguinus spixii	= *Saguinus geoffroyi*	*Zati*	= *Macaca*

3. COMMON NAMES OF PRIMATES

The principal synonyms for lemurs, monkeys and apes are listed below. This list is not definitive but includes all the common English, German, Dutch and French names for primate species. Purely local or dialect names are not included unless they have become adopted by American or European usage.

COMMON NAME	GENERIC NAME	SPECIFIC NAME
Abyssinian guereza	*Colobus*	*C. guereza*
Agile Gibbon	*Hylobates*	*H. agilis*
Agile Mangabey	*Cercocebus*	*C. galeritus agilis*
Allen's Galago	*Galago*	*G. alleni*
Allen's Monkey	*Cercopithecus*	*C. nigroviridis*
Ampongi	*Avahi*	*A. laniger*
Angwantibo	*Arctocebus*	*A. calabarensis*
Anubis baboon	*Papio*	*P. anubis*
Ashy Titi	*Callicebus*	*C. moloch donacophilus*
Assamese macaque	*Macaca*	*M. assamensis*
Atbarapavian	*Papio*	*P. anubis*
Atélé araignée	*Brachyteles*	*B. arachnoides*
Aye-Aye	*Daubentonia*	*D. madagascariensis*
Azara's Capuchin	*Cebus*	*C. apella cay*
Babakoto	*Indri*	*I. indri*
Baboons	*Papio*	
Babouin	*Papio*	
Bald Chimpanzee	*Pan*	*P. troglodytes*
Bald Leaf Monkey	*Presbytis*	*P. frontatus*
Bald Tamarins	*Saguinus*	
Bald Uakari	*Cacajao*	*C. calvus*

COMMON NAME	GENERIC NAME	SPECIFIC NAME
Bandar	*Macaca*	*M. mulatta*
Banded Leaf Monkey	*Presbytis*	*P. melalophos*
Bandro	*Hapalemur*	*H. simus*
Barbary Ape	*Macaca*	*M. sylvana*
Barbe's Lutong	*Presbytis*	*P. phayrei phayrei*
Bare-Faced Tamarins	*Saguinus*	
Bärenmaki	*Arctocebus*	*A. calabarensis*
Bärenmakak	*Macaca*	*M. speciosa*
Bärenpavian	*Papio*	*P. ursinus*
Bärenstummelaffe	*Colobus*	*C. polykomos*
Barombi guereza	*Colobus*	*C. badius preussi*
Barrigudos	*Lagothrix*	
Bartaffe	*Macaca*	*M. silenus*
Baviaan	*Papio*	
Bay Colobus	*Colobus*	*C. badius badius*
Bear Macaque	*Macaca*	*M. speciosa*
Bear-Monkey	*Presbytis*	*P. senex monticola*
Bearded Sakis	*Chiropotes*	
Berggorilla	*Gorilla*	*G. g. beringei*
Beringe's Gorilla	*Gorilla*	*G. g. beringei*
Berok	*Macaca*	*M. nemestrina*
Biet's Monkey	*Rhinopithecus*	*R. roxellanae bieti*
Black Ape	*Cynopithecus*	*C. niger*
Black Colobus	*Colobus*	*C. polykomos satanas*
Black-faced Chimpanzee	*Pan*	*P. troglodytes troglodytes*
Black-footed Guenon	*Cercopithecus*	*C. pogonias nigripes*
Black Gibbon	*Hylobates*	*H. concolor*
Black-Handed Spider Monkey	*Ateles*	*A. geoffroyi*
Black-Handed Titi	*Callicebus*	*C. personatus melanochir*
Black-Headed Uakari	*Cacajao*	*C. melanocephalus*
Black Langur	*Presbytis*	*P. johnii*
Black Lemur	*Lemur*	*L. macaco*
Black Mangabey	*Cercocebus*	*C. aterrimus or C. albigena*
Black-Pencilled Marmoset	*Callithrix*	*C. penicillata*
Black Saki	*Chiropotes*	*C. satanas*
Black Sifaka	*Propithecus*	*P. diadema holomelas*
Black Spider Monkey	*Ateles*	*A. paniscus*
Black-Tailed Bushbaby	*Galago*	*G. alleni*
Black-Tailed Marmoset	*Callithrix*	*C. argentata*
Black and White Colobus	*Colobus*	*C. guereza or C. polykomos*
Blaumaulmeerkatze	*Cercopithecus*	*C. cephus*
Bleeding Heart Baboon	*Theropithecus*	*T. gelada*
Blue Monkey	*Cercopithecus*	*C. mitis stuhlmanni*
Bobbyjohn	*Papio*	*P. ursinus*
Bokombouli	*Hapalemur*	*H. griseus*
Bonobo	*Pan*	*P. paniscus*

COMMON NAME	GENERIC NAME	SPECIFIC NAME
Bonnet Macaque	*Macaca*	*M. radiata*
Bonneted Langur	*Presbytis*	*P. pileatus*
Bornean Slow Loris	*Nycticebus*	*N. coucang borneanus*
Bosman's potto	*Perodicticus*	*P. potto potto*
Boutourlini's guenon	*Cercopithecus*	*C. mitis boutourlinii*
Brauner Kapuziner	*Cebus*	*C. nigrivittatus*
Brauner Wollaffe	*Lagothrix*	*L. lagothricha*
Breitschanziger Halpmaki	*Hapalemur*	*H. simus*
Brelich's Monkey	*Rhinopithecus*	*R. roxellanae brelichi*
Broad-Nosed Lemur	*Hapalemur*	*H. simus*
Broad-Nosed Gentle Lemur	*Hapalemur*	*H. simus*
Brown Capuchin	*Cebus*	*C. apella*
Brown Colobus	*Colobus*	*C. badius*
Brown-Headed Spider Monkey	*Ateles*	*A. fusciceps*
Brown Howler	*Alouatta*	*A. fusca*
Brown Lemur	*Lemur*	*L. macaco fulvus*
Brown-Headed Tamarin	*Saguinus*	*S. pileatus*
Brown Woolly Monkey	*Lagothrix*	*L. lagothricha*
Brüllaffen	*Alouatta*	
Budeng	*Presbytis*	*P. cristatus*
Buff-Headed Marmoset	*Callithrix*	*C. flaviceps*
Buffon's Tarsier	*Tarsier*	*T. syrichta*
Buschelohriger Katzenmaki	*Cheirogaleus*	*C. trichotis*
Büttikofer's Monkey	*Cercopithecus*	*C. petaurista buettikoferi*
Campbell's Monkey	*Cercopithecus*	*C. campbelli*
Capped Gibbon	*Hylobates*	*H. lar pileatus*
Capuchins	*Cebus*	
Capucyner	*Cebus*	
Cat Lemur	*Lemur*	*L. catta*
Celebes Ape	*Cynopithecus*	*C. niger*
Celebes Macaque	*Macaca*	*M. maurus*
Celebes Tarsier	*Tarsius*	*T. spectrum*
Cercocèbe agile	*Cercocebus*	*C. galeritus*
Cercocèbe à collier blanc	*Cercocebus*	*C. torquatus*
Cercocèbe à crête	*Cercocebus*	*C. galeritus*
Cercocèbe à gorge blanc	*Cercocebus*	*C. albigena*
Cercopithèque Diadème	*Cercopithecus*	*C. mitis*
Cercopithèque Callitriche	*Cercopithecus*	*C. sabaeus*
Cercopithèque noir et vert	*Cercopithecus*	*C. nigroviridis*
Cercopithèque pain-à-cacheter	*Cercopithecus*	*C. ascanius*
Ceylon Hutaffe	*Macaca*	*M. sinica*
Chacma Baboon	*Papio*	*P. ursinus*
Chamek	*Ateles*	*A. paniscus*
Chimpanzees	*Pan*	
Chimpanzee nain	*Pan*	*P. paniscus*

COMMON NAME	GENERIC NAME	SPECIFIC NAME
Choga	*Pan*	*P. troglodytes troglodytes*
Chirogale à oreilles velues	*Cheirogaleus*	*C. trichotis*
Cinnamon Ringtail	*Cebus*	*C. albifrons*
Coaita	*Ateles*	
Collared Titi	*Callicebus*	*C. torquatus*
Colobe	*Colobus*	
Colobe à Huppe	*Colobus*	*C. verus*
Colobe à Camail	*Colobus*	*C. polykomos*
Colobe Ferrugineux	*Colobus*	*C. badius*
Colobe Ourson	*Colobus*	*C. polykomos*
Common Marmoset	*Callithrix*	*C. jacchus*
Common Treeshrew	*Tupaia*	*T. glis*
Congo Red Monkey	*Cercopithecus*	*C. mitis kandti*
Coquerel's Dwarf Lemur	*Microcebus*	*M. coquereli*
Coquerel's Sifaka	*Propithecus*	*P. verreauxi coquereli*
Cotton-tops	*Saguinus*	*S. oedipus*
Couxio	*Chiropotes*	
Crab-eating Macaque	*Macaca*	*M. fascicularis*
Crested Celebes Macaque	*Cynopithecus*	*C. niger*
Crested Langurs	*Presbytis*	*P. cristatus*
Crested Mangabey	*Cercocebus*	*C. albigena*
Cross's Monkey	*Cercopithecus*	*C. preussi*
Crossley's Dwarf Lemur	*Cheirogaleus*	*C. major crossleyi*
Cross-marked Leaf Monkey	*Presbytis*	*P. melalophos cruciger*
Crowned Sifaka	*Propithecus*	*P. verreauxi coronatus*
Cynomolgus	*Macaca*	*M. fascicularis*
Deville's Tamarin	*Saguinus*	*S. weddelli*
Devil Monkey	*Aotus*	*A. trivirgatus*
Diademed Monkey	*Cercopithecus*	*C. mitis*
Diademed Sifaka	*Propithecus*	*P. diadema*
Dianameerkatze	*Cercopithecus*	*C. diana*
Diana Monkey	*Cercopithecus*	*C. diana*
Dickkopfkapuziner	*Cebus*	*C. apella*
Doguera Baboon	*Papio*	*P. anubis*
Dog-Faced Lemur	*Indri*	*I. indri*
Doggett's Monkey	*Cercopithecus*	*C. mitis doggetti*
Doucs	*Pygathrix*	*P. nemaeus*
Douroucouli	*Aotus*	*A. trivirgatus*
Drill	*Mandrillus*	*M. leucophaeus*
Dryas guenon	*Cercopithecus*	*C. diana dryas*
Dusky Leaf Monkey	*Presbytis*	*P. obscurus*
Dusky Titi	*Callicebus*	*C. moloch cupreus*
Dwarf Bushbaby	*Galago*	*G. demidovii*
Dwarf Gibbon	*Hylobates*	*H. klossii*
Dwarf Lemurs	*Cheirogaleus*	
Dwarf Siamang	*Hylobates*	*H. klossii*

COMMON NAME	GENERIC NAME	SPECIFIC NAME
E. African Potto	*Perodicticus*	*P. potto ibeanus*
Eastern Mountain Gorilla	*Gorilla*	*G. g. beringei*
Eastern Lowland Gorilla	*Gorilla*	*G. g. manyema*
Eastern Tarsier	*Tarsius*	*T. spectrum*
Ei-A	*Aotus*	*A. trivirgatus*
Emperor Tamarin	*Saguinus*	*S. imperator*
Endrina	*Indri*	*I. indri*
Entellus langur	*Presbytis*	*P. entellus*
Eroide	*Brachyteles*	*B. arachnoides*
Erxleben's Monkey	*Cercopithecus*	*C. pogonias grayi*
Everett's Langur	*Presbytis*	*P. aygula hosei*
Everett's Tupaia	*Urogale*	*U. everetti*
Fahnenschwanzspitzhörnchen	*Ptilocercus*	*P. lowii*
Fat-tailed dwarf lemur	*Cheirogaleus*	*C. medius*
Feather-tailed Tree-shrew	*Ptilocercus*	*P. lowii*
Fettschwanzmaki	*Cheirogaleus*	*C. medius*
Flachlandgorilla	*Gorilla*	*G. g. gorilla*
Flocky Lemur	*Avahi*	*A. laniger*
Fork-crowned Dwarf-Lemur	*Phaner*	*P. furcifer*
Formosanmakak	*Macaca*	*M. cyclopis*
Forsyth-Major's Sifaka	*Propithecus*	*P. verreauxi majori*
Fotsiefaka	*Avahi*	*A. laniger*
François' Schlankaffe	*Presbytis*	*P. francoisi*
Full-bottom monkey	*Colobus*	*C. polykomos*
Gaberstrerfiger Zwergmaki	*Phaner*	*P. furcifer*
Galago à Queue Touffue	*Galago*	*G. crassicaudatus*
Galago Mignon	*Galago*	*G. elegantulus*
Galago Pâle	*Galago*	*G. elegantulus pallidus*
Gehaubter Kapuziner	*Cebus*	*C. apella*
Gelada	*Theropithecus*	*T. gelada*
Gelber babuin	*Papio*	*P. cynocephalus*
Gentle Lemurs	*Hapalemur*	
Geoffroy's Marmoset	*Callithrix*	*C. geoffroyi*
Geoffroy's Tamarin	*Saguinus*	*S. geoffroyi*
Giant Rhesus	*Macaca*	*M. nemestrina*
Gibbon cendré	*Hylobates*	*H. moloch*
Gibbons	*Hylobates*	
Gibraltar Ape	*Macaca*	*M. sylvana*
Goeldi's Marmoset	*Callimico*	*G. goeldii*
Goeldi's Monkey	*Callimico*	*C. goeldii*
Gold Monkey	*Cercopithecus*	*C. mitis kandti*
Golden-bellied Monkey	*Cercopithecus*	*C. pogonias*
Golden Langur	*Presbytis*	*P. geei*
Golden Marmoset	*Callithrix*	*C. chrysoleuca*
Golden Lion Marmoset	*Leontideus*	*L. rosalia*
Golden Monkey	*Rhinopithecus*	*R. roxellanae roxellanae*

COMMON NAME	GENERIC NAME	SPECIFIC NAME
Golden Potto	*Arctocebus*	*A. calabarensis*
Golden-headed Tamarin	*Leontideus*	*L. chrysomelas*
Gorille	*Gorilla*	
Gorille du côte	*Gorilla*	*G. g. gorilla*
Gorille de montagne	*Gorilla*	*G. g. beringei.* or *G. g. manyema*
Grauwangen Mangabe	*Cercocebus*	*C. albigena*
Grauer Babuin	*Papio*	*P. anubis ibeanus*
Grauer Halbmaki	*Hapalemur*	*H. griseus*
Grauer Wollaffe	*Lagothrix*	*L. lagothricha lugens*
Gray's Monkey	*Cercopithecus*	*C. pogonias grayi*
Great Bushbaby	*Galago*	*G. crassicaudatus*
Great Gibbon	*Symphalangus*	*S. syndactylus*
Greater Dwarf Lemur	*Cheirogaleus*	*C. major*
Green Monkey	*Cercopithecus*	*C. sabaeus*
Grey Gibbon	*Hylobates*	*H. moloch*
Grey-cheeked Mangabey	*Cercocebus*	*C. albigena*
Grey Lemur	*Hapalemur*	*H. griseus*
Grey Woolly Monkey	*Lagothrix*	*L. lagothricha lugens*
Grivet	*Cercopithecus*	*C. aethiops*
Grosses Lowenäffchen	*Leontideus*	*L. rosalia*
Grüne Meerkatz	*Cercopithecus*	*C. aethiops*
Guenons	*Cercopithecus*	
Guariba	*Alouatta*	
Guereza	*Colobus*	*C. guereza*
Guinea Baboon	*Papio*	*P. papio*
Guineapavian	*Papio*	*P. papio*
Guineaschimpanze	*Pan*	*P. troglodytes*
Günther's Treeshrew	*Tupaia*	*T. minor*
Hainan Gibbon	*Hylobates*	*H. concolor hainanus*
Hairy-eared Dwarf Lemur	*Cheirogaleus*	*C. trichotis*
Hairy-faced tamarins	*Saguinus*	
Half-a-tail	*Perodicticus*	*P. potto*
Halsbande Mangabe	*Cercocebus*	*C. torquatus*
Hamadryas Baboon	*Papio*	*P. hamadryas*
Hamlynmeerkatze	*Cercopithecus*	*C. hamlyni*
Hamlyn's Monkey	*Cercopithecus*	*C. hamlyni*
Hanuman Langur	*Presbytis*	*P. entellus*
Hapale	*Callithrix*	
Hattock	*Lepilemur*	*L. mustelinus*
Haubenmangabe	*Cercocebus*	*C. galeritus*
Hendee's Woolly Monkey	*Lagothrix*	*L. flavicauda*
Highland Gorilla	*Gorilla*	*G. g. beringei*
Himalayan Langur	*Presbytis*	*P. entellus schistaceus*
Himalayan Macaque	*Macaca*	*M. assamensis*
Hocheur	*Cercopithecus*	*C. nictitans*
Hoelman	*Presbytis*	*P. entellus*

COMMON NAME	GENERIC NAME	SPECIFIC NAME
Hooded Capuchin	*Cebus*	*C. apella cay*
Hoolock Gibbon	*Hylobates*	*H. hoolock*
Horsfield's Tarsier	*Tarsius*	*T. bancanus*
Hose's Leaf Monkey	*Presbytis*	*P. aygula hosei*
Houlemann	*Presbytis*	*P. entellus*
Howlers	*Alouatta*	
Hulman	*Presbytis*	*P. entellus*
Hulok	*Hylobates*	*H. hoolock*
Humboldt's Woolly Monkey	*Lagothrix*	*L. lagothricha lagothricha*
Hurleur	*Alouatta*	
Husarnaffe	*Erythrocebus*	*E. patas*
Hutaffe	*Macaca*	*M. radiata*
Illiger's Tamarin	*Saguinus*	*S. illigeri*
Indisches Spitzhörnchen	*Anathana*	*A. ellioti*
Indochinese Bear Macaque	*Macaca*	*M. arctoides*
Indris	*Indri*	*I. indri*
Japanese macaque	*Macaca*	*M. fuscata*
Javaneraffe	*Macaca*	*M. fascicularis*
Java Monkey	*Macaca*	*M. fascicularis*
Javaspitzhörnchen	*Tupaia*	*T. javanica*
Jew Monkey	*Chiropotes*	*C. satanas chiropotes*
John's Langur	*Presbytis*	*P. johnii*
Judenaffe	*Chiropotes*	*C. satanas chiropotes*
Kalahari Chacma	*Papio*	*P. ursinus ruacana*
Kalzenmaki	*Lemur*	*L. catta*
Kapuziner	*Cebus*	*C. capucinus*
Kasi	*Presbytis*	*P. senex or johnii*
Katanga Monkey	*Cercopithecus*	*C. ascanius katangae*
Katta	*Lemur*	*L. catta*
Katzenmaki	*Lemur*	*L. catta*
Katzenachtaffe	*Aotus*	*A. trivirgatus*
Kilimanjaro Blue Monkey	*Cercopithecus*	*C. albogularis kibonotensis*
King Colobus	*Colobus*	*C. polykomos*
Kikuyu Colobus	*Colobus*	*C. guereza kikuyuensis*
Kirk's Colobus	*Colobus*	*C. kirkii*
Klammeraffe	*Ateles*	
Kleideraffe	*Pygathrix*	*P. nemaeus*
Kleiner plumplori	*Nycticebus*	*N. pygmaeus*
Kloss's Gibbon	*Hylobates*	*H. klossii*
Koboldmaki	*Tarsius*	
Kolb's Monkey	*Cercopithecus*	*C. albogularis kolbi*
Kooloo-Kamba	*Pan*	*P. troglodytes troglodytes*
Kra monkey	*Macaca*	*M. fascicularis*
Kuif-mangabey	*Cercocebus*	*C. albigena. C. aterrimus*
Langurs	*Presbytis*	
Laotian Lutong	*Presbytis*	*P. francoisi laotum*

COMMON NAME	GENERIC NAME	SPECIFIC NAME
Large Treeshrew	*Tupaia*	*T. tana*
Leaf (eating) Monkeys	*Presbytis or Colobus*	
Le Cercocèbe Noir	*Cercocebus*	*C. aterrimus*
Le Colobe Bai	*Colobus*	*C. badius*
Le Colobe Noir	*Colobus*	*C. satanas*
Leeuwaapje	*Leontideus*	
Le Grand Galago	*Galago*	*G. crassicaudatus*
(Les) Mones	*Cercopithecus*	*C. mona*
Leontocebus	*Leontideus or Saguinus*	
Lesser Bushbaby	*Galago*	*G. senegalensis*
Lesser Mouse Lemur	*Microcebus*	*M. murinus*
Lesser Slow Loris	*Nycticebus*	*N. pygmaeus*
Lesser Tree-Shrew	*Tupaia*	*T. minor*
L'Hoest's Monkey	*Cercopithecus*	*C. lhoesti*
Lion Marmosets	*Leontideus*	
Lion-tailed Macaque	*Macaca*	*M. silenus*
Liszt Monkey	*Saguinus*	*S. oedipus*
Little Lion Monkeys	*Leontideus*	
Long-Haired Spider Monkey	*Ateles*	*A. belzebuth*
Lönnberg's Tamarin	*Saguinus*	*S. pluto*
Long-legged Baboon	*Papio*	*P. cynocephalus*
Loris parresseux	*Nycticebus*	*N. coucang*
Lowe's Monkey	*Cercopithecus*	*C. campbelli lowei*
Lowland Bornean Leaf Monkey	*Presbytis*	*P. aygula sabanus*
Lowland Gorilla	*Gorilla*	*G. g. gorilla*
Lungoor	*Presbytis*	*P. entellus*
Lutongs	*Presbytis*	eg. *P. cristatus*
Mac	*Lemur*	*L. catta*
Macaque à face rouge	*Macaca*	*M. fuscata*
Macaque de Büffon	*Macaca*	*M. fascicularis*
Macaque commun	*Macaca*	*M. radiata*
Macaque couronne	*Macaca*	*M. sinica*
Macaque maure	*Macaca*	*M. maurus*
Madras Langur	*Presbytis*	*P. entellus priam*
Madras Treeshrew	*Anathana*	*A. ellioti*
Magot	*Macaca*	*M. sylvana*
Maimon	*Macaca*	*M. nemestrina*
Makak	*Macaca*	
Malbrouk	*Cercopithecus*	*C. pygerythrus cynosuros*
Malaysian Tarsier	*Tarsius*	*T. bancanus*
Mandrill	*Mandrillus*	*M. sphinx*
Maned Tamarins	*Leontideus*	
Mangabeys	*Cercocebus spp.*	
Mangabé enfumé	*Cercocebus*	*C. atys*
Mangabé huppé	*Cercocebus*	*C. albigena. C. aterrimus*

COMMON NAME	GENERIC NAME	SPECIFIC NAME
Mantelaffe	Colobus	C. guereza
Mantelmangabe	Cercocebus	C. albigena
Mantelpavian	Papio	P. hamadryas
Marikina	Saguinus	
Marimonda	Ateles	
Marmosets	Callithrix	
	Cebuella	
	Saguinus	
	Leontideus	
Maroon Leaf Monkey	Presbytis	P. rubicundus
Masked Titi	Callicebus	C. personatus
Mausmaki	Microcebus	M. murinus
Mawas	Pongo	P. pygmaeus abelii
Mbega	Colobus	C. guereza
Meerkat	Cercopithecus	
Mentawi Leaf Monkey	Presbytis	P. potenziani
Mentawischlankaffe	Presbytis	P. potenziani
Mentawi Islands Langur	Simias	S. concolor
Mias	Pongo	P. pygmaeus pygmaeus
Mico	Callithrix	C. argentata
Mico de Noche	Aotus	A. trivirgatus
Midget Tree-Shrew	Tupaia	T. minor
Milius' Dwarf Lemur	Cheirogaleus	C. major major
Milius' Katzenmaki	Cheirogaleus	C. major major
Miller's Mouse-Lemur	Microcebus	M. murinus
Milne-Edwards' Potto	Perodicticus	P. potto edwardsi
Milne-Edwards' Sifaka	Propithecus	P. diadema edwardsi
Military Monkey	Erythrocebus	E. patas
Mindanao Tarsier	Tarsius	T. syrichta carbonarius
Mitred Leaf Monkey	Presbytis	P. aygula aygula
Mohrenäffchen	Saguinus	S. tamarin
Mohrenmaki	Lemur	L. macaco
Mohrenmangabe	Cercocebus	C. atys
Moloney's Monkey	Cercopithecus	C. albogularis moloneyi
Monameerkatze	Cercopithecus	C. mona
Mona Monkey	Cercopithecus	C. mona
Mongoose Lemur	Lemur	L. mongoz
Montane Red-Tailed Guenon	Cercopithecus	C. ascanius montanus
Montane Rhesus	Macaca	M. assamensis
Monschsaffe	Pithecia	P. monachus
Mongoose Lemur	Lemur	L. mongoz
Mongozmaki	Lemur	L. mongoz
Monk Saki	Pithecia	P. monachus
Moor Macaque	Macaca	M. maurus
Mountain Guereza	Colobus	C. guereza
Mountain Gorilla	Gorilla	G.g. beringei or G.g. manyema

COMMON NAME	GENERIC NAME	SPECIFIC NAME
Moustached Tamarin	*Saguinus*	*S. mystax*
Mouse Lemur	*Microcebus*	
Moustac à queue rousse	*Cercopithecus*	*C. cephus cephus*
Mountain Tree-Shrew	*Tupaia*	*T. montana*
Moustached Monkey	*Cercopithecus*	*C. cephus*
Mountain Monkey	*Cercopithecus*	*C. lhoesti*
Martin's Monkey	*Cercopithecus*	*C. nictitans martini*
Mulatto Monkey	*Ateles*	*A. belzebuth*
Müller's Tree-shrew	*Tupaia*	*T. muelleri*
Murilemur	*Microcebus*	
Nachtaffe	*Aotus*	*A. trivirgatus*
Nacktbrustpavian	*Theropithecus*	*T. gelada*
Narvasha Vervet	*Cercopithecus*	*C. pygerythus callidus*
Nasaenaffe	*Nasalis*	*N. larvatus*
Nasique	*Nasalis*	*N. larvatus*
Negro Langur	*Presbytis*	*P. cristatus*
Needle-clawed Bushbaby	*Galago*	*G. elegantulus*
Needle-clawed Galago	*Galago*	*G. elegantulus*
Needle-nailed Galago	*Galago*	*G. elegantulus*
Negro Tamarin	*Saguinus*	*S. tamarin*
Neusaap	*Nasalis*	*N. larvatus*
Nicobar Tree-shrew	*Tupaia*	*T. nicobarica*
Night Monkey	*Aotus*	*A. trivirgatus*
Nigger Monkeys	*Lagothrix*	
Nilgiri Langur	*Presbytis*	*P. johnii*
Northern Yellow Baboon	*Papio*	*P. cynocephalus ibeanus*
Nisnas	*Erythrocebus*	*E. patas pyrrhonotus*
Northern Smooth-Tailed Tree-Shrew	*Dendrogale*	*D. murina*
Oedipomidas	*Saguinus*	
Olive Baboon	*Papio*	*P. anubis*
Olive Colobus	*Colobus*	*C. verus*
Orang-utan	*Pongo*	*P. pygmaeus*
Ouandern	*Macaca*	*M. silenus*
Ouakari	*Cacajao*	
Ouarine	*Alouatta*	
Ouistiti	*Callithrix*	
Ouistiti Melanure	*Callithrix*	*C. argentata*
Ouistiti Mignon	*Cebuella*	*C. pygmaea*
Owl Monkey	*Aotus*	*A. trivirgatus*
Owl-faced Monkey	*Aotus*	*A. trivirgatus*
Owl-faced Monkey	*Cercopithecus*	*C. hamlyni*
Pagi Islands Langur	*Simias*	*S. concolor*
Pageh-Stumpfnasenaffe	*Simias*	*S. concolor*
Painted monkey	*Pygathrix*	*P. nemaeus*
Painted Tree-Shrew	*Tupaia*	*T. picta*

COMMON NAME	GENERIC NAME	SPECIFIC NAME
Paitan Langur	*Presbytis*	*P. aygula sabanus*
Palawan Tree-shrew	*Tupaia*	*T. palawanensis*
Pallas' Tarsier	*Tarsius*	*T. spectrum*
Papion	*Papio*	
Parauacu	*Pithecia*	*P. monachus*
Patas	*Erythrocebus*	*E. patas patas*
Pavian	*Papio*	
Peaked Mangabey	*Cercocebus*	*C. aterrimus*
Pen-Tailed Tree-shrew	*Ptilocercus*	*Ptilocercus lowii*
Perrier's Sifaka	*Propithecus*	*P. diadema perrieri*
Phayre's Schlankaffe	*Presbytis*	*P. phayrei*
Philippinen-Koboldmaki	*Tarsius*	*T. syrichta*
Philippine Tarsier	*Tarsius*	*T. syrichta*
Philippinenspitzhörnchen	*Urogale*	*U. everetti*
Philippines Tree-shrew	*Urogale*	*U. everetti*
Pied Tamarin	*Saguinus*	*S. bicolor*
Pig-tailed Baboon	*Papio*	*P. ursinus*
Pig-tailed langur	*Simias*	*S. concolor*
Pig-tailed macaque	*Macaca*	*M. nemestrina*
Pinché	*Saguinus*	*S. oedipus*
Plain-headed Mangabey	*Cercocebus*	*C. galeritus*
Plumplori	*Nycticebus*	*N. coucang*
Pluto Monkey	*Cercopithecus*	*C. mitis mitis*
Pöppig's Woolly Monkey	*Lagothrix*	*L. lagothricha poeppigii*
Potto	*Perodicticus*	*P. potto*
Potto de Calabar	*Arctocebus*	*A. calabarensis*
Potto doré	*Arctocebus*	*A. calabarensis*
Preuss's Monkey	*Cercopithecus*	*C. preussi*
Proboscis Monkey	*Nasalis*	*N. larvatus*
Purple-faced Langur	*Presbytis*	*P. senex*
Putty-nosed Guenons	*Cercopithecus*	*C. nictitans*
Pygmy Chimpanzee	*Pan*	*P. paniscus*
Pygmy Slow Loris	*Nycticebus*	*N. pygmaeus*
Pygmy Gibbon	*Hylobates*	*H. klossii*
Pygmy Marmoset	*Cebuella*	*C. pygmaea*
Raffles' Tarsier	*Tarsius*	*T. bancanus*
Rat de Madagascar	*Microcebus*	*M. murinus*
Red Titi	*Callicebus*	*C. moloch cupreus*
Reed Titi	*Callicebus*	*C. moloch donacophilus*
Red Uakari	*Cacajao*	*C. rubicundus*
Reed Lemur	*Hapalemur*	*H. simus*
Retroussé-nosed monkeys	*Rhinopithecus*	
Rhesus monkey	*Macaca*	*M. mulatta*
Rhodesian chacma	*Papio*	*P. ursinus griseipes*
Sacred baboon	*Papio*	*P. hamadryas*
Rib-Faced Baboon	*Mandrillus*	*M. sphinx*

COMMON NAME	GENERIC NAME	SPECIFIC NAME
Riesengalago	*Galago*	*G. crassicaudatus*
Ringtailed Lemur	*Lemur*	*L. catta*
Ringtail Monkey	*Cebus*	*C. apella*
Roloway	*Cercopithecus*	*C. diana roloway*
Rotbauchmaki	*Lemur*	*L. rubriventer*
Roterpavian	*Papio*	*P. papio*
Roter schlankaffe	*Presbytis*	*P. melalophos*
Roter stummelaffe	*Colobus*	*C. badius*
Rothandäffchen	*Saguinus*	*S. midas*
Rotkopfmangabe	*Cercocebus*	*C. torquatus*
Rotnassenmeerkatze	*Cercopithecus*	*C. cephus*
Rotschwänziger Wieselmaki	*Lepilemur*	*L. mustelinus ruficaudatus*
Roxellane's monkey	*Rhinopithecus*	*R. roxellanae*
Ruffed lemur	*Lemur*	*L. variegatus*
Sacred Langur	*Presbytis*	*P. entellus*
Saguin	*Callithrix*	*C. jacchus*
Sajou	*Cebus*	
Saki	*Pithecia*	
Saki à nez blanc	*Chiropotes*	*C. albinasus*
Saki satan	*Chiropotes*	*C. satanas satanas*
Sakiwinki	*Pithecia*	
Samango	*Cercopithecus*	*C. albogularis labiatus*
Samat's Dwarf Lemur	*Cheirogaleus*	*C. medius samati*
Sapajous	*Cebus*	
Satansaap	*Chiropotes*	*C. satanus*
Satansaffe	*Chiropotes*	*C. satanas satanas*
Satansaffer	*Chiropotes*	*C. satanas*
Satansaffe	*Colobus*	*C. polykomos satanas*
Savannah Monkey	*Cercopithecus*	*C. aethiops, sabaeus etc.*
Scarlet-Fever Faced Monkey	*Cacajao*	*C. calvus*
Schlarlachgesicht Uakari	*Cacajao*	*C. calvus*
Schlankaffe	*Presbytis*	
Schlanklori	*Loris*	*Loris tardigradus*
Schlegel's Guenon	*Cercopithecus*	*C. neglectus*
Schmidt's Monkey	*Cercopithecus*	*C. ascanius schmidti*
Schopfhulman	*Presbytis*	*P. pileatus*
Schopfstummlaffe	*Colobus*	*C. verus*
Schnurrbartäffchen	*Saguinus*	*S. mystax*
Schwarzkopfmaki	*Lemur*	*L. macaco fulvus*
Schwarzpinseläffchen	*Callithrix*	*C. penicillata*
Schwarzköpf Uakari	*Cacajao*	*C. melanocephalus*
Schwarze Schopfmangabe	*Cercocebus*	*C. aterrimus*
Schwein's affe	*Macaca*	*M. silenus*
Schweinfurth's Chimpanzee	*Pan*	*P. troglodytes schweinfurthii*
Sclater's white-nosed monkey	*Cercopithecus*	*C. erythrotis sclateri*
Semnopithecine	*Presbytis*	

COMMON NAME	GENERIC NAME	SPECIFIC NAME
Semnopithèque	*Presbytis*	
Semnopithèque blanchâtre	*Presbytis*	*P. senex*
Senegal galago	*Galago*	*G. senegalensis*
Shan states lutong	*Presbytis*	*P. phayrei shanicus*
Short-tailed indris	*Indri*	*I. indri*
Siamangs	*Symphalangus*	
Sifakas	*Propithecus*	
Sifak	*Propithecus*	
Silberäffchen	*Callithrix*	*C. argentata*
Silbergibbon	*Hylobates*	*H. moloch*
Silky Marmoset	*Callithrix*	*C. chrysoleuca*
Silky Sifaka	*Propithecus*	*P. diadema candidus*
Silver Gibbon	*Hylobates*	*H. moloch*
Silvery Gibbon	*Hylobates*	*H. moloch*
Silver(ed) Leaf Monkey	*Presbytis*	*P. cristatus*
Silver Monkey	*Cercopithecus*	*C. mitis doggetti*
Silvery Marmoset	*Callithrix*	*C. argentata*
Singe de Nuit	*Aotus*	*A. trivirgatus*
Singe de Pocock	*Cercopithecus*	*C. nigroviridis*
Singe des paleturiers	*Cercopithecus*	*C. talapoin*
Singe vert	*Cercopithecus*	*C. sabaeus*
Slender Loris	*Loris*	*L. tardigradus*
Slender Treeshrew	*Tupaia*	*T. gracilis or T. glis longipes*
Slingeraap	*Ateles*	
Slow Loris	*Nycticebus*	*N. coucang*
Small Treeshrew	*Tupaia*	*T. javanica*
Smoky Woolly Monkey	*Lagothrix*	*L. lagothricha lagothricha*
Smooth-Tailed Treeshrew	*Dendrogale*	
Snow monkey	*Rhinopithecus*	*R. roxellanae bieti*
Snub-Nosed Lemur	*Hapalemur*	*H. simus*
Snub-Nosed Monkey	*Rhinopithecus*	
Soko-Mutu	*Pan*	*Pan troglodytes*
Sooty Mangabey	*Cercocebus*	*C. atys*
South Indian Langurs	*Presbytis*	*P. entellus priam*
Southern Smooth-tailed Tree-shrew	*Dendrogale*	*D. melanura*
Spectacled Leaf-Monkey	*Presbytis*	*P. obscurus*
Spectral Tarsier	*Tarsius*	*T. spectrum*
Spider-Monkey	*Ateles*	
Spinnenaffen	*Brachyteles*	*B. arachnoides*
Spitzhörnchen	*Tupaia*	
Spookdientje	*Tarsius*	
Sportive Lemur	*Lepilemur*	*L. mustelinus*
Spot-Nosed Guenon	*Cercopithecus*	*C. nictitans*
Springtamarin	*Callimico*	*C. goeldii*
Squirrel Monkey	*Saimiri*	

COMMON NAME	GENERIC NAME	SPECIFIC NAME
Staartloze aap	*Macaca*	
Stair's Monkey	*Cercopithecus*	*C. albogularis erythrarchus*
Stampfli's Monkey	*Cercopithecus*	*C. nictitans stampflii*
Striped Treeshrew	*Tupaia*	*T. dorsalis*
Stuhlmann's Monkey	*Cercopithecus*	*C. mitis stuhlmanni*
Stumpfnasenaffe	*Rhinopithecus*	
Stumptailed macaque	*Macaca*	*M. speciosa*
Sunda Island Gibbon	*Hylobates*	*H. moloch*
Sureili	*Presbytis*	
Sundanesicher Schlankaffe	*Presbytis*	*P. aygula*
Sunda Island Leaf Monkey	*Presbytis*	*P. aygula*
Swamp Monkey	*Cercopithecus*	*C. nigroviridis*
Sykes' Monkey	*Cercopithecus*	*C. albogularis albogularis*
Talapoin	*Cercopithecus*	*C. talapoin*
Tamarins	*Saguinus*	
Tamarinus	*Saguinus*	
Tamarin nègre	*Saguinus*	*S. tamarin*
Tamarin Rosalia	*Leontideus*	*L. rosalia*
Tana	*Tupaia*	*T. tana*
Tantalus Monkey	*Cercopithecus*	*C. aethiops tantalus*
Terrestrial Treeshrew	*Tupaia*	*T. tana*
Thicktailed Bushbaby	*Galago*	*G. crassicaudatus*
Thomas's Leaf Monkey	*Presbytis*	*P. aygula thomasi*
Thoth Baboon	*Papio*	*P. hamadryas*
Tibet Langur	*Rhinopithecus*	*R. roxellanae*
Tickell's Slow Loris	*Nycticebus*	*N. coucang tenasserimensis*
Titis	*Callicebus*	
Tonkin Monkey	*Rhinopithecus*	*R. avunculus*
Tonkin Snub-nosed Monkey	*Rhinopithecus*	*R. avunculus*
Tonkinese lutong	*Presbytis*	*P. francoisi*
Toque Monkey	*Macaca*	*M. sinica*
Totenköpfchen	*Saimiri*	
Toupaie d'Elliot	*Anathana*	*A. ellioti*
Toupaie ferrugineux	*Tupaia*	*T. glis*
Toupaie murin	*Dendrogale*	*D. murina*
Transvaal Chacma	*Papio*	*P. ursinus orientalis*
Treeshrews	*Tupaia*	
Treemouse	*Ptilocercus*	*P. lowii*
True Langur	*Presbytis*	*P. entellus*
Tschego	*Pan*	*P. troglodytes troglodytes*
Tufted Capuchin	*Cebus*	*C. apella*
Uakaris	*Cacajao*	
Unka	*Hylobates*	*H. agilis*
Van Beneden's Monkey	*Colobus*	*C. verus*
Van der Decken's Sifaka	*Propithecus*	*P. verreauxi deckeni*
Varecia	*Lemur*	*L. variegatus*

COMMON NAME	GENERIC NAME	SPECIFIC NAME
Vari	*Lemur*	*L. variegatus*
Variegated Langur	*Pygathrix*	*P. nemaeus*
Varikia	*Lemur*	*L. catta*
Verreaux's Sifaka	*Propithecus*	*P. verreauxi*
Vervet	*Cercopithecus*	*C. pygerythrus*
Volbartmeerkatze	*Cercopithecus*	*C. lhoesti*
Waiti-Feici-Wanaku	*Pithecia*	*P. pithecia*
Black-Feici-Wanaku	*Pithecia*	*P. pithecia*
Wanaku	*Pithecia*	*P. pithecia*
Wanderoo or Wandern	*Macaca*	*M. silenus*
Wau-wau	*Hylobates*	*H. moloch*
Weasel Lemur	*Lepilemur*	*L. mustelinus*
Weddell's Tamarin	*Saguinus*	*S. weddelli*
Weeper Capuchin	*Cebus*	*C. nigrivittatus*
Weisstirnschlankaffe	*Presbytis*	*P. frontatus*
Weissbartschlankaffe	*Presbytis*	*P. senex*
Weissbartstummelaffe	*Colobus*	*C. polykomos*
Weisscheitelmangabe	*Cercocebus*	*C. atys lunulatus*
Western Gorilla	*Gorilla*	*G. gorilla gorilla*
Weisshändiger Gibbon	*Hylobates*	*H. lar*
Weissnasenaffe	*Chiropotes*	*C. albinasus*
Weissnasenmeerkatze	*Cercopithecus*	*C. nictitans*
Weisspinseläffchen	*Callithrix*	*C. jacchus*
Weissschwanzguereza	*Colobus*	*C. guereza caudatus*
Western Colobus	*Colobus*	*C. guereza caudatus*
Western Gorilla	*Gorilla*	*G. g. gorilla*
Western Tarsier	*Tarsius*	*T. bancanus*
Western Yellow Baboon	*Papio*	*P. cynocephalus kindae*
White-cheeked Gibbon	*Hylobates*	*H. concolor*
White-collared Mangabey	*Cercocebus*	*C. torquatus*
White-Collared Titi	*Callicebus*	*C. torquatus*
White-Eared Marmoset	*Callithrix*	*C. aurita*
White Eyelid Monkeys	*Cercocebus*	
White Faced Capuchin	*Cebus*	*C. capucinus*
White-Footed Tamarin	*Saguinus*	*S. leucopus*
White-Fronted Capuchin	*Cebus*	*C. albifrons*
White-Fronted Leaf Monkey	*Presbytis*	*P. frontatus*
White-handed Gibbon	*Hylobates*	*H. lar*
White-Nosed Saki	*Chiropotes*	*C. albinasus*
Whiteside's Guenon	*Cercopithecus*	*C. ascanius whitesidei*
White-Tailed Guereza	*Colobus*	*C. guereza caudatus*
White Tamarin	*Saguinus*	*S. melanoleucus*
White-thighed Guereza	*Colobus*	*C. polykomos vellerosus*
White-Throated Capuchin	*Cebus*	*C. capucinus*
White-Throated Monkey	*Cercopithecus*	*C. albogularis*
White Uakari	*Cacajao*	*C. calvus*

COMMON NAME	GENERIC NAME	SPECIFIC NAME
Widow Monkey	*Callicebus*	*C. torquatus*
Wied's Tamarin	*Leontideus*	*L. chrysomelas*
Wieselmaki	*Lepilemur*	*L. mustelinus*
Wolf's Monkey	*Cercopithecus*	*C. wolfi wolfi*
Wollaffe	*Lagothrix*	
Wollmaki	*Avahi*	*A. laniger*
Woolly Lemur	*Avahi*	*A. laniger*
Woolly Monkeys	*Lagothrix*	
Woolly Spider Monkey	*Brachyteles*	*B. arachnoides*
Yellow Baboon	*Papio*	*P. cynocephalus*
Yellow Monkey	*Cercopithecus*	*C. pygerythrus johnstoni*
Yellow-Nosed Monkey	*Cercopithecus*	*C. ascanius whitesidei*
Zweifarben Tamarin	*Saguinus*	*S. bicolor*
Zwergchimpanzee	*Pan*	*P. paniscus*
Zwergmeerkatze	*Cercopithecus*	*C. talapoin*
Zwergpavian	*Papio*	*P. anubis neumanni*
Zwergseidenäffchen	*Cebuella*	
Zwerg-"Siamang"	*Hylobates*	*H. klossii*
Zotteleaffe	*Pithecia*	*P. monachus*

4. TAXONOMIC NOTES

Alouatta

Following Hall and Kelson (1959), the specific name *Alouatta palliata* Gray, 1849, for the Central American or Mantled Howler, is rejected on the grounds that it is antedated by *A. villosa* Gray, 1845.

According to Hershkovitz (1964), *A. fusca* E. Geoffroy, 1812 is the correct name for the brown howler, *A. guariba* Humboldt, 1812 being a junior homonym of *A. guariba* E. Geoffroy, 1806.

Avahi

Following Schwarz (1931, *Proc. zool. Soc. Lond.*, p. 425, footnote), the prior *Lichanotus* Illiger, 1811 has been rejected as it is a synonym of *Indri* Geoffroy and Cuvier, 1795, containing the same two species.

Cacajao

In this genus Fiedler (1956) and Hill (1960) include four species, one of which, *Cacajao roosevelti* Allen, 1914, is considered to be a synonym of *Chiropotes albinasus* (Goodwin, G. G. *Bull. Am. Mus. nat. Hist.* **102**: 262, 1953).

Callimico

The genus *Callimico*, with 36 teeth as in Cebidae, and claws on hands and feet as in Callitrichidae, has given rise to differences of opinion as to its systematic position. It is usually considered as the sole genus of subfamily Callimiconinae. Simpson (1945) placed Callimiconinae in the Cebidae, considering the dental characters to be more important taxonomically than the characters of the hands and feet; in this, he was followed by Cabrera (1957). Pocock (1925c) and Wood Jones (1929) were exponents of the opposite view. From recent anatomical studies, Hill (1957: Preface, p. viii) concludes that *Callimico* is a primitive tamarin, and therefore that Callimiconinae must be placed in the Callitrichidae, a view that is followed here.

Callithrix

Although Simpson (1945) includes *Cebuella* in the genus *Callithrix*, it is retained here as a separate genus, following Cabrera (1957). The Bare-eared Marmoset, placed in the genus *Mico* Lesson, 1840, by Hill (1957), is considered a species of *Callithrix*, *C. argentata*. See Comparative Taxonomy of the Callitrichinae below.

COMPARATIVE TAXONOMY OF THE CALLITRICHINAE (Generic Name)

	Simpson 1945	Hershkovitz 1949a	Cabrera 1957	Hill 1957	Hill 1960	Hershkovitz 1966a and b
Marmosets: ("short-tusked"; i.e. with elongated lower incisors and incisiform lower canines)						
Typical Marmosets	*Callithrix*		*Callithrix*	*Hapale*	*Hapale*	*Callithrix*
Bare-eared Marmosets	*Callithrix*		*Callithrix*	*Mico*	*Mico*	*Callithrix*
Pygmy Marmosets	*Callithrix*		*Cebuella*	*Cebuella*	*Cebuella*	—
Tamarins: ("long-tusked"; i.e. with normal lower canine-incisor relationship)						
Black-faced hairy-faced Tamarins	*Leontocebus*	*Marikina* (*Tamarin*)	*Leontocebus* (*Tamarin*)	*Tamarin*	*Tamarin*	*Saguinus*
White-moustached hairy-faced Tamarins	*Leontocebus*	*Marikina* (*Tamarin*)	*Leontocebus* (*Tamarin*)	*Tamarinus*	*Leontocebus*	*Saguinus*
Bare-faced Tamarins	*Leontocebus*	*Marikina* (*Marikina*)	*Leontocebus* (*Marikina*)	*Marikina*	*Marikina*	*Saguinus*
Crested Bare-faced Tamarins or Pinchés	*Leontocebus*	*Marikina* (*Oedipomidas*)	*Leontocebus* (*Oedipomidas*)	*Oedipomidas*	*Oedipomidas*	*Saguinus*
Golden Lion Tamarins	*Leontocebus*	*Leontocebus*	*Leontideus*	*Leontocebus*	*Leontideus*	

Cebuella

Although Simpson (1945) includes *Cebuella* in the genus *Callithrix*, it is retained here as a separate genus, following Cabrera (1957). *See* Comparative Taxonomy of the Callitrichinae, above.

N

Cercocebus

Schwarz (1928a) provides for four species of *Cercocebus* in two species-groups. Booth (1956b) shows *C. atys* to be a separate species with two races. Following Booth, we have included *C. atys* in Schwarz' *torquatus* group. For subspecies of the genus, we have followed Schwarz (*loc. cit.*). A useful discussion of the place of mangabeys in the systematics of Cercopithecinae is that of Tappen (1963).

Cercopithecus

Taxonomy of *Cercopithecus* is still largely a matter of dispute and is likely to remain so until the whole genus is reviewed from an ecological as well as a morphological viewpoint, particularly the *mitis*, *cephus* and *nictitans* groups.

We have followed Allen's (1939) revision of Schwarz' (1928b) classification for species groups, excepting for *C. talapoin*. Schwarz (*loc. cit.*) regarded all closely related groups that replace each other geographically as subspecies regardless of biological considerations; thus Schwarz' "species-groups" are in effect species containing a number of subspecies. The species-group concept is broadly equivalent to the taxon "superspecies" suggested by Rensch (1929), discussed at length by Mayr (1963) and used for *Cercopithecus* by Hill (1966b).

C. talapoin and *C. nigroviridis* we have placed in separate subgenera; this procedure follows that of Fiedler (1956) in the case of *C. nigroviridis*. Verheyen (1962) also has three subgenera including *Erythrocebus* and *Allenopithecus* but not including the talapoin monkey which is placed within the subgenus *Cercopithecus*. Rode (1938) would include *Miopithecus* as a separate genus; and Zuckerman (1933) accepts generic status for the talapoin on the important grounds of its sexual skin. Hill (1966b) places *Allenopithecus* and *Miopithecus* in separate genera.

We have followed Booth's (1955) revision of Mona monkeys in which five species, e.g. *C. mona*, *C. campbelli*, *C. wolfi*, *C. pogonias* and *C. denti* are included within the Mona group (also Hill, 1966b).

For species and subspecies we have followed Hill (1966b).

Colobus

Many modern authors place all African Colobinae in one genus (Allen, 1939, Rode, 1937, and Fiedler, 1956) following Schwarz, 1929. Schwarz (*loc. cit.*) placed all black and white *Colobus* in a single species, *polykomos*, with four sections, i.e. *polykomos*, *satanas*, *angolensis* and *abyssinicus*. Pocock (1936) did not accept Schwarz' view, preferring to regard Schwarz' "sections" as species. Booth (1954) also regards Schwarz' procedure as an oversimplification. Rode (1937) follows Schwarz except for *C. satanas* which he separates; Fiedler (1956) does likewise though he retains *satanas* in the *polykomos* species section. Allen (1939) in his Checklist of African Mammals includes all the black and white group under *C. polykomos*. Verheyen (1962), on the basis of skull morphology, recognizes two good species: *C. polykomos* and *C. abyssinicus* (=*guereza*), a procedure that is followed here. Verheyen (*loc. cit.*) treats *C. satanas* as a race of *C. polykomos*.

Pocock (1936) separates *Procolobus* Rochebrune 1887 from *Colobus*, with *verus* Van Beneden, 1838 as the type; within this genus, Pocock includes the red colobus group. Hill (1952), after studying the external and visceral anatomy of *Procolobus*, reserves this name for the olive species, *verus*. Hill points out that, if this position is accepted, the red Colobus must be separated at generic level; he recommends resuscitation of *Piliocolobus* Rochebrune 1887 for the *badius* group, a recommendation followed by Booth (1954).

Verheyen (1962), on craniological and craniometric evidence, gives *Procolobus* and *Piliocolobus* subgeneric status within the genus *Colobus*, a procedure that is followed here.

The name, *Colobus abyssinicus* Oken, 1816, for the Abyssinian Colobus, is not available (International Commission on Zoological Nomenclature, Opinion 417, 1956). The next available name, *Colobus guereza* Rüppell, 1835, is therefore employed.

Cynopithecus

At present only a tentative arrangement is possible with regard to the Celebes monkeys. Büttikofer (1917), although placing all the Celebes monkeys in the genus *Cynopithecus*, divides them into two distinct groups: "Macaques" (5 species), and "Crested Macaques" (3 species). In his "Crested Macaques" group, he includes *C. niger* Desmarest, 1822, *C. nigrescens* Temminck, 1849 and *C. hecki* Matschie, 1901. Laurie and Hill (1954) consider these to be synonymous; following their checklist, *Cynopithecus* is here retained as a separate genus with one species *C. niger*.

Galago

Schwarz (1931a) recognized two genera, *Galago* and *Euoticus*, within the Galaginae. Hill (1953) prefers to remove *G. demidovii* from *Galago* and place it in a separate genus *Galagoides* A. Smith, 1833, principally on account of its distinctive placentation (Gérard, 1929, 1931 and 1932; *but see* J. P. Hill, 1965).

Fiedler (1956) has relegated both *Euoticus* and *Galagoides* to subgenera of *Galago*, a procedure followed here on the grounds, as far as *Euoticus* is concerned, of Hayman's (1937) observation that *G. senegalensis inustus* Schwarz, 1930 also presents the ungual specializations of *Euoticus* and should be placed in this genus. *Inustus*, it would appear, is the link which indicates the true taxonomic affinities of *Galago* and *Euoticus*. It does not appear to us that *Galagoides* is sufficiently distinct from *Galago* or *Euoticus* to be separated generically. For subspecies, we have followed Allen (1939) and Hill (1953).

Gorilla

The accepted classification of gorillas (Coolidge, 1929) divides the species into two subspecies: *G. g. gorilla* (western or lowland gorillas) and *G. g. beringei* eastern or mountain). Except that some authors prefer to regard these two as full species, the Coolidge revision is generally employed today. However, not only did Haddow and Ross (1951) point out irregularities in Coolidge's methods, but recently the realization has been growing that not all eastern gorillas live on mountains.

A recent revision (Groves, 1966) recognizes the eastern lowland gorillas as forming a third subspecies (*G. g. manyema* Rothschild, 1908) equidistant from the other two; distinguishing characters are to be found in both skull and postcranial skeleton. The gorillas of the Mitumba mountains of the eastern Congo are somewhat intermediate between the subspecies *manyema* and *G. g. beringei* of the Virunga Volcanoes—in skull morphology as well as in altitude—but are morphologically nearer to the former, probably because of genetic continuity.

Hylobates

Many authors, including Miller (1933), Ellerman and Morrison-Scott (1951) and Simonetta (1957), place all the Gibbons and the Siamang in one genus with four subgenera. Following Schultz (1930 and 1933b), *Symphalangus* is here given generic status, but the subgenera *Brachitanytes* (Schultz, 1932) and *Nomascus* (Miller, 1933) are not employed.

Although Schultz (1933b) gives *Hylobates pileatus* and *Hylobates leucogenys* specific status, they are here given only subspecific rank, following Ellerman and Morrison-Scott (1951), Delacour (1951), and Simonetta (1957). The latter author makes the Sunda Island Gibbon (*H. moloch*) conspecific with *H. lar*, following Sody (1949).

Lagothrix

On his travels in South America, Humboldt saw dark-brown furry skins used as saddle-cloths by the Peruvians for their mules. On the basis of these skins he described (1812) a new species of Howler monkey which he named *Simia flavicauda*. Thomas (1927a) described a newly discovered monkey from Peru as *Lagothrix* (*Oreonax*) *hendeei*. It was very similar to *Simia flavicauda* Humboldt, particularly in the yellow-striped prehensile tail, but Thomas in a further paper (1927b) maintained that the two were taxonomically distinct. Cabrera (1957) considered *Simia flavicauda* Humboldt to be indeterminable. Fooden's arguments in favour of *L. hendeei* Thomas and *S. flavicauda* Humboldt being identical are set forth on pp. 242 and 243 of his paper "A revision of the woolly monkeys (Genus *Lagothrix*)" (*J. Mammal*. **44**: 213–247, 1963).

Lemur

Following Schwarz (1936) and Petter (1962c), *Lemur fulvus* is accepted as conspecific with *L. macaco* in view of their many similarities of structure and behaviour and, more significantly, of the existence of intermediate forms (*L. fulvus flavifrons* and *L. fulvus sanfordi*) as discussed by Petter (1965). *L. macaco* Linnaeus, 1766 has priority over *L. fulvus* E. Geoffroy, 1812.

Petter (1962c), following Gray (1863), proposes to separate *L. variegatus* generically from *Lemur* and place it in a monotypic genus *Varecia*. It does not appear to us that there is sufficient evidence at this time to justify such a step—although we recognize that it may well become necessary.

Lepilemur

The genus *Lepilemur* has recently been reviewed by Petter (1960) who regards it as consisting of a single species, *Lepilemur mustelinus* I. Geoffroy, 1851, with five subspecies.

He further suggests (1965) that from the point of view of ecology and ethology this genus differs profoundly from the remaining members of the Lemurinae. Morphologically, as Mivart (1873) was the first to observe, many characters of the vertebral column, thorax and hand, link this genus with the Indriidae, with which family *Lepilemur* shares its locomotor characteristics. The similarity of locomotor behaviour is reflected in similarity of limb and hand proportions. Davies and Hill (1954a) comment on the differences in gastric morphology of *Lepilemur* from that of other Lemurinae, indicating that, in certain features, it resembles that of *Propithecus* and other primate leaf-eaters; at the same time Davies and Hill point out the many similarities of the alimentary system with other Lemurinae. There seems little doubt in view of the wide dissimilarity in the dentition (*inter alia*) that this affinity is a matter of parallelism arising in two separate groups having a common ancestral stock in which, as it now seems possible (Napier and Walker—in press), vertical clinging and leaping was the typical mode of locomotion. The authors, in support of Petter's recommendation, suggest that *Lepilemur* be placed in a separate subfamily of Lemuridae, the Lepilemurinae.

Macaca

Pending the comprehensive revision of the genus by Fooden, the checklists of Allen (1939), Chasen (1940), Ellerman and Morrison-Scott (1951) and Laurie and Hill (1954) are combined here; an additional subspecies of *M. maurus* (*ochreata* Ogilby, 1840) is included in the systematic list (Hooijer, 1950). The Philippines macaques recognized by Lawrence (1939): *M. mindora* Hollister, 1913, and by Sanborn (1952): *M. philippinensis philippinensis* Geoffroy, 1843 and *M. philippinensis mindanensis* Mearns, 1905, are here considered as subspecies of *M. fascicularis*.

Macaca fascicularis Raffles, 1821 replaces *M. irus* F. Cuvier, 1818 as the earliest name properly proposed for the crab-eating macaque (Miller, 1942, Fooden, 1964a). The name, *Macaca speciosa* I. Geoffroy, 1826, used in the text for the stumptailed macaque, must in future be replaced by *Macaca arctoides* I. Geoffroy, 1831 (*see* Fooden, 1967).

In spite of Fooden's proposition (1964a) that the crab-eating macaque, *M. fascicularis*, and the rhesus macaque, *M. mulatta*, should be considered conspecific, they are here retained as separate species.

Mandrillus

M. poensis Zukowsky, 1922, is a subspecies of *M. leucophaeus* from Fernando Póo, distinguished by its small size. Tappen (1960) proposed that it should be granted specific rank.

M. insularis Zukowsky, 1925 (a Mandrill), was also said to be from Fernando Póo, but this is probably a mistaken locality.

Nycticebus

A new species, *N. intermedius*, based on an adult ♀ from Hoa Binh, North Vietnam, has been described by Tien (1960); it is intermediate in size between *N. coucang* and *N. pygmaeus* (Head and body length: 230 mm 1 ♀).

Pan

Validation of generic name: The name *Pan* was first published by Oken in "*Lehrbuch der Naturgeschichte*" Vol. 3, 1816, a work rejected by the International Commission on Zoological Nomenclature on nomenclatorial grounds in Opinion 417, 1956. The next available name is *Chimpansee* Voigt, 1831 (Hershkovitz, 1949b). Ruling 3 of Opinion 417 invited zoologists to submit applications for the validation, under the plenary powers of the Commission, of any of Oken's names, if, in their opinion, rejection would lead to instability or confusion in nomenclature. Application for the validation of *Pan* was made in 1950 and revised in 1965. Consequently the generic name for the chimpanzee is at present *sub judice* and current usage (*Pan* Oken, 1816) is therefore continued here. (Article 80, *International Code of Zoological Nomenclature*, 1964.)

Races of Chimpanzee: A fourth race of *P. troglodytes*, *P. t. calvus* du Chaillu, 1860, is some-
times recognized. The common names for *P. t. calvus* are the Choga, the Black-faced
Chimpanzee and the Kooloo-kamba. This form is here regarded as synonymous with
P. t. troglodytes.

The distinguishing features of *P. t. calvus* are a black face, black hands and feet, and a
gorilla-like external nose resembling a "squashed tomato" (L. G. Smith—private communication). Its distribution is said to be from the Cameroons south to Gabon. Rode (1936) points
out that with age the pigmentation of the face of *P. t. troglodytes* "... devient plus foncée et
finalement noire". He also observes that among adult chimpanzees in the wild pigmentation
of the face is more marked than it is in captivity in temperate climatic zones, which may
explain why Kooloo-kambas appear to be more common in Africa than in European Zoos!

The Bonobo or pygmy chimpanzee: the Bonobo was first described as a subspecies of
P. troglodytes by Schwarz (1929). Its taxonomic position was discussed by Coolidge (1933b)
and by Schouteden (1931). In 1954, Tratz and Heck placed it in a separate genus, *Bonobo*.
Here, the authors have followed Allen (1939) in giving the Bonobo full species rank.

Papio

Müller's description of *Papio* (1776) referred to a mandrill (Hopwood, 1947). Unless
therefore mandrills are included in the genus (*see* Fiedler, 1956) the taxon is invalid for typical
baboons and *Chaeropithecus* Gervais, 1839 becomes the valid name; this nomenclature is
followed by Ellerman, Morrison-Scott and Hayman (1953). *Papio* Erxleben, 1777, though
strictly invalid, is here retained in the interests of stability. In the light of the most recent
revision (Jolly, 1964), *P. hamadryas* is placed in the genus *Papio* but in a separate species
group. We regard, as the correct name for the olive baboon, *Papio anubis* Lesson, 1827
[=*P. doguera*] (Hill, 1959; Hershkovitz, 1960), and for the Chacma baboon, *Papio ursinus*
Kerr, 1792 [=*P. comatus*].

Presbytis

Following Ellerman and Morrison-Scott, 1951, and Chasen, 1940, the Asiatic Colobinae
are placed in five genera: *Rhinopithecus*, *Pygathrix*, *Nasalis*, *Simias* and *Presbytis*: the latter is
divided into four species groups which have sometimes been given generic status (*see* Hill,
1939a; Pocock, 1939; Washburn, 1944, and Hooijer, 1962) as follows:

Presbytis aygula group [=*Presbytis* Eschscholtz, 1821]	4 species
Presbytis entellus group [=*Semnopithecus* Desmarest, 1822]	1 species
Presbytis senex group [=*Kasi* Reichenbach, 1862]	2 species
Presbytis cristatus group [=*Trachypithecus* Reichenbach, 1862]	7 species.

A possible eighth species of the *P. cristatus* group, *P. leucocephalus*, has been described by
Pang-Chieh (1957); limited range in Fusui country (Funan, S. Kwangsi). *See also* Jarvis (1966).

Saguinus

Leontocebus Wagner, 1840, is rejected as the valid name for the tamarins (other than the
Golden Lion Tamarin, *Leontideus rosalia* Linnaeus, 1766) because it is antedated by *Saguinus*
Hoffmannsegg, 1807. Moreover, the retention of *Leontocebus* for this group may cause

confusion; since 1912, when Miller (*U.S. nat. Mus. Bull.* **79**: 380) selected as the type species *Midas leoninus* Geoffroy, 1812 (=*Simia leonina* Humboldt, 1812 (*Rec. Obs. Zool.*, p. 14, plate 5), *Leontocebus* has been considered to be allied to or identical with *Leontideus rosalia*, the Golden Lion Tamarin. Humboldt's figure, Plate 5, gives the impression of a golden-maned tamarin. However, in 1956 Cabrera drew attention to the discrepancies between the drawing (by an artist who never saw the animal) and Humboldt's description; he showed that Humboldt's animal was a white-moustached tamarin and *not* a maned tamarin. For the maned tamarins of the *rosalia* type, Cabrera proposed a new genus name *Leontideus* (Type species: *Simia rosalia* Linnaeus, 1766). Thus, the name *Leontocebus*, for many years associated with a maned tamarin, now means every other type of tamarin but that one, i.e. the hairy-faced tamarins (with or without white moustache) = *Saguinus* (*Saguinus*); the bare-faced tamarins = *Saguinus* (*Marikina*); and the crested bare-faced tamarins or Pinchés = *Saguinus* (*Oedipomidas*).

The above arrangement of the tamarins is that of Hershkovitz (1949a) and Cabrera (1957); Hershkovitz (1966a) uses species groups, rather than subgenera, to indicate the groupings of the different forms of the genus. *See* Comparative Taxonomy of the Callitrichinae, p. 371.

Saimiri

Cabrera (1957) considered that, pending a conscientious revision of the genus, the numerous species which have been described must be reduced to two, *S. sciureus* (from South America) and *S. oerstedii* (from Central America), and that even the latter is possibly only a subspecies of the former. Cabrera's arrangement is followed here.

Hill (1960), following Cruz Lima (1945) recognizes four South American species; for descriptions and localities, *see* Hill (1960, 1965).

As *Saimiri* is in extensive use as a laboratory animal, basic work on the taxonomy of the genus is overdue (Hershkovitz, 1965).

Symphalangus

A. H. Schultz, in his paper "Observations on the growth, classification and evolutionary specialization of Gibbons and Siamangs" (*Hum. Biol.* **5**: 212–255, 385–428, 1933), places *Symphalangus*, on account of its many distinctive morphological characters, in a separate genus, an arrangement which is followed here.

Tupaia

For the classification of the Tupaiinae the authors have followed Lyon (1913) and Simpson (1945) in retaining four genera (*Tupaia, Anathana, Dendrogale* and *Urogale*) within the subfamily. They feel, however, that in the light of modern taxonomic trends a fresh look at the Tupaiinae will lead to a reduction in the number of genera. Fiedler (1956) already includes *Anathana* in the genus *Tupaia*.

Lyonogale Conisbee, 1953 [=*Tana* Lyon, 1913] has been retained as a subgenus of *Tupaia*, following Medway, 1965. *Lyonogale* was considered by Chasen and Kloss (1931) and Davis (1962) to be inseparable from *Tupaia*, a view accepted by Fiedler (1956).

The subgeneric name *Lyonogale* is substituted for the preoccupied *Tana* Lyon, 1913 (*see* Conisbee, 1953).

Habitats of Primates

1. GEOGRAPHICAL RANGE

With very few exceptions, the vast majority of living primates are restricted to the tropics. In this region, their main habitats are the forests and the savannahs between the latitudes 25° N and 30° S. As a rule, primates do not extend into temperate zones, in fact the macaques (and possibly *Rhinopithecus*) are the only primates to have done so (Fig. 4). In China, macaques (*M. mulatta*) are found near Pekin although it may well be that they were introduced there. In Japan, the Japanese macaque (*M. fuscata*) reaches as far north as 41° on the island of Honshu. Limiting factors to the northerly migration of primates in Asia are concerned partly with temperatures but particularly with food-availability (Jolly, 1964). The higher the latitude, the more restricted becomes the growing season and the shorter the daylight period in winter. The combination of these two factors would make it extremely difficult for monkeys to find sufficient food during the daylight hours. African primates seem to be able to adapt well to cold conditions so that low temperatures alone would not be expected to limit their range. New World monkeys on the other hand appear to be extremely sensitive to temperatures much below 70° F.

The main blocks of primate distribution are (1) African (including Madagascan), (2) South-east Asian and (3) South American. Whereas S. American stocks have been independent since the Eocene, the African and Asian stocks are closely related and share members of four sub-families, i.e. Colobinae, Cercopithecinae, Lorisinae and Ponginae. The only common genus to the African and South-east Asian blocks is *Macaca*.

Apart from the main primate blocks there are a number of islands on which primates are found today; here they live as natural populations, descendants of forms introduced, in the first place, by man. In the West Indies, on the islands of St. Kitts and Grenada, are populations of *Cercopithecus sabaeus* and *Cercopithecus mona* respectively; *Macaca fascicularis* [= *irus*] are to be found on the island of Mauritius. The only monkeys resident on the continent of Europe are the Barbary "apes" of Gibraltar (*M. sylvana*) introduced sometime prior to 1704 when the British took over. In a somewhat different category, are the research islands such as Barro Colorado in the Panama Canal and Cayo Santiago in the Caribbean. In the former live a number of New World genera including howlers, spider monkeys and capuchins; on Cayo Santiago there is a thriving study colony of *Macaca mulatta* introduced some 25 years ago.

2. ECOLOGY IN AFRICA

In Africa, bordering the savannah belt to the north and south, and constituting formidable ecological barriers to primate migration, are belts of arid grasslands, desert and scrub. Some of the savannah-living African primates, such as the baboons, range beyond the limits of the savannah belt into sub-desert regions.

The vegetational zonation in Central Africa is seen in Fig. 6, which represents a sample strip of West Central Africa some 1300 miles in length, extending from the Congo (Brazzaville) in the south on the Equator, northwards through the Ubangi-Shari, Chad and ending south

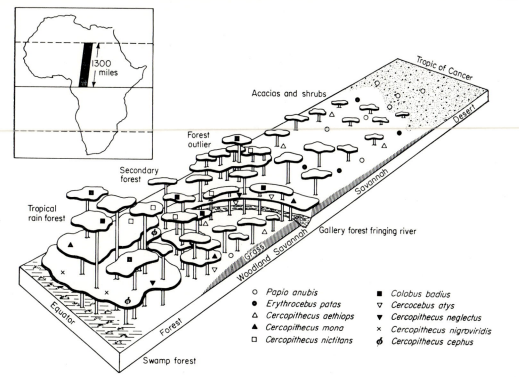

FIG. 6. Vegetational zones in sample strip 1300 miles in length from Congo to Tibesti plateau showing resident primates

of Tibesti. Altitudinal differences are not considered in this strip which, in fact, represents a plateau varying between 1000 and 2500 feet above sea level. The main vegetational zones lie in an east–west direction roughly parallel to the Equator, the width of each zone being determined by local climatic factors of rainfall and temperature. Generally speaking rainfall decreases from south to north. In the equatorial region the temperature is high all the year round and the rainfall is continuous showing two maxima in May–June and September–October. These conditions change at about 5° N to a climate where temperatures are even higher at the maximal point of the annual range which occurs in March; about 40 inches of rain fall in the summer, but the winters are dry. At 15° N grassland begins to give way to shrub and finally to desert where temperatures show marked seasonal fluctuations and rainfall is practically nil. In vegetational terms the main succession is: (1) tropical rain forest: (2) savannah: (3) steppe: (4) desert. (Table I.)

TYPE 1. TROPICAL RAIN FOREST BIOME

The chief characteristic is a dense evergreen closed canopy with abundance of thick-stemmed lianes and herbaceous epiphytes. Many of the trees bear buttress roots. There is an absence of grasses on the forest floor which supports ill-defined herb and shrub strata. The forest canopy is itself stratified into three more or less well-defined storeys, the highest storey extending up to 150 feet or more (Richards, 1957). There are a number of sub-types (Table I) of tropical rain forest including mangrove swamp, swamp forest, secondary forest and montane forest.

Primate Fauna

There are two major habitats within a tropical rain forest and a number of minor ones. The major habitats are the forest floor and the canopy (here used to indicate all the crowns of trees *above* the shrub layer). The principal primate inhabitants of the floor in West Central Africa are *Mandrillus*, *Pan* and *Gorilla gorilla*; in the canopy a variety of *Cercopithecus*, *Colobus* and *Cercocebus* are found. The prosimians are represented by *Galago*, *G. (Euoticus)*, *Perodicticus* and *Arctocebus*.

TYPE 2. SAVANNAH BIOME

Salient features of savannah are a mixture of grassland and trees. The two main sub-types are Woodland Savannah and Open Savannah. Tall grasses, which show a seasonal cycle terminated by burning, are the dominant vegetation of the Woodland Savannah. Open savannah has widely spaced flat-topped trees, 20–30 ft high, acacias (fever trees, umbrella trees) and boababs being frequent varieties. Common sub-types in savannah country are *gallery forests* bordering streams and *forest outliers*; both vegetational types are closely related to rain forest morphologically and occur where soil conditions are favourable, e.g. along banks of rivers or streams and in moist, well-drained valleys.

Primate Fauna

In the savannah of the Central African Republic the more terrestrial of the guenons are found, particularly the *Cercopithecus aethiops* group. Among the fully terrestrial forms *Papio* and *Erythrocebus* abound. In gallery forests and rain forest outliers *Colobus*, *Cercopithecus* and *Cercocebus* (especially *C. galeritus* and *C. atys*) are found; also *Galago*.

TYPE 3. STEPPE BIOME

This zone which bears a variety of regional synonyms (e.g. Thornland in French Equatorial Africa) forms a transition between savannah and desert. Low, widely-spaced acacias and other spiny trees are characteristic of this belt, where they form sporadic closed canopy thickets. Grass is in tussocks and rather sparse. The zone gradually deteriorates north of Lake Chad into sub-desert.

Primate Fauna

Only the thoroughly terrestrial genera, such as *Papio*, *Erythrocebus* and (more rarely) the grivets *C. aethiops*, inhabit the zone.

TYPE 4. DESERT BIOME

In the sub-Saharan zone of Chad the only vegetation consists of sparse dwarf shrubs whose life cycle occupies only a few weeks following the short, irregular rainy season. Further north there is barren desert with a rocky sub-stratum and a sandy soil; an occasional wadi relieves the monotony which, by virtue of subterranean water, can support sparse, perennial shrubs.

TABLE I

A Summary of the Vegetational Zones and Related Primate Fauna of Sub-Saharan Africa

	Vegetation zone	Sub-type	Vegetation and climate	Primate genera
Type I	Tropical rain forest Alternative terms: Moist forest Lowland rain forest Tropical high forest Forêt dense		3 strata constituting an open and closed canopy with emergents Temp.—steady with narrow range Rainfall—high Rel. humidity—high	Cercopithecus Colobus Pan Gorilla Cercocebus Mandrillus Perodicticus Galago Arctocebus
		Mangrove	Specialized mangroves lining estuaries and creeks to tidal limits	
		Secondary forest	Tropical rain forest that has been cultivated and subsequently abandoned	
		Swamp forest	Similar but more open and irregular in structure	
		Montane rain forest Alternative terms: Highland forest Cloud forest	3000 ft up to 8000 ft (depending on climatic conditions). Varies from evergreen forest to woodland with tree fern and bamboo thickets. Lianes	Pan Gorilla Cercopithecus Colobus Papio
		Bamboo forest	7000 ft–10,000 ft. Stands of bamboo from 20–35 ft. Ground cover sparse	
Type II	Savannah Alternative terms: Sour veldt (S.Af.) High grass (E.Af.)	Woodland	Trees 20 ft–50 ft high especially *Isoberlinia* Grass 6 ft–15 ft high	Cercopithecus (esp. C. aethiops) Erythrocebus Colobus Papio Cercocebus Galago
		Open savannah	Trees widely spaced Grass 6 ft–15 ft high	
		Forest outliers Alternative terms: Bowl forest Kurmi Copses	Islands of tropical rain forest. Occurs in hollows and ravines where edaphic conditions are favourable	
		Gallery forest Alternative terms: Riverine forest Fringing forest	Tropical rain forest on river banks	
Type III	Steppe Alternative terms: Thornland Sweet veldt (S.Af.) Short grass (E.Af.) Desert grass Orchard steppe	Wooded steppe	Open and closed woodlands or thickets. *Acacia* and *Commiphora* Short grasses	Cercopithecus (esp. C. aethiops) Erythrocebus Papio

Primate Fauna

Papio may range occasionally into this region.

 While this account refers directly to the sample strip inset in Fig. 6, the succession is typical of many regions in Africa, north and south of the Equator. Table I includes the primate fauna inhabiting the strip, but also lists forms found in similar vegetational zones elsewhere in Africa, including montane and bamboo forest which does not appear on the strip.

<h1 style="text-align:center">3. MINOR HABITATS OF PRIMATES
AND FOREST STRATIFICATION</h1>

It has become apparent in recent years that in order to assess the taxonomic inter-relationships of monkey populations, a vertical dimension must be added to the more familiar two-dimensional distribution or "range" maps. The forest canopy consists of several horizontal strata that provide a number of different ecological niches for tree-living fauna. This principle of stratification (a concept which recalls Humboldt's description of the Amazonian canopy as "a forest above a forest") has been known among botanists and foresters for some time, and

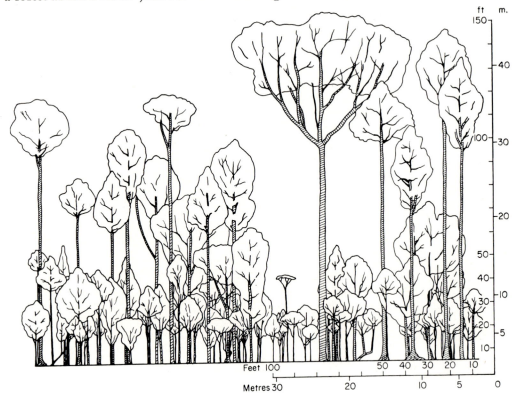

FIG. 7. Profile diagram of primary rain forest (Shasha Forest Reserve, Nigeria), showing stratification of canopy. Strip is 200 ft (6 m) long and 25 ft (7·6 m) wide. (From Richards, 1957, "Tropical Rain Forest", Cambridge University Press).

the existence of discrete storeys in tropical rain forest has been, and still is, a matter of considerable dispute. The situation has been largely resolved in certain areas by the technique of constructing profile diagrams of narrow sample strips of specially cleared forest (Fig. 7). Studies of stratification have been carried out in Nigeria, on the Ivory Coast, in Gabon, in Uganda, in South America and in the East Indies; although the edaphic conditions and the botanical nature of the tree and plant communities vary greatly from place to place, the principle of stratification appears to hold true.

Three strata are recognized. From below upwards, they consist of (1) understorey, 25–50 ft high; (2) middle storey, 50–120 ft high; (3) upper storey, 120–150 ft high.

The understorey consists of trees whose crowns, varying about a mean, form a completely *closed canopy*, the whole stratum being closely bound by woody creepers into a solid mass of foliage. The middle storey is an irregular layer of trees which occasionally form a closed canopy but whose crowns are usually in lateral contact. The upper storey consists of trees with broad umbrella-like crowns that form a discontinuous layer. In addition, giant trees (emergents) that reach as high as 200 ft are occasionally found. The lowest branches of one layer usually make contact with the highest branches of the layer below, so that the whole canopy constitutes a vertical continuum.

The principle of stratification of the tropical rain forest has opened a new field of study for primatologists that should lead to clarification of many taxonomic problems. In addition, this concept promises rich rewards for the study of locomotor behaviour and phylogeny.

TABLE II

Vertical Range of Monkeys in Forest of S.W. Ghana (Booth, A. H., 1956)

| | Sleeping | | | Travelling | | | | Feeding | | | | Food | |
	Upper	Middle	Lower	Upper	Middle	Lower	Ground	Upper	Middle	Lower	Ground	Fruit	Leaves
Colobus badius	+	–	–	+ +	+	–	–	+ +	+	(+)	–	–	+
Colobus polykomos	+	+	–	+	+	–	–	(+)	+	+	–	–	+
Colobus verus	–	+	+	–	+	+	–	–	(+)	+	–	–	+
Cercopithecus diana	+	+	–	+	+	–	–	+	+	(+)	–	+	–
Cercopithecus campbelli	–	+	(+)	(+)	+	+	(+)	–	+	+	–	+	–
Cercopithecus petaurista	–	+	+	–	+	+ +	(+)	–	(+)	+ +	–	+	+
Cercocebus atys	–	+	+	–	+	+	+ +	–	–	–	+	+	–

The principal implications of stratification *vis-à-vis* locomotor adaptations of primates are as follows:

(1) The presence or absence of gaps between crowns of adjacent trees in relation to leaping and brachiating activities during travel.

(2) The pattern of distribution and density of primate food items such as leaves, fruit and flowers, within the crowns of feeding-trees, in relation to the climbing behaviour and prehensile adaptations of the limbs of arboreally living primates.

With these implications in mind it is desirable that an attempt should be made to express stratification in terms that are more meaningful for primate biology than the A, B, C strata (or their synonyms) of botanical usage. It is suggested that for this purpose it is probably sufficient to divide the canopy simply into "open" and "closed" layers. The upper storey is invariably a discontinuous stratum whose component trees have umbrella-shaped crowns (wider than deep) arising from a candelabra arrangement of distal branches (Richards, 1957). The maximum density of fruit and leaves thus tends to be sited peripherally; in order to reach and feed on the leaves, the animal is forced to move far out from the trunk into a milieu that is largely composed of small flexible branches; in such a setting the suspensory activities of the hands, feet and the balancing or suspensory activities of the tail (particularly in some New World monkeys) are called into play. The lower or under-storey invariably forms a continuous stratum with smaller crowns that are deeper than they are wide; at this level the leaves are more homogeneously distributed throughout the crown and feeding can be carried out largely in a dense milieu of rigid branches interlaced with lianes. This setting places, proportionately, a less intense demand on prehensility of extremities.

From the point of view of primate locomotion it would appear that animals that under experimental conditions select a small branch setting show a larger brachiation or arm-swinging component in their locomotor behaviour (Avis, 1962). Field observation, in addition, indicates that the black and white colobus monkeys (*Colobus polykomos* and *C. guereza*) which tend to be open canopy dwellers (Booth, 1957) cross wide gaps by leaping and swinging by the arms; this mode of locomotion of these animals has been termed semibrachiation (Napier, 1963). There is, thus, some evidence that the essential characteristics of the forest canopy for primate ecology are, firstly, a matter of *contiguity* of crowns; and secondly, of crown *shape* and *leaf density*; it would seem likely that both these factors may be correlated with stratification.

The trees of the middle storey of the canopy are characteristically in lateral contact (Richards, 1957) although there are frequently gaps between the crowns. The crowns themselves may be of either the upper or lower storey ("A" or "C" stratum) type. Therefore, whether the middle storey is to be grouped with the upper or lower storey for the purpose of the present classification, is somewhat equivocal. From the relatively few observations on stratification of living primate population, it would appear on the whole that there are more primate species which are common to both middle and lower storeys than there are species common to middle and upper storeys. (Booth, 1955, 1956, 1957; Haddow, 1952, Sanderson, 1940). In view of this it would seem more appropriate to place the middle storey with the lower storey in the following classification:

TABLE III

| Open canopy | Crowns discontinuous | Broad, umbrella shaped crowns, with predominantly peripheral foliage | Upper storey |
| Closed canopy | Crowns in lateral contact or overlapping | Small narrow crowns with more homogeneously distributed foliage | Lower storey
Middle storey |

It is unnecessary to emphasize the provisional nature of this classification and the hypotheses on which it is based, but it may provide a useful starting point for further study of the ecology of arboreal primates. Many factors of primate behaviour and morphology, other than those mentioned, would have to be considered, particularly body size in relation to branch size and dietary preferences in relation to the preferred stratum.

Limbs and Locomotion

1. LOCOMOTION IN PRIMATES

It might appear from the classification of locomotor patterns (Table I) that primates fall into a number of discrete behavioural categories such as Vertical Clinging, Brachiation and so on, and that field or captivity observations of a particular species would serve to pinpoint their precise category. This is far from the truth. Locomotor differences between groups of

TABLE I

Locomotor Classification

Category	Sub-type	Activity	Primate genera
1. Vertical Clinging and Leaping		Leaping in trees and hopping on the ground.	*Avahi, Galago, Hapalemur, Lepilemur, Propithecus, Indri, Tarsius*
2. Quadrupedalism	(i) Slow climbing type.	Cautious climbing—no leaping or branch running.	*Arctocebus, Loris, Nycticebus, Perodicticus*
	(ii) Branch running and walking type.	Climbing, springing, branch running and jumping.	*Aotus, Cacajao, Callicebus, Callimico, Callithrix, Cebuella, Cebus, Cercopithecus, Cheirogaleus, Chiropotes, Lemur, Leontideus, Phaner, Pithecia, Saguinus, Saimiri, Tupaia*
	(iii) Ground running and walking type.	Climbing, ground running.	*Macaca, Mandrillus, Papio, Theropithecus, Erythrocebus*
	(iv) New World semi-brachiation type.	Arm-swinging with use of prehensile tail; little leaping.	*Alouatta, Ateles, Brachyteles, Lagothrix*
	(v) Old World semi-brachiation type.	Arm-swinging and leaping.	*Colobus, Nasalis, Presbytis, Pygathrix, Rhinopithecus, Simias*
3. Brachiation	(i) True brachiation.	Gibbon type of brachiation.	*Hylobates, Symphalangus*
	(ii) Modified brachiation.	Chimpanzee and orang-utan type of brachiation.	*Gorilla, Pan, Pongo*
4. Bipedalism		Striding.	*Homo*

primates are quantitative rather than qualitative. The differences lie principally in the degree to which the forelimbs and the hindlimbs are used to jump, swing, climb or run, and the frequency with which each type of behaviour is employed by a particular species in different ecological situations.

Any classification within a relatively homogeneous group showing continuous variation, inevitably leads to an over-simplification as a result of the need to compromise. Classifications however are desirable to provide a perspective, a basis for discussion and a framework on which further investigations can be built.

BIOMECHANICAL CLASSIFICATIONS

Primates are a fairly homogeneous group in respect of the anatomy of the limb skeleton, particularly of the hindlimb. The similarity of hindlimb structure is apparent both osteologically and osteometrically. A series of femora from a wide variety of species show, apart from allometric considerations, a remarkable similarity of form. Measurements of lower limb proportions, (the Crural Index for example) show very little variation between taxa or between functional locomotors groups and are therefore of extremely limited value as diagnostic indices. The hindlimbs of primates are primarily supporting structures and the anatomy of the limbs is in accordance with biomechanical requirements for resisting the compression forces exerted by the ground during walking and running. All primates walk and therefore they all possess the same basic structural characters. Variation in these characters will depend on how often and under what circumstances they use their hindlimbs for walking and for other purposes. For example the hindlimbs of chimpanzees and orangs, are adapted for suspension, having a notably free range of movement, particularly at the hip and foot joints. This character and the special prehensile adaptations of their feet permit them to scramble and climb among slender branches of trees supporting the body weight at very awkward angles. Chimpanzees and orangs very often use their hindlimbs alone to suspend the body. On the ground however chimpanzees walk quadrupedally and even bipedally, their legs in this situation supporting the body from below. Other primates such as the quadrupedal howlers, spider monkeys and woolly monkeys of South America, also occasionally use their hindlimbs for suspension; so also do galagos and pottos. In fact, it would be true to say that the majority of primates can, and sometimes do, suspend themselves by their feet. Since all primates support themselves on the hindlimbs and many suspend themselves in this manner, a classification of locomotion simply in terms of the supporting and suspending functions of the hindlimbs is unlikely to be very satisfactory.

The situation with regard to the forelimbs is very similar. The limbs are used for both support and suspension, and are therefore subject to both compression and tensile forces. All primates, except gibbons and man, walk quadrupedally using their forelimbs as props. Equally all primates, with again few exceptions, use the arms to suspend the body from above. The most striking examples of arm-swinging primates are of the gibbons and the siamangs; in certain ecological situations these primates use arm-suspension exclusively. The New World spider and woolly monkeys and some of the African and Asian Colobinae frequently employ arm-suspension as a means of locomotion. Other primates such as the guenons and the macaques only occasionally use this method of locomotion. Arm-suspension in the primates therefore comprises a *spectrum* of activity from the habitual to the occasional and can not be used very meaningfully, as it stands, as a means of classifying locomotion. However it is possible using the same criteria of suspension and support to grade the *degree* of these activities as demonstrated by different groups of primates; this involves an arbitrary segmentation of a continuous spectrum of activity as shown in Table II. Such a method can help to differentiate the function in certain groups but it contributes little to classification of primate locomotion as a whole.

TABLE II

Analysis of Limb Function in Anthropoidea

| | Forelimb | | Hindlimb | |
	Suspension	Support	Suspension	Support
Brachiators	+ + +	+(+)	+ +	+ + +
Semibrachiators (New World)	+ +	+ +	+	+ + +
Semibrachiators (Old World)	+(+)	+ + +	−	+ + +
Quadrupeds	(+)	+ + +	−	+ + +

Finally a much more meaningful method of quantification of supporting and suspensory activities has been developed by Ashton and Oxnard (1963, 1964a, 1965) and Oxnard (1963). They have undertaken extensive studies into the stress patterns of primate forelimbs in terms of both muscular and osteological form and proportions, and have subjected their results to appropriate statistical techniques. Theirs is essentially a metrical method, and the results provide a quantitative assessment of the whereabouts, in the spectrum of forelimb use (from suspension to support), of any particular species, living or fossil.

BEHAVIOURAL CLASSIFICATION

A classification by means of total locomotor pattern (Table I) involves the consideration of both fore- and hindlimbs together; it is in fact concerned with locomotor behaviour of living animals rather than simply with their biomechanical adaptations. In adopting this method of classification, the basic problem—the segmentation of a continuous phenomenon into discrete categories—is by no means solved, but the available categories are wider; such factors as speed of movement, use of tail, body and limb postures and ecological situation can be woven into a classification. The principal categories (Table I) can be defined as follows:

1. Vertical Clinging and Leaping

A type of arboreal locomotor behaviour in which the body is held vertically at rest and pressed to the trunk or main branch of a tree; movement from place to place is effected by a leap or jump from one vertical support to another. The forelimbs take no part in propelling the body during leaping. Vertical clinging and leaping primates usually hop bipedally when moving rapidly on the ground, but assume a quadrupedal gait when moving slowly.

2. Quadrupedalism

A type of locomotion which can take place on the ground or in the trees; its principal component is four-legged walking or running. In an arboreal situation the hands and feet may be used, in a prehensile fashion, to provide stability. The movements of springing, jumping and leaping are associated with this mode of locomotion. Quadrupedalism also involves the vertical movement of climbing using all four extremities. Movement may be rapid as in galloping on the ground or it may be cautious and slow. Quadrupedal primates in certain situations show a variable amount of arm-swinging with or without the additional use of a prehensile tail.

Sub-types of Quadrupedalism Category

i. *Slow Climbing*. A type of quadrupedal locomotion in which three of the four extremities are applied to the branch at any given moment. Movement is always slow and cautious. The limbs may act to suspend the body or to support it.

ii. *Branch Running and Walking*. Generalized quadrupedal locomotion in which running or walking in trees usually involves prehensile grasp with forelimbs or hindlimbs or both. The hand is usually plantigrade. Climbing, jumping or leaping in a dog-like fashion is also seen.

iii. *Ground Running and Walking*. Generalized quadrupedal locomotion in which running or walking on the ground does not usually involve prehensile grasp of limbs. The hands usually digitigrade in posture. Branch walking, frequently with a digitigrade hand posture, is seen, also climbing and dog-like leaping.

iv. *New World Semibrachiation*. A type of arboreal locomotion in which the forelimbs are used extended above the head to suspend the body or to propel it through space. The forelimbs may be used alone or in association with the hindlimbs and the prehensile tail. Quadrupedal walking and running constitute a major part of the habit. Leaping is uncommon.

v. *Old World Semibrachiation*. Differing from the New World type mainly in the extent to which leaping is employed. During leaping the arms reach out ahead of the body to grasp a handhold or to check momentum. Hand over hand progression is seldom seen. Quadrupedalism is common.

3. Brachiation

A form of locomotion in which the typical component is arm-swinging by which means the body, suspended from above, is propelled through space. The hindlimbs are used to support the body in trees or on the ground either in the erect or in the quadrupedal position. In some brachiating primates the hindlimbs may be used to suspend the body.

Sub-types of Brachiation Category

i. *True Brachiation*. A form of arboreal locomotion in which the forelimbs alone are used fully extended above the head to suspend or to propel the body through space by means of hand over hand progress. Arm-swinging may be used to provide momentum to cross wide gaps between forest trees. Bipedal walking on branches and bipedal walking on the ground constitute part of the total pattern.

ii. *Modified Brachiation*. A form of arboreal locomotion in which the forelimbs extended above the head play a major role in suspending the body or propelling it through space. The hindlimbs contribute to the pattern to a greater or lesser extent, being used to provide partial support for the body from below. Hindlimbs may also be used to suspend the body from above. On the ground quadrupedal walking, the weight of the forebody being taken on the knuckles or bunched fists, is commonly seen; occasional bipedalism is also seen.

4. Bipedalism

A form of locomotion in which the body is habitually supported on the hindlimbs which move alternately to propel it through space; the gait is characterized by the act of striding which involves a heel-toe propulsive movement.

All four categories are serially linked by some facet of locomotor pattern common to each successive pair. Vertical clingers when moving slowly on the ground are quadrupedal. Quadrupeds may suspend themselves by the arms alone in the manner of brachiating primates. Brachiating primates when on the ground and in the trees adopt bipedalism for short distances. Thus, the sequence Vertical Clinging—Quadrupedalism—Brachiation—Bipedalism forms a continuum of locomotor activity which only arbitrarily can be segmented into discrete categories. In terms of living primates a number of transitional forms are found which it is difficult to assign to a particular group. *Lemur catta* for instance is generally regarded as quadrupedal but field and captivity studies (Napier and Walker, 1967) indicate a considerable element of vertical clinging and leaping behaviour in its repertoire. Spider monkeys, though quadrupedal, frequently swing by their arms for considerable distances as Erikson (1963) has pointed out; Ashton *et al.* (1965) have shown that in the morphological characters of its shoulder girdle *Ateles* has an equivocal position, intermediate between the categories of Brachiation and Quadrupedalism. Among the brachiating primates, the gibbons adopt a bipedal gait when on the ground. There are many other examples of primates which are intermediate in their locomotor patterns between one category and another.

Fossil evidence strongly suggests that the dominant trend in primate locomotor evolution has been in the direction of greater and greater dependency on the forelimbs. Palaeontology also suggests that Vertical Clinging and Leaping constituted the principal locomotor pattern of the ancestral primate stocks of the Eocene.* A somewhat generalized vertical clinger having the characteristic short arms and long legs, but probably lacking the extreme specialization of *Tarsius*, then evolved into a quadrupedal form simply by a relative increase in the length of the forelimb and a relative decrease in the length of the hindlimb. These changes would give rise to an animal something like the modern *Lemur* whose forelimbs are still rather short and hindlimbs rather long relative to trunk height. Further adaptive change in relative limb-length would produce a more generalized quadrupedal morphology such as is seen in the Asian langurs and the African *Colobus* monkeys. These Old World monkeys are termed semibrachiators, a subtype of the quadrupedal category; their locomotion involves a major element of leaping and a minor element of arm-swinging. As has been suggested elsewhere (Napier and Davis, 1959; Napier, 1963) modern semibrachiators may represent a stage in primate locomotor phylogeny when brachiation, in its fullest expression, was evolving. In the palaeontological record it has been suggested (Napier and Davis *loc. cit.*) that *Proconsul africanus* was the representative of this stage of locomotor evolution.

The derivation of bipedalism is somewhat equivocal. There appear to be two possibilities. Firstly that bipedalism evolved from quadrupedalism; and secondly that it evolved out of an early stage of brachiation. Most authorities now agree that human bipedal gait could not have been derived from fully evolved brachiation as Keith (1923) and many others at one time believed. The two alternatives noted above, are not really alternatives at all. As has been already mentioned, quadrupedalism and brachiation are not wholly discrete categories; the

---

* A preliminary analysis of neontological and palaeontological evidence supporting this hypothesis has been carried out by Napier and Walker (1967).

TABLE III

Jumping Type (*Callicebus*)	Swinging and Hanging Type (*Ateles*)
1. Cervical spine short	Long
2. Foramen magnum directed more posteriorly	Directed more downwards
3. Occipital condyles feebly projecting	Strongly projecting
4. Atlas with shallow anterior articular facets for condyles	Anterior facets deep and concave.
5. Odontoid horizontal	Odontoid directed upwards and forwards at an angle with the centrum of C.2
6. Thoracic spine short; lumbar region long	Lumbar region shortened and with fewer vertebrae
7. Lumbar spinous processes weak and inclined forwards	Stronger and steeper
8. Articular surfaces plane, horizontal on lumbar vertebrae and sacrum	Steeply concave; tendency to lumbar lordosis
9. No special features in caudal vertebrae	Specializations in caudal vertebrae
10. Thorax narrow transversely; deep dorso-ventrally	Thorax broader, dorso-ventrally flattened, with strong arched ribs
11. Scapula of normal shape with glenoid directed laterally; spinous process horizontal. Limited excursion at shoulder	Scapula axially elongated; glenoid with upward trend; spinous process very oblique; greater excursion possible at shoulder joint
12. Clavicle only 12 per cent, trunk-length (in *Aotus*) and 15% (in *Saimiri*)	Long, 25 per cent, trunk length (*Cebus* 18 per cent, *Alouatta* 20%)
13. Processes for muscular attachment on humerus feebler; bicipital groove and olecranon fossa shallow. Shaft in section rounded	Processes strongly marked, bicipital groove and olecranon fossa deep.
14. Elongation in all long bones of hind limb Femur (shaft) antero-posterior diameter greater than transverse Great trochanter less developed	Not specially elongated Great trochanter prominent
15. Tibia platycnemic and retroverted	Not as in *Callicebus*
16. Inner margins of malleoli parallel	Inner margins of malleoli converging posteriorly
17. Trochlear surface of talus describing more than a semi-circle.	Trochlear surface narrowing cranio-caudally
18. Tuber calcanei long	Shorter proportionally

Table III is from Hill (1956) after Priemel (1937).

Quadrupedalism sub-type—semibrachiation—contains elements of both categories. Washburn (1950) stated "Spider monkeys brachiate (*sic*) . . . they also move in a quadrupedal fashion . . . the combination of brachiation and quadrupedal locomotion . . . shows how the ape-type of locomotion may have arisen". Straus (1949) stated that man's catarrhine ancestors ". . . probably indulged in some swinging by the arms and in that sense might be regarded as primitive brachiators."

Whether in fact bipedalism evolved out of specialized quadrupedalism or unspecialized brachiation is entirely unimportant, inasmuch as these two locomotor designations are virtually synonymous.

Locomotion among living primates must be viewed in the light of phylogeny in order to understand the significance of its continuous nature. Bridging forms, that do not comfortably sit in one category or another, are the modern descendants of ancestral primates whose locomotor evolution came to a halt at a point best adapted to their ecological needs; it is not surprising that this point should often lie *between* major categories.

Field studies of primates in their natural habitats very often reveal the variety of their locomotor habits—langurs for instance are known to run, walk, leap, jump, climb, hop and even swing by their arms (Ripley, 1967). Baboons run, walk, jump and climb. Chimpanzees run and walk bipedally, climb, hop, and brachiate (Reynolds, 1965). In the face of such a plethora of activities, all of which are adaptive for their particular way of life, it is difficult purely on behavioural grounds to place them in a single, meaningful category. It is important to assess their behaviour, as far as it is possible, in the light of their past evolution, a procedure which naturally involves a consideration of morphology. Within the broad range of the locomotor potentialities of any one species what element has been of major significance in their past history as reflected in the palaeontology of the group and in the present morphology of the species? In other words, on what particular aspect of their locomotion has natural selection operated most forcibly?

While locomotor categories are expressed here in behavioural terms, their basis is essentially morphological. In order to recognize the brachiating affinities of the gorilla, for instance, recourse to morphology must be made as there is little in its present behaviour which supports such a classification. The concept of semibrachiation is as much a matter of morphology as behaviour, as Ashton and Oxnard (1963) have shown; the differences between a Springer and a Climber [in Priemel's (1937) terminology] are based essentially on morphological distinctions (Table III).

2. LIMB PROPORTIONS AND INDICES

The measurements from which the Limb Indices were derived were made on skeletal material. Although there is some variation in the exact measuring points used by different authors, to all intents and purposes the *greatest length of the bone* has been measured. Different measuring techniques probably, therefore, contribute in small part to the range of variation seen in the Indices.

The following dimensions have been used by the authors. An indication is given where the authors' measurements differ from those of other authorities.

Humerus   Greatest length. Head of humerus to capitulum.
Radius   Centre of head to midpoint of distal end. Styloid process length excluded. (Styloid process included by all other authors.)

Alouatta

Lagothrix

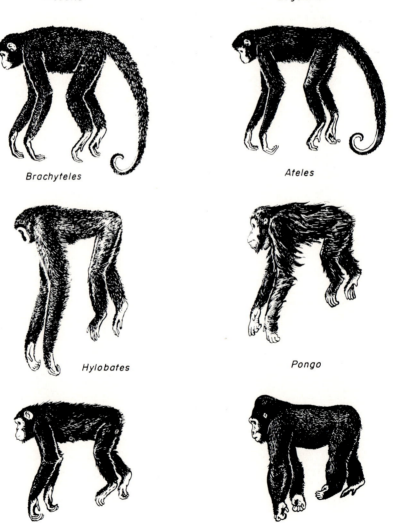

Brachyteles

Ateles

Hylobates

Pongo

Pan

Gorilla

Fɪɢ. 8. Profile views of four New World monkeys (Semibrachiators) and four Anthropoid apes (Brachiators) reduced to common trunk length. By courtesy of G. E. Erikson, from "Brachiation in New World Monkeys and Anthropoid Apes" *Symp. Zool. Soc. Lond.* No. **10**: 135–164.

Femur   Greatest length. Tip of greater trochanter to lateral condyle. [Erikson, G. E. (1963) employs "head of femur to medial condyle".]

Tibia   Centre of lateral surface of femoral condyle to midpoint of distal end. Medial malleolus excluded. (Medial malleolus included by all other authors.)

The Indices are constructed thus:

Brachial Index: $\dfrac{\text{Radius length} \times 100}{\text{Humerus length}}$

Crural Index: $\dfrac{\text{Tibia length} \times 100}{\text{Femur length}}$

Intermembral Index: $\dfrac{\text{Humerus} + \text{Radius length} \times 100}{\text{Femur} + \text{Tibia length}}$

LIMB INDICES

Name	Brachial index	Crural index	Intermembral index	Authority
Alouatta	(17) 91 84–96	(11) 88 84–92	(34) 98 92–105	A.E.*M.S.
Aotus	(5) 88 85–90	(5) 96 95–97	(12) 74 72–75	A.M.S.
Arctocebus	(2) 96 95, 98	(2) 85 85, 85	(2) 90 90, 90	A.
Ateles	(63) 101 93–108	(8) 95 93–102	(34) 105 99–109	A.E.*M.S.
Avahi	(4) 117 110–123	(4) 86 84–87	(4) 56 55–56	A.M.Mi.
Brachyteles	(7) 94 89–102	(1) 87	(7) 105 102–110	A.E.*
Callicebus	(2) 88 83, 92	(2) 99 97, 100	(2) 73 72, 73	A.
Callimico	(3) 100 97–103	(3) 101 98–105	(3) 76 71–81	A.
Callithrix	(38) 88 84–91	(38) 101 98–105	(38) 76 73–78	A.M.We.*
Cebuella	(1) 88	(1) 101	(1) 80	A.
Cebus	(15) 93 88–98	(15) 95 89–103	(15) 81 77–85	A.M.S.

Key to authorities:

A   = Authors   M-E = Milne-Edwards, A. (1898)
E   = Erikson, G. E. (1963)   S   = Schultz, A. H. (1930, 1937, 1953)
H-C = Hall-Craggs, E. C. B. (1965)   W   = Washburn, S. L. (1942)
M = Mollison (1910)   We = Wettstein, E. B. (1963)   Symbol * = Principal authority.
Mi = Mivart (1873)

Name	Brachial index	Crural index	Intermembral index	Authority
Cercocebus	(2) 99 98, 100	(2) 86 85, 87	(2) 86 82–90	A.
Cercopithecus	(29) 96 87–102	(24) 98 90–100	(37) 84 79–91	A.*M.S.
Chiropotes	(3) 88 84–90	(2) 98 92, 104	(2) 76 75, 76	A.M.
Colobus	(8) 95 90–100	(8) 91 86–97	(8) 79 77–83	A.M.S.
Cynopithecus	(3) 103 99–108	(4) 88 85–91	(3) 93 89–95	M.
Daubentonia	(6) 100 98–101	(6) 95 92–98	(6) 71 70–72	A.*M.
Erythrocebus	(5) 107 104–113	(5) 98 94–104	(7) 92 86–99	A.M.S.
Euoticus	—	—	(5) 63 62–64	H-C
Galago	(9) 109 100–125	(9) 94 86–112	(10) 62 51–71	A.M.S.
Galagoides	—	—	(2) 65 65–66	H-C
Gorilla	(181) 80 73–86	(179) 80 73–86	(178) 117 110–125	A.M.S.
Hapalemur	(1) 110	(1) 86	(1) 65	A.
Hylobates	(66) 113 105–124	(66) 88 78–94	(55) 129 121–138	A.M.S.
Indri	(13) 121 116–125	(13) 84 81–88	(13) 64 61–66	A.M.S.
Lagothrix	(22) 89 84–93	(2) 88 87, 89	(22) 98 93–100	A.E.S.
Lemur	(17) 106 99–113	(17) 93 90–96	(17) 70 68–72	A.S.
Leontideus	(3) 93 89–98	(2) 100 100, 100	(2) 82 78, 86	A.
Lepilemur	(6) 114 109–119	(6) 89 85–92	(6) 64 62–66	Mi.S.
Loris	(8) 115 111–117	(8) 98 95–102	(8) 92 89–98	A.M.
Macaca	(122) 97 91–102	(123) 92 86–98	(116) 89 83–95	A.M.S.
Mandrillus	(7) 104 98–116	(8) 89 85–100	(7) 94 88–99	A.M.
Nasalis	(22) 100 93–104	(12) 89 85–92	(12) 93 89–97	A.M.S.
Nycticebus	(5) 100 95–112	(5) 96 94–100	(7) 90 87–94	A.M.S.
Pan	(128) 93 87–100	(128) 84 78–90	(128) 107 102–114	A.M.S.

Name	Brachial index	Crural index	Intermembral index	Authority
Papio	(14) 104 99–113	(14) 85 80–91	(22) 95 92–100	A.M.S.
Perodicticus	(4) 104 102–105	(4) 92 91–93	(6) 88 86–90	A.M.S.
Pithecia	(3) 89 87–92	(4) 93 92–95	(4) 76 73–77	A.M.
Pongo	(103) 100 92–109	(103) 92 85–94	(103) 144 135–150	A.M.S.
Presbytis	(88) 104 91–119	(87) 90 86–94	(87) 78 73–84	A.M.W.
Propithecus	(10) 109 105–113	(10) 86 80–87	(10) 64 63–66	A.S.*
Ptilocercus	(3) 105·8 100–110	(3) 100	(3) 80 78–81	A.
Pygathrix	(4) 104 100–107	(1) 88	(3) 93 92–94	W.*M-E
Rhinopithecus	(1) 95	(1) 86	(1) 89	M-E
Saguinus	(11) 88 81–93	(11) 100 96–102	(11) 75 73–78	A.
Saimiri	(9) 89 85–92	(9) 98 92–100	(9) 77 75–80	A.M.
Symphalangus	(31) 111 106–116	(31) 86 83–90	(31) 148 142–155	M.S.*
Tarsius	(5) 128 121–135	(14) 100 95–102	(8) 55 53–59	A.S.
Theropithecus	(1) 106	(1) 97	(1) 94	M.
Tupaia	(7) 95 90–100	(7) 104 101–110	(8) 73 69–76	A.

3. OPPOSABILITY OF THE THUMB IN PRIMATES

The hands of primates are pentadactyl. In certain prosimians, such as *Perodicticus* and *Arctocebus*, the index finger has become reduced and, in the latter genus, the middle finger has also undergone reduction in length. The South American spider monkeys, *Ateles* and the African genus *Colobus*, are thumbless. The hands of all primates are convergent and, with the exception of treeshrews, all are prehensile. Convergence is a compound movement occurring at the metacarpo-phalangeal joints and consists of flexion and adduction leading to the approximation of the tips of the digits; the opposite movement is divergence, a movement of extension and abduction leading to a fanning of the digits. All primates, including man, possess convergent-divergent digits. The approximation of the tips of the digits in convergence, and their spread in divergence, depends on the arched form of the carpus and metacarpus; the fingers are, in effect, set upon a curved surface (Fig. 9a).

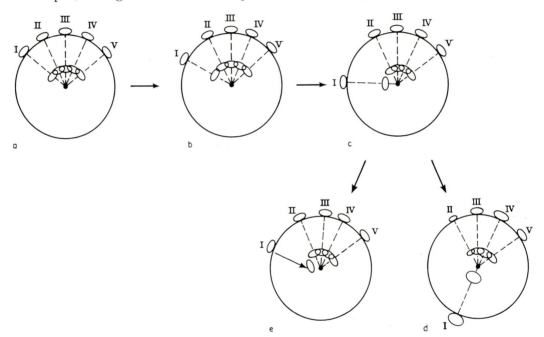

FIG. 9. Diagrams show grades of thumb mobility in primates.

 a. Convergent digits, non-prehensile hand, non-opposable thumb.
 b. Prehensile hand, non-opposable thumb, e.g. *Callithrix*.
 c. Prehensile hand, pseudo-opposable thumb (New World Monkey Type, e.g. *Cebus*).
 d. Prehensile hand, pseudo-opposable thumb (Prosimian Type, e.g. *Perodicticus*).
 e. Prehensile hand, opposable thumb (Old World Monkey type, e.g. *Macaca* and *Homo*).

Arrows indicate possible phylogenetic sequence of functional morphology of the hand.

 Prehensile hands are convergent hands in which the digits approximate in such a manner that an object may be grasped and held securely by one hand against the effect of external influences (e.g. gravity) which are tending to displace it (Fig. 9b). The behavioural correlate of prehensility is one-handed feeding.

 Variation of hand function within the primate order is principally a matter of the length and the degree of divergence and opposability of the thumb. Prehensile hands can be classified into three main types, depending on the degree to which the thumb moves independently.

(1) With non-opposable thumbs.
(2) With pseudo-opposable thumbs.
(3) With opposable thumbs.

If function and behaviour were the only considerations, Types (2) and (3) could both be regarded as "opposable" in the sense that the thumb can be directed towards one or more of the remaining digits so that the palmar surfaces of the thumb and fingers lie parallel to, and opposite, each other. In terms of morphology, however, the underlying mechanism by which opposition is brought about in Types (2) and (3) differs considerably. The concept of opposition of the thumb has been studied and defined in terms of man and the connotation is, therefore, a strictly human one. This being so, opposition or opposability of the thumb should be terms reserved for the functional and morphological pattern of thumb movement seen in man and, incidentally, most other catarrhine primates.

Opposition may be defined in the following terms: a movement by which the pulp surface of the thumb, undergoing flexion and rotation at the carpo-metacarpal joint, can be placed squarely in contact with, or diametrically opposite to, the pulp surface of one or all of the remaining digits.

The occurrence of the three types in primate families is as follows:

(1) Non-opposable thumb: Treeshrew, tarsier, marmoset families.
(2) Pseudo-opposable thumb: New World monkey (excluding marmoset) and prosimian families.
(3) Opposable thumb: Old World monkey, ape and human families.

THE NON-OPPOSABLE THUMB

Among primates the simplest expression of the prehensile hand is found in the marmosets. The fingers and "thumb" are moderately long, long enough for the hand to be folded upon itself and, thus, to provide a mechanism for a stable grasp and one-handed feeding. The fingers are clawed at their tips with a modified nail which Clark (1936) referred to as a tegula. The thumb is slightly divergent in the living hand, but the pattern of contrahentes indicates little, if any, functional selection of the thumb. However, the confluence of the volar pads to form a "palm" indicates a functional advance of the marmoset hand over that of the treeshrews where the touch pads are still discrete.

A different type of hand altogether is seen in *Tarsius*. The phalanges are extremely long and the metacarpals short—the thumb in the living form usually appears well differentiated from the rest of the hand, but the site of this divergence is at the metacarpo-phalangeal joint and not the carpo-metacarpal joint (Napier, 1961; Day and Napier, 1963). The thumb is not opposable within the general meaning of the word, but the movement of abduction-adduction and rotation of the metacarpo-phalangeal joint provides a considerable range of freedom of the distal half of the thumb. This movement at the metacarpo-phalangeal joint of the pollex is retained in some measure by most primates although it is much reduced in man (Napier, 1952). The carpo-metacarpal joint in *Tarsius* permits only a very limited range of movement.

The pattern of contrahentes in the hand of *Tarsius* is somewhat specialized, indicating that the thumb plays a mobile and independent role in the function of the hand: the form of the contrahens to the thumb foreshadows the specialization of this muscle in higher primates where it becomes known as the adductor pollicis. In addition, there is an extra slip on the radial border of the first contrahens which is possibly homologous with the deep head of flexor pollicis brevis of higher primates (Day and Napier, 1963), it is attached distally to the radial border of the proximal phalanx of the thumb and, presumably, produces the moderate degree of medial rotation found at this joint. A well developed abductor pollicis brevis is also present. The digits are longer than the length of the carpus and metacarpus combined, and the thumb is also longer (*see* Hand Indices, p. 401).

THE PSEUDO-OPPOSABLE THUMB

Among living primates this type of hand is found in New World monkeys (excluding the marmosets and the thumbless *Ateles*), but is also found in the Miocene hominoid, *Proconsul africanus* (Napier and Davis, 1959). The element of rotation at the carpo-metacarpal joint is lacking and the articulation itself is substantially of the "hinge" variety in contrast to the "saddle" type of joint which provides the mechanism of the true opposability found in living Old World monkeys. The hand of the capuchin monkey, though somewhat specialized, is fairly typical of the Cebidae. The thumb is lined up in series with the remaining digits but is separated from the rest by a deep inter-digital cleft. The thumb can be abducted at least 45° from the index finger. Movements within the carpo-metacarpal joint are limited to angular displacements, rotations being absent. Owing to the presence of the transverse carpal and metacarpal arches in the hand, the digits are naturally disposed along a curved plane, thus abduction movements would tend to displace the thumb ventrally with respect to the remaining digits. As a result, following an abduction movement, the palmar plane of the thumb comes to lie at an angle to the palmar surface of the remaining digits (Fig. 9c); flexion movements from this abducted opposition produces a degree of functional opposability. In the absence of a rotatory movement at the carpo-metacarpal joint this type of movement is termed pseudo-opposability.

Alison Bishop (1964), who has studied hand function in certain New World monkeys, confirms the absence of opposition and states that the thumb flexes with the fingers in the same plane. Contrahentes muscles are present and consist of a central raphe giving attachment to contrahentes I and V, that to I being the longer (Forster, 1916). The deep head of flexor pollicis brevis is absent as might be expected in the absence of true opposability (Day and Napier, 1963), and the thumb is long.

The prosimians (other than tarsier and the treeshrew) also possess pseudo-opposable thumbs. The divergence between the thumb and index finger is considerably more marked than in the Cebidae. In the potto for instance, the thumb has diverged from the index finger through 180° (Fig. 9d). Flexion of the thumb from this widely divergent starting position, results in its close opposition to the fourth digit. Once again the movement, though functionally opposition, is in fact morphologically a pseudo-opposition as no element of rotation of the carpo-metacarpal joint is involved during the movement. Other prosimians, for instance the galago, the slow loris and the indris show a similar—though less extreme—specialization.

THE OPPOSABLE THUMB

All living primates of the Old World, that possess thumbs, show opposability; the functional effectiveness of the opposition in different genera is shown by the Opposability Index which reflects the relative lengths of the thumb and forefinger. The Index (*see* Hand Proportions, p. 401) expresses the length relationship between the thumb and index fingers and can only meaningfully be applied to those primates in which true opposability is present—the Old World monkeys and apes.

The extremes of disproportion between 1st and 2nd digits is shown by *Pongo*. The *Presbytis* group also show a surprising disproportion, but the range of variation within the group is enormous, and clearly many more specimens are needed, particularly of the *entellus* langur. This species, which is probably responsible for the upper limit of the *Presbytis* range, has altogether a longer thumb than the more arboreally habituated langurs.

When the Opposability Index is compared with the Thumb Index it is apparent that *Erythrocebus* has a short thumb and yet, in spite of that, a high Opposability Index. This can be explained by the extreme shortness of its digits (*see* Phalangeal Index). The short thumb of *Erythrocebus* allies it taxonomically with the *Cercopithecus* group, rather than adaptively, with *Papio* and *Mandrillus* whose thumbs are considerably longer. *Erythrocebus* also shows the short index finger characteristic of *Cercopithecus* and *Macaca*; once again it is adaptively distinguished from *Papio* whose index finger more closely matches the middle finger in length. The relatively short index finger is an adaptation of arboreal quadrupeds, while the relatively long index finger is an adaptation in ground-living quadrupeds such as *Papio*, and is related to their digitigrade gait; in arboreal genera, such as *Pongo* and *Hylobates*, the thumb is also short, but here it is an adaptation to the manual grasp of brachiating forms.

The selective advantage of a high opposability index is apparent in the behaviour of ground-living monkeys in which grass-plucking (or "manual grazing") is an important feature of the feeding repertoire.

The saddle conformation of the catarrhine carpo-metacarpal joint permits flexion-extension, abduction-adduction and rotation. The word "rotation" here is really a misnomer, the movement is strictly a conjunct rotation which is an entirely different type of movement (Napier, 1955); the *effect* however is one of medial rotation (Fig. 9e).

Movement at the metacarpo-phalangeal, or middle joint, of the thumb substantially aids opposability in man as well as in non-human catarrhines. The motion that takes place at this joint is identical with that found in *Tarsius* where, it will be remembered, it constitutes the principal movement of the thumb; in man however the movement has only a small range.

4. HAND PROPORTIONS AND INDICES

All measurements from which the Hand Indices are derived were collected by the authors using the following dimensions (*see* Fig. 10):

Carpus: Length of carpus in the line of the 3rd digit.
Metacarpus: Greatest length of the 3rd metacarpal.
Phalanges: Greatest length of phalanges of 3rd digit.
Thumb: Base of metacarpal, measured from lateral (radial) aspect to tip of terminal phalanx.
Index: Base of metacarpal to tip of terminal phalanx.

The following Indices were then constructed:

Hand Length Index: $$\frac{\text{Total length of hand} \times 100}{\text{Humerus} + \text{radius} + \text{hand length}}$$

Phalangeal Index: $$\frac{\text{Phalangeal length} \times 100}{\text{Hand length}}$$

Thumb Length Index: $$\frac{\text{Thumb length} \times 100}{\text{Total hand length}}$$

Opposability Index: $$\frac{\text{Thumb length} \times 100}{\text{Index ray length}}$$

Opposability Index has been assessed only in the catarrhine primates in which true opposability is present.

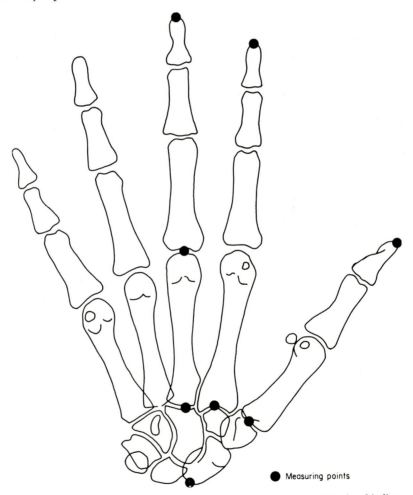

● Measuring points

FIG. 10. Diagram of hand to show measuring points used in determining hand indices.

HAND INDICES

Name	Hand length index	Phalangeal index	Thumb length index	Opposability index
Alouatta	(5) 27 27–28	(18) 58 56–59	(18) 47 45–49	—
Aotus	(4) 30 29–31	(4) 57 55–60	(4) 48 46–51	—
Arctocebus	(2) 24 24, 24	(2) 58 56, 56	(2) 55 54, 54	—
Ateles	(6) 27 25–29	(6) 53 49–54	—	—
Avahi	(2) 34 33, 35	(2) 58 59, 58	(2) 42 42, 43	—
Callicebus	(2) 28 29, 28	—	—	—
Callimico	(2) 32 32, 33	(2) 57 56, 58	(2) 52 51, 53	—
Callithrix	(14) 29 29–33	(14) 53 51–56	(12) 54 51–56	—
Cebuella	(1) 30	—	(1) 64	—
Cebus	(5) 27 26–28	(6) 52 50–53	(6) 50 46–52	—
Cercocebus	(3) 26 26–27	(3) 49 47–50	(3) 38 37–40	
Cercopithecus	(13) 26 25–28	(19) 50 47–52	(13) 38 35–42	(11) 53 48–55
Chiropotes	(1) 29	(1) 53	(1) 51	
Colobus	(3) 30 30–31	(3) 54 53–55	—	—
Daubentonia	(4) 42 40–43		(1) 43	
Erythrocebus	(3) 23 22–24	(3) 42 41–43	(3) 37 33–39	(3) 42 47–57
Galago	(6) 30 28–32	(6) 63 60–67	(6) 50 44–56	—
Gorilla	(10) 25 23–26	(18) 48 48–49	(16) 38 36–40	(16) 48 43–51
Hapalemur	(1) 30	(1) 60	(1) 47	—
Hylobates	(5) 26 24–28	(10) 52 52–54	(6) 36 35–41	(5) 47 43–50
Indri	(2) 33	(2) 55	(1) 45	
Lagothrix	(2) 26 26, 26	(2) 56 56, 57	(2) 42 40, 44	—
Lemur	(3) 29 28–29	(6) 55 54–60	(5) 46 45–48	—
Leontideus	(3) 31 30–32	(4) 54 52–56	45 41–52	—

N.B. Figures in brackets indicate size of samples

Name	Hand length index	Phalangeal index	Thumb length index	Opposability index
Lepilemur	(1) 32	(1) 56	(1) 42	
Loris	(6) 22 19–25	(3) 56 56–56	(6) 53 50–58	—
Macaca	(18) 27 26–28	(19) 49 47–53	(18) 39 38–43	(18) 54 48–59
Mandrillus	(3) 27 26–29	(5) 48 47–49	(3) 44 42–46	(3) 57 56–57
Microcebus	(1) 32	(1) 60	(1) 43	—
Nasalis	(5) 28 28–29	(6) 53 51–54	(6) 34 33–35	(4) 46 45–48
Nycticebus	(4) 23 19–26	(4) 59 56–62	(4) 51 46–58	—
Pan	(9) 30 29–31	(14) 50 48–52	(4) 33 33–35	(7) 42 38–44
Papio	(7) 23 22–25	(17) 44 41–45	(10) 41 38–44	(13) 57 53–60
Perodicticus	(4) 29 28–31	(4) 59 57–64	(3) 49 46–50	—
Pithecia	(4) 28 27–29	(4) 57 57–64	(3) 48 46–50	—
Pongo	(6) 28 27–30	(11) 50 49–52	(6) 30 27–34	(6) 39 36–44
Presbytis	(13) 29 27–30	(13) 53 50–56	(12) 30 27–34	(12) 42 36–47
Propithecus	(2) 33 32,33	(1) 56	(2) 47	—
Ptilocercus	(2) 27 25, 28	(2) 51 48, 54	(2) 53 53, 53	—
Pygathrix	(1) 26·8	—	—	—
Rhinopithecus	(1) 25·1	—	—	—
Saguinus	(11) 31 29–33	(10) 52 51–55	(10) 53 51–55	
Saimiri	(6) 28 26–29	(6) 54 53–57	(5) 46 43–49	—
Tarsius	(3) 40 39–40	(6) 64 61–65	(6) 45 42–47	—
Theropithecus	—	(1) 42	(1) 46	—
Tupaia	(6) 28 26–30	(6) 45 38–50	(6) 45 42–48	—

N.B. Opposability Index assessed only in catarrhine primates in which true opposability is present. Figures in brackets indicate size of samples.

Data on Macaques

1. *Macaca*: SYSTEMATIC LIST

Species	Subspecies	Author	Name in common usage	Probable range
M. sylvana (Type species)	—	Linnaeus, 1758	Barbary Ape	Morocco, Algeria: Gibraltar (introduced)
M. sinica	sinica	Linnaeus, 1771	Toque monkey	Ceylon: low country dry zone
	aurifrons	Pocock, 1931		Ceylon: low-country wet zone and central hill zone
	opisthomelas	Hill, 1942		Ceylon: Highlands
M. radiata	radiata	E. Geoffroy, 1812	Bonnet monkey	Peninsular India: S. of Satara and R. Godavari
	diluta	Pocock, 1931		Peninsular India: southern Kerala
M. silenus	—	Linnaeus, 1758	Lion-tailed Macaque	Peninsular India: Western Ghats from 14° N. to Cape Comorin
M. nemestrina	nemestrina	Linnaeus, 1766	Pig-tailed Macaque	Malaya, Sumatra, Borneo, Bangka I.
	leonina	Blyth, 1863		Upper Burma, Tenasserim, Mergui Archipelago, Thailand. Andaman Is. (introduced)
	blythii	Pocock, 1931		? Naga Hills, Assam
	pagensis	Miller, 1903		Pagai Is., Mentawai Is., W. Sumatra
M. fascicularis	fascicularis	Raffles, 1821	Crab-eating Macaque	Malay Peninsula: Langkawi I., Terutoa I., Penang I. and Singapore. Sumatra, Riau and Lingga Archipelagos, Bangka I., Belitung I., Banjak Is., Musala I., Batu Is., Borneo and coastal islands, Karimata Is.
	aurea	E. Geoffroy, 1831		Lower Burma, Tenasserim, Mergui Archipelago, S.W. Thailand
	umbrosa	Miller, 1902		Gt. Nicobar, Little Nicobar and Katchall Is.
	valida	Elliot, 1909		Cochin China
	atriceps	Kloss, 1919		Koh Kram I., S.E. Thailand
	argentimembris	Kloss, 1911		Great Redang Is., E. coast Malaya
	capitalis	Elliot, 1910		Peninsular Thailand: islands of Ko Phangan and Ko Samui
	laeti	Elliot, 1909		Tioman and Tinggi Is., E. coast Malaya
	pumila	Miller, 1900		Anamba Is., Tambelan Is., N. and S. Natuna Is.
	fusca	Miller, 1903		Simalur I., W. Sumatra
	lasiae	Lyon, 1916		Lasia I., W. Sumatra
	phaeura	Miller, 1903		Nias I., W. Sumatra
	mordax	Thomas and Wroughton, 1909		Java, Bali
	cupida	Elliot, 1910		Matasiri I., Java Sea
	baweana	Elliot, 1910		Bawean I., Java Sea

O

1. *Macaca*: SYSTEMATIC LIST (*continued*)

Species	Subspecies	Author	Name in common usage	Probable range
	philippinensis	I. Geoffroy, 1843		Luzon, Philippines
	mindanesis	Mearns, 1905		Mindanao and Basilan, Philippines
	mindora	Hollister, 1913		Mindoro I., Philippines
	tua	Kellogg, 1944		Maratua I., E. Borneo
	limitis	Schwarz, 1913		Timor
	sublimitis	Sody, 1933		Lombok, Sumbawa, Sumba, Flores; introduced into Atauro (Pulau Kambing)
M. mulatta	*mulatta*	Zimmermann, 1780	Rhesus monkey	Nepal, Bhutan, Assam, Burma, Northern Peninsular India, Thailand, Indo-China, China, S. of the R. Yangtse Kiang, also Szechwan and part of Hopeh; Hainan I.
	vestita	Milne-Edwards, 1892		Nam Tsho (Tengri-Nor), Tibet, possibly E. to Pat'ang, W. Szechwan
	villosa	True, 1894		S. Kashmir, Upper Punjab, Northern Uttar Pradesh
	mcmahoni	Pocock, 1932		E. Afghanistan, Chitral
M. assamensis	*assamensis*	M'Clelland, 1839	Assamese Macaque	From Assam, S. to the Sundarbans, Mishmi and Naga Hills, N. Burma, Yunnan, Vietnam
	pelops	Hodgson, 1840		Himalayas: southern foothills from Uttar Pradesh through Nepal and Sikkim to Bhutan
M. cyclopis	—	Swinhoe, 1862	Formosan Rock Macaque	Formosa (Taiwan)
M. speciosa	*speciosa*	F. Cuvier, 1825	Stump-tailed Macaque	Assam, Upper Burma, Southern China, Vietnam
	arctoides	I. Geoffroy, 1831		Cochin China
	melanota	Ogilby, 1839		Tenasserim, S.W. and peninsular Thailand
	thibetana	Milne-Edwards, 1870		Szechwan, China
M. fuscata	*fuscata*	Blyth, 1875	Japanese Macaque	Honshu, Shikoku and Kiushu, Japan (*not* Hokkaido)
	yakui	Kuroda, 1941		Yakushima I., Japan
M. maurus	*maurus*	F. Cuvier, 1823	Moor Macaque	Southwestern peninsula of Celebes
	brunnescens	Matschie, 1901		Muna and Butung Is., S.E. Celebes
	togeana	Sody, 1949		Malengi I., Togian Islands, N.E. Celebes
	ochreata	Ogilby, 1840		Southeastern peninsula of Celebes

Systematic list is based on the checklists of Allen (1939), Chasen (1940), Ellerman and Morrison-Scott (1951) and Laurie and Hill (1954). Reference has also been made to Allen (1938), Lawrence (1939), Hooijer (1950) and Sanborn (1952).

2. DIFFERENTIATING CHARACTERISTICS OF ADULT MACAQUES

Species	General Colour and Texture	Arrangement of Crown Hairs	Face	Tail	Special Peculiarities
M. sylvana Barbary ape	Black and yellow giving a mottled yellowish-grey effect. Rough coat. Paler underparts.	Forehead and crown covered with erect golden-brown hairs.	Dark flesh-colour, sometimes freckled. Whiskers encroach on to cheeks. Relatively short-faced.	Absent.	Conspicuous circular swelling of sexual skin at oestrus is blue-grey in colour. Adjacent furred area of rump is also involved.
M. sinica Toque monkey	Golden or reddish brown. Paler underparts.	Whorl on crown radiates long hairs outwards forming a circular cap [Toque] set forward on crown.	Lower part of forehead bare. Red blotching of face begins at puberty in ♀♀ only, and may increase over several years until uniformly red. Short hairs form whorl on cheeks.	Longer than head and body length. Smooth-haired.	Penis large; glans has crescentic thickening above the orifice and is angularly pointed below. Sexual skin is reddish-purple throughout menstrual cycle. Disagreeable odour in ♀♀ due to discharge of mucus from the vagina.
M. radiata Bonnet monkey	Grey-brown. Paler underparts.	Long hairs on crown radiate outwards and backwards with distinct central parting, forming a cap [Bonnet] set back on crown.	Bare: light pink or red. Short hairs on forehead grow outwards from centre parting. No whorl on cheeks.	Longer than head and body length. Smooth-haired.	Penis large; glans has crescentic thickening above the orifice and is angularly pointed below. Sexual skin is bright red or purple throughout menstrual cycle. Discharge of mucus in ♀♀ as in M. sinica.
M. nemestrina Pig-tailed macaque	Buff to dark brown, darker on head, back and tail. Paler underparts.	Central whorl on crown radiates short dark-brown hairs outwards forming a thick cap of erect hairs.	Bare: light brown. Eyelids strongly marked. Relatively long-faced.	One-third head and body length, carried arched over back. Smooth-haired.	Conspicuous swelling and reddening of sexual skin during oestrus, involving buttocks and root of tail.
M. fascicularis Crab-eating macaque	Pale yellowish-brown or grey to dark brown. Paler underparts.	Crown hairs directed backwards; sometimes forming short crest on mid-line.	Cheek hairs form fringe of whiskers on and around face. Triangle of pale naked skin on inner side of eyelids.	Equal to head and body length or longer. Smooth-haired.	Penis small with round button-shaped glans. Sexual skin swelling involves a small area of base of tail and is slate-grey in colour.
M. silenus Lion-tailed macaque	Black.	Large grey ruff encircles face except on forehead where it is parted by outwardly directed crown hairs.	Black and bare.	Half to two-thirds of head and body length; smooth-haired with terminal tuft.	Conspicuous pink swelling of sexual skin at oestrus.
M. mulatta Rhesus monkey	Brown: greyer foreparts, more rufous hindparts. Paler underparts.	Crown hairs directed backwards.	Bare; flesh-coloured becoming red at oestrus in 10% of ♀♀.	About half head and body length, well-haired; pendulous.	Swelling and reddening of sexual skin occurs at oestrus in 50% ♀♀ and may involve thighs, buttocks and hips. More pronounced in adolescent ♀♀.
M. assamensis Assamese macaque	Yellowish-brown to dark brown.	Median parting above brows; crown hairs directed backwards.	Flesh-colour around mouth, darker below eyes. Fringe of dark hairs directed backwards from cheek to ear.	Variable: between one-third and two-thirds head and body length; well-haired, pendulous.	As in M. mulatta.
M. cyclopis Formosan Rock macaque	Slatey-brown with darker limbs. Thick woolly fur.	Crown hairs dark and directed backwards.	Flesh-coloured. Forehead bare; dark-whiskered cheeks. Relatively short-faced.	About half to two-thirds head and body length. Stout and bushy; pendulous.	Conspicuous swelling and reddening of sexual skin at oestrus involving root of tail, buttocks and back of thighs.
M. speciosa Stump-tailed macaque	Dark chestnut brown becoming darker and grizzled with age. Typically shaggy.	Hair radiates from centre of crown, long at back and sides, very short in front. Forehead bald in adults.	Forehead bare and wrinkled. Face pink or red, sometimes with dark freckles.	Sparsely-haired stump, turned to one side.	Glans penis very long and tapering. Reddening of sexual skin at oestrus with little swelling. Unpleasant musky odour in young animals.
M. fuscata Japanese macaque	Yellowish-brown shaggy fur.	Hair directed backwards and outwards from centre of forehead.	Narrow bare area above brow. Face pink, becoming red at oestrus.	Very short; furry; with terminal tuft.	Sexual skin, normally pink, becomes red at oestrus, particularly in adolescent ♀♀. Swelling is less common.
M. maurus Moor macaque	Black or dark brown, sometimes with paler forearms, legs, inner side of thighs and buttocks.	Crown hairs directed backwards.	Brownish-black and bare; strong brow ridges.	Sparsely-haired tubercle.	2 types of sexual swelling observed: (1) Prominent pink spherical swelling above callosities, concealing tail and involving adjacent furred area of rump. (2) Diffuse pink involving only buttocks and sometimes backs of thighs; (neither rump nor tail).

REFERENCES

1. Pocock, R. I. (1939)
2. Hill, W. C. Osman (1939b)
3. Pocock, R. I. (1925a)
4. Pocock, R. I. (1921)
5. Simonds, P. (1965)
6. Kuehn, R. E. et al. (1965)
7. Carpenter, C. R. (1942b)
8. Swinhoe, R. (1862)
9. Tokuda, K. (1961–62)
10. Büttikofer, J. (1917)
11. Montagna, W. et al. (1966)
12. Spiegel, A. (1954)

3. WEIGHTS AND DIMENSIONS OF MACAQUE SPECIES

	Body weight ♂♂ (g)	Body weight ♀♀ (g)	Head and body length ♂♂ (mm)	Head and body length ♀♀ (mm)	Tail length ♂♂ (mm)	Tail length ♀♀ (mm)
M. sylvana	11,145 (1)	—	559, 620 (2)	600 (1)	—	—
M. sinica	4427–8392 (6)	3405–4313 (5)	442–533 (5)	432–452 (3)	549–622 (5)	465–569 (3)
M. radiata	5670–8853 (10)	2930–4420 (10)	513–599 (11)	345–523 (13)	508–686 (11)	482–634 (13)
M. silenus	6754 (1)	—	508–610 (5)	457 (2)	254–386 (5)	254, 318 (2)
M. nemestrina	6243–14,500 (14)	4654–10,896 (3)	495–595 (10)	467–564 (3)	160–245 (10)	137–193 (3)
M. fascicularis	3500–8286 (32)	2500–5680 (17)	412–648 (24)	385–503 (7)	435–655 (24)	400–545 (7)
M. mulatta	5557–10,896 (12)	4370–10,659 (47)	483–635 (15)	470–531 (17)	203–305 (15)	189–284 (17)
M. assamensis	10,442–12,712 (3)	—	559–650 (6)	528, 680 (2)	193–351 (6)	235, 386 (2)
M. cyclopis	—	—				
M. speciosa	—	—	549–700 (8)	503–569 (6)	41–100 (8)	10–61 (6)
M. fuscata	11,100–18,000 (6)	8300–16,300 (5)	535–607 (22)	472–601 (22)	81–124 (22)	72–103 (22)
M. maurus	8800, 10,100 (2)	5105 (1)	445–665 (7)	530–570 (5)	44–64 (5)	38–55 (3)

Numbers in brackets refer to the numbers of specimens.
Data from: Allen (1938), Altmann (1962), Davis (1962), Hartman (1938), Hazama (1965), Iwamoto *et al.* (1966), personal communication, Kellogg (1944), Lyon (1907, 1908), Miller (1907a and b), Pocock (1939), Schultz (1933a), Spiegel (1956), Sody (1949), Washburn (1942); British Museum (Natural History) Records, and Veterinary Officer's Reports, Zoological Society of London.

4. DATA ON REPRODUCTION IN MACAQUE SPECIES

	M. mulatta	Ref.	M. fuscata	Ref.	M. radiata	Ref.	M. nemestrina	Ref.	M. fascicularis	Ref.
Menstrual cycle (mode)	28 days	1	28 days	2	31 days	3, 4	31 days	5	28 days	6
Duration of oestrus (mean)	9·2 days	7	9·3 days	8	Not known		Not known		About 11 days	6
Gestation period	164 days (146–180)	1	— (170–180)	9	163 days (153–169)	4	170 days (162–186)	5	167 days (153–179)	6
Birth season	March–June (a few in Sept.)	10	March to August	10	January–April (a few in June and July)	10	Not known		Not known	
Birth weight range (g)	330–600	11	450–500*	12	330–370	4	Not known		230–470	13
Lactation	7–14 months	1	About 6 months	9	Not known		About 8 months	14	14–18 months	6
Sexual maturity ♂♂	4·5 years	1	4·5 years	15	3–4 years	16	Not known		4·2 years	6
♀♀	3·5 years	17	3·5 years	15	3–4 years	16	Not known		4·3 years	6

REFERENCES

1. Hartman, C. G. (1932)
2. Nigi, H. (1966) Personal communication
3. Zuckerman, S. (1930)
4. Hartman, C. G. (1938)
5. Kuehn, R. E., Jensen, G. D. and Morrill, R. K. (1965)
6. Spiegel, A. (1954)
7. Carpenter, C. R. (1942a)
8. Tokuda, K. (1961–62)
9. Kawai, M. (1966) Personal communication
10. Lancaster, Jane B. and Lee, R. B. (1965)
11. Schultz, A. H. (1933a)
12. Hazama, N. (1964)
13. Spiegel, A. (1956)
14. Zuckerman, S. (1937)
15. Itani, J., Tokuda, K., Furuya, Y., Kano, K. and Shin, Y. (1963)
16. Simonds, P. (1965)
17. Koford, C. B. (1965)

5. ZOO LONGEVITY RECORDS OF MACAQUE SPECIES

M. sylvana	21 years 5 months	Philadelphia Zoo, U.S.A.
M. sinica	29 years 4 months	Colombo Zoo, Ceylon
M. radiata	18 years 9 months	Philadelphia Zoo, U.S.A.
M. silenus	17 years 7 months	Philadelphia Zoo, U.S.A.
M. nemestrina	26 years 4 months	Milwaukee Zoo, U.S.A.
M. fascicularis	15 years 5 months	Bronx Zoo, New York
M. mulatta	21 years 6 months	National Zoological Park, Washington
M. assamensis	6 years 0 months	Calcutta Zoo
M. cyclopis	2 years 7 months	National Zoological Park, Washington
M. speciosa	19 years 8 months	National Zoological Park, Washington
M. fuscata	19 years 3 months	San Diego Zoo, U.S.A.
M. maurus	28 years 1 month	Philadelphia Zoo, U.S.A.

Data from Jones (1962)

Vital Statistics of Primates

1. GESTATION PERIODS OF PRIMATES

Alouatta	Not known	*Indri*	Not known
Anathana	Not known	*Lagothrix*	225 days approx.
Aotus	Not known	*Lemur*	120–135 days
Arctocebus	131 days*	*Leontideus*	Not known
Ateles	139 days approx.	*Lepilemur*	120–150 days
Avahi	Not known	*Loris*	160–174 days*
Brachyteles	Not known	*Macaca*	146–186 days
Cacajao	Not known	*Mandrillus*	245 days approx.
Callicebus	Not known	*Microcebus*	59–62 days
Callimico	Not known	*Nasalis*	166 days approx.
Callithrix	140 days	*Nycticebus*	193 days*
Cebuella	Not known	*Pan*	225 days
Cebus	180 days approx.	*Papio*	154–183 days
Cercocebus	Not known	*Perodicticus*	Not known
Cercopithecus		*Phaner*	Not known
(Cercopithecus)	180–213 days approx.	*Pithecia*	Not known
Cercopithecus		*Pongo*	275 days
(Miopithecus)	196 days*	*Presbytis*	168 days approx.
Cheirogaleus	70 days	*Propithecus*	150 days approx.
Chiropotes	Not known	*Ptilocercus*	Not known
Colobus	Not known	*Pygathrix*	Not known
Cynopithecus	155–175 days	*Rhinopithecus*	Not known
Dendrogale	Not known	*Saguinus*	140 days approx.
Daubentonia	Not known	*Saimiri*	168–182 days
Erythrocebus	170 days (estimated)	*Simias*	Not known
Galago		*Symphalangus*	230–235 days
crassicaudatus	130–135* days	*Tarsius*	180 days approx.
Galago senegalensis	144–146 days	*Theropithecus*	Not known
Gorilla	251–289 days	*Tupaia*	41–50 days
Hapalemur	Not known	*Urogale*	54–56 days approx.
Hylobates	210 days approx.		

* Based on one or two observations.

2. CHROMOSOME DIPLOID NUMBERS OF THE PRIMATES

		20 +	30 +	40	42	44	46	48	50 +	60 +	70 +	80
Tupaiidae												
Tupaia	T. glis									60, 62		
Urogale	U. everetti	26*				44						
Lemuridae												
Lemur	L. catta								56			
	L. variegatus						46					
	L. macaco macaco					44						
	L. macaco fulvus							48				
	L. macaco rufus									60		
	L. macaco albifrons									60		
Hapalemur	H. griseus griseus								54			
	H. griseus olivaceus								58			
Cheirogaleus												
	C. major									66		
Microcebus	M. murinus									66		
Propithecus	P. verreauxi							48				
Lorisidae												
Galago	G. senegalensis		38									
	G. crassicaudatus									62		
Nycticebus	N. coucang								50			
	N. pygmaeus								50			
Perodicticus												
	P. potto									62		
Tarsiidae												
Tarsius	T. bancanus											80
Cebidae												
Aotus	A. trivirgatus						·		54			
Callicebus	C. moloch						46					
Pithecia	P. pithecia						46					
Cacajao	C. rubicundus						46					
Alouatta	A. seniculus					44						
Cebus	C. apella								54			
	C. capucinus								54			
Saimiri	S. sciureus					44						
Ateles	A. geoffroyi		34									
	A. belzebuth		34									
	A. paniscus		34									
Lagothrix	L. lagothricha									62		
Brachyteles	B. arachnoides		34*									

	20 +	30 +	40	42	44	46	48	50 +	60 +	70 +	80
Callitrichidae											
Callithrix C. jacchus						46					
C. chrysoleuca						46					
Cebuella C. pygmaea					44						
Saguinus S. illigeri						46					
Leontideus L. rosalia						46					
Callimico C. goeldii							48				
Cercopithecidae											
Cercopithecus											
C. aethiops									60		
C. diana								58	60		
C. neglectus								58	62		
C. mona									66		
C. cephus									66		
C. nictitans									66	70	
C. mitis										72	
C. lhoesti										72	
C. nigroviridis									60		
C. talapoin								54			
Erythrocebus											
E. patas								54			
Cercocebus All species				42							
Mandrillus M. sphinx				42							
M. leucophaeus				42							
Papio All spp. (except											
P. ursinus)				42							
Theropithecus											
T. gelada				42							
Macaca All species				42							
Cynopithecus											
C. niger				42							
Colobus C. polykomos					44						
Presbytis P. obscurus					44						
P. entellus								50			
Hylobatidae											
Hylobates H. lar, H. agilis					44						
H. hoolock					44						
Symphalangus											
S. syndactylus								50			
Pongidae											
Pongo P. pygmaeus							48				
Pan P. troglodytes							48				
Gorilla G. gorilla							48				
Hominidae											
Homo H. sapiens						46					

* Tentative data.

3. LONGEVITY RECORD IN CAPTIVITY†

Alouatta	3 yr 9 mo	*Indri*	—	
Anathana	—	*Lagothrix*[14]	12 yr 0 mo	
Aotus	11 yr 7 mo	*Lemur*	27 yr 1 mo	
Arctocebus	4 yr 6 mo	*Leontideus*	10 yr 4 mo	
Ateles[12]	20 yr 0 mo	*Lepilemur*	0 yr 3 mo	
Avahi	—	*Loris*	7 yr 0 mo	
Brachyteles	1 yr 8 mo	*Macaca*	29 yr 4 mo	
Cacajao	8 yr 9 mo	*Mandrillus*	28 yr 6 mo	
Callicebus	4 yr 2 mo	*Microcebus*	15 yr 5 mo	
Callimico	2 yr 4 mo	*Nasalis*[5]	4 yr 6 mo	
Callithrix[1]	12 yr 0 mo	*Nycticebus*	12 yr 8 mo	
Cebuella[12]	4 yr 11 mo	*Pan*[6]	41 yr 0 mo	
Cebus[2]	40 yr approx.	*Papio*	29 yr 10 mo	
Cercocebus	20 yr 9 mo	*Perodicticus*	8 yr 11 mo	
Cercopithecus		*Phaner*	—	
(*Cercopithecus*)	31 yr 0 mo	*Pithecia*	13 yr 8 mo	
(*Allenopithecus*)	8 yr 8 mo	*Pongo*	30 yr 8 mo	
(*Miopithecus*)	22 yr 3 mo	*Presbytis*[7]	20 yr 0 mo	
Cheirogaleus	8 yr 8 mo	*Propithecus*[8]	7 yr 0 mo	
Chiropotes	15 yr 0 mo	*Ptilocercus*	—	
Colobus		*Pygathrix*	0 yr 4 mo	
(*Colobus*)[3]	24 yr 0 mo	*Rhinopithecus*	—	
(*Piliocolobus*)	2 yr 0 mo	*Saguinus*		
(*Procolobus*)	—	(*Saguinus*)	7 yr 6 mo	
Cynopithecus	16 yr 7 mo	(*Oedipomidas*)	7 yr 8 mo	
Dendrogale	—	(*Marikina*)	9 yr 10 mo	
Daubentonia[4]	3 yr 0 mo	*Saimiri*[9]	21 yr 0 mo	
Erythrocebus	20 yr 2 mo	*Simias*	—	
Galago		*Symphalangus*	16 yr 2 mo	
(*Galago*)	14 yr 0 mo	*Tarsius*[10]	12 yr 0 mo	
(*Galagoides*)	2 yr 10 mo	*Theropithecus*	10 yr 5 mo	
(*Euoticus*)	—	*Tupaia*		
Gorilla	33 yr 5 mo	(*Tupaia*)[11]	5 yr 6 mo	
Hapalemur	12 yr 1 mo	(*Lyonogale*)	2 yr 4 mo	
Hylobates	31 yr 6 mo	*Urogale*[13]	7 yr 0 mo	

† Data from Jones (1962) unless otherwise stated.

REFERENCES

1. International Zoo Year Book, Vol. II (1960)
2. Hill, C. A. (1964b)
3. Hill, C. A. (1964a)
4. International Zoo Year Book, Vol. II (1960)
5. Pournelle, G. H. (1966)
6. Riopelle, A. J. (1963)
7. Hill, C. A. (1964a)
8. Hill, W. C. Osman (1953)
9. Hume, E. M. (1957)
10. Ulmer, F. A. (1960)
11. Sprankel, H. (1965) (Personal communication)
12. Crandall, L. S. (1964)
13. Rabb, G. B. (1965) (Personal communication)
14. Badham, M. (1966) (Personal communication)

4. COMPARATIVE WEIGHTS OF PRIMATES

(Order based on heaviest weight of ♂)

	No. ♂♂	Grams	No. ♀♀	Grams
Ptilocercus	4	46 av.	—	—
Tarsius	10	95–165	8	87–154
Tupaia glis	—	177 av.	—	159 av.
Galago senegalensis	10	300 av.	9	229 av.
Saguinus (Saguinus)	3	264–341	4	264–395
Loris	16	85–348	7	85–270
Urogale	1	355	—	—
Callithrix	4	175–360	9	167–335
Callimico	—	472 av.	—	—
		(11 ♀♀ + ♂♂)		
Saguinus (Oedipomidas)	5	300–510	3	337–567
Leontideus	1	553	1	480
Callicebus	1	681	—	—
Aotus	2	825, 1020	2	780, 1249
Saimiri	14	550–1135	5	365–750
Galago crassicaudatus	10	1241 av.	13	1034 av.
Cercopithecus (Miopithecus)	2	1230, 1280	2	745, 820
Perodicticus	2	1025, 1400	2	1000, 1200
Pithecia	6	1578 av.	5	1406 av.
Nycticebus	9	1012–1675	3	1105–1370
Lemur	3	2103 av.	2	1703, 2384
Hapalemur	1	2625	1	2550
Chiropotes	2	2770, 3130	—	—
Cebus	18	1150–3320	—	—
Colobus (Procolobus)	7	3300–4400	5	2900–4100
Cercopithecus (Cercopithecus)	38	3178–6356	36	1816–3859
Ateles	2	5470, 6887	1	5824
Simias	—	—	1	7151
Alouatta	4	7392 av.	4	5720 av.
Hylobates	41	4300–7928	30	4110–6800
Lagothrix	7	3600–10,000	7	5000–6500
Cynopithecus	—	10,000–11,200	—	5100–7700
Erythrocebus	3	7483–12,600	4	4082–7100
Brachyteles	—	—	1	9500
Symphalangus	5	9500–12,700	5	9000–11,600
Macaca	87	3500–18,000	88	2500–16,300
Mandrillus sphinx	1	19,522	—	—
Presbytis	76	3650–20,884	79	3178–17,706
Nasalis	21	11,700–23,608	18	8165–11,794
Theropithecus (estimated)	1	20,500	1	13,620
Papio	—	22,000–30,000	—	11,000–15,000

	No. ♂♂	Grams	No. ♀♀	Grams
Pan	2	48,900 av.	4	40,600 av.
Pongo	4	69,000 av.	5	37,000 av.
Gorilla (estimated)	—	140,000–180,000	—	75,000–110,000

5. COMPARATIVE DIMENSIONS OF PRIMATES

(Order based on longest head and body length of male)

	No.	Sex	Head and body length (mm)	Tail length (mm)
Microcebus murinus	1	—	130	170
Dendrogale	9	♂♂	103–130	110–145
	7	♀♀	107–150	105–145
Tupaia (Tupaia) minor	25	♂♂	105–142	142–165
	19	♀♀	118–170	130–165
Ptilocercus	6	♂♂	120–143	165–180
	5	♀♀	120–140	170–180
Cebuella	6	—	130–144	197–210
Tarsius	9	♂♂	85–159	135–274
	14	♀♀	95–160	189–239
Galago (Galagoides)	—		125–160	182–199
Galago (Galago) senegalensis	10	♂♂	151–173	217–250
	10	♀♀	150–163	205–248
Anathana	5	♂♂	160–180	169–195
	3	♀♀	177–185	165–187
Callimico	2	♂♂	190, 215	255, 325
	1	♀	190	270
Callithrix	50	♂♂	173–220	243–375
	43	♀♀	158–240	247–385
Tupaia (Tupaia) glis	158	♂♂	140–230	129–215
	164	♀♀	143–225	130–205
Urogale	5	♂♂	182–235	148–170
	2	♀♀	200, 202	147, 150
Galago (Euoticus)	—	—	187–235	280–332
Tupaia (Lyonogale)	32	♂♂	161–240	145–196
	28	♀♀	175–240	140–190
Saguinus (Oedipomidas)	5	♂♂	219–245	362–382
	1	♀	250	370
Microcebus coquereli	—	—	250	280
Arctocebus	6	♂♂	220–251	8 approx.
	2	♀♀	231, 263	8 approx.
Loris	11	♂♂	186–264	—
	9	♀♀	198–249	—
Cheirogaleus	5	—	190–267	165–250
Phaner	—	—	250–275	325–350

	No.	Sex	Head and body length (mm)	Tail length (mm)
Saguinus (Marikina)	4	♂♂	219–292	349–368
	6	♀♀	210–250	235–420
Saguinus (Saguinus)	23	♂♂	170–310	275–420
	25	♀♀	155–280	325–425
Avahi	2	—	300, 330	390, 395
Lepilemur	3	—	280–356	254–280
Leontideus	6	—	227–370	300–360
Cercopithecus (Miopithecus)	1	♂	350	375
	2	♀♀	340, 370	360, 380
Saimiri	34	♂♂	249–370	367–465
	12	♀♀	225–295	370–445
Hapalemur	2	♂♂	365, 370	365
	3	♀♀	260–330	240–350
Galago crassicaudatus	4	♂♂	319–373	439–473
	4	♀♀	297–336	415–426
Nycticebus	15	♂♂	265–380	—
	14	♀♀	268–335	—
Callicebus	71	—	287–390	331–493
Daubentonia	—	—	400	560–600
Perodicticus	11	♂♂	337–406	50–81
	6	♀♀	355–417	56–72
Chiropotes	3	♂♂	400–407	380
	1	♀	460	350
Lemur (except L. variegatus)	11	—	303–456	370–560
Aotus	20	—	240–475	220–418
Pithecia	11	♂♂	355–480	315–510
	12	♀♀	300–425	255–545
Colobus (Procolobus)	8	♂♂	430–480	570–640
	6	♀♀	435–490	570–640
Cacajao	4	♂♂	435–485	155–185
	3	♀♀	365–445	150–165
Cercopithecus (Allenopithecus)	2	♂♂	460, 510	500, 525
	1	♀	410	355
Propithecus	4	—	458–534	483–560
Simias	3	♂♂	490–550	130–190
	3	♀♀	460–550	100–150
Cebus	77	♂♂	320–565	342–560
	51	♀♀	323–480	290–510
Lagothrix	58	♂♂	414–568	560–690
	51	♀♀	390–580	597–730
Ateles	17	♂♂	370–590	630–823
	30	♀♀	344–660	613–920
Colobus (Piliocolobus)	34	♂♂	455–610	550–800
	23	♀♀	470–600	412–790
Lemur variegatus	1	—	612	611

	No.	Sex	Head and body length (mm)	Tail length (mm)
Cercocebus	25	♂♂	515–615	690–940
	24	♀♀	435–580	590–895
Brachyteles	6	♂♂	462–630	650–741
	3	♀♀	470–565	740–800
Hylobates	62	♂♂	403–635	—
	38	♀♀	408–622	—
Cercopithecus (Cercopithecus)	107	♂♂	410–645	575–1090
	96	♀♀	315–520	480–1020
Colobus (Colobus)	37	♂♂	490–690	670–890
	28	♀♀	485–640	645–880
Indri	1	—	700	30
Mandrillus leucophaeus	1	♂	700	120
Macaca	115	♂♂	412–700	0–686
	81	♀♀	345–680	0–634
Alouatta	35	♂♂	465–720	490–748
	34	♀♀	390–573	490–711
Nasalis	11	♂♂	555–723	660–745
	4	♀♀	540–605	570–620
Theropithecus	2	♂♂	690,740	460,500
	2	♀♀	500,650	325,410
Erythrocebus	10	♂♂	575–750	620–740
Papio	5	♂♂	735–785	520–600
	4	♀♀	562–660	415–530
Presbytis	162	♂♂	415–787	495–1092
	131	♀♀	432–695	599–1016
Cynopithecus	4	♂♂	520–800	10–20
	4	♀♀	500–610	10–20
Mandrillus sphinx	1	♂	810	70
Pygathrix	6	♂♂	550–820	600–769
	2	♀♀	597, 630	597, 665
Rhinopithecus	7	♂♂	560–830	610–920
	5	♀♀	500–740	510–1040
Symphalangus	9	♂♂	468–846	—
	9	♀♀	460–630	—
Pan	7	♂♂	770–925	—
	4	♀♀	700–850	—
Pongo	7	♂♂	953 av.	—
	11	♀♀	777 av.	—

REFERENCES

Affolter, M. (1938). Les organes cutanés brachiaux ♂ *Hapalemur griseus*. *Bull. Acad. malgache* **20**: 77–100.

Akeley, Carl E. (1922). Hunting gorillas in Central Africa. *Wld's Work* **44**: 169–183, 307–318, 393–399, 525–533.

Allen, G. M. (1939). A checklist of African mammals. *Bull. Mus. comp. Zool. Harv.* **83**: 1–763.

Allen, G. M. (1938). *The mammals of China and Mongolia*, Part I. New York: American Museum of Natural History.

Allen, G. M., Lawrence, B., and Loveridge, A. (1936). Scientific results of an expedition to rain forest regions in E. Africa. III. Mammals. *Bull. Mus. comp. Zool. Harv.* **79**: 31–126.

Allen, G. M., and Loveridge, A. (1942). Scientific results of a fourth expedition to forested areas in East and Central Africa. I. Mammals. *Bull. Mus. comp. Zool. Harv.* **89**: 145–214.

Allen, J. A. (1916). Mammals collected on the Roosevelt Brazilian expedition, with field notes by Leo E. Miller. *Bull. Am. Mus. nat. Hist.* **35**: 559–610.

Allen, J. A. (1925). Primates collected by the American Museum Congo Expedition. *Bull. Am. Mus. nat. Hist.* **47**: 283–499.

Altmann, S. A. (1959). Field observations on a howling monkey society. *J. Mammal.* **40**: 317–330.

Altmann, S. A. (1962). A field study of the sociobiology of Rhesus monkeys, *Macaca mulatta*. *Ann. N.Y. Acad. Sci.* **102**: 338–435.

Amoroso, E. C. (1959). Comparative anatomy of the placenta. *Ann. N.Y. Acad. Sci.* **75**: 855–872.

Andrew, R. J. (1962). The situations that evoke vocalisation in primates. *Ann. N.Y. Acad. Sci.* **102**: 296–315.

Andrew, R. J. (1963). Evolution of vocalisation in monkeys and apes. *Symp. zool. Soc. Lond.* **10**: 89–101.

Andrew, R. J. (1964). Displays of the primates. In *Evolutionary and genetic biology of primates*, Vol. II. (Ed. Buettner-Janusch, J.) New York and London: Academic Press.

Ankel, F. (1965). Der canalis sacralis als indikator für die länge der caudalregion der Primaten. *Folia primat.* **3**: 263–276.

Ansell, W. F. H. (1960). *Mammals of northern Rhodesia*. Lusaka: Govt. Printer.

Appelman, F. J. (1954). Über *Theropithecus gelada* Rüppell. *Zool. Gart.* **20**: 95–98.

Appelman, F. J. (1957). Noch einige worte über *Theropithecus gelada* Rüppell. *Zool. Gart.* **23**: 246–247.

Asdell, S. A. (1946). *Patterns of mammalian reproduction*. London: Constable.

Ashton, E. H., Healy, M. J. R., Oxnard, C. E., and Spence, T. F. (1965). Canonical analysis of the primate shoulder. *J. Zool. Lond.* **147**: 406–429.

Ashton, E. H., and Oxnard, C. E. (1963). The musculature of the primate shoulder. *Trans. zool. Soc. Lond.* **29**: 553–650.

Ashton, E. H., and Oxnard, C. E. (1964a). Functional adaptations in the primate shoulder. *Proc. zool. Soc. Lond.* **142**: 49–66.

Ashton, E. H., and Oxnard, C. E. (1964b). Locomotor patterns in primates. *Proc. zool. Soc. Lond.* **142**: 1–28.

Ashton, E. H., and Zuckerman, S. (1950a). Influence of geographic isolation on the skull of the green monkey (*Cercopithecus aethiops sabaeus*). Part I. *Proc. R. Soc. B.* **137**: 212–238.

Ashton, E. H., and Zuckerman, S. (1950b). Some quantitative dental characteristics of the chimpanzee, gorilla and orang-outang. *Phil. Trans. R. Soc.* **234**: 471–484.

Ashton, E. H., and Zuckerman, S. (1952). The mastoid process in the chimpanzee and gorilla. *Am. J. phys. Anthrop.* **10**: 145–153.

Attenborough, D. (1957). *Zoo quest for a dragon*. London: Lutterworth Press.

Attenborough, D. (1961). *Zoo quest to Madagascar*. London: Lutterworth Press.

Attenborough, D. (1963). *Zoo quest to Madagascar*. B.B.C. film.

Aulmann, G. (1932). Geglückte Wachzucht eines Orang-Utan im Düsseldorfer Zoo. *Zool. Gart.* **5**: 81–90.

Avila-Pires, F. D. de (1966). On criteria for selection of laboratory primates. *Laboratory Primate Newsletter* **5**, No. 2: 21–22.

Avis, Virginia (1962). Brachiation: the crucial issue for man's ancestry. *Southwestern J. Anthrop.* **18**: 119–148.

Avon, F. (1963). Drills and Mandrills. *Animal Life* **13**.

Ayer, A. A. (1948). *The anatomy of* Semnopithecus entellus. Madras: Indian Publ. House Ltd.

Banks, E. (1926). in Clark, W. E. Le Gros. The anatomy of the pen-tailed treeshrew. *Proc. zool. Soc. Lond.* 1179–1309.

Banks, E. (1949). *A naturalist in Sarawak.* Kuching: The Kuching Press.

Banks, E. (1961). The distribution of mammals and birds in the South China Sea and West Sumatran Islands. *Bull. natn. Mus. St. Singapore* **30**: 92–96.

Bard, P., and Mountcastle, V. B. (1948). Some forebrain mechanisms involved in the expression of rage. *Res. Publ. Assoc. Nerv. Disorders.* 362–404.

Barnett, C. H., and Napier, J. R. (1953). Rotatory mobility of the fibula in Eutherian mammals. *J. Anat.* **87**: 207–213.

Barnicot, N. A., and Jolly, C. J. (1966). Haemoglobin polymorphism in the orang-utan and an animal with four major haemoglobins. *Nature, Lond.* **210**: 640–642.

Barnicot, N. A., Huens, E. R., and Jolly, C. J. (In press). Biochemical studies on Hb variants of the Irus Macaque. *Proc. R. Soc.* B.

Bartlett, E. (1871). Notes on the monkeys of Eastern Peru. *Proc. zool. Soc. Lond.* 217–220.

Bates, G. L. (1905). Notes on the mammals of the South Cameroons and the Benito. *Proc. zool. Soc. Lond.* 65–85.

Bates, H. W. (1863). *"The Naturalist on the River Amazons."* Vols. I and II. London: John Murray.

Beattie, J. (1927). Anatomy of the Common Marmoset. (*Hapale jacchus* Kuhl) *Proc. zool. Soc. Lond.* 513–718.

Beddard, F. (1884). Some points in the structure of *Hapalemur griseus. Proc. zool. Soc. Lond.* 391–399.

Beddard, Frank E. (1908). Some notes on the anatomy of *Chiromys madagascariensis. Proc. zool. Soc. Lond.* 694.

Belt, J. (1874). *A Naturalist in Nicaragua.* London: E. Bumpus.

Benchley, B. (1938). Notes on birth and infancy of a baby gibbon. *Zoonooz* **10**, No. 8: 1–7.

Benchley, B. (1942). *My friends, the apes.* Boston: Little, Brown & Co.

Bender, M. A., and Chu, E. H. Y. (1963). Chromosomes of primates. In *Evolutionary and genetic biology of primates*, Vol. I. (Ed. Buettner-Janusch, J.) New York and London: Academic Press.

Bender, M. A., and Mettler, L. E. (1958). Chromosome studies of Primates. *Science, N.Y.* **128**: 186–190.

Benirschke, K., Anderson, J. M., and Brownhill, L. E. (1962). Marrow chimerism in marmosets. *Science, N.Y.* **138**: 513–515.

Bernstein, I. S. (1964). The integration of Rhesus monkeys introduced to a group. *Folia primat.* **2**: 50–63.

Bernstein, I. S. (1965). Activity patterns in a *Cebus* monkey group. *Folia primat.* **3**: 211–224.

Bernstein, I. S., and Mason, W. A. (1963). Group formation by Rhesus monkeys. *Anim. Behav.* **11**: 28–31.

Biegert, J. (1961). *Primatologia* II. Teil I. Lieferung 3: Volarhaut der Hände und Füsse. Basel: S. Karger.

Biegert, J. (1964). The evaluation of characteristics of the skull, hands and feet for primate taxonomy. In *Classification and Human Evolution.* (Ed. Washburn, S. L.) Viking Press Publ. Anthrop, No. 37. New Work: Wenner-Gren Foundation.

Bigourdan, J., and Prunier, R. (1937). Quoted in Tappen (1960).

Bingham, H. C. (1932). Gorillas in a native habitat. *Carnegie Inst. Wash. Publ.* **426**: 1–66.

Bischoff, T. L. W. (1870). Beiträge zur Anatomie des *Hylobates leuciscus*. *Abh. Math. Phys. Cl. Ak. Wiss. München* **10**: 199–297.

Bishop, A. (1962). Hand control in lower primates. *Ann. N.Y. Acad. Sci.* **102**: 316–337.

Bishop, A. (1964). Use of the hand in lower primates. In *Evolutionary and genetic biology of primates*. Vol. II. (Ed. Buettner-Janusch, J.) New York and London: Academic Press.

Bode, N. C. (1952). Sakis, Elves of the Amazon. *Zoonooz* **25**, No. 4: 5–6.

Bode, N. C. (1953). "Just like Daddy" Saki, Jr. *Zoonooz* **26**, No. 12: 5.

Böker, H. (1932). Beobachtungen und Untersuchungen an Säugetieren während einer biologisch-anatomischen Forschreise nach Brasilien im Jahre 1928. *Morph. Jb.* **70**: 1–66.

Bolk, L. (1914). *Odontologische Studien*, Vol. 2, *Die Morphogenie der Primatzähne*. Jena: G. Fischer.

Bolk, L. (1915). Über Lagerung, Verschiebung und Neigung des Foramen magnum am Schädel der Primaten. *Z. Morph. Anthrop.* **17**: 611–692.

Bolk, L. (1926). *Das Problem der Menschwerdung*. Jena: G. Fischer.

Bolwig, N. (1959). A study of the behaviour of the Chacma baboon. *Behaviour* **14**: 136–163.

Bonhote, J. L. (1907). On a collection of mammals made by Dr. Vassal in Annam. *Proc. zool. Soc. Lond.* 3–11.

Booth, A. H. (1954). A note on the Colobus monkeys of the Gold and Ivory Coast. *Ann. Mag. nat. Hist.* **7** (12): 857–860.

Booth, A. H. (1955). Speciation in the Mona monkeys. *J. Mammal.* **36**: 434–449.

Booth, A. H. (1956a). The Cercopithecidae of the Gold and Ivory coasts: geographic and systematic observations. *Ann. Mag. natn. Hist.* **9** (12): 476–480.

Booth, A. H. (1956b). The distribution of Primates in the Gold Coast. *Jl. W. Afr. Sci. Ass.* **2**: 122–133.

Booth, A. H. (1957). Observations on the natural history of the Olive Colobus monkey, *Procolobus verus* (van Beneden). *Proc. zool. Soc. Lond.* **129**: 421–430.

Booth, A. H. (1958). The Zoogeography of West African primates: A Review. *Bull. Inst. fr. Afr. Noire* **20**: 587–622.

Booth, C. (1962). Some observations on the behaviour of *Cercopithecus* monkeys. *Ann. N.Y. Acad. Sci.* **102**: 477–487.

Boulenger, E. G. (1936). *Apes and monkeys*. London: Harrap.

Bourlière, F., Petter-Rousseaux, A., and Petter, J. J. (1962). Regular breeding in captivity of the lesser mouse lemur. *International Zoo Yearbook* Vol. 3. (Eds. Jarvis, C. and Morris, D.) London: Zoological Society.

Bourlière, F., and Petter-Rousseaux, A. (1966). Existence probable d'un rythme métabolique saisonnier chez les Cheirogaleinae (Lemuroidea). *Folia primat.* **4**: 249–256.

Bowden, D., Winter, P., and Ploog, D. (1967). Pregnancy and delivery behaviour in the squirrel monkey (*Saimiri sciureus*) and other primates. *Folia primat.* **5**: 1–42.

Brain, C. K. (1965). Observations on the behaviour of Vervet monkeys, *Cercopithecus aethiops*. *Zoologica Africana* **1**: 13–27.

Brooks, A. Barbara (1963). More notes on *Saimiri sciureus*. *Laboratory Primate Newsletter* **2**, **4**: 3–4.

Buettner-Janusch, J., and Twickell, J. B. (1961). Alkali-resistant Hemoglobins in prosimian primates. *Nature, Lond.* **192**: 669.

Buettner-Janusch, J. (1962). Biochemical genetics of the primates—Hemoglobins and Transferrins. *Ann. N.Y. Acad. Sci.* **102**: 235–248.

Buettner-Janusch, J. (1963a). An introduction to the primates. In *Evolutionary and Genetic Biology of the Primates*. Vol. I. (Ed. Buettner-Janusch, J.) New York and London: Academic Press.

Buettner-Janusch, J. (1963b). Hemoglobins and Transferrins of baboons. *Folia primat.* **1**: 73–87.

Buettner-Janusch, J. (1964). The breeding of galagos in captivity and some notes on their behaviour. *Folia primat.* **2**: 93–110.

Buettner-Janusch, J., and Andrew, R. J. (1962). The use of the incisors by primates in grooming. *Am. J. phys. Anthrop.* **20**: 129–132.

Buettner-Janusch, J., and Buettner-Janusch, V. (1963). Haemoglobins of *Galago crassicaudatus*. *Nature, Lond.* **197**: 1018–1019.

Buettner-Janusch, J., and Buettner-Janusch, V. (1964). Hemoglobins of primates. In *Evolutionary and genetic biology of primates*, Vol. II. (Ed. Buettner-Janusch, J.) New York and London: Academic Press.

Burmeister, H. C. C. (1846). *Beiträge zur Kenntnis der Gattung Tarsius*. Berlin: G. Reimer.

Burmeister, H. C. C. (1854–56). *Systematische Uebersicht der Thiere Brasiliens*. Berlin.

Butler, H. (1960). Some notes on the breeding cycle of the Senegal Galago *Galago senegalensis senegalensis* in the Sudan. *Proc. zool. Soc. Lond.* **135**: 423–430.

Butler, H. (1966). Some notes on the distribution of primates in the Sudan. *Folia primat.* **4**: 416–423.

Butler, H. (1967). Seasonal breeding of the Senegal Galago (*Galago senegalensis senegalensis*) in the Nuba mountains, Republic of the Sudan. *Folia primat.* **5**: 165–175.

Büttikofer, J. (1917). Die Kurzschwanzaffen von Celebes. *Zoöl. Med. Mus. Leiden* **3**: 1–86.

Butterfield, R. S. (1954). The slow loris as a pet. *Malay. Nat. J.* **9**: 43–49.

Buxton, A. P. (1951). Further observations on the night-resting habits of monkeys in a small area on the edge of the Semliki forest, Uganda. *J. Anim. Ecol.* **20**: 31–32.

Cabrera, A. (1900). Quoted in Hershkovitz, P. (1963). *Mammalia* **27**: 1–79.

Cabrera, A. (1956). Sobre la identificacion de *Simia leonina* Humboldt. *Neotropica* **2**: No. 8: 49–53.

Cabrera, A. (1957). *Catalogo de los mamiferos de America del Sur*. Instituto Nacional de Investigacion de la Ciencias Naturales, Ciencio Zoologica. IV: No. 1, Buenos Aires y Peru.

Cabrera, A., and Ruxton, A. E. (1926). On the mammals of Luluabourg. *Ann. Mag. nat. Hist.* **17**: 591–602.

Cain, S. A., and Castro, G. M. de O. (1959). *Manual of vegetation analysis*. New York: Harper.

Campbell, C. B. G. (1966). Taxonomic status of treeshrews. *Science N.Y.* **153**: 436.

Cansdale, G. S. (1944). *Galago demidovii*. *J. Soc. Preserv. Fauna Emp.* **50**: 7.

Cansdale, G. S. (1946). *Animals of West Africa*. London: Longmans, Green & Co.

Cantor, T. (1846). Catalogue of Mammalia inhabiting the Malayan peninsula and islands. *J. Asiat. Soc. Beng.* **15**: 171–241.

Carmichael, L., Kraus, M. B., and Reed, T. (1961). The Washington National Zoological Park gorilla infant, Tomoko. *International Zoo Yearbook*. Vol. III. (Eds. Jarvis, C. and Morris, D.). London: Zoological Society.

Carpenter, C. R. (1934). A field study of the behaviour and social relations of howling monkeys. *Comp. Psychol. Monogr.* **10** (48): 1–168.

Carpenter, C. R. (1935). Behaviour of the Red Spider Monkey (*Ateles geoffroyi*) in Panama. *J. Mammal.* **16**: 171–180.

Carpenter, C. R. (1938). A survey of wildlife conditions in Atjeh of North Sumatra with special reference to the Orang-utan. *Amsterdam, Netherlands Committee for International Nature Protection*. Communications No. 12: 1–34.

Carpenter, C. R. (1940). A field study in Siam of the behaviour and social relations of the gibbon (*Hylobates lar*). *Comp. Psychol. Monogr.* **16** (5): 1–212.

Carpenter, C. R. (1941). The menstrual cycle and body temperature in two gibbons. *Anat. Rec.* **79**, No. 3: 291–296.

Carpenter, C. R. (1942a). Sexual behaviour of free-ranging Rhesus monkeys (*Macaca mulatta*). *J. comp. Psychol.* **33**: 113–162.

Carpenter, C. R. (1942b). Societies of monkeys and apes. *Biological Symposia* **8**: 177–204.

Carpenter, C. R. (1954). Tentative generalization on the grouping behaviour of non-human primates. *Hum. Biol.* **26**: 267–276.

Carpenter, C. R. (1958). Quoted in Altmann, S. A. (1962). *Ann. N.Y. Acad. Sci.* **102**: 338–435.

Carpenter, C. R. (1965). The howlers of Barro Colorado Island. In *Primate Behaviour* (Ed. Devore, I.) New York: Holt, Rinehart and Winston.

Catchpole, H. R., and Fulton, J. F. (1943). The oestrus cycle in *Tarsius*: observations on a captive pair. *J. Mammal.* **24**: 90–93.

Causey, O. R., Laemmert, H. W., and Hayes, G. S. (1948). The home range of Brazilian Cebus monkeys in a region of small residual forests. *Ann. J. Hyg.* **47**: 304–314.

Chacko, L. W. (1954). A comparative study of the distribution of the fibre size in the optic nerve of mammals. *J. anat. Soc. India* **3**: 11–23.

Chacko, L. W. (1955). The lateral geniculate body in gibbon (*Hylobates hoolook*). *J. anat. Soc. India* **4**: 69–81.

Chance, M. R. A. (1956). Social structure of a colony of *Macaca mulatta*. *Br. J. Anim. Behav.* **4**: 1–13.

Chapman, F. M. (1937). My monkey neighbours on Barro Colorado. *Nat. Hist., N.Y.* **40**: 471–479.

Chase, R. E., and De Garis, C. F. (1939). Arteriae coronariae (cordis) in the higher primates. *Am. J. phys. Anthrop.* **24**: 427–448.

Chasen, F. N. (1935). On a collection of mammals from the Natuna islands, South China Sea. *Bull. Raffles Mus.* **10**: 5–42.

Chasen, F. N. (1940). A handlist of Malaysian mammals. *Bull. Raffles Mus.* **15**: 1–209.

Chasen, F. N., and Kloss, C. Boden (1927). Spolia Mentawensia.—Mammals. *Proc. zool. Soc. Lond.* 797–840.

Chasen, F. N., and Kloss, C. Boden (1931). On a collection of mammals from the lowlands and islands of North Borneo. *Bull. Raffles Mus.* **6**: 1–82.

Chiarelli, B. (1961). Chromosomes of the Orang-utan (*Pongo pygmaeus*). *Nature, Lond.* **192**: 285.

Chiarelli, B. (1962a). Comparative morphometric analysis of primate chromosomes. I. The chromosomes of anthropoid apes and of man. *Caryologia* **15**: 99–12.

Chiarelli, B. (1962b). Comparative morphometric analysis of primate chromosomes. II. The chromosomes of the genera *Macaca, Papio, Theropithecus* and *Cercocebus*. *Caryologia* **15**: 401–420.

Chiarelli, B. (1963a). Comparative morphometric analysis of primate chromosomes. III. The chromosomes of the genera *Hylobates, Colobus* and *Presbytis*. *Caryologia* **16**: 637–648.

Chiarelli, B. (1963b). Sensitivity to P.T.C. in primates. *Folia primat.* **1**: 88–94.

Chiarelli, B. (1963c). Observations on P.T.C. tasting and on hybridization in primates. *Symp. zool. Soc. Lond.* No. 10: 277–279.

Chiarelli, B. (1966a). Marked chromosome in catarrhine monkeys. *Folia primat.* **4**: 74–80.

Chiarelli, B. (1966b). Caryology and taxonomy of the catarrhine monkeys. *Am. J. phys. Anthrop.* **24**: 155–170.

Chu, E. H. Y., and Bender, M. A. (1961). Chromosome cytology and evolution in primates. *Science, N.Y.* **133**: 1399–1405.

Chu, E. H. Y., and Bender, M. A. (1962). Cytogenetics and evolution of primates. *Ann. N.Y. Acad. Sci.* **102**: 253–266.

Chu, E. H. Y., and Giles, N. H. (1957). A study of chromosome complements. *Am. Nat.* **91**: 273–282.

Clark, W. E. Le Gros. (1924a). On the brain of *Tupaia minor*. *Proc. zool. Soc. Lond.* 1053–1074.

Clark, W. E. Le Gros. (1924b). The myology of the tree-shrew (*Tupaia minor*). *Proc. zool. Soc. Lond.* 461–497.

Clark, W. E. Le Gros. (1924c). Notes on the living tarsier (*Tarsius spectrum*). *Proc. zool. Soc. Lond.* 217–223.

Clark, W. E. Le Gros. (1926). The anatomy of the pen-tailed tree shrew. *Proc. zool. Soc. Lond.* 1179–1309.

Clark, W. E. Le Gros. (1929). The thalamus of *Tupaia minor*. *J. Anat., Lond.* **63**: 117–216.

Clark, W. E. Le Gros. (1931). The brain of *Microcebus murinus*. *Proc. zool. Soc. Lond.* 463–486.

Clark, W. E. Le Gros. (1932a). A morphological study of the lateral geniculate body. *Br. J. Ophthalmol.* **16**: 264–284.

Clark, W. E. Le Gros. (1932b). The brain of Insectivora. *Proc. zool. Soc. Lond.* 975–1013.

Clark, W. E. Le Gros. (1936). The problem of the claw in primates. *Proc. zool. Soc. Lond.* 1–24.

Clark, W. E. Le Gros (1959). *The antecedents of man*. Edinburgh: University Press.

Clark, W. E. Le Gros, and Leakey, L. S. B. (1951). *The Miocene Hominoidea of East Africa*. Fossil Mammals of Africa, No. 1. London: British Museum (N.H.).

Cole, J. (1963). *Macaca nemestrina* studied in captivity. *Symp. zool. Soc. Lond.* No. 10: 105–114.

Collias, N. E., and Southwick, C. H. (1952). A field study of population density and social organisation in howling monkeys. *Proc. Am. Phil. Soc.* **96**: 144–156.

Collyer, F. (1936). Variation and diseases of the teeth of animals. London; John Bate, Sons and Danielsson.

Conaway, C. H., and Sorenson, M. W. (1966). Reproduction in tree shrews. In *Comparative Biology o Reproduction in Mammals. Symp. zool. Soc. Lond.*, No. 15, London and New York: Academic Press.

Conisbee, L. R. (1953). *A list of the names proposed for genera and subgenera of recent mammals, from the publication of T. S. Palmer's "Index generum mammalium" 1904 to the end of 1951*. London: British Museum (Natural History).

Coolidge, H. J. (1929). A revision of the Genus *Gorilla*. *Mem. Mus. comp. Zool. Harv.* **50**: 291–381.

Coolidge, H. J. (1933a). Notes on a family of breeding gibbons. *Hum. Biol.* **5**: 288–294.

Coolidge, H. J. (1933b). *Pan paniscus*, pigmy chimpanzee from south of the Congo river. *Am. J. phys. Anthrop.* **18**: 1–57.

Corner, E. J. H. (1955). Botanical collecting with monkeys. *Proc. R. Inst. G.B.* **36**: 1.

Crandall, Lee S. (1964). *Management of wild animals in captivity*. Chicago and London: Univ. Chicago Press.

Crook, J. H. (in press). Gelada baboon herd structure and movement. *Symp. zool. Soc. Lond.*

Cruz Lima, E. da (1945). *Mammals of Amazonia*, Vol. I. *General Introduction and Primates*. Rio de Janeiro: Livraria Agir Editora.

Cuming, H. (1838). On the habits of some species of Mammalia from the Philippine Islands. *Proc. zool. Soc. Lond.* 67–68.

Cummins, Harold, and Spragg, S. D. S. (1938). Dermatoglyphics in the chimpanzee: description and comparison with man. *Hum. Biol.* **10**, 4: 457–510.

Dahr, P. (1937). Zur Frage der serologischen Verschiedenheit von Altweltaffen (Catarrhini) und Neuweltaffen (Platyrrhini). *Z. Immun. Forsch.* **90**: 376–406.

Daitz, H. M. (1953). Note on the fibre content of the fornix system in man. *Brain* **76**: 509–512.

Dandelot, P. (1959). Note sur la classification des cercopithèques du groupe Aethiops. *Mammalia* **23**: 357–368.

Dart, Raymond A. (1963). The carnivorous propensity of baboons. *Symp. zool. Soc. Lond.* No. 10: 49–56.

Darwin, C. (1872). *The expression of the emotions in man and animals*. London: John Murray.

Davenport, R. K. (1967). The Orang-utan in Sabah. *Folia primat.* **5**: 247–263.

Davies, D. V. (1947). The cardiovascular system of the slow loris. *Proc. zool. Soc. Lond.* **117**: 377–410.

Davies, D. V., and Hill, W. C. Osman (1954a). The abdominal portion of the alimentary system in *Hapalemur* and *Lepilemur*. *Proc. R. Soc. Edinb.*, B. **65**: 182–204.

Davies, D. V., and Hill, W. C. Osman (1954b). The reproductive organs in *Lepilemur* and *Hapalemur*. *Proc. R. Soc. Edinb.*, B. **65**: 251–270.

Davis, D. Dwight (1938). Notes on the anatomy of the treeshrew *Dendrogale*. *Field Mus. Publ. Chicago Zool.* **20**: 383–407.

Davis, D. Dwight (1958). Mammals of the Kelabit plateau, northern Sarawak. *Fieldiana: Zool.* **39**: 119–147.

Davis, D. Dwight (1962). Mammals of the lowland rain-forest of north Borneo. *Bull. natn. Mus. St. Singapore* **31**: 1–129.

Davis, P. R. and Napier, J. R. (1963). A reconstruction of the skull of *Proconsul africanus* (R.S. 51.) *Folia primat.* **1**: 20–28.

Day, M. H., and Napier, J. R. (1963). Functional significance of the deep head of flexor pollicis brevis in primates. *Folia primat.* **1**: 122–134.

De Beaux, O. (1925). Mammiferi dell' Abissinia raccolti dal Signor Ugo Ignesti addetto alla R. agenzia commerciale di Gondar. *Atti Soc. ital. Sci. nat.* **64**: 196–218.

De Beaux, O. (1943). Mammalia in Missione Biologica Sagan—Omo Zoologia I. R. *Acad. Ital. Centro studi Africa orient. ital.* **6**: 15–57.

Déchambre, E. (1935). Observations sur les makis de la ménagerie du Jardin des Plantes. *Bull. Mus. natn. Hist. nat.*, Paris **7**: 315–319.

Deinhardt, F., and Deinhardt, J. (1966). The use of platyrrhine monkeys in medical research. *Symp. zool. Soc. Lond.* **17**: 127–159.

Dekeyser, P. L. (1952). A propos de la tête osseuse d'un cynocéphale du Tibesti. *Bull. Inst. Fr. Afr. noire* **14**: 537–544.

Dekeyser, P. L. (1955). *Les mammifères de l'Afrique noire Française.* 2nd Ed. Dakar: I.F.A.N.

Dekeyser, P. L., and Derivot, J. (1960). Sur de nouveaux specimens de Cynocéphales du Tibesti. *Bull. Inst. Fr. Afr. noire* **22**. Ser. A., 4.

Delacour, J. (1951). La systématique des gibbons indochinois. *Mammalia* **15**: 118–123.

Deraniyagala, P. E. P. (1955). A new race of leaf-monkey from Ceylon. *Spolia zeylan.* **27**: 293–294.

Deville, E. (1855). Quoted in Hershkovitz, P. (1963). *Mammalia* **27**: 1–80.

DeVore, Irven (1963). Problems of monkey and ape behaviour. In *Classification and Human Evolution.* (Ed. Washburn, S. L.) Viking Fund Publications in Anthropology No. 37. New York: Wenner-Gren Foundation.

DeVore, I., and Washburn, S. L. (1963). Baboon ecology and human evolution. In *African Ecology and Human Evolution.* (Eds. Howell, F. C. and Bourlière, F.) Viking Fund Publications in Anthropology No. 36. New York: Wenner-Gren Foundation.

Ditmars, R. L. (1933). Development of the Silky Marmoset. *Bull. N.Y. zool. Soc.* **36**, (6): 175–176.

Dollman, G. S. (1912). A new snub-nosed monkey. *Proc. zool. Soc. Lond.* 503–504.

Dollman, G. (1937). Quoted in Hill, W. C. Osman (1957).

Donisthorpe, Jill (1958). A pilot study of the Mountain Gorilla (*G. g. beringei*) in S.W. Uganda, February to September, 1957. *S. Afr. J. Sci.* **54**: 195–217.

Doran, A. H. G. (1879). Morphology of the mammalian ossicula auditus. *Trans. Linn. Soc.* **1**: 371–497.

Drake-Brockman, R. E. (1910). *The mammals of Somaliland.* London: Hurst and Blackett, Ltd.

Draper, William A. (1963). Laboratory maintenance of the tree shrew. *Laboratory Primate Newsletter* **2**, 4: 1–2.

Du Brul, E. Lloyd (1965). The skull of the Lion Marmoset, *Leontideus rosalia* Linnaeus. *Am. J. phys. Anthrop.* **23**: 261–276.

Duckworth, W. L. H. (1915). *Morphology and Anthropology.* 2nd Edit. Vol. I. Cambridge: University Press.

Durrell, G. (1954). *The Bafut Beagles.* London: Rupert Hart-Davis.

Eckardt, H. (1930). Vergleichende morphologische Studien an den molaren des Orang-utan und des Gibbon. *Z. Morph. Anthrop.* **18**: 323–350.

Edinger, T. (1948). Evolution of the horse brain. *Mem. geol. Soc. Am.* **25**: 1–777.

Eibl-Eibesfeldt, I. (1953). Eine besondere Form des Duftmarkierens beim Reisengalago, *Galago crassicaudatus* E. Geoffroy, 1812. *Säugertierkundliche Mitt.* **1**: 171–173.

Elftman, Herbert (1944). The bipedal walking of the chimpanzee. *J. Mammal.* **25**: 67–70.

Elftman, H., and Atkinson, W. B. (1950). The abdominal viscera of the gorilla. In *The Anatomy of the Gorilla* (Ed. Gregory, W. K.) New York: Columbia Univ. Press.

Ellefson, J. O. (In press). Territorial behaviour in the common white-handed gibbon, *Hylobates lar.*

Ellerman, J. R., and Morrison-Scott, T. C. S. (1951). *Checklist of Palearctic and Indian mammals 1758–1946*. London: British Museum (Nat. Hist.).

Elliot, D. G. (1913). *A review of the primates*. Vols. I, II and III. New York: American Museum of Natural History.

Elliot-Smith, G. (1902). Catalogue of the physiological series of comparative anatomy in the Museum of the Royal College of Surgeons. **2** (2nd edit.). London: Taylor and Francis.

Ellis, R. A., and Montagna, W. (1962). The Skin of Primates VI. *Am. J. phys. Anthrop.* **20**: 79–93.

Emlen, J. T., and Schaller, G. B. (1960). Distribution and status of the mountain gorilla (*Gorilla gorilla beringei*) 1959. *Zoologica* **45** (1): 41–52.

Enders, R. K. (1930). Notes on some mammals from Barro Colorado island, Canal Zone. *J. Mammal.* **11**: 280–292.

English, W. L. (1934). Notes on the breeding of a Douroucouli (*Aotus trivirgatus*) in captivity. *Proc. zool. Soc. Lond.* 143–144.

Erikson, G. E. (1962). Quoted in Hill, W. C. Osman. 1962a.

Erikson, G. E. (1963). Brachiation in New World monkeys and in anthropoid apes. *Symp. zool. Soc. Lond.* **10**: 135–164.

Evans, C. S. (In press). Maintenance of the Philippine tarsier (*T. syrichta*) in a research colony.

Evans, F. Gayner (1942). The osteology and relationships of the Elephant Shrews. *Bull. Am. Mus. nat. Hist.* **80**: 83–125.

Fanning, Elizabeth A. (1962). Third molar emergence in Bostonians. *Am. J. phys. Anthrop.* **20**: 339–345.

Fick, R. (1895). Vergleichend–anatomische Studien an einem erwachsenen Orang-utang. *Arch. Anat.* 1–100.

Fiedler, W. (1956). Ubersicht über das system der Primates. In *Primatologia*. Vol. I. (Eds. Hofer, H., Schultz, A. H., and Starck, D.) Basel: S. Karger.

Fitzgerald, A. (1935). Rearing of marmosets in captivity. *J. Mammal.* **16**: 181–188.

Fitzinger, L. J. (1853). Untersuchung ueber die Existenz verscheidener Arten unter den asiatischen Orang-Affen. *Sber. Akad. Wiss. Wien* 400–449.

Flower, S. S. (1929). List of vertebrated animals exhibited in the gardens of the Zoological Society of London. 1828–1927 Vol. I. *Mammals*.

Fooden, J. (1963). A revision of the Woolly Monkeys (Genus *Lagothrix*). *J. Mammal* **44**: 213–247.

Fooden, J. (1964a). Rhesus and crab-eating macaques: intergradation in Thailand. *Science, N.Y.* **143**: 363–365.

Fooden, J. (1964b). Stomach contents and gastro-intestinal proportions in wild-shot Guianian monkeys. *Am. J. phys. Anthrop.* **22**: 227–232.

Fooden, J. (1967). Identification of the stump-tailed monkey, *Macaca speciosa* I. Geoffroy, 1826. *Folia primat.* **5**: 153–164.

Forbes, H. O. (1897). *A Handbook to the Primates*. Vols. I and II. London: Edward Arnold.

Fox, H. (1929). The birth of two anthropoid apes. *J. Mammal.* **10**: 37–51.

Franks, D. (1963). The blood groups of primates. *Symp. zool. Soc. Lond.* **10**: 221–250.

Freedman, L. (1957). Fossil Cercopithecoidea of South Africa. *Ann. Transv. Mus.* **23**: 121–262.

Freedman, L. (1962). Growth of muzzle length relative to calvaria length in *Papio. Growth* **26**: 117–128.

Frisch, J. E. (1959). Research in primate behaviour in Japan. *Am. Anthrop.* **61**: 584–596.

Frisch, J. E. (1963). Sex-differences in the canines of the gibbon (*Hylobates lar*). *Primates* **4**, No. 2: 1–10.

Furry, D. E., Lowery, R. T., and Beischer, D. E. (1963). Laboratory maintenance of Squirrel Monkeys. *Laboratory Primate Newsletter* **2**, 3: 1–4.

Furuya, Y. (1961–62a). The social life of the silvered leaf monkeys (*Trachypithecus cristatus*). *Primates* **3**, No. 2: 41–60.

Furuya, Y. (1961–62b). On the ecological survey of the wild crab-eating monkeys in Malaya. *Primates* **3**, No. 1: 75–76.

Gabis, R. V. (1960). Les os des membres des singes cynomorphes. *Mammalia* **24**, No. 4: 577–607.

Garner, R. L. (1900). *Apes and Monkeys: their life and language*. Quoted in Hill, W. C. Osman, 1960.

Gavan, J. A. (1953). Growth and development of the Chimpanzee. *Hum. Biol.* **25**: 93–143.

Gavan, J. A., and Swindler, Daris R. (1966). Growth rates and phylogeny in primates. *Am. J. phys. Anthrop.* **24**: 181–190.

Gavin, J., Noades, J., Tippett, P., Sanger, R., and Race, R. R. (1964). Blood group antigen Xg[a] in gibbon. *Nature, Lond.* **204**: 322.

Gee, E. P. (1955). A new species of langur in Assam. *J. Bombay nat. Hist. Soc.* **53**: 252–254.

Gee, E. P. (1961). The distribution and feeding habits of the Golden Langur, *Presbytis geei* Gee (Khajuria, 1956). *J. Bombay nat. Hist. Soc.* **58**: 1–12.

Gérard, P. (1929). Contribution à l'étude de la placentation chez les lémuriens à propos d'une anomalie de la placentation chez *Galago demidoffi* (Fisch.). *Arch. Anat. microsc.* **25**: 56–68.

Gérard, P. (1931). Les stades précoces de l'ontogénèse chez *Galago demidoffi* et le problème du mésoblaste primitif chez l'embryon humain. *Bull. Acad. Méd. Belg.* **1931**: 662–682.

Gérard, P. (1932). Études sur l'ovogénèse et l'ontogénèse chez les Lémuriens du genre *Galago*. *Arch. Biol. (Belg.)* **43**: 93–151.

Gilbert, C., and Gillman, J. (1951). Pregnancy in the baboon (*P. ursinus*). *S. Afr. J. Med. Sci.* **16**: 115–124.

Gilmore, R. M. (1943). Mammalogy in an epidemiological study of jungle yellow fever in Brazil. *J. Mammal.* **24**: 144–162.

Gloor, P. (1960). Amygdala. In *Handbook of Physiology*. Section I. *Neurophysiology*. (Ed. Field, J.). Washington: Amer. Physiol. Soc.

Goodall, J. (1962). Nest building behaviour in the free ranging chimpanzee. *Ann. N.Y. Acad. Sci.* **102**: 455–467.

Goodall, J. (1963). Feeding behaviour of wild chimpanzees. *Symp. zool. Soc. Lond.* No. 10: 39–47.

Goodall, J. (1965). Chimpanzees of the Gombe Stream Reserve. in *Primate Behaviour*. (Ed. De Vore, I) New York: Holt, Rinehart and Winston.

Goodman, M. (1962a). Evolution and immunological species specificity of human serum proteins. *Hum. Biol.* **34**: 104–150.

Goodman, M. (1962b). Immunochemistry of the primates and primate evolution. *Ann. N.Y. Acad. Sci.* **102**: 219–234.

Goodman, M. (1963). Man's place in the phylogeny of the primates as reflected in serum proteins. In *Classification and Human Evolution*. (Ed. Washburn, S. L.) Viking Publ. in Anthropology No. 37. New York: Wenner-Gren Foundation.

Goodman, M. (1964). The specificity of proteins and the process of primate evolution. In *Protides of the Biological fluids*, Proceedings of 12th Colloquium, Bruges 1964. (Ed. Peeters, H.) Amsterdam: Elsevier.

Goodman, M. (In press). Molecular records of primate evolution.

Goodwin, G. G. (1953). Catalogue of the type specimens of recent mammals in the American Museum of Natural History. *Bull. Am. Mus. nat. Hist.* **102**: 262.

Goswell, M. J., and Gartlan, J. S. (1965). Pregnancy, birth and early infant behaviour in captive Patas monkey, *Erythrocebus patas*. *Folia primat.* **3**: 189–200.

Grand, T. I. (1967). The functional anatomy of the ankle and foot of the slow loris. (*Nycticebus coucang*.) *Am. J. phys. Anthrop.* **26**: 207–218.

Grand, T. I., Duro, E., and Montagna, W. (1964). Observations on the development of a Potto born in captivity. *Am. J. phys. Anthrop.* **22**: 329–332.

Grandidier, D., and Petit, G. (1932). *Zoologie de Madagascar*. Paris.

Gray, J. E. (1848). Description of a new genus of insectivorous Mammalia, or Talpidae, from Borneo. *Proc. zool. Soc. Lond.* 23–24.

Gregory, W. K. (1920). On the structure and relations of *Notharctus*. *Mem. Am. Mus. nat. Hist.*, **N.S. 3**, 2: 49–243.

Groves, C. P. (1966). Variation in the skulls of Gorillas with particular reference to ecology. Ph.D. Thesis. Univ. of London.

Groves, C. P. (1967). Ecology and taxonomy of the gorilla. *Nature, Lond.* 890–893.

Grüner, M., and Krause, P. (1963). Biologische Beobachtungen an Weisspinseläffchen *Hapale jacchus* (L. 1758) im Berliner Tierpark. *Zool. Gart.* **28**: 108–114.

Haddow, A. J. (1952). Field and laboratory studies on an African monkey, *Cercopithecus ascanius schmidti* Matschie. *Proc. zool. Soc. Lond.* **122**: 297–394.

Haddow, A. J. (1956). Blue monkey group in Uganda. *Uganda Wildlife and Sport* 1: 22–26.

Haddow, A. J., and Ross, R. W. (1951). A critical review of Coolidge's measurements of gorilla skulls. *Proc. zool. Soc. Lond.* **121**: 43–54.

Haddow, A. J., Smithburn, K. C., Mahaffy, A. F., and Bugher, J. C. (1947). Monkeys in relation to epidemiology of yellow fever in Bwamba County, Uganda. *Trans. R. Soc. Trop. Med. Hyg.* **40**: 677–700.

Haines, R. W. (1955). The anatomy of the hand of certain insectivores. *Proc. zool. Soc. Lond.* **125**: 761–777.

Hall, E. R., and Kelson, K. R. (1959). *The mammals of North America*, Vol. I. New York: The Ronald Press Company.

Hall, K. R. L. (1962a). Numerical data, maintenance activities and locomotion of the wild Chacma baboon, *Papio ursinus*. *Proc. zool. Soc. Lond.* **139**: 181–220.

Hall, K. R. L. (1962b). Sexual, agonistic and derived social behaviour patterns of the wild Chacma baboon, *P. ursinus*. *Proc. zool. Soc. Lond.* **139**: 283–327.

Hall, K. R. L. (1963). Variations in the ecology of the Chacma baboon, *Papio ursinus*. *Symp. zool. Soc. Lond.* **10**: 1–28.

Hall, K. R. L. (1964). Aggression in monkey and ape societies. In *Natural History of Aggression*. (Eds. Carthy, J. D. and Ebling, F. J.) Institute of Biology Symposia No. 13. London and New York: Academic Press.

Hall, K. R. L. (1966). Behaviour and ecology of the wild Patas monkey, *Erythrocebus patas*, in Uganda. *J. Zool. Lond.* **148**: 15–87.

Hall, K. R. L., and Goswell, M. J. (1964). Aspects of social learning in captive Patas monkeys, *Erythrocebus patas*. *Primates.* **5**: 59–70.

Hall, K. R. L., Boelkins, R. C., and Goswell, M. J. (1965). Behaviour of Patas monkeys in captivity with notes on the natural habitat. *Folia primat.* **3**: 22–49.

Hall, K. R. L., and DeVore, Irven (1965). Baboon social behaviour. In *Primate Behaviour*. (Ed. DeVore, I.) New York: Holt, Rinehart and Winston.

Hall, K. R. L., and Gartlan, J. S. (1965). Ecology and behaviour of the Vervet monkey, *Cercopithecus aethiops*, Lolui Island, Lake Victoria. *Proc. zool. Soc. Lond.* **145**: 37–56.

Hall, K. R. L., and Mayer, Barbara (1966). Hand preferences and dexterities of captive Patas monkeys. *Folia primat.* **4**: 169–185.

Hall-Craggs, E. C. B. (1961). The blood vessels of the heart of *Gorilla gorilla beringei*. *Am. J. phys. Anthrop.* **19**: 373–378.

Hall-Craggs, E. C. B. (1965a). The jump of the lesser Galago (*Galago senegalensis*). Ph.D. Thesis. Univ. of London.

Hall-Craggs, E. C. B. (1965b). An osteometric study of the hindlimb of the Galagidae. *J. Anat. Lond.* **99**: 119–126.

Hamerton, J. L. (1963). Primate chromosomes. *Symp. zool. Soc. Lond.* **10**: 211–219.

Hamerton, J. L. *et al.* (1961). Somatic chromosomes of the gorilla. *Nature, Lond.* **192**: 225–228.

Hamlett, G. W. D. (1939). Reproduction in American monkeys. I. Estrous, ovulation and menstruation in *Cebus*. *Anat. Rec.* **73**: 171–187.

Hampton, J. K. (1964). Laboratory requirements and observations of *Oedipomidas oedipus*. *Am. J. phys. Anthrop.* **22**: 239–244.

Hampton, J. K., Hampton, S. H., and Landwehr, B. T. (1966). Observations on a successful breeding colony of the marmoset, *Oedipomidas oedipus*. *Folia primat.* **4**: 265–287.

Hanson, H. M. (1963). Laboratory note on *Saimiri sciurea*. *Laboratory Primate Newsletter* **2**: No. 1: 1–3.

Harlow, H. F., and Harlow, M. K. (1961). A study of animal affection. *Natural History* **70**: 48–55.

Harlow, H. F., and Harlow, M. K. (1962). Social deprivation in monkeys. *Scient. Am.* **207**: 136–146.

Harlow, H. F., and Harlow, M. K. (1965). The affectional systems. In *Behaviour of Nonhuman Primates*. (Eds. Schrier, A. M., Harlow, H. F., and Stollnitz, F.) New York and London: Academic Press.

Harlow, H. F., Harlow, M. K., and Hansen, E. W. (1963). The maternal affectional system in Rhesus monkeys. In *Maternal Behaviour in Mammals*. (Ed. Rheingold, H. L.) New York: Wiley.

Harlow, H. F., and Zimmerman, R. R. (1959). Affectional responses in the infant monkey. *Science, N.Y.* **130**: 421–432.

Harms, J. W. (1956). Fortpflanzungsbiologie. In *Primatologia*, Vol. I. (Eds. Hofer, H., Schultz, A. H., and Stark, D.) Basel: S. Karger.

Harms, J. W. (1956). Schwangerschaft und Geburt. In *Primatologia*, Vol. I. (Eds. Hofer, H., Schultz, A. H., and Starck, D.) Basel: S. Karger.

Harrison, J. L. (1954). The natural food of some rats and other mammals. *Bull. Raffles Mus.* **25**: 157–165.

Harrison, J. L. (1962). The apes and monkeys of Malaya (including the Slow Loris). Popular Pamphlet No. 9, Malayan Museum Pamphlets. Singapore: National Museum.

Harrison, J. L., and Lim, B. L. (1950). Notes on some small mammals of Malaya. *Bull. Raffles Mus.* **23**: 300–309.

Harrisson, Barbara (1960). A study of Orang-utan behaviour in semi-wild state. *Sarawak Mus. J.* **9**: 422–447.

Harrisson, Barbara (1962). Getting to know about *Tarsius*. *Malay. Nat. J.* **16**: 197–204.

Harrisson, B. (1963). Trying to breed *Tarsius*. *Malay. Nat. J.* **17**: 218–231.

Harrisson, T. (1962). Leaf-monkeys at Fraser's Hill. *Malay. Nat. J.* **16**: 120–125.

Hartman, C. G. (1928). The period of gestation in the monkey, *Macacus rhesus*, first description of parturition in monkeys, size and behaviour of the young. *J. Mammal.* **9**: 181–194.

Hartman, C. G. (1932). Studies in the reproduction of the monkey *Macacus* (*Pithecus*) *rhesus* with special reference to menstruation and pregnancy. *Contr. Embryol.* **23**: 1–161.

Hartman, C. G. (1938). Some observations on the Bonnet macaque. *J. Mammal.* **19**: 468–474.

Hartman, C. G., and Straus, W. L. (1933). *The anatomy of the Rhesus monkey (Macaca mulatta)*. New York: Hafner Publishing Co.

Hartmann, R. (1885). *Anthropoid Apes*. London: Kegan Paul Trench & Co.

Hawkins, A., and Olszewski, J. (1957). Glial nerve cell index for cortex of the whale. *Science, N.Y.* **126**: 76–77.

Hayes, K. J., and Hayes, C. (1951). The intellectual development of a home raised chimpanzee. *Proc. Am. Phil. Soc.* **95**: 105–109.

Hayman, R. W. (1935). On a collection of mammals from the Gold Coast. *Proc. zool. Soc. Lond.* 915–937.

Hayman, R. W. (1937). A note on *Galago senegalensis inustus* Schwarz. *Ann. Mag. nat. Hist.* **20**: 149–151.

Hazama, N. (1964). Weighing wild Japanese monkeys in Arashiyama. *Primates* **5**, Nos. 3 & 4: 81–104.

Hediger, H. (1950). *Wild animals in captivity*. London: Butterworths Scientific Publ.

Hediger, H. (1955). *Studies of the psychology and behaviour of captive animals in zoos and circuses*. New York: Criterion.

Henckel, K. O. (1928). Das primordialcranium von *Tupaja* und der Ursprung der Primaten. *Z. Anat. EntwGesch.* **84**: 204–227.

Hershkovitz, P. (1949a). Mammals of Northern Colombia. Preliminary Report No. 4: Monkeys (Primates), with taxonomic revisions of some forms. *Proc. U.S. natn. Mus.* **98**: 323–427.

Hershkovitz, P. (1949b). Status of names credited to Oken, 1816. *J. Mammal.* **30**: 289–307.

Hershkovitz, P. (1958). Type localities and nomenclature of some American primates. *Proc. biol. Soc. Wash.* **71**: 53–56.

Hershkovitz, P. (1963). A systematic and zoogeographic account of the monkeys of the genus *Callicebus* (Cebidae) of the Amazonas and Orinoco river basins. *Mammalia* **27**: 1–80.

Hershkovitz, P. (1964). Primates. Comparative Anatomy and Taxonomy. Vol. IV (1962). A critical review with a summary of the volumes on New World Primates. *Am. J. phys. Anthrop.* **21** (3): 391–398.

Hershkovitz, P. (1965). Primate research and systematics. *Science, N.Y.* **147**: 1156–1157.

Hershkovitz, P. (1966a). Taxonomic notes on Tamarins, genus *Saguinus* (Callithricidae, Primates), with descriptions of four new forms. *Folia primat.* **4**: 381–395.

Hershkovitz, P. (1966b). On the identification of some marmosets. Family Callithricidae (Primates). *Mammalia* **30**: 327–332.

Heuglin, M. T. von (1863). Beitrage zur Zoologie Afrika's—über einige Säugethiere des Bäschlo— Gebietes. *Nova Acta Acad. Caesar Leop. Carol.* **30**: 10–14.

Hewes, G. W. (1961). Food transport and the origin of human bipedalism. *Am. Anthrop.* **63**: 687–710.

Hildebrand, Milton (1967). Symmetrical gaits of primates. *Am. J. phys. Anthrop.* **26**: 119–130.

Hill, C. A. (1964a). Primate senior citizens. *Zoonooz* **37**, No. 5: 14–15.

Hill, C. A. (1964b). Oldest zoo monkey dies: was sterile. *Primate Laboratory Newsletter* **3**, No. 4: 17.

Hill, J. E. (1960). The Robinson collection of Malaysian mammals. *Bull. Raffles Mus.* **29**: 1–112.

Hill, J. E., and Carter, T. D. (1941). The Mammals of Angola, Africa. *Bull. Am. Mus. nat. Hist.* **78**: 3–211.

Hill, J. P. (1932). Developmental history of the Primates (Croonian Lecture). *Phil. Trans.*, B. **221**: 45–178.

Hill, J. P. (1965). On the placentation of *Tupaia*. *J. Zool. Lond.* **146**: 278–304.

Hill, W. C. Osman (1934). A monograph on the purple-faced leaf-monkeys (*Pithecus vetulus*). *Ceylon J. Sci.* (B) **19**: 23–88.

Hill, W. C. Osman (1936). On a hybrid leaf-monkey: with remarks on the breeding of leaf-monkeys in general. *Ceylon J. Sci.* (B) **20**: 135–148.

Hill, W. C. Osman (1937a). On the breeding and rearing of certain species of primates in captivity. *Spolia zeylan.* **20**: 369–389.

Hill, W. C. Osman (1937b). Treatment of the Slender Loris in captivity. *Loris.* **1**: 85–88.

Hill, W. C. Osman (1938a). A curious habit common to lorisoids and platyrrhine monkeys. *Ceylon J. Sci.* (B) **21**: 66–67.

Hill, W. C. Osman (1938b). Observations on a giant Sumatran orang. *Am. J. phys. Anthrop.* **24**: 449–505.

Hill, W. C. Osman (1939a). An annotated systematic list of the leaf-monkeys. *Ceylon J. Sci.* (B) **21**: 277–305.

Hill, W. C. Osman (1939b). The menstrual cycle of the Toque macaque. *Ceylon J. Sci.* (D) **5**: 21–36.

Hill, W. C. Osman (1952). The external and visceral anatomy of the Olive Colobus monkey. (*Procolobus verus.*) *Proc. zool. Soc. Lond.* 127–186.

Hill, W. C. Osman (1953). *Primates. Comparative Anatomy and Taxonomy.* Vol. I. Strepsirrhini. Edinburgh; University Press.

Hill, W. C. Osman (1955a). *Primates. Comparative Anatomy and Taxonomy.* Vol. II. Tarsioidea. Edinburgh: University Press.

Hill, W. C. Osman (1955b). A note on the integumental colours with reference to genus *Mandrillus*. *Säuget. Mitt.* **3**: 145–151.

Hill, W. C. Osman (1956a). Body odour in lorises. *Proc. zool. Soc. Lond.* **127**: 580.

Hill, W. C. Osman (1956b). Behaviour and adaptations of the Primates. *Proc. R. Soc. Edinb.* B **66**: 94–110.

Hill, W. C. Osman (1957). *Primates. Comparative anatomy and taxonomy.* Vol. III. Hapalidae. Edinburgh: University Press.

Hill, W. C. Osman (1959a). Aborted mid-term foetus of *Aotes trivirgatus infulatus* (Feline Douroucouli). *Proc. zool. Soc. Lond.* **132**: 148.

Hill, W. C. Osman (1959b). Anatomy of *Callimico goeldii*. *Trans. Am. Phil. Soc.* **49**, Part 5.

Hill, W. C. Osman (1960). *Primates. Comparative Anatomy and Taxonomy.* Vol. IV. Cebidae. Part A. Edinburgh: University Press.

Hill, W. C. Osman (1962a). *Primates. Comparative Anatomy and Taxonomy.* Vol. V. Cebidae. Part B. Edinburgh: University Press.

Hill, W. C. Osman (1962b). Reproduction in the squirrel monkey, *Saimiri sciurea*. *Proc. zool. Soc. Lond.* **139**: 671–672.

Hill, W. C. Osman (1964a). The external anatomy of *Allenopithecus*. *Proc. R. Soc. Edinb.* **68**, 4: 302–326.

Hill, W. C. Osman (1964b). The maintenance of langurs (Colobidae) in captivity; experiences and some suggestions. *Folia primat.* **2**: 222–231.

Hill, C. A. (1967). A note on the gestation period of the Siamang (*Hylobates syndactylus*). *Ind. Zoo. Yearbook*, **7** (in press).

Hill, W. C. Osman (1965). Tentative identification of laboratory squirrel monkeys (*Saimiri*). *Laboratory Primate Newsletter* **4**, No. 3: 1–4.

Hill, W. C. Osman (1966a). Laboratory breeding, behavioural development and relations of the Talapoin (*Miopithecus talapoin*). *Mammalia* **30**: 353–370.

Hill, W. C. Osman (1966b). *Primates. Comparative Anatomy and Taxonomy.* Vol. VI. Cercopithecoidea. Edinburgh: University Press.

Hill, W. C. Osman, and Booth, A. H. (1957). Voice and larynx in African and Asian Colobidae. *J. Bombay nat. Hist. Soc.* **54**: 309–321.

Hill, W. C. Osman, Porter, A., and Southwick, M. D. (1952). The natural history, endoparasites and pseudo-parasites of the tarsiers (*Tarsius carbonarius*) recently living in the Society's menagerie. *Proc. zool. Soc. Lond.* 79–119.

Hinde, R. G., and Rowell, T. E. (1962). Communication by postures and facial expression in the Rhesus monkey (*Macaca mulatta*). *Proc. zool. Soc. Lond.* **138**: 1–21.

Hines, M. (1942). The development and regression of reflexes, postures and progression in the young macaque. *Contr. Embryol. Carneg. Inst.* **196**: 155–209.

Hofer, H. (1954). Beobachtungen am Hirnrelief der aussen-fläche des Schädels, am Endocranium und der Hirnform des Südamerikanischen Nachtaffen (*Aotes*) *Ber. oberhess. Ges. Nat. u. Heilk.* **27**: 90–110.

Hofer, H. (1957). Über die Bewegungen des Potto. *Natur. Volk* **87**: 409–418.

Hofer, H. (1958). Über das Bewegungsspiel der Klammeraffen. *Natur. Volk* **88**: 397–407.

Hofer, H. (1960). Beobachtungen an Brüllaffen (*Alouatta*). *Natur. Volk* **90**: 241–251.

Holloway, Ralph L. (1966). Cranial capacity, neural reorganization and hominid evolution. A search for more suitable parameters. *Am. Anthrop.* **68**: 103–121.

Hooff, J. A. R. A. M. van (1962). Facial expressions in higher primates. *Symp. zool. Soc. Lond.* **8**: 97–125.

Hoogstraal, H. (1947). The inside story of the tarsier. *Chicago nat. Hist. Mus. Bull.* **18**, Nos. 11 and 12.

Hooijer, D. A. (1950). Man and other mammals from Toalian sites in south-western Celebes. *Verh. K. Akad. Wet.* **46** (2): 1–160.

Hooijer, D. A. (1962). Quaternary langurs and macaques from the Malay archipelago. *Zool. Verh. Leiden* **55**: 1–64.

Hopwood, A. T. (1947). The generic names of the Mandrill and Baboon with notes on some of the genera of Brisson, 1762. *Proc. zool. Soc. Lond.* **117**: 533–534.

Hornaday, W. T. (1885). Two years in the Jungle. London.

Hose, C. (1893). *Mammals of Borneo*. London:

Hrdlička, A. (1907). Anatomical observations on a collection of Orang skulls from western Borneo: with a bibliography. *Proc. U.S. natn. Mus.* **31**: 539–568.

Hsu, T. C., and Johnson, M. L. (1963). Karyotypes of two mammals from Malaya. *Am. Nat.* **97**: 127–129.

Hsuing, G. D., Black, F. L., and Henderson, J. R. (1964). Susceptibility of primates to viruses. In *Evolutionary and genetic biology of primates*, Vol. II. (Ed. Buettner-Janusch, J.) New York and London: Academic Press.

Huber, E. (1931). *Evolution of facial musculature and facial expression*. Oxford: University Press.

Huber, E. (1933). Facial musculature and its innervation. Chapter 8 in *Anatomy of Rhesus monkey*. (Eds. Hartmann, C. G. and Straus, W. L.) New York: Hafner Publish. Co.

Humboldt, A. de, and Bonpland, A. (1812). Recueil d'observations de zoologie et d'anatomie comparée. Paris: Smith & Gide.

Hume, E. M. (1957). Monkey Welfare. The Nutrition of Laboratory Animals. *Coll. Pap. Lab. Anim. Bur.* **5**: 61–68.

Husson, A. M. (1957). *Studies on the fauna of Suriname and other Guyanas* **i**: 13–40.

Huxley, J. S. (1932). *Problems of relative growth*. London: Methuen.

Ilse, D. R. (1955). Olfactory marking of territory in two young male Loris, *Loris tardigradus lydekkerianus*, kept in captivity in Poona. *Br. J. Anim. Behav.* **3**: 118–120.

Imanishi, K. (1957). Social behaviour in Japanese monkeys, *Macaca fuscata*. *Psychologia* **1**: 47–54.

International Zoo Year Book, (1959–1963). Vols. I–V. (Eds. Morris, D. and Jarvis, C.) London: Zoological Society of London.

Itani, J. (1959). Paternal care in the wild Japanese monkey, *Macaca fuscata fuscata*. *Primates* **2**, No. 1: 61–93.

Itani, J. (1963). Vocal communication of the wild Japanese monkey. *Primates* **4**, No. 2: 11–66.

Itani, J., Tokuda, K., Furuya, Y., Kano, K., and Shin, Y. (1963). The social construction of natural troops of Japanese monkeys, in Takasakiyama. *Primates* **4**, No. 3: 1–42.

I.U.C.N. (1964). *Animals and plants threatened with extinction*. Survival Service Commission of International Union for the Conservation of Nature.

Jacob, G. F., and Tappen, N. C. (1957). Abnormal haemoglobin in monkeys. *Nature, Lond.* **180**: 241–242.

Jacob, G. F., and Tappen, N. C. (1958). Haemoglobins in monkeys. *Nature, Lond.* **181**: 197–198.

James, W. Warwick (1960). *The jaws and teeth of primates*. London: Pitman Medical Publishing Co. Ltd.

Jarvis, C. (1965). Census of Rare Animals. In *International Zoo Year Book*, **5**: (Ed. Jarvis, C.) London: Zoological Society.

Jarvis, C. (1966). Zoos in China. *Animals* **8**, No. 17: 450–455, No. 19: 522–527.

Jay, Phyllis C. (1963a). The Indian langur monkey (*Presbytis entellus*). In *Primate Social Behaviour*. (Ed. Southwick, C. H.) Princeton, New Jersey: D. Van Nostrand, Co. Inc.

Jay, Phyllis C. (1963b). Mother–infant relations in langurs. In *Maternal behaviour in mammals*. (Ed. Rheingold, H. L.) New York: Wiley.

Jay, Phyllis C. (1965). The common langur of North India. In *Primate Behaviour*. (Ed. DeVore, I.) New York: Holt, Rinehart and Winston.

Jeannin, A. (1936). *Les mammifères sauvages du Cameroun*. Paris: Lechevalier.

Jennison, G. (1927). *Table of gestation periods and number of young*. London: Black.

Jentinck, F. A. (1890). Note xxii on a collection of mammals from Billiton. *Notes Leyden Mus.* **12**: 149–154.

Jolly, C. J. (1963). A suggested case of evolution by sexual selection in primates. *Man* **221**: 177–178.

Jolly, C. J. (1965). *The origins and specializations of the long-faced Cercopithecoidea.* University of London, Ph.D. Thesis.

Jolly, C. J. (1966). Introduction to the Pithecoidea with notes on their use as laboratory animals. *Symp. zool. Soc. Lond.* **17**: 427–457.

Jolly, C. J., and Barnicot, N. A. (1966). Serum and red cell protein variations of the Celebes black ape. *Folia primat.* **4**: 169–185.

Jones, F. Wood (1916). *Arboreal Man.* London: Edward Arnold.

Jones, F. Wood (1929). *Man's place among the mammals.* London: Edward Arnold.

Jones, M. L. (1962). Mammals in captivity—primate longevity. *Laboratory Primate Newsletter* **1**, No. 3: 3–13.

Jones, T. S., and Cave, A. J. E. (1960). Diet, longevity and dental disease in the Sierra Leone Chimpanzee: *Proc. zool. Soc. Lond.* **135**: 147–155.

Jouffroy, F. K. (1962). La musculature des membres chez les Lémuriens de Madagascar. Etude descriptive et comparative. *Thès. Paris Mammalia* Serie A.3860.

Jouffroy, F. K., and Lessertisseur, J. (1960). Les spécialisations anatomiques de la main chez les singes à progression suspendue. *Mammalia* **24**: 93–151.

Kanagasuntheram, R., and Jayawardene, F. L. W. (1957). The intrinsic muscles of the hand of the slender loris. *Proc. zool. Soc. Lond.* **128**: 301–312.

Kaufman, J. H. (1965). Studies on the behaviour of captive treeshrews. *Folia primat.* **3**: 50–74.

Kawai, M., and Mizuhara, H. (1959). An ecological study of the wild mountain gorilla (*G. g. beringei*). *Primates* **2**: 1–42.

Kawamura, S. (1959). The process of sub-culture propagation among Japanese macaques. *Primates* **2**, No. 1: 43–60.

Keith, A. (1891). Anatomical notes on Malay apes. *J. Straits Brch. R. Asiat. Soc.* 77–89.

Keith, A. (1896). An introduction to the study of anthropoid apes. IV. The Gibbon. *Nat. Sci.* **9**: 372–379.

Keith, A. (1899). On the Chimpanzees and their relationship to the Gorilla. *Proc. Zool. Soc. Lond.* 296–312.

Kelemen, G., and Sade, J. (1960). The vocal organ of the howling monkey (*Alouatta palliata*). *J. Morph.* **107**: 123–140.

Kellogg, R. (1944). A new macaque from an island off the east coast of Borneo. *Proc. biol. Soc. Wash.* **57**: 75–76.

Kellogg, R., and Goldman, E. A. (1944). Review of the spider monkeys. *Proc. U.S. natn. Mus.* **96**: 1–45.

Kellogg, W. N., and Kellogg, L. A. (1933). *The ape and the child.* New York: McGraw-Hill.

Kern, J. A. (1964). Observations on the habits of the Proboscis monkey, *Nasalis larvatus* (Wurmb), made in the Brunei Bay area, Borneo. *Zoologica* **49**: 183–192.

Kern, J. A. (1965). The Proboscis monkey. *Animals* **6**, No. 9: 522–526.

Khajuria, H. (1952). Taxonomic status of the Celebes ashy-black monkey—a remarkable case of convergence. *Rec. Indian Mus.* **50**: 301–305.

Khajuria, H. (1956). A new langur (Primates : Colobidae) from Goalpara District, Assam. *Ann. Mag. nat. Hist.* **9** (12): 86–88.

Klinger, H. P. (1963). The somatic chromosomes of some primates (*Tupaia glis, Nycticebus coucang, Tarsius bancanus, Cercocebus aterrimus, Symphalangus syndactylus*). *Cytogenetics* **2**: 140–151.

Klinger, H. P., Hamerton, J. L., Mutton, D., and Lang, E. M. (1963). The chromosomes of Hominoidea. In *Classification and Human Evolution.* (Ed. Washburn, S. L.) Viking Press Publ. in Anthrop. No. 37 for Wenner-Gren Foundation. Chicago: Aldine Publ. Co.

Kloss, C. Boden (1911). On a collection of mammals and other vertebrates from the Trengganu archipelago. *J. fed. Malay St. Mus.* **4**: 135–143.

Kloss, C. Boden (1929). Some remarks on the gibbons with the description of a new sub-species. *Proc. zool. Soc. Lond.* 113–127.

Klüver, H. (1933). *Behaviour Mechanisms in Monkeys.* Chicago: University Press.

Koch, W. (1937). *Bericht über das Ergebnis der Obduktion des Gorilla Bobby des Zoologisches Gartens zu Berlin.* Jena: G. Fischer.

Koford, C. B. (1963). Group relations in an island colony of Rhesus monkeys. In *Primate Social Behaviour.* (Ed. Southwick, C. H.) Princeton, N.J.: D. Van Nostrand Co.

Koford, C. B. (1965). Population dynamics of Rhesus monkeys on Cayo Santiago. In *Primate Behaviour.* (Ed. DeVore, I.) New York: Holt, Rinehart and Winston.

Kohlbrügge, J. H. F. (1890). Versuch einer Anatomie des Genus *Hylobates. Max Weber's Zoologisches Ergebnisse einer Reise in Niederländ. Ost. Indien,* Vol. I: 211–355, Vol. II: 139–206.

Kohler, W. (1925). *The mentality of Apes.* New York: Harcourt.

Kortlandt, A. (1962). Chimpanzees in the wild. *Scient. Am.* **206** (5): 128–138.

Kortlandt, A. (1966). Chimpanzee ecology and laboratory management. *Laboratory Primate Newsletter,* **5,** 3: 1–11.

Kortlandt, A., and Kooij, M. (1963). Protohominid behaviour in primates (Preliminary Communication). *Symp. zool. Soc. Lond.* **10:** 61–88.

Kreig, H. (1930). Biologische Reisenstudien in Südamerika. Die Affen des Gran Chaco und seiner Grenzgebiete. *Z. Morph. Ökol. Tiere* **18:** 760–785.

Kuehn, R. E., Jensen, G. D., and Morrill, R. K. (1965). Breeding *Macaca nemestrina*: a program of birth engineering. *Folia primat.* **3:** 251–262.

Kühlhorn, F. (1939). Beobachtungen über das Verhalten von Kapuzineraffen im freier Wildbahn. *Z. Tierpsychol.* **3:** 147–151.

Kühlhorn, F. (1943). Über die Jugendentwicklung eines aufgezogenen Kapuziner-affen. *Natur Volk* **83:** 115–119.

Kühlhorn, F. (1954). Gefügegesetzliche Untersuchungen an Neuweltaffen (*Cebus apella* L. und *Alouatta caraya* Humboldt) *Z. Saügetierk* **20:** 13–36.

Kuhn, H. J. (1964). Zur Kenntnis von Bau und Funktion des Magens der Schlankaffen (Colobinae). *Folia primat.* **2:** 193–221.

Kummer, H. (1956). Rang-Kruterien bei Mantelpavianen. *Rev. Suisse. Zool.* **63:** 288–297.

Kummer, H. (1957). Soziales Verhalten einer Mantelpavianen-gruppe *Schweiz. Z. Psychol.* No. 23.

Kummer, H., and Kurt, F. (1963). Social units of a free-living population of Hamadryas baboons. *Folia primat.* **1:** 1–19.

Lamberton, C. (1911). Contribution à l'étude des moeurs du aye-aye. *Bull. Acad. Malgache* **8:** 129–140.

Lamberton, C. (1939). *Mém. Acad. Malgache* **27:** 5–203.

Lampert, H. (1926). Zur Kenntnis des Platyrrhinenkehlkopfes. *Gegenbaurs morph. Jb.* **55:** 607–654.

Lancaster, Jane B., and Lee, R. B. (1965). The annual reproductive cycle in monkeys and apes. In *Primate Behaviour.* (Ed. DeVore, I.) New York: Holt, Rinehart and Winston.

Lang, E. M. (1959). The birth of a Gorilla at Basle Zoo. In *International Zoo Yearbook,* Vol. I. (Eds. Morris, D. and Jarvis, C.) London: Zoological Society.

Lang, E. M. (1961). Jambo, the second Gorilla born at Basle Zoo. *International Zoo Yearbook,* Vol. III. (Eds. Jarvis, C. and Morris, D.) London: Zoological Society.

Lang, H. (1923). A new genus of African monkey. *Am. Mus. Novit.* **87:** 1–5.

Lange, V., and Schmitt, J. (1963). Das Serumeiweissbild der Primaten unter besonderer Berücksichtigung der Haptoglobine und Transferrine. *Folia Primat.* **1:** 208–250.

Laurie, E. M. O., and Hill, J. E. (1954). *List of Land Mammals of New Guinea, Celebes and adjacent islands, 1758–1952.* London: British Museum (Natural History).

Lavauden, L. (1933). Le Aye-Aye. *La terre et la vie* **3:** 142–152.

Lawrence, Barbara (1933). Howler monkeys of the *palliata* group. *Bull. Mus. comp. Zool. Harv.* **75:** 314–354.

Lawrence, B. (1939). Collections from the Philippine Islands. *Bull. Mus. comp. Zool. Harv.* **86:** 28–73.

Lehmann, F. C. (1963). Quoted in Fooden, J. (1963). A revision of the woolly monkeys (*Genus Lagothrix*). *J. Mammal.* **44**: 213–247.

Lettelier, F., and Petter, J. J. (1961). Note sur un *Lepilemur* en captivité au vivarium du Jardin des Plantes de Paris. *Mammalia* **25**: 571–572.

Lim, Boo Liat (in press). Note on the food habits of the *Ptilocercus lowii* Gray (Pentail Treeshrew) and the *Echinosorex gymnurus* Raffles (Moonrat) in West Malaysia with reference to "ecological labelling" by parasite patterns. *J. Zool.*

Lönnberg, E. (1938). Remarks on some members of the genera *Pithecia* and *Cacajao* from Brazil. *Arkiv. Zool.* **30A**, No. 18: 1–25.

Lönnberg, E. (1940a). Notes on Marmosets. *Arkiv. Zool.* **32A**, No. 10: 1–21.

Lönnberg, E. (1940b). Notes on some members of the genus *Saimiri*. *Arkiv. Zool.* **32A**, No. 21: 1–18.

Lorenz, R. (1966a). Waschen bei zwei arten der gattung *Presbytis*. *Folia primat.* **4**: 191–193.

Lorenz, R. (1966b). Sollte jemand das grosse Glück haben. *Freunde des Kölner Zoo* Heft 1; 11–14.

Lorenz, R., and Heinemann, H. (in press). *Folia primat.*

Lowther, F. de L. (1939). The feeding and grooming habits of the galago. *Zoologica* **24**: 477–480.

Lowther, F. de L. (1940). A study of the activities of a pair of *Galago senegalensis moholi* in captivity. *Zoologica* **25**: 433–462.

Lucas, N. S., Hume, E. M., and Smith, H. H. (1927). On the breeding of the common marmoset (*Hapale jacchus* Linn.) in captivity when irradiated with ultra-violet rays. *Proc. zool. Soc. Lond.* 447–451.

Lucas, N. S., Hume, E. M., and Smith, H. H. (1937). The breeding of the common marmoset in captivity. *Proc. zool. Soc. Lond.* **107**: 205–211.

Lumsden, W. H. R. (1951). The night-resting habits of monkeys in a small area on the edge of the Semliki Forest, Uganda. *J. Anim. Ecol.* **20**: 11–30.

Lydekker, R. (1893–94). *The Royal Natural History*. London and New York: Frederick Warne and Co.

Lydekker, R. (1905). Colour evolution in Guereza monkeys. *Proc. zool. Soc. Lond.* 325–329.

Lyon, M. W. (1907a). Notes on the slow lemurs. *Proc. U.S. nat. Mus.* **31**: 527–539.

Lyon, M. W. (1907b). Mammals of Banka, Mendanau and Billiton islands between Sumatra and Borneo. *Proc. U.S. natn. Mus.* **31**: 575–612.

Lyon, M. W. (1908a). Mammals collected in western Borneo by Dr. W. L. Abbott. *Proc. U.S. nat. Mus.* **33**: 547–572.

Lyon, M. W. (1908b). Mammals collected in eastern Sumatra during 1903, 1906 and 1907 with descriptions of new species and sub-species. *Proc. U.S. nat. Mus.* **34**: 619–679.

Lyon, M. W. (1911). Mammals collected by Dr. W. L. Abbott on Borneo and some of the small adjacent islands. *Proc. U.S. natn. Mus.* **40**: 53–146.

Lyon, M. W. (1913). Treeshrews: an account of the mammalian family Tupaiidae. *Proc. U.S. natn. Mus.* **45**: 1–188.

McCann, C. (1933). Notes on the colouration and habits of the white-browed gibbon or hoolock (*Hylobates hoolock* Harl.). *J. Bombay nat. Hist. Soc.* **36**: 395–405.

McCann, C. (1934). Observations on some of the Indian langurs. *J. Bombay nat. Hist. Soc.* **36**: 618–628.

McClure, H. Elliott (1964). Some observation of primates in Climax Dipterocarp forest near Kuala Lumpur, Malaya. *Primates* **5**: 3 and 4: 39–58.

MacKenzie, A. F., and Jones, T. S. (1952). The economic problems of the monkey population in Sierra Leone. *Proc. zool. Soc. Lond.* **122**: 541.

MacRoberts, M. (1965). Quoted in Washburn, S. L., Jay, Phyllis C., and Lancaster, Jane B. (1965). *Science, N.Y.* **150**: 1541–1547.

Mahan, J. L., and Rumbaugh, D. M. (1963). Observational learning in squirrel monkeys. *Perceptual and motor skills* **17**: 686.

Makino, S. (1952). Quoted in Bender, M.A., and Chu, E. H. Y. (1963). In *Evolutionary and Genetic Biology of Primates*, Vol. I. (Ed. Buettner-Janusch, J.) New York and London: Academic Press.

Malbrant, R., and Maclatchy, A. (1949). *Faune de l'equateur Africain Français*, Tome II, Mammifères. Paris: Paul Lechevalier.

Malinow, M. R. (1966). An electrocardiographic study of *Macaca mulatta*. *Folia primat.* **4**: 51–65.

Manley, G. H. (1966a). Reproduction in lorisoid primates. *Symp. zool. Soc. Lond.* **15**: 493–509.

Manley, G. H. (1966b). Prosimians as laboratory animals. *Symp. zool. Soc. Lond.* **17**: 11–39.

Martin, R. D. (1966). Treeshrews: unique reproductive mechanism of systematic importance *Science, N.Y.* **152**: 1402–1404.

Mason, W. A. (1960). The effects of social restriction on the behaviour of Rhesus monkeys. I. Free social behaviour. *J. comp. physiol. Psychol.* **53**: 582–589.

Mason, W. A. (1961a). The effects of social restriction on the behaviour of Rhesus monkeys. II. Tests of gregariousness. *J. comp. physiol. Psychol.* **54**: 287–290.

Mason, W. A. (1961b). The effects of social restriction on the behaviour of Rhesus monkeys. III. Dominance tests. *J. comp. physiol. Psychol.* **54**: 694–699.

Mason, W. A. (In press). Social organization of the South American monkey *Callicebus moloch*: a preliminary report. *Tulane Studies in Zoology*.

Matthews, L. H. (1946). Notes on the genital anatomy and physiology of the gibbon (*Hylobates*). *Proc. zool. Soc. Lond.* **116**: 339–364.

Matthews, L. H. (1956). Sexual skin of the Gelada Baboon (*Theropithecus gelada*). *Trans. zool. Soc. Lond.* **28**, pt. 7: 543–552.

Mayr, E. (1963). *Animal species and evolution.* London: Oxford University Press.

Medway, Lord (1961). The status of *Tupaia splendidula* Gray, 1865. *Treubia* **25**: 269–272.

Medway, Lord (1965). Mammals of Borneo: Field keys and annotated checklist. Singapore: Malaysian Branch of the Royal Asiatic Society.

Meister, W., and Davis, D. Dwight (1956). Placentation of the pygmy treeshrew, *Tupaia minor*. *Fieldiana: Zool.* **35**: 73–84.

Meister, W., and Davis, D. Dwight (1958). Placentation of the terrestrial treeshrew, *Tupaia tana*. *Anat. Rec.* **132**: 541–554.

Merfield, F. G., and Miller, H. (1956). *Gorilla Hunter.* (*Gorillas were my Neighbours* in G.B.) New York: Farrer, Straus.

Midlo, C. (1934). Form of hand and foot in Primates. *Am. J. phys. Anthrop.* **19**, 3: 337–389.

Midlo, C., and Cummins, H. (1942). *Palmar and plantar dermatoglyphics in primates.* Philadelphia: Wistar Institute.

Miles, R. C. (1957). Learning-set formation in the squirrel monkey. *J. comp. physiol. Psychol.* **50**: 356–357.

Miles, R. C. (1958). Color vision in the squirrel monkey. *J. comp. physiol. Psychol.* **50**: 356–357.

Miller, F. W. (1930). Notes on some mammals of the Southern Matto Grosso, Brazil. *J. Mammal.* **11**: 10–22.

Miller, G. S. (1903). Seventy new Malayan mammals. *Smithsonian misc. Coll.* **45**: 1–73.

Miller, G. S. (1907a). Mammals collected by Dr. W. L. Abbott in the Karimata islands, Dutch East Indies. *Proc. U.S. natn. Mus.* **31**: 55–66.

Miller, G. S. (1907b). The mammals collected by Dr. W. L. Abbott in the Rhio-Linga Archipelago. *Proc. U.S. natn. Mus.* **31**: 247–286.

Miller, G. S. (1933). The classification of Gibbons. *J. Mammal.* **14**: 158–159.

Miller, G. S. (1942). Zoological results of the George Vanderbilt Sumatran Expedition, 1936/39. Part V. Mammals collected by Frederick A. Ulmer, Jr. on Sumatra and Nias. *Proc. Acad. nat. Sci. Phila.* **94**: 127.

Miller, L. E. Quoted in Allen, J. A. (1916). Mammals collected on the Roosevelt Brazilian Expedition, with field notes by Leo. E. Miller. *Bull. Am. Mus. nat. Hist.* **35**: 83–87, 113–125.

Miller, L. E. (1916). Quoted in Fooden, J. (1963). A revision of the woolly monkeys (*Genus Lagothrix*). *J. Mammal.* **44**: 213–247.

Miller, L. E. (1916). Quoted in Hershkovitz, P. (1963). A systematic and zoogeographic account of the monkeys of the genus *Callicebus* (Cebidae) of the Amazonas and Orinoco river basins. *Mammalia*. **27**: 1–80.

Miller, Ruth A. (1943). Adaptations in the forelimbs of slow lemurs. *Am. J. Anat.* **73**: 153–184.

Milne-Edwards, A. (1895). Observations sur deux Orang-outans morts à Paris. *Nouv. Archs. Mus. Hist. nat.*, *Paris* 31–114.

Milne-Edwards, M. H., and A. (1868–74). *Récherches pour servir à l'histoire naturelle des mammifères*, Vols. I and II: 233–243; 36, 37. Paris: Librairie de l'Académie de Médecine.

Milne-Edwards, A., and Pousargues, E. de (1898). Le Rhinopithèque de la vallée du haut Mékong (*Rhinopithecus bieti* Milne-Edwards). *Nouv. Archs Mus. Hist. nat.*, *Paris* (3) 10: 121–142.

Mitchell, P. Chalmers (1905). On the intestinal tract of mammals. *Trans. zool. Soc.* **17**: 437–536.

Mitchell, P. Chalmers (1916). Further observations on the intestinal tract of mammals. *Proc. zool. Soc. Lond.* 183–251.

Mivart, St. George (1873). On *Lepilemur* and *Cheirogaleus* and on the zoological rank of the Lemuroidea. *Proc. zool. Soc. Lond.* 484–510.

Mizuhara, H. (1964). Social changes of Japanese monkey troops in Takasakiyama. *Primates* **5**, No. 1–2: 27–52.

Mollison, T. (1910). Die Körperproportionen der Primaten. *Morph. Jb.* **42**: 79–299.

Monard, A. (1938). Primates de la Guinée Portugaise. *Arq. Mus. Bocage*, **9**: 121–144.

Montagna, William (1962). The Skin of Lemurs. *Ann. N.Y. Acad. Sci.*, **102**: 190–209.

Montagna, W. (1965). The Skin. *Scient. Am.* **212**: 56–66.

Montagna, W., and Ellis, R. A. (1963). New approaches to the study of the skin of primates. In *Evolutionary and Genetic Biology of Primates*, Vol. I. (Ed. Buettner-Janusch, J.) New York and London: Academic Press.

Montagna, W., and Machida, H. (1966). The skin of primates. 32. The Philippine Tarsier (*Tarsius syrichta*). *Am. J. Phys. Anthrop.* **25**: 71–75.

Montagna, W., Machida, H., and Perkins, E. (1966). The skin of primates. 23. The Stump-tail Macaque (*Macaca speciosa*). *Am. J. phys. Anthrop.* **24**: 71–85.

Montagna, W., and Yun, I. S. (1962). Further observations on (the skin) of *Perodicticus potto*. *Am. J. phys. Anthrop.* **20**: 441–450.

Moor-Jankowski, J., Huser, H. J., Wiener, A. S., Kalter, S. S., Pallotta, A. J., and Guthrie, C. B. (1965). Hematology, blood groups, serum isoantigens, and preservation of blood of the Baboon. In *The Baboon in Medical Research*. (Ed. Vagtborg, H.) Austin: University of Texas Press.

Moor-Jankowski, J., and Wiener, A. S. (1964). Blood groups and serum specificities of apes and monkeys. *Laboratory Primate Newsletter* **3**, No. 4: 1–14.

Moor-Jankowski, J., Wiener, A. S., and Gordon, E. B. (1964). Blood Groups of Apes and Monkeys. III. The M-N Blood factors of Apes. *Folia primat.* **2**: 129–148.

Moor-Jankowski, J., Wiener, A. S., and Gordon, E. B. (1965). Simian blood groups. A "new" factor, A^{ba}, of Celebes black ape red cells demonstrated with rabbit antisera. *Folia primat.* **3**: 245–250.

Moor-Jankowski, J., Wiener, A. S., and Rogers, C. M. (1964). Human blood group factors in non-human primates. *Nature, Lond.* **202**: 663–665.

Moorrees, C. F. A. (1957). *The Aleut dentition*. Camb., Mass.: Harv. Univ. Press.

Morris, Desmond (1962). *Biology of Art*. London: Methuen.

Morris, Ramona and Desmond (1966). *Men and Apes*. London; Hutchinson & Co.

Morrison-Scott, T. C. S. (1965). *Pan* Oken, 1816, and *Panthera* Oken, 1816 (Mammalia): Proposed conservation under the plenary powers. Z.N.(S). 482. *Bull. zool. Nom.* **22**, 4: 230–232.

Mott, F. (1924). A study by serial sections of the structure of the larynx of *Hylobates syndactylus* (Siamang gibbon). *Proc. zool. Soc. Lond.* 1161–1170.

Murie, J., and Mivart, St. G. (1872). On the anatomy of the Lemuroidea. *Trans. zool. Soc. Lond.* **7**: 1–114.

Nanda, R. S. (1954). Agenesis of 3rd molar in man. *Am. J. Orthodontics* **40**: 698–706.

Napier, J. R. (1955). The form and function of the carpo-metacarpal joint of the thumb. *J. Anat. Lond.* **89**: 362–369.

Napier, J. R. (1952). Attachments and function of the abductor pollicis brevis. *J. Anat. Lond.* **86**: 335–341.

Napier, J. R. (1960). Studies of the hand of living primates. *Proc. zool. Soc. Lond.* **134**: 647–657.

Napier, J. R. (1961). Prehensility and opposability in the hands of primates. *Symp. zool. Soc. Lond.* **5**: 115–132.

Napier, J. R. (1963). Brachiation and brachiators. *Symp. zool. Soc. Lond.* **10**: 183–195.

Napier, J. R. (1964). Evolution of bipedal walking in the hominids. *Arch. Biol.* **75**: 673–708.

Napier, J. R. (In litt.). The structure and function of the primate hand in relation to locomotion.

Napier, J. R., and Davis, P. R. (1959). The forelimb bone and associated remains of *Proconsul africanus*. *Fossil Mammals of Africa.* No. 17. London. British Museum (N.H.)

Napier, J. R., and Walker, A. C. (1967). Vertical clinging and leaping, a newly recognised category of locomotor behaviour among primates. *Folia primat.* **6**: 180–203.

Narayan Rao, C. R. (1927). Observation on the habits of the Slow Loris *Loris lydekkerianus*. *J. Bombay nat. Hist. Soc.* **32**: 206–208.

Nayak, U. V. (1933). *A comparative study of the Lorisinae and Galaginae.* Ph.D. Thesis: London University.

Negus, V. E. (1929). *The mechanism of the larynx.* London: Heinemann.

Negus, V. E. (1949). *The comparative anatomy and physiology of the larynx.* London: Heinemann.

Nicholls, L. (1939). Period of gestation of *Loris*. *Nature, Lond.* **143**: 246.

Nissen, H. W. (1931). A field study of the Chimpanzee. *Comp. Psychol. Monogr.* **8**: 1–122.

Nissen, H. W. (1951). Social behaviour in primates. In *Comparative Psychology*, 3rd Ed. (Ed. Stone, E. P.) Englewood Cliffs: Prentice-Hall.

Nissen, H. W. (1956). Individuality in behaviour of chimpanzees. *Am. Anthrop.* **58**: 407–413.

Nissen, H. W., and Riesen, A. H. (1945). The deciduous teeth of the Chimpanzee. *Growth* **9**: 265–274.

Nissen, H. W., and Riesen, A. H. (1949). Retardation in onset of ossification in Chimpanzee related to various environmental and physiological factors. *Anat. Rec.* **105**: 665–675.

Nissen, Henry W., and Riesen, Austin H. (1964). The eruption of the permanent dentition of Chimpanzee. *Am. J. phys. Anthrop.* **22**: 285–294.

Noback, C. R., and Moskowitz, N. (1963). The primate nervous system: functional and structural aspects in phylogeny. In *Evolutionary and genetic biology of primates*, Vol. I. (Ed. Buettner-Janusch, J.) New York and London: Academic Press.

Nolte, Angela (1955). Field observations on the daily routine and social behaviour of common Indian monkeys with special reference to the Bonnet monkey (*Macaca radiata* Geoffroy). *J. Bombay nat. Hist. Soc.* **53**: 177–184.

Nolte, Angela (1958). Beobachtungen über das Instinktverhalten von Kapuzineraffen (*Cebus apella* L.) im der Gefangenschaft. *Behaviour* **13**: 183–207.

Oates, J. (1966). Secrets of Spanish Guinea. *Animals* **8**: 254–259.

Oboussier, H., and Maydell, G. A. von (1960). Zur Kenntnis von *Presbytis entellus* (Dufresnes, 1797). *Zool. Anz.* **164**, 1–2: 141–154.

Ochs, K. (1964). Pygmies in my drawing-room. *Animals* **3**, No. 6: 142–145.

Ogilvie, A. W. (1923). Breeding of the gibbon in captivity. *J. nat. Hist. Siam.* **6**: 137.

Olivier, G. *et al.* (1952–1964). Le squelette post-cranien du Semnopithèque. *Mammalia* **16–28**.

Olivier, G., Libersa, C., and Fenart, R. (1955). Le crâne du Semnopithèque. *Mammalia* **19**: 1–286.

Osborn, Rosalie M. (1963). Behaviour of the Mountain Gorilla. *Symp. zool. Soc. Lond.* **10**: 29–37.

Osgood, W. H. (1932). Mammals of the Kelley-Roosevelts and Delacour Asiatic Expeditions. *Field. Mus. nat. Hist. Zool.* **18**: 191–339.

Owen, R. (1831). On the anatomy of the orang-utang. *Proc. zool. Soc. Lond.* pp. 4, 9, 28, 67.

Owen, R. (1837). On a new orang. *Proc. zool. Soc. Lond.* 91–96.

Owen, R. (1843). Notes on the dissection of a female orang-utang. *Proc. zool. Soc. Lond.* 123–134.

Owen, R. (1862). Osteological contributions to the Natural History of the chimpanzees (*Troglodytes*) and the orangs (*Pithecus*). No. VI. Characters of the skull of the male *Pithecus morio*. *Trans. zool. Soc. Lond.* **4**: 165–178.

Owen, R. (1866). On the Aye-Aye (*Chiromys* Cuvier). *Trans. zool. Soc. Lond.* **5**: 33–101.

Owen, R. D., and Anderson, D. R. (1962). Blood groups in Rhesus monkeys. *Ann. N.Y. Acad. Sci.* **97**: 1–8.

Oxnard, C. E. (1963). Locomotor adaptations in the primate forelimb. *Symp. zool. Soc. Lond.* **10**: 165–182.

Oxnard, C. E. (1966). Vitamin B$_{12}$ nutrition in some primates in captivity. *Folia primat.* **4**: 424–431.

Pang-Chien, T'an (1957). Rare catches by Chinese animal collectors. *Zoo Life* **12**: 61–63.

Panouse, J. B. (1957). Les mammifères du Maroc. *Trav. Inst. Scient. chérif.* **5**.

Patterson, E. L. (1942). The myology of *Rhinopithecus roxellanae* and *Cynopithecus niger*. *Proc. zool. Soc. Lond.* **112**: 31–104.

Patterson, J. T., and Stone, W. S. (1952). *Evolution in the genus Drosophila*. New York: MacMillan and Co.

Perrier de la Bathie, H. (1921). La végétation malgache. *Ann. Mus. Colonial Marseille*, 3rd Series **9**: 1–268.

Petter, J. J. (1960). Remarques sur la systématique du genre *Lepilemur*. *Mammalia* **24**: 76–86.

Petter, J. J. (1962a). Ecological and behavioural studies of Madagascan lemurs in the field. *Ann. N.Y. Acad. Sci.* **102**: 267–281.

Petter, J. J. (1962b). Remarques sur l'écologie et l'ethologie comparées des Lémuriens Malgaches. *La Terre et la Vie* **4**: 394–416.

Petter, J. J. (1962c). Recherches sur l'ecologie et l'ethologie des Lémuriens Malgaches. *Mem. Mus. nat. Hist.* **27** (1): 1–146.

Petter, J. J. (1965). The lemurs of Madagascar. In *Primate behavior*. (Ed. DeVore, I.) New York: Holt, Rinehart and Winston.

Petter, J. J., and Petter-Rousseaux, A. (In press). *The aye-aye of Madagascar*.

Petter-Rousseaux, A. (1962). Recherches sur la biologie des primates inférieurs. *Mammalia* **26**, Suppl.: 1–88.

Petter-Rousseaux, A. (1964). Reproductive physiology and behavior of the Lemuroidea. In *Evolutionary and genetic biology of primates*, Vol. II. (Ed. Buettner-Janusch, J.) New York and London: Academic Press.

Phillips, W. W. A. (1931). The food of the Ceylon Slender Loris in captivity. *Spolia Zeylan.* **16**: 205–208.

Pitman, C. R. S. (1935). The gorillas of the Kayonsa Region. *Proc. zool. Soc. Lond.* 477–494.

Ploog, D. W., Blitz, J., and Ploog, F. (1963). Studies on social and sexual behavior of the squirrel monkey (*Saimiri sciureus*). *Folia primat.* **1**: 29–66.

Pocock, R. I. (1905). Observations upon a female specimen of the Hainan Gibbon (*Hylobates hainanus*) now living in the Society's Gardens. *Proc. zool. Soc. Lond.* 169–180.

Pocock, R. I. (1907). A monographic revision of the monkeys of the genus *Cercopithecus*. *Proc. zool. Soc. Lond.* 677–746.

Pocock, R. I. (1917a). Lemurs of the *Hapalemur* Group. *Ann. Mag. nat. Hist.* (8) **19**: 343–352.

Pocock, R. I. (1917b). The genera of Hapalidae (Marmosets). *Ann. Mag. nat. Hist.* (8) **20**: 247–258.

Pocock, R. I. (1918). On the external characters of Lemurs and of *Tarsius*. *Proc. zool. Soc. Lond.* 19–53.

Pocock, R. I. (1920). On the external characters of the South American monkeys. *Proc. zool. Soc. Lond.* 91–113.

Pocock, R. I. (1921). The systematic value of the glans penis in Macaque monkeys. *Ann. Mag. nat. Hist.* (9) **7**: 224–229.

Pocock, R. I. (1924). A new genus of monkeys. *Proc. zool. Soc. Lond.*, Abstr. **248**: 17.

Pocock, R. I. (1925a). The external characters of catarrhine monkeys and apes. *Proc. zool. Soc. Lond.* 1479–1579.

Pocock, R. I. (1925b). Notes on Cercopithecine genera, *Rhinostigma* and *Miopithecus*. *Ann. Mag. nat. Hist.* (9) **16**: 264–268.

Pocock, R. I. (1925c). Additional notes on the external characters of some platyrrhine monkeys. *Proc. zool. Soc. Lond.* 27–47.

Pocock, R. I. (1927). The gibbons of the genus *Hylobates*. *Proc. zool. Soc. Lond.* 719–741.

Pocock, R. I. (1928). The langurs or leaf-monkeys of British India. *J. Bombay nat. Hist. Soc.* **32**: 472–504, 661–677.

Pocock, R. I. (1934). The monkeys of the genera *Pithecus* (or *Presbytis*) and *Pygathrix* found to the east of the Bay of Bengal. *Proc. zool. Soc. Lond.* 895–961.

Pocock, R. I. (1936). External characters of a female specimen of a Red Colobus monkey. *Proc. zool. Soc. Lond.* 939–944.

Pocock, R. I. (1939). *The Fauna of British India, Mammalia.* Vol. I. London: Taylor and Francis, Ltd.

Polak, C. (1908). Die Anatomie des genus *Colobus*. *Verh. K. ned. Akad. Wet.* **2**: 1–247.

Poll, M. (1940). Les cercopithèques de group talapoin. *Revue Zool. Bot. afr.* **33**: 126–135.

Polyak, S. (1957). *The vertebrate visual system.* Chicago: University of Chicago Press.

Pournelle, G. H. (1959). Allen's Monkey. *Zoonooz* **32**, No. 10.

Pournelle, G. H. (1960). Observations on a captive Proboscis monkey. *Sarawak Mus. J.* **9**: 458–460.

Pournelle, G. H. (1962). Observations on the birth and early development of Allen's monkey. *J. Mammal.* **43**: 265–266.

Pournelle, G. H. (1965). The Gorilla—its status in captivity. *Zoonooz* **38**, No. 9: 9–10.

Pournelle, G. H. (1966). Birth of a Proboscis monkey. *Zoonooz* **39**, No. 3: 3–7.

Powell, T. P. S., Guillery, R. W., and Cowan, W. M. (1957). A quantitative study of the fornix-mamillo-thalamic system. *J. Anat.* **91**: 419–437.

Preuschoft, H. (1963). Beitrag zur Funktion des Pongidenfusses. *J. Morph. Anthrop.* **53**: 19–28.

Priemel, G. (1937). Die platyrrhinen Affen als Bewegungstypen unter besonderer Berücksichtigung der Extremformen *Callicebus* und *Ateles*. *Z. Morph. Ökol. Tiere.* **33**: 1–52.

Ramiswami, L. S., and Anand Kumar, T. C. (1962). Reproductive cycle of the slender loris. *Naturwissenschaften* **49**: 115–116.

Rand, A. L. (1935). Habits of Madagascan mammals. *J. Mammal.* **16**: 89–104.

Raven, H. C. (1936). Genital swelling in a female gorilla. *J. Mammal.* **17**: 416.

Raven, H. C. (Memorial Volume) (1950). *The anatomy of the Gorilla.* (Ed. Gregory, W. K.) New York: Columbia Univ. Press.

Rempe, Udo (1961). Einige beobachtungen an Bonobos. *Pan paniscus* Schwarz, 1929. *Z. wiss. Zool.* **165**: 81–87.

Rensch, B. (1929). *Das Prinzip geographischer Rassenkreise und das Problem der Artbildung.* Berlin: Borntraeger.

Reynolds, Vernon, and Reynolds, Frances (1955). Chimpanzees of the Budongo Forest. In *Primate Behaviour.* (Ed. De Vore, I.) New York: Holt, Rinehart and Winston.

Ribiero, A. de Miranda (1940). Commentaries on South American primates. *Mem. Inst. Oswaldo Cruz.* **35** (4): 779–851.

Richards, P. W. (1957). *Tropical Rain Forest.* Cambridge Univ. Press.

Ridley, H. N. (1895). Mammals of the Malay peninsula. *Nat. Sci.* **6**: 23–29.

Riesen, A. H., and Kinder, E. F. (1952). *The postural development of infant Chimpanzees.* New Haven, Conn.: Yale Univ. Press.

Riopelle, A. J. (1963). Growth and behavioural changes in chimpanzees. *Z. Morph. Anthrop.* **53**: 53–61.

Ripley, S. (1967). The leaping of langurs. *Am. J. phys. Anthrop.* **26**: 149–170.

Roberts, A. (1951). *Mammals of South Africa.* Johannesburg:

Robinson, H. C. (1905). Notes on the occurrence in Selangor of three vertebrates new to the Malayan peninsula. *J. Straits Brch. R. Asiat. Soc.* **44**: 224–225.

Rode, P. (1936). Sur quelques caractères différentiels de la tête osseuse des Cercopithèques et des Cercocèbes. *Mammalia* **1**: 59–64.

Rode, P. (1937). *Les primates de l'Afrique.* Paris: Librairie Larose.

Rode, P. (1938). Considérations sur la systématique des simiens africains. *Mammalia* **2**: 182–186.

Rosevear, D. R. (1935a). The lemurs of Nigeria. *Niger. Fld.* **4**: 16–21.

Rosevear, D. R. (1935b). The monkeys and baboons of Nigeria. *Niger. Fld.* **4**: 138–151.

Rosevear, D. R. (1953). *Checklist and atlas of Nigerian mammals.* Lagos: Nigerian Government.

Rosvold, H. E., Mirsky, A. F., and Pribram, K. H. (1954). Influence of amygdalectomy on social behaviour in monkeys. *J. comp. physiol. Psychol.* **47**: 173–178.

Rothfield, L., and Harmon, P. J. (1954). On the relation of the hippocampalfornix systems to the control of rage responses in cats. *J. comp. Neurol.* **101**: 265–282.

Rothschild, W. (1908). Note on *Gorilla gorilla diehli* (Matschie). *Novit. zool.* **15**: 391–392.

Rothschild, W. (1923). Exhibition of adult male mountain gorilla. *Proc. zool. Soc. Lond.* 176–177.

Roux, G. H. (1947). The cranial development of certain Ethiopian "Insectivores" and its bearing on the mutual affinities of the group. *Acta. zool., Stockh.* **28**: 165–397.

Rowell, Thelma E. (1966). Forest living baboons in Uganda. *J. Zool., Lond.* **149**: 344–364.

Rowell, Thelma E., and Hinde, R. A. (1962). Vocal communication by the Rhesus monkey (*Macaca mulatta*). *Proc. zool. Soc. Lond.* **138**: 279–294.

Rumbaugh, D. M. (1963). Squirrel monkey maintenance at San Diego State College. *Laboratory Primate Newsletter* **2**, 3: 2–4.

Rumbaugh, D. M. (1965a). The gibbon infant, Gabrielle; its growth and development. *Zoonooz* **38**, 12: 10–15.

Rumbaugh, D. M. (1965b). Maternal care in relation to infant behavior in the squirrel monkey *Psychological Reports.* Southern Universities Press. **16**: 171–176.

Rumbaugh, D. M. (1965c). The birth of a lowland gorilla. *Zoonooz* **38**, 9: 12–17.

Rumbaugh, D. M. (1967). The Siamang infant. Sarah . . . its growth and development. *Zoonooz* **40**, 3: 12–18.

Rumbaugh, D. M., and McQueeney, J. A. (1963). Learning-set formation and discrimination reversal: learning problems to criterion in the squirrel monkey. *J. comp. physiol. Psychol.* **56**: 435–439.

Rüppell, E. (1835–1840). *Neue Wirbeltiere zu der Fauna von Abyssinien gehörig.* Frankfurt-am-Main: Siegmund Schmerber.

Russell, A. E., and Zuckerman, S. (1935). A "sexual skin" in a marmoset. *J. Anat. Lond.* **69**: 356–362.

Sabater Pi, Jorge (1964). Distribucion actual de los Gorilas de Llanura en Rio Muni. *Publicaciones del Servicio Municipal del Parque Zoologico de Barcelona.*

Sade, D. S. (1964). Seasonal cycle in size of testes of free-ranging *Macaca mulatta. Folia primat.* **2**: 171–180.

Sanborn, C. C. (1952). Philippine zoological expedition, 1946–47. Mammals. *Fieldiana: Zool.* **33**: 110–112.

Sanderson, I. T. (1937). *Animal treasure.* London: Macmillan & Co.

Sanderson, I. T. (1940). The mammals of the North Cameroons forest area. *Trans. zool. Soc. Lond.* **24**: 623–725.

Sanderson, I. T. (1949). A brief review of the mammals of Suriname (Dutch Guiana) based upon a collection made in 1938. *Proc. zool. Soc. Lond.* **119**: 755–789.

Sanderson, I. T. (1957). *The Monkey Kingdom.* London: Hamish Hamilton.

Sandwith, H. (1866). Quoted by Owen R. (1866). On the Aye-Aye (*Chiromys* Cuvier). *Trans. zool. Soc. Lond.* **5**: 33–101.

Sarasin, P., and F. (1905). *Reisen in Celebes*, Vol. I. Wiesbaden: C. W. Kreidel's Verlag.

Sauer, E. G. Franz, and Sauer, Eleonore M. (1963). The South-West African bush-baby of the *Galago senegalensis* group. *Jl S.W. Africa scient. Soc.* **16**: 5–35.

Schaller, G. B. (1961). The orang-utan in Sarawak. *Zoologica* **46** (2): 73–82.

Schaller, George B. (1963). *The Mountain Gorilla: Ecology and Behaviour*. Chicago: University of Chicago Press.

Schaller, George B. (1965). The behaviour of the Mountain Gorilla. In *Primate Behaviour*. (Ed. DeVore, I.) New York: Holt, Rinehart and Winston.

Schenkel, R., and Schenkel-Hulliger, Lotte (In press). On sociology of free-ranging Colobus (*Colobus guereza caudatus* Thomas, 1885).

Schlegel, H., and Müller, S. (1839–44). Bijdragen tot de natuurlijke historie van den Orang-oetan (Simia satyrus). *Verhandelingen over de Natuurlijke beschiedenis der Nederlandsche overseesche bezittingen, de Leden der Natuurkundige commissie in Indie en andere Schrijvers*. (Ed. Temminck, C. J.) Zoologie.

Schneider, G. (1905). Ergebnisse zoologischer Forschungsreisen in Sumatra. Säugetiere (Mammalia). *Zool. Jb.* **23**: 1–172.

Schouteden, H. (1931). Le chimpanzé de la rive gauche du Congo. *Revue zool. Bot. afr.* **20** (*Bull. Cercle zool. Congol.* **7**: 114–119).

Schouteden, H. (1947). De Zoogdieren van Belgisch-Congo. *Annls. Mus. r. Congo belge Sér. 8vo.* **3**, Ser. 2.

Schultz, A. H. (1921). Fetuses of the Guiana howling monkey. *Zoologica, N.Y.* **12**: 243–262.

Schultz, A. H. (1926). Foetal growth of man and other primates. *Q. Rev. Biol.* **1**: 465–521.

Schultz, A. H. (1927). Studies on the growth of the gorilla and of other higher primates. *Mem. Carneg. Mus.* **11**: 1–87.

Schultz, A. H. (1929). Technique of measuring the outer body of human foetuses and of primates in general. *Contr. Embryol.* **20**: 213–257. (Carnegie Inst. Wash. 394.)

Schultz, A. H. (1930). The skeleton of the trunk and limbs of higher primates. *Hum. Biol.* **2**: 303–438.

Schultz, A. H. (1932). The generic position of *Symphalangus klossii*. *J. Mammal.* **13**: 368–369.

Schultz, A. H. (1933a). Growth and Development. Chapter II. *The anatomy of the rhesus monkey*. (Eds. Hartman, C. G., and Straus, W. L.) New York: Hafner Publishing Co.

Schultz, A. H. (1933b). Observations on the growth, classification and evolutionary specialization of gibbons and siamangs. *Hum. Biol.* **5**: 212–255, 385–428.

Schultz, A. H. (1934a). *Science, N.Y.* **79**: 185–186, quoted in Hill, W. C. Osman (1960). *Primates. Comparative Anatomy and Taxonomy*. Vol. IV. Edinburgh: University Press.

Schultz, A. H. (1934b). Some distinguishing characters of the mountain gorilla. *J. Mammal.* **15**: 51–61.

Schultz, A. H. (1937). Proportions, variability and asymmetries of the long bones of the limbs and the clavicles in man and apes. *Hum. Biol.* **9**: 281–328.

Schultz, A. H. (1938). Genital swelling in the female orang-utan. *J. Mammal.* **19**: 363–366.

Schultz, A. H. (1940a). The size of the orbit and eye in primates. *Am. J. phys. Anthrop.* **26**: 389–408.

Schultz, A. H. (1940b). Growth and development of the chimpanzee. *Contr. Embryol.* **28**: 1–63.

Schultz, A. H. (1941a). The relative size of the cranial capacity in primates. *Am. J. phys. Anthrop.* **28**: 273–287.

Schultz, A. H. (1941b). Growth and development of the orang-utan. *Contr. Embryol.* **29**: 57–110.

Schultz, A. H. (1942). Growth and development of the Proboscis monkey. *Bull. Mus. comp. Zool. Harv.* **89**: 279–314.

Schultz, A. H. (1944). Age changes and variability in gibbons. *Am. J. phys. Anthrop.* N.S. **2**: 1–129.

Schultz, A. H. (1948). Number of young at birth and the number of nipples in primates. *Am. J. phys. Anthrop.* N.S. **6**: 1–23.

Schultz, A. H. (1950). The specializations of man and his place among the catarrhine primates. In *Origin and Evolution of Man. Cold. Spr. Harb. Symp. quant. Biol.* **15**: 37–53.

Schultz, A. H. (1953). The relative thickness of the long bones and the vertebrae in primates. *Am. J. phys. Anthrop.* N.S. **11**: 277–312.

Schultz, A. H. (1956). Post-embryonic age changes. In *Primatologia*, Vol. I. (Eds. Hofer, H., Schultz, A. H., and Starck, D.) Basel: S. Karger.

Schultz, A. H. (1960). Age changes in primates and their modification in man. In *Human Growth* 1–20. London: Pergamon Press.

Schultz, A. H. (1961). Vertebral Column and Thorax. In *Primatologia*, IV, Lief. 5. (Eds. Hofer, H., Schultz, A. H., and Starck, D.) Basel: S. Karger.

Schultz, A. H. (1963a). Foot skeleton in primates. *Symp. zool. Soc. Lond.* **10**: 199–206.

Schultz, A. H. (1963b). Age changes, sex differences and variability as factors in the classification of Primates. In *"Classification and Human Evolution"*. (Ed. Washburn, S. L.) Viking Publ. in Anthrop. No. 37. New York: Wenner-Gren Foundation.

Schultz, A. H. (1964). A gorilla with exceptionally large teeth and supernumerary premolars. *Folia primat.* **2**: 149–160.

Schuman, E. L., and Brace, C. L. (1954). Dentition of the Liberian chimpanzee. *Hum. Biol.* **26**: 239–268.

Schwarz, E. (1928a). The species of the genus *Cercocebus*. *Ann. Mag. nat. Hist.* (10), **1**: 644–670.

Schwarz, E. (1928b). Notes on the classification of the African monkeys of the genus *Cercopithecus*, Erxleben. *Ann. Mag. nat. Hist.* (10), **1**: 649–663.

Schwarz, E. (1928c). Bemerkungen über den roten Stummelaffen. *Z. Saügetierk.* **3**: 92–97.

Schwarz, E. (1929). Das Vorkommen des Schimpanses auf dem linken Kongo-Ufer. *Revue Zool. Bot. afr. Tervuren* **16**: 425–433.

Schwarz, E. (1929). On the local races and distribution of the Black and White Colobus monkeys. *Proc. zool. Soc. Lond.* 585–598.

Schwarz, E. (1930). *Galago senegalensis inustus. Revue Zool. Bot. afr.* **19**: 391.

Schwarz, E. (1931a). On the African long-tailed lemurs or galagos. *Ann. Mag. nat. Hist.* (10), **7**: 41–66.

Schwarz, E. (1931b). On the African short-tailed lemurs or pottos. *Ann. Mag. nat. Hist.* (10), **8**: 249–256.

Schwarz, E. (1931c). A revision of the genera and species of Madagascan Lemuridae. *Proc. zool. Soc. Lond.* 399–428.

Schwarz, E. (1934). On the local races of the chimpanzee. *Ann. Mag. nat. Hist.* (10), **13**: 576–583.

Schwarz, E. (1936). A propos du *Lemur macaco* Linnaeus. *Mammalia* **1**: 24–25.

Sclater, W. L. (1900). *The Mammals of South Africa, I.* London: Porter.

Scott, James (1963). Factors determining skull form in primates. *Symp. zool. Soc. Lond.* No. 10, 127–134.

Selenka, E. (1898). *Stud. EntwGesch. Tiere* **6**: Menschenaffen. Wiesbaden.

Seth, P. K. (1964). Crista sagittalis in relation to the nuchal crest in *Nycticebus coucang. Am. J. phys. Anthrop.* **22**: 53–64.

Shamel, H. H. (1930). Mammals collected on the island of Koh Tau off the east coast of the Malay peninsula. *J. Mammal.* **11**: 71–73.

Shaw, G. A. (1879). A few notes upon four species of Lemurs, specimens of which were brought alive to England in 1878. *Proc. zool. Soc. Lond.* 132–136.

Shaw, G. A. (1883). A few rough notes on Aye-Aye. *Proc. zool. Soc. Lond.* 44.

Shell, W. F., and Riopelle, A. J. (1958). Progressive discrimination learning in platyrrhine monkeys. *J. comp. physiol. Psychol.* **51**: 467–470.

Shortridge, G. C. (1934). *Mammals of South-west Africa.* London: Heinemann.

Simonds, P. E. (1965). The Bonnet macaque in south India. In *Primate Behavior* (Ed. DeVore I.) New York: Holt, Rinehart and Winston.

Simonetta, A. (1957). Catalogo e sinonimia annotata degli ominoidi fossili ed attuali (1758–1955). *Atti Della Soc. tosc. Sci. nat. Pisa.* **64**, B: 53–112.

Simons, E. L. (1962). Two new primate species from the African Oligocene. *Postilla*, No. **64**: 1–12.

Simons, E. L. (1963). Critical reappraisal of Tertiary primates. In *Evolutionary and Genetic Biology of Primates*, Vol. I. (Ed. Buettner-Janusch, J.) New York and London: Academic Press.

Simons, E. L., and Russell, D. E. (1960). The cranial anatomy of *Necrolemur. Breviora* No. **127**, 1–14.

Simpson, D. A. (1952). Efferent fibres of the hippocampus in the monkey. *J. Neurol. Neurosurg. Psychiat.* **15**: 79–92.

Simpson, G. G. (1945). The principles of classification and a classification of mammals. *Bull. Am. Mus. nat. Hist.* **85**: 1–350.

Snedigar, R. (1949). Breeding of the Philippine tree-shrew, *Urogale everetti* Thomas. *J. Mammal.* **30**: 194–195.

Snow, C. C., and Vice, T. (1965). Organ weight allometry and sexual dimorphism in the olive baboon, *Papio anubis*. In *The Baboon in Medical Research*. (Ed. Vagtborg, H.) Austin: Univ. of Texas Press.

Sody, H. J. V. (1949). Notes on some primates, Carnivora and the Barbirusa from the Indo-Malayan and Indo-Australian regions. *Treubia* **20**: 121–190.

Sonntag, C. F. (1924). *Morphology and evolution of the apes and man.* London: John Bate, Sons and Danielsson Ltd.

Sorensen, M. W., and Conaway, C. H. (1964). Laboratory maintenance of treeshrews. *Laboratory Primate Newsletter* **3**, 2: 1–2.

Sorenson, M. W., and Conaway, C. H. (1966). Observations on the social behaviour of treeshrews in captivity. *Folia primat.* **4**: 124–145.

Southwick, C. H. (1962). Patterns of intergroup social behavior in primates with special reference to rhesus and howling monkeys. *Ann. N.Y. Acad. Sci.* **102**: 436–454.

Southwick, C. H., Beg, M. A., and Siddiqi, M. R. (1961). A population survey of Rhesus monkeys in villages, towns and temples in northern India. *Ecology* **42**, No. 3: 538–547.

Southwick, C. H., Beg, M. A., and Siddiqi, M. R. (1965). Rhesus monkeys in north India. In *Primate Behaviour*. (Ed. DeVore, I.) New York: Holt, Rinehart and Winston.

Spatz, W. B. (1966). Zur Ontogenese der Bulla Tympanica von *Tupaia glis* Diard, 1820. *Folia primat.* **4**: 26–50.

Spiegel, A. (1954). Beobachtung und Untersuchung an Javamakaken. *Zool. Gart.* **20**: 227–270.

Spiegel, A. (1956). Uber das Körperwachstum der Javamakaken. *Zool. Anz.* **156**: 1–8.

Sprankel, H. (1961a). Histologie und biologische Bedeutung eines jugulosternalen Duftdrüsenfeldes bei *Tupaia glis* (Diard, 1820). *Verh. dt. zool. Ges.* 198–206.

Sprankel, H. (1961b). Über Verhaltenweisen und Zucht von *Tupaia glis* (Diard, 1820) in Gefangenschaft. *Z. wiss. Zool.* **165**: 186–220.

Sprankel, H. (1965). Untersuchungen an *Tarsius*. I. Morphologie des Schwanzes. *Folia primat.* **3**: 153–188.

Stanley, W. B. (1919). Carnivorous apes in Sierra Leone. *Sierra Leone Studies*: 3–19

Starck, D., and Frick, H. (1958). Beobachtungen an Aethiopischen Primaten. *Zool. Jb.* **86**: 41–70.

Steiner, Paul E. (1954). Anatomical observations in a *Gorilla gorilla*. *Am. J. phys. Anthrop.* **12**: 145–180.

Stevenson-Hamilton, J. (1947). *Wild Life in South Africa.* London: Cassell.

Stott, K. (1946). Twinning in a green guenon. *J. Mammal.* **27**: 394.

Stott, K. (1962). Addicted to ape watching. *Zoonooz* **35**, No. 10: 10–15.

Stott, K., and Selsor, G. J. (1961a). The Orang-utan in N. Borneo. *Oryx* **5**: 6.

Stott, K., and Selsor, G. J. (1961b). Observations of the maroon leaf-monkey in North Borneo. *Mammalia* **25**: 184–189.

Straus, W. L. (1936). The thoracic and abdominal viscera of the primates. *Proc. Am. phil. Soc.* **76**: 1–85.

Straus, W. L. (1941). Locomotion of gibbons. *Am. J. phys. Anthrop.* **27**: 199–207.

Straus, W. L. (1942). Rudimentary digits in primates. *Q. Rev. Biol.* **17**: 228–243.

Straus, W. L. (1949). Riddle of man's ancestry. *Q. Rev. Biol.* **24**: 200–223.

Straus, W. L. (1962). Fossil evidence for the evolution of the erect bipedal posture. *Clin. orthop.* **25**: 9–19.

Straus, W. L. (1963). The Classification of *Oreopithecus*. In *Classification and Human Evolution*. (Ed. Washburn, S. L.) Viking Fund Publ. in Anthrop. No. 37. New York: Wenner-Gren Foundation.

Straus, W. L., and Wislocki, G. B. (1932). On certain similarities of the sloth and slow lemur. *Bull. Mus. comp. Zool. Harv.* **74**: 45–56.

Subramoniam, S. (1956). Some observations on the habits of the slender loris, *Loris tardigradus* (Linnaeus). *J. Bombay nat. Hist. Soc.* **54**: 387–398.

Sugiyama, Y. (1964). Group composition, population density and some sociological observations of Hanuman langurs (*Presbytis entellus*). *Primates* **5**, Nos. 3–4: 7–37.

Swinhoe, R. (1862). On the mammals of the island of Formosa (China). *Proc. zool. Soc. Lond.* 347–365.

Takeshita, H. (1961–62). On the delivery behaviour of squirrel monkeys and a Mona monkey. *Primates* **3**: 59–72.

Tanner, J. M. (1962). *Growth at adolescence.* 2nd Ed. Oxford: Blackwell.

Tappen, N. C. (1960). African monkey distribution. *Curr. Anthrop.* **1**: 91–120.

Tappen, N. C. (1963). Genetics and systematics in the study of primate evolution. *Symp. zool. Soc. Lond.* No. **10**: 267–276.

Tate, G. H. H. (1939). Mammals of Guiana Region. *Bull. Am. Mus. nat. Hist.* **76**: 151–229.

Tate, G. H. H. (1954). On *Cebus apella* (Linnaeus), with a note on *Cebus capucinus* (Linnaeus). *J. Mammal.* **35**: 415–418.

Taylor, E. H. (1934). *Philippine land mammals.* Manila: Bureau of Science.

Temminck, C. J. (1835). *Monographies de Mammalogie.* Vol. II. Leiden.

Tennent, J. E. (1861). Sketches of the natural history of Ceylon. 4th Edit. **1**. London: Longmans Green.

Thomas, O. (1903). A new monkey. *Proc. zool. Soc. Lond.* 224–225.

Thomas, O. (1908). On mammals from the Malay peninsula and islands. *Ann. Mag. nat. Hist.* (8) **2**: 301–306.

Thomas, O. (1922). On the systematic arrangement of the marmosets. *Ann. Mag. nat. Hist.* (9) **9**: 196–199.

Thomas, O. (1927a). A remarkable new monkey from Peru. *Ann. Mag. nat. Hist.* (9) **19**: 156–157.

Thomas, O. (1927b). The Godman-Thomas Expedition to Peru. V. On mammals collected by Mr. R. W. Hendee in the province of San Martin, N. Peru, mostly at Yurac Yacu. *Ann. Mag. nat. Hist.* (9) **19**: 361–375.

Thomas, O. (1927c). The Delacour exploration of French Indo-China—Mammals. *Proc. zool. Soc. Lond.* 41–58.

Thomas, O. (1928a). The Delacour exploration of French Indo-China—Mammals. *Proc. zool. Soc. Lond.* 139–150.

Thomas, O. (1928b). The Godman-Thomas Expedition to Peru. The mammals of the Rio Ucayali. *Ann. Mag. nat. Hist.* (10) **2**: 249–265.

Thomas, O., and Hinton, M. A. C. (1923). On mammals collected by Captain Shortridge during the Percy Sladen and Kaffrarian expedition to the Orange River. *Proc. zool. Soc. Lond.* **32**: 483–499.

Thomas, O., and Hinton, M. A. C. (1923). On mammals collected by Captain Shortridge during the Percy Sladen and Kaffrarian expedition to the Orange River. *Proc. zool. Soc. Lond.* **32**: 483–499.

Thomas, O., and Wroughton, R. C. (1911). On mammals from the Rhio archipelago and Malay peninsula. *J. fed. Malay St. Mus.* **4**: 99–128.

Tien, D. V. (1960). Sur une nouvelle espèce de *Nycticebus* au Vietnam. *Zool. Anz.* **164**: 240–243.

Tigges, J. (1964). On visual learning capacity, retention and memory in *Tupaia glis* Diard, 1820. *Folia primat.* **2**: 232–245.

Tokuda, K. (1961–62). A study on the sexual behaviour in the Japanese monkey troop. *Primates* **3**, No. 2: 1–40.

Tomes, C. S. (1923). *A manual of dental anatomy.* London: J. & A. Churchill, Ltd.

Tower, D. B. (1954). Structural and functional organisation of mammalian cerebral cortex. The correlation of neurone density with brain size. *J. comp. Neurol.* **101**: 19–53.

Tratz, E., and Heck, H. (1954). Der Afrikanische Anthropoide "Bonobo", eine neue Menschen-affengattung. *Säugietierk. Mitt.* **2**: 97–101.

Tuttle, Russell H. (1967). Knuckle-walking and the evolution of hominoid hands. *Am. J. phys. Anthrop.* **26**: 171–206.

Tuttle, Russell H., and Rodgers, Charles M. (1966). Genetic and selective factors in reduction of the hallux in *Pongo pygmaeus*. *Am. J. phys. Anthrop.* **24**: 191–198.

Ullrich, W. (1954). Quoted in Hill, W. C. Osman (1962). *Primates*, Vol. V. Edinburgh: University Press.

Ulmer, F. A. (1957). Breeding of Orang-utans. *Zool. Gart.* **23**: 57–65.

Ulmer, F. A. (1960). A longevity record for the Mindanao tarsier. *J. Mammal.* **41**: 512.

Ulmer, F. A. (1963). Observations on the tarsier in captivity. *Zool. Gart.* **27**: 106–121.

Vagtborg, H. (1965). *The Baboon in medical research.* (Ed. Vagtborg, H.) Austin: University of Texas.

Vallois, H. V. (1955). Ordre des Primates. Traité de Zoologie. Vol. 17. (Mammifères). (Ed. Grassé, P. P.) Paris.

Vandenbergh, J. G. (1963). Feeding, activity and social behaviour of the treeshrew, *Tupaia glis*, in a large outdoor enclosure. *Folia primat.* **1**: 199–207.

Van Valen, Leigh (1965). Tree shrews, primates, and fossils. *Evolution* **19**: 137–151.

Verheyen, W. N. (1959). Summary of the results of a craniological study of the African primate genera *Colobus* Illiger, 1811 and *Cercopithecus* Linnaeus, 1758. *Revue Zoo. Bot. afr.* **60**: 1–2.

Verheyen, W. N. (1962). Contribution à la craniologie comparée des primates. *Musée Roy. Afrique Centrale—Tervuren, Belgique.* Ser. 8. *Sci. Zool.* **105**: 1–256.

Veterinary Officer's Reports. Zoological Society of London (1961–66).

Vevers, G. M., and Weiner, J. S. (1963). Use of a tool by a captive Capuchin monkey. *Symp. zool. Soc. Lond.* No. **10**: 115–117.

Vogel, C. (1962). Untersuchungen an *Colobus*-Schädeln aus Liberia unter besonderer Berück-sichtigung der Crista sagittalis. *Z. Morph. Anthrop.* **52**: 306–332.

Wade, P. (1958). Breeding season among mammals in the lowland rainforest of North Borneo. *J. Mammal.* **39**: 429–433.

Wagner, H. O. (1956). Freilandbeobachtungen an Klammeraffen. *Z. Tierpsychol.* **13**: 302–313.

Walker, A. E., and Thomson, A. F. (1950). Behaviour alterations following lesions of the medial surface of the temporal lobes. *Folia psychiat. neurol. neurochir. neerl.* **53**: 444–452.

Walker, A. E., Thomson, A. F., and McQueen, J. D. (1953). Behaviour and the temporal rhinence-phalon in monkeys. *Bull. Johns Hopkins Hosp.* **93**: 65–93.

Wallace, A. R. (1856). On the Orang-Utan or Mias of Borneo. *Ann. Mag. nat. Hist.* (2) **17**: 471–476.

Wallace, A. R. (1869). *The Malay Archipelago.* London: Macmillan and Co.

Washburn, S. L. (1942). Skeletal proportions of adult langurs and macaques. *Hum. Biol.* **14**: 444–472.

Washburn, S. L. (1944). The genera of Malaysian langurs. *J. Mammal.* **25**: 289–294.

Washburn, S. L. (1950). Thoracic viscera of the gorilla. In *Anatomy of the Gorilla.* (Ed. Gregory, W. K.) New York: Columbia Univ. Press.

Washburn, S. L. (1957). Ischial callosities as sleeping adaptations. *Am. J. phys. Anthrop.* **15**: 269–280.

Washburn, S. L., and DeVore, I. (1961). The social life of baboons. *Scient. Am.* **204**: 62–71.

Washburn, S. L., Jay, Phyllis C., and Lancaster, Jane B. (1965). Field studies of Old World monkeys and apes. *Science, N.Y.* **150**: 1541–1547.

Watt, H. J. (1925). Quoted in Noback, Charles R., and Moskowitz, Norman (1963).

Webb, C. S. Notes on mammal collecting in Madagascar (unpublished). Quoted in Hill, W. C. Osman (1953). *Primates. Comparative Anatomy and Taxonomy.* Vol. I. Edinburgh: University Press.

Webb, C. S. (1953). *A wanderer in the wind.* London: Hutchinson.

Welch, F. D. (1911). Observations on different gibbons of the genus *Hylobates* now or recently living in the Society's gardens and on *Symphalangus syndactylus*. *Proc. zool. Soc. Lond.* 353–358.

Wettstein, E. B. (1963). Variabilität, Geschlechtunterschiede und Alterveränderungen bei *Callithrix jacchus*. L. *Morph. Jb.* **104**, 2: 185–271.

Wharton, C. H. (1948). Seeking Mindanao's strangest creatures. *Natn. geogr. Mag.* **94**: 388–408.

Wharton, C. H. (1950a). Notes on the Philippine tree shrew *Urogale everetti* (Thomas, 1892). *J. Mammal.* **31**: 352–354.

Wharton, C. H. (1950b). The tarsier in captivity. *J. Mammal.* **31**: 260–269.

Wiener, A. S., Baldwin, M., and Gordon, E. B. (1963). Blood groups in chimpanzees. *Expl. Med. Surg.* **21**: 159–163.

Wiener, A. S., Candela, P. B., and Goss, L. J. (1942). Blood Group factors in the blood, organs and secretions of primates. *J. Immunol.* **45**: 229–235.

Wiener, A. S., and Gordon, E. B. (1960). The blood groups of Chimpanzees. A-B-O Groups and M-N types. *Am. J. phys. Anthrop.* **18**: 301–311.

Wiener, A. S., and Moor-Jankowski, J. (1965). Primate blood groups and evolution. *Science, N.Y.* **148**: 255–256.

Wiener, A. S., Moor-Jankowski, J., and Gordon, E. B. (1963). Blood groups of apes and monkeys. V. Studies on the human blood group factors, A, B, H and Le in Old and New World monkeys. *Am. J. phys. Anthrop.* **22**: 175–187.

Wiener, A. S., Moor-Jankowski, J., and Gordon, E. B. (1966). Blood Groups of Apes and Monkeys. VI. Further studies on human blood factors A, B, H and Le in monkeys. *Folia primat.* **4**: 81–102.

Williams, C. A. (1964). Immunochemical analysis of serum proteins of the primates: a study of molecular evolution. In *Evolutionary and genetic biology of primates*, Vol. II. (Ed. Buettner-Janusch, J.) New York and London: Academic Press.

Williams, C. A., and Wemyss, C. T. (1961). Experimental and evolutionary significance of similarities among serum protein antigens of man and lower primates. *Ann. N.Y. Acad. Sci.* **94**: 77.

Williams, L. (1965). *Samba and the monkey mind*. London: Bodley Head.

Williams, L. (1967). Breeding Humboldt's woolly monkey *L. lagotricha* at Murraytown Woolly Monkey Sanctuary. *In* International Zoo Year Book, Vol. VII. (Ed. Jarvis, C.) London: Zoological Society of London.

Winkelman, R. K. (1963). Nerve endings in the skin of primates. In *Evolutionary and genetic biology of primates*, Vol. I. (Ed. Buettner-Janusch, J.) New York and London: Academic Press.

Wislocki, G. B. (1930a). *Contr. Embryol. Carneg. Instn.* **22**: 173–192. Quoted in Hill, W. C. Osman (1960). *Primates. Comparative Anatomy and Taxonomy*. Vol. IV. Edinburgh: University Press.

Wislocki, G. B. (1930b). A study of scent glands in the marmosets, especially *Oedipomidas geoffroyi*. *J. Mammal.* **11**: 475–482.

Wislocki, G. B. (1933). The reproductive systems. Chapter 9. *The anatomy of the Rhesus monkey*. (Eds. Hartman, C. G., and Straus, W. L.) New York: Hafner Publishing Co.

Wislocki, G. B., and Straus, W. L. (1933). On the blood vascular bundles in the limbs of certain Edentates and Lemurs. *Bull. Mus. comp. Zool. Harv.* **74**: 1–16.

Wislocki, G. B., and Schultz, A. H. (1925). On the nature of modifications of the skin in the sternal region of certain primates. *J. Mammal.* **6**: 236–243.

Woodburne, L. S. (1963). Notes on *Saimiri sciurea* as an experimental animal. *Laboratory Primate Newsletter* **2**, No. 1: 4–7.

Woollard, H. H. (1925). The anatomy of *Tarsius spectrum*. *Proc. zool. Soc. Lond.* 1071–1184.

Yamada, M. (1963). A study of blood-relationship in the natural society of the Japanese macaque. *Primates* **4**, No. 3: 43–65.

Yeager, C. H., Painter, T. S., and Yerkes, R. M. (1940). The chromosomes of the chimpanzee. *Science, N.Y.* **91**: 74–75.

Yerkes, R. M., and Yerkes, A. W. (1929). *The great apes*. New Haven, Conn.: Yale University Press.

Yerkes, R. M. (1943). *Chimpanzees, a laboratory colony*. New Haven, Conn.: Yale University Press.

Yoshiba, K. (1964). The Orang-utan in North Borneo. *Primates* **5**: Nos. 1–2: 11–26.

Young, W. J., Merz, T., Ferguson-Smith, M. A., and Johnston, A. W. (1960). Chromosome number of the chimpanzee, *Pan troglodytes*. *Science, N.Y.* **131**: 1672–1673.

Ziegler, Alan C. (1964). Brachiating adaptations of chimpanzee upper limb musculature. *Am. J. phys. Anthrop.* **22**: 15–32.

Zoological Society of London. Veterinary Officer's Reports (1961–1966).

Zoonooz (1964a). *Zoonooz* **37**, No. 6: 7

Zoonooz (1964b). *Zoonooz* **37**, No. 5: 14.

Zuckerkandl, E. (1900). Zur anatomie von *Chiromys madagascariensis*. *Denkschr. Öst. Akad. Wiss.* **68**, 89–200.

Zuckerkandl, E., Jones, R. T., and Pauling, L. (1960). A comparison of animal hemoglobins by tryptic peptide pattern analysis. *Proc. natn. Acad. Sci. U.S.A.* **46**, 134–9.

Zuckerman, S. (1930). The menstrual cycle of the primates. General nature and homology. *Proc. zool. Soc. Lond.* 691–754.

Zuckerman, S. (1931). The menstrual cycle of the primates. IV. Observations on the lactation period. *Proc. zool. Soc. Lond.* 593–602.

Zuckerman, S. (1932a). The social life of monkeys and apes. London.

Zuckerman, S. (1932b). The menstrual cycle of the primates. Part 6. *Proc. zool. Soc. Lond.* 1059–1075.

Zuckerman, S. (1933). *Functional affinities of man, monkeys and apes*. London: Kegan Paul, Trench, Trubner & Co. Ltd.

Zuckerman, S. (1937). The duration and phases of the menstrual cycle in Primates. *Proc. zool. Soc. Lond.* **107**: 315–346.

Zuckerman, S. (1953). The breeding season of mammals in captivity. *Proc. zool. Soc. Lond.* **122**: 827–950.

Zuckerman, S., and Parkes, A. S. (1932). The menstrual cycle of primates. Part V. *Proc. zool. Soc. Lond.* 139–191.

Zukowsky, L. (1922). Der Dril von Fernando Po. *Arch. Naturgesch.* **88**: Sect. A. pt. 3: 184–192.

Zukowsky, L. (1925). Der Mandrill von Fernando Po. *Arch. Naturgesch.* **91**: Sect. A. No. 5: 132–136.

INDEX TO ANIMALS

(*Figures in italics indicate illustrations*)